SO-ABY-253

John Friedlander
II. M & P

Currents,
Fields,
and Particles

TECHNOLOGY PRESS BOOKS IN SCIENCE AND ENGINEERING

FLUID POWER CONTROL   edited by John F. Blackburn, Gerhard Reethof, and
 J. Lowen Shearer
FRACTURE   edited by B. L. Averbach, D. K. Felbeck, G. T. Hahn, and D. A. Thomas
RANDOM VIBRATION   edited by Stephen H. Crandall
KINETICS OF HIGH-TEMPERATURE PROCESSES   edited by W. D. Kingery
BASIC DATA OF PLASMA PHYSICS   by Sanborn C. Brown
MOLECULAR SCIENCE AND MOLECULAR ENGINEERING   by Arthur R. von Hippel
NOISE IN ELECTRON DEVICES   edited by Louis D. Smullin and Hermann A. Haus
THE PHYSICAL CHEMISTRY OF STEELMAKING   edited by John F. Elliott
LECTURES ON ORDINARY DIFFERENTIAL EQUATIONS   by Witold Hurewicz
NOTES ON ANALOG-DIGITAL CONVERSION TECHNIQUES   edited by Alfred K. Susskind
ATMOSPHERIC EXPLORATIONS   edited by Henry G. Houghton
CERAMIC FABRICATION PROCESSES   edited by W. D. Kingery
CURRENTS, FIELDS, AND PARTICLES   by Francis Bitter
THE THEORY AND TECHNIQUE OF SHIP DESIGN   by George C. Manning
SPHEROIDAL WAVE FUNCTIONS   by J. A. Stratton, P. M. Morse, L. J. Chu,
 J. D. C. Little, and F. J. Corbato
PRINCIPLES OF ELECTRIC UTILITY ENGINEERING   by C. A. Powel
DIELECTRIC MATERIALS AND APPLICATIONS   edited by Arthur R. von Hippel
PHYSICAL METEOROLOGY   by John C. Johnson
THE MATHEMATICS OF CIRCUIT ANALYSIS   by E. A. Guillemin
MAGNETIC CIRCUITS AND TRANSFORMERS   by Members of the Electrical Engineering
 Staff, M.I.T.
APPLIED ELECTRONICS Second Edition   by Truman S. Gray
ELECTRIC CIRCUITS   by Members of the Electrical Engineering Staff, M.I.T.
METHODS OF OPERATIONS RESEARCH   by Philip M. Morse and George E. Kimball
AN INDEX OF NOMOGRAMS   compiled and edited by Douglas P. Adams
THE EXTRAPOLATION, INTERPOLATION, AND SMOOTHING OF STATIONARY TIME
 SERIES   by Norbert Wiener
INDEX FOSSILS OF NORTH AMERICA   by H. W. Shimer and R. R. Shrock
WAVELENGTH TABLES   measured and compiled under the direction of G. R. Harrison
TABLES OF ELECTRIC DIPOLE MOMENTS   compiled by L. G. Wesson
ANALYSIS OF THE FOUR-BAR LINKAGE   by John A. Hrones and George L. Nelson

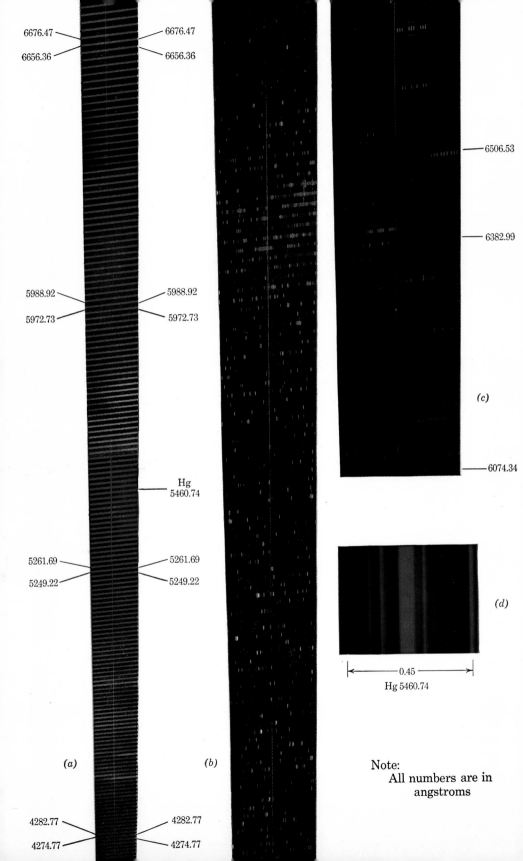

6676.47
6656.36

6676.47
6656.36

6506.53

6382.99

5988.92
5972.73

5988.92
5972.73

(c)

6074.34

Hg
5460.74

5261.69
5249.22

5261.69
5249.22

(d)

0.45
Hg 5460.74

(a)

(b)

Note:
All numbers are in
angstroms

4282.77

4282.77

4274.77

4274.77

FRONTISPIECE

(a) The continuous spectrum of a white light photographed with a grating crossed with an echelle ($\frac{1}{2}$ actual size).

(b) A portion of the line spectrum of thorium (actual size).

(c) The Zeeman effect of some of the red lines of neon in a field of 75,000 gauss (actual size). Single lines are split up in this way by a magnetic field.

(d) The detailed structure (hyperfine structure) of a line in the mercury spectrum.

Spectrograms taken on "Ansco Color" film. For further discussion of these spectra, see Appendix VIII.

Currents,
Fields,
and Particles

by FRANCIS BITTER

Professor of Physics
Massachusetts Institute of Technology

Published jointly by
The Technology Press of
Massachusetts Institute of Technology
and
John Wiley & Sons, Inc., New York

FOURTH PRINTING, AUGUST, 1960

Copyright © 1956, by The Massachusetts Institute of Technology

All Rights Reserved. This book or any part
thereof must not be reproduced in any form
without the written permission of the publisher.

Library of Congress Catalog Card Number: 52-42835

Printed in the United States of America

This book is dedicated to the imaginative and inspiring leaders of M.I.T.

KARL T. COMPTON and VANNEVAR BUSH

and their successors,

JAMES R. KILLIAN, JR., and JULIUS A. STRATTON

Preface

This book in its present form is the result of a six-year effort to base the second year of a two-year physics course on atomic physics. Its main objective is to give the student an appreciation of one of the great achievements of man—the development of a series of abstract concepts which make it possible to see deeply into the nature of creation. A second objective is to lay the groundwork for the training of future scientists, engineers, and others who will benefit from an understanding of the laws of nature. In choosing illustrative examples and problems for this purpose, an effort has been made to go beyond the usual range of electrical circuits and optical instruments and to include a variety of ideas in the general area of the physics of solids and gases and the structure of atoms because these matters are fast becoming a part of engineering curricula of all sorts.

The book contains more material than can be covered in a single academic year by most students. For this reason a good deal of the text is in small type. This is not to indicate that it is unimportant, but that it is supplementary to the main argument. It takes on some aspects of the supplementary study which in more advanced courses involves the use of library facilities. Much of it may be omitted, or included only for those students who wish to understand the subject more thoroughly.

An effort has been made to include problems that require many steps in their solution in order to supplement the usual pattern of presenting an argument and then essentially repeating it in the form of questions. This not only adds variety and interest but has been found useful as a stimulant to occasional review of earlier portions of the text. The problems marked with a star will, as a rule, be too difficult for most students. They are included to help the teacher in keeping alive the interest of the exceptional student who is bored with work at the pace required for the class. Some of these problems include considerable discussion and may form the basis for further independent study. Others appear to be mere mathematical exercises but should be considered as illustrations of the sort of analysis which forms an important part of any research program.

I further wish to acknowledge the debt I owe to many colleagues and authors. In particular, I must mention F. W. Sears' *Principles of Physics*, from which I began teaching physics in 1946, after having been diverted into other fields for the best part of fifteen years; N. H. Frank's *Introduction to Electricity and Optics*, which brought to my attention once again the pleasure and satisfaction of studying a clear, thorough exposition of difficult new concepts; the excellent texts of Shortley and Williams, and of Furry, Purcell, and Street, both recently published, to which I have constantly referred in order to see how other authors have incorporated new ideas; L. B. Arguimbau's *Vacuum Tube Circuits*, which I have had to study to remedy a gap in my experience; and finally R. W. Pohl's *Einführung in die Physik*, a book which seems to me outstanding in its clarity and in the completeness of its discussion of fundamentals.

I wish to thank Sumner P. Davis for his valuable occasional assistance over a period of years, and for preparing the colored frontispiece, an achievement that only a few specialists will properly appreciate. I also particularly want to thank Professor Heinrich Medicus, with whom I have had many discussions concerning the organization and presentation of the material to be included in the course. These discussions have been most illuminating and have repeatedly led me to revise my own ideas of how best to proceed.

Finally, I am very much indebted to N. H. Frank and J. A. Stratton, whose sympathetic encouragement and support are in no small measure responsible for my perseverance in this attempt to present a few facts and ideas clearly enough so that the reader may agree with Walt Whitman's exclamation, "As if the beauty and sacredness of the demonstrable must fall behind that of the mythical!"

FRANCIS BITTER

Cambridge, Massachusetts
1956

Contents

CHAPTER 1

The Basic
Electrical Quantities
and Their Measurement

1.1 ELECTRICAL FORCES; COULOMB'S LAW

Electrical and magnetic phenomena have been observed in one form or another for thousands of years. Until the end of the eighteenth century, however, these observations were largely qualitative and unrelated. Such phenomena as the orientation of the compass needle or the electrical displays during thunderstorms were merely curious and strange aspects of nature. With the advent of quantitative measurements, an ever-deepening insight into the nature of the structure of matter was obtained. The universal attribute, mass, had to be expanded to include the notion of charges out of which atoms are made. Finally, during the twentieth century, the detailed study of charged particles led to the formulation of quantum mechanics and a satisfactory description of atomic structure. The first step in this evolution was an adequate description of the two forces at a distance which the charged components of matter can exert on each other. The simpler of these is the electrostatic force measured and analyzed by Charles A. Coulomb in 1785.

One force at a distance, namely, gravity, is described by Newton's famous law

$$F \propto \frac{mm'}{r^2}$$

illustrated in Fig. 1.1a. Electrical forces follow a similar law, called *Coulomb's law*

$$F \propto \frac{qq'}{r^2} \tag{1.1}$$

illustrated in Fig. 1.1b. Here q and q' represent quantities of electrical charge, just as m and m' in Newton's law represent quantities of mass.

Charges may be produced in a variety of ways, the oldest of which is simply by friction. Rubbing a glass rod with a piece of silk, or a hard-rubber rod with a piece of fur, for example, will leave the rubbed surfaces charged. These charges may then be transferred by contact to other light bodies to demonstrate electrostatic forces.

Although Newton's and Coulomb's equations are so similar, the physical manifestations of gravitational and electrical forces are very different. There are two reasons for this difference. The first is the

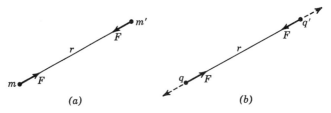

Fig. 1.1. (a) The gravitational force F acting between two masses, m and m'. (b) The electrical force F acting between two charges, q and q'. The electrical force may be attractive or repulsive, but it always acts along the line joining the two charges.

magnitude of the forces that can be produced in the laboratory. An illustration of the differences encountered may be taken from everyday experience. The weight of a human hair is a small but measurable force. It is a gravitational force exerted on the hair by an adjacent object, namely, the earth. The gravitational force exerted on a hair by a nearby comb can readily be computed. It is negligible compared to the weight of the hair, yet a comb can, under certain circumstances, exert a different force at a distance which is many times the weight of the hair. It can lift the hair up against the gravitational force and make it stand on end. This effect is due to an electrical force. Friction can separate electric charges, leaving some on the hair and some on the comb, and it is these separated charges that attract each other and produce the observed effects.

The second important difference between gravitational and electric forces is that, whereas the former are invariably attractive, the latter may be either attractive or repulsive, as is illustrated in Fig. 1.2. There is only one kind of mass, and all masses attract each other. There are, however, two kinds of electric charge; positive and negative. Positive charges repel each other, as do negative charges, but positive charges attract negative charges. It is a consequence of these facts that a given quantity of positive charge can be canceled by an equal quantity of negative charge. Such a cancelation is possible electrically, but not gravitationally. In the hair and comb experiment, for instance, the hairs stand up separately. They repel each other because they have attached to them charges of like sign. They are all attracted to the comb because it has attached to it charges of the opposite sign. The material bodies involved, namely, hair and comb, seem to exert forces on each other because of the electric charges that are attached to them. The electric charges are not permanently and irrevocably attached to

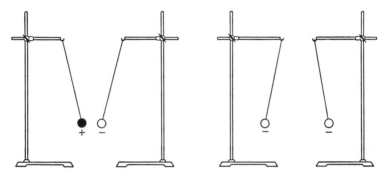

FIG. 1.2. (a) The attractive force between oppositely charged spheres. (b) The repulsive force between similarly charged spheres.

the hair and comb. The electric forces of attraction will now and again pry some of the charge loose, and this may flow through the air or along the arm toward the charge having the opposite sign, and so produce a partial cancelation.

The quantitative application of Eq. 1.1 requires the specification of units. In general, Coulomb's law may be written

$$F = k \frac{qq'}{r^2} \tag{1.2}$$

where the magnitude of the constant k depends on the units used. Perhaps the simplest procedure is that adopted in the *centimeter-gram-second (cgs) electrostatic system* of units. The constant $k = 1$, so that Coulomb's law becomes

$$F = \frac{qq'}{r^2} \tag{1.3}$$

Here q is in electrostatic units (esu), r is in centimeters (cm), and F is in dynes. The esu of charge is called the *statcoulomb*. It is defined as that quantity of charge which, placed 1 cm away from a like charge, will experience a force of 1 dyne. This system is very convenient when we are concerned with purely electrostatic interactions, but it has certain disadvantages when we come to consider moving charges and magnetic effects.

The system of units used in this book is the *rationalized meter-kilogram-second (mks) system*. It was adopted in 1935 by the International Electrotechnical Commission and is gradually replacing other systems in scientific and technical work. The unit of charge is the *coulomb*. It is defined in terms of electrical currents in a way which we shall take up further on. The magnitude of the coulomb is such that the proportionality constant k in Coulomb's law has the value

$$k = 8.98776 \times 10^9 \frac{\text{newton-meter}^2}{\text{coulomb}^2}$$

if the charges are in a vacuum. We shall in general round this off to

$$k = 9 \times 10^9 \frac{\text{n-m}^2}{\text{coulomb}^2} \tag{1.4}$$

Coulomb's law is usually not written in terms of this proportionality constant k but of a related constant, called the *permittivity*, and defined as follows:

$$\epsilon_0 = \frac{1}{4\pi k} \approx 8.85 \times 10^{-12} \frac{\text{coulomb}^2}{\text{n-m}^2} \quad \text{(approx.)} \tag{1.5}$$

The form of Coulomb's law that we finally adopt is then

$$F = \frac{1}{4\pi\epsilon_0} \frac{qq'}{r^2} \text{ newtons} \qquad \blacktriangleright(1.6)\blacktriangleleft$$

In this equation ϵ_0 has the value* of Eq. 1.5, the charges q and q' are expressed in coulombs, and the distance r between them in meters.

Coulomb's law specifies the magnitude of either one of two equal and opposite forces, namely, that which the charge q exerts on the charge q', or the equal but oppositely directed force which the charge q' exerts on the charge q. If the two charges under consideration have the same sign, the forces are repulsive. If they have opposite signs, the forces which they exert are attractive.

---

* When the factor 4π is written out explicitly in the definition of ϵ_0, as has been done here, one obtains the so-called rationalized mks system. Some writers define ϵ_0 by the equation $k = 1/\epsilon_0$. This definition leads to the so-called unrationalized mks system. One must be careful when reading works on electricity to determine whether rationalized or unrationalized units are being used. We shall use only the former in this book.

In the form shown in Eq. 1.6, Coulomb's law describes the force between charges in a vacuum. It is found experimentally that, if charges are embedded in non-conducting substances such as oil or glass, for example, Coulomb's law must be modified. The permittivity will have a value differing from that specified in Eq. 1.5. The first two chapters will be confined, however, to the case of charges in a vacuum. The permittivity of air is so nearly equal to that of a vacuum that Eq. 1.6 will also be applied to charges in air.

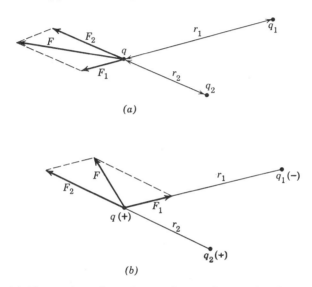

FIG. 1.3. (a) The resultant force F exerted on a charge q by charges q_1 and q_2 having the same sign as q. (b) The resultant force F exerted on a positive charge q by a negative charge q_1 and a positive charge q_2.

If several charges are present, the resultant force exerted on some one charge may be found through adding the forces exerted by the separate charges vectorially. This is illustrated in Fig. 1.3. Thus, if we are concerned with the force on a charge q in the presence of a charge q_1 of like sign at a distance r_1 from q, and another charge q_2 of like sign at a distance r_2 from q, we have the situation shown in Fig. 1.3a.

$$\mathbf{F} = \mathbf{F}_1 + \mathbf{F}_2 = \frac{1}{4\pi\epsilon_0} \left(\frac{\vec{qq_1}}{r_1{}^2} + \frac{\vec{qq_2}}{r_2{}^2} \right) \tag{1.7}$$

This procedure may readily be extended to any number of charges. It must be remembered, however, that unlike charges attract each other. Hence if we modify the situation illustrated in Fig. 1.3a by reversing the sign of q_1 so that we might suppose q and q_2 to be positive, but q_1 negative, we should have the situation shown in Fig. 1.3b.

The force exerted by n charges q_1, q_2, q_3, q_4, $\cdots$, q_s, $\cdots$, q_n on a charge q may be written

$$\mathbf{F} = \frac{1}{4\pi\epsilon_0} \sum_{s=1}^{n} \frac{\overrightarrow{qq_s}}{r_s^2} \tag{1.8}$$

where the summation is to be a vector sum for all the possible values of s from 1 to n.

As will become apparent from quantitative applications of Coulomb's law, the coulomb is an extremely large quantity of charge seldom physically realized in the laboratory. One more often deals with microcoulombs (μc) or micromicrocoulombs ($\mu\mu$c). The use of such prefixes as scale factors is described below.

Note about Scale Factors

The following prefixes have these meanings:

Prefix	Abbreviation	Meaning
Mega or meg	M	10^6
kilo	k	10^3
milli	m	10^{-3}
micro	μ	10^{-6}
micromicro	$\mu\mu$	10^{-12}

Examples: Megavolt, megohm, megacycle; kilovolt, kilometer, kilowatt; millivolt, milligram, milliampere; microampere, microcoulomb, micromicrocoulomb.

An Example of the Application of Coulomb's Law

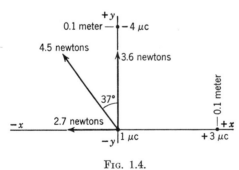

Fig. 1.4.

The application of Eq. 1.7 is illustrated in the following example. A charge of 1 μc is located at the origin of a rectangular coordinate system as shown in Fig. 1.4. A charge of 3 μc is located at a point 0.1 meter from the origin on the positive x axis, and a charge of -4 μc 0.1 meter from the origin on the positive y axis. What is the resultant electrical force on the charge at the origin?

Let us consider first the force produced by the 3-μc charge on the x axis. The force on the charge at the origin due to this charge is repulsive, since both have the same sign, and in the direction of the x axis, since both charges are on this axis. We have for the magnitude of the force due to the first charge

$$F_1 = 9 \times 10^9 \frac{(1 \times 10^{-6})(3 \times 10^{-6})}{(0.1)^2} = 2.7 \text{ newtons}$$

Similarly, the force due to the second charge is attractive, and in the direction of the positive y axis. Its magnitude is

$$F_2 = 9 \times 10^9 \frac{(1 \times 10^{-6})(4 \times 10^{-6})}{(0.1)^2} = 3.6 \text{ newtons}$$

The resultant of these two mutually perpendicular forces is

$$F = \sqrt{F_1{}^2 + F_2{}^2} = 0.9\sqrt{3^2 + 4^2} = 4.5 \text{ newtons}$$

The angle which the resultant makes with the positive y axis is θ, where $\tan \theta = \frac{3}{4}$, or approximately 37°.

1.2 INSULATORS AND CONDUCTORS

Matter is composed of *atoms*, having diameters of the order of 10^{-10} meter. At the center of an atom is a very small positively charged *nucleus*. Nuclear diameters range from 10^{-15} to 10^{-14} meter. Around atomic nuclei there is a cloud of *electrons*. In electrically neutral atoms the negative charge of the electrons just balances the positive charge of the nucleus.

Small clusters of atoms are called *molecules*. Thus oxygen gas is made up of pairs of oxygen atoms held together by chemical forces, vibrating and rotating about their centers of mass. Hydrogen, nitrogen, and oxygen are examples of gases, under normal conditions, made up of diatomic molecules, designated H_2, N_2, and O_2 respectively. Water molecules consist of three atoms, two hydrogen and one oxygen, designated H_2O. Ammonia contains four atoms, NH_3, and so on.

Atoms and molecules need not be electrically neutral. If for some reason there is an excess of charge of one sign, the particle is called an *ion*. Ions in a gas or liquid will move in response to electrical forces. The details of the motion will depend on the applied force and on the collisions between the ions and their neighbors.

Matter may be classified electrically into two categories, according to whether electrical forces will produce moving charges or not. Ionized gases or liquids are examples of electrical conductors, because electrical forces acting on the charged particles will produce motion, as illustrated in Fig. 1.5. Gases and most liquids containing only neutral atoms are insulators.

In solids, atoms are so closely packed together that it is difficult for two atoms to change places. Although such exchanges do occur, they are so rare that for the purposes of the present discussion we shall suppose that ions in a solid do not move in response to electrical forces. The mechanism of electrical conduction in solids, hence, is different from that in gases or liquids. Metals are electrical conductors, and they conduct because they contain free electrons. In an insulator, each atom may be thought of as holding its electrons in a cloud around its nucleus. In a metal, in addition to these bound electrons, there are some free electrons that can move about. If a metallic wire is connected into an electrical circuit, the free electrons can flow out at one terminal and are replaced by other free electrons entering the wire at

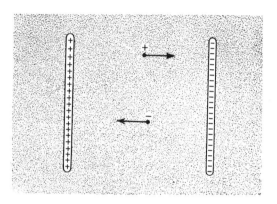

Fig. 1.5.   The forces acting on positive and negative ions in the presence of charged bodies.   An ionized gas is an example of a conducting medium.

the other terminal. If an isolated piece of metal is given an excess charge, for example by having a charged object rubbed against it, the excess charge is free to move around on or in the metal. Excess charge on an insulator, such as a glass plate, for example, will tend to remain where it is placed. It is bound and not free to move.

1.3   ELECTRICAL ENERGY; THE VOLT

In the first section we introduced the concepts of a quantity of charge, measured in terms of statcoulombs or coulombs, and of the forces which charges exert on each other. In this section we shall take up the volt. The definition of the volt follows quite simply when we consider electrical phenomena from the point of view of the energies involved rather than from the point of view of the forces which charges exert on each other. The one follows from the other. In teaching mechanics, the usual procedure is to start with a discussion of forces and first express a relationship between force and motion in the form $F = ma$. Subsequently it is shown that for many problems a much more useful formulation involves not forces but energy and "quantity of motion," or momentum. Without concerning ourselves with the detail involved in the description of varying forces, we can compute many important characteristics of the motion of objects by applying the principles of the conservation of energy and momentum. For example, it is possible to compute the maximum altitude reached by a ball thrown upward with a given initial velocity, or the changes in velocity produced in an elastic collision between two particles, without having to solve for the motion in detail. We shall find, similarly, that considerations involving electrical energy will enable us to compute much about electrical phenomena that would be difficult if we were required to explore the electrical forces in full detail.

In electrical problems the electrostatic potential energy is an important quantity. Let us explore the space surrounding the charged terminals of a current generator or battery with a very small charge. This small charge, or "test body" as we shall call it, is assumed to have a charge sufficiently small so that its presence will not alter the position of other charges as it is moved about. The test body will experience a force at any given point in space. The magnitude and direction of this force can be computed from Coulomb's law. If we move the test body from point to point, its potential energy will change. If we move the test body in a direction opposite to that in which the electrical forces act, we must do work, and this work goes to increase the potential energy of the test body. The mechanical analog would consist of lifting a mass against the downward pull of gravity. In lifting the mass we move it in a direction opposite to the downward pull, and the work we do in lifting it is precisely equal to the increase in its potential energy. The electrical forces will in general vary in magnitude and direction from point to point, so that we cannot write a simple expression like mgh for the potential energy, as we could for gravitational forces in the laboratory, which were uniform in magnitude and direction. But in spite of this complication, we may assign a given potential energy to our test body at every point in space (except for an arbitrary constant specifying the point at which we shall designate the potential energy to be zero). The change in potential energy in going from some point A to some point B will be the work required to move the test body from A to B.

This potential energy concept is particularly useful when we come to consider electrical circuits. We shall be considering charges flowing through various electrically interconnected circuit elements from one terminal of a battery to another. We shall find that electrical forces must be present in order to make the charges move, but that it is almost never necessary to resort to a detailed description of the forces. Instead, we consider the potential energy of a small quantity of charge at various points in the circuit and from this deduce the resultant flow of charge. It is most fortunate for our study that this potential energy of a quantity of charge is, first of all, so revealing and, second, so easy to measure.

Let us again return to a consideration of mechanical problems. Suppose we plan to dig a deep ditch from one end of Kansas to the other, connecting two water reservoirs, and we wish to decide in advance how much water is going to flow along the ditch and in which direction. It would, of course, be necessary to know something of the size and construction of the proposed ditch, but the most important point of all, the point which determines the direction of the flow and for a canal of any given size also the rate of flow, would be the difference in the water level of the two reservoirs. Stated more generally, the direction of flow and the rate of flow will be determined by the difference in the gravitational potential energy mgh of a test body m, or the difference in the gravitational potential gh, at the two reservoirs.

Similarly, if we have two points in a circuit, A and B, and we wish to predict how much current will flow through a wire connected to A and B, we must, first of all, know the difference in potential energy of a coulomb of charge at A and at B. If the potential energy at A is higher than at B, then positive charge will spontaneously move "downhill," as it were, from A to B. The potential energy per coulomb is the important quantity. It is called the *electrostatic potential*. Its dimensions are joules/coulomb in the mks system of units, and 1 *joule/coulomb is called a volt.*

Potential, like potential energy, has an arbitrary absolute magnitude, but differences in potential energy are unambiguous and it is differences in potential that are significant. Thus, if V_A and V_B are the potential energies of 1 coulomb at points A and B, then the difference in potential between A and B, usually written V_{AB}, is just $V_A - V_B$. The work $W_{B \to A}$ required to carry a charge q from B to A is the potential energy of the charge q at A, or qV_A minus the potential energy of the charge q at B, or qV_B. We have, therefore

$$W_{B \to A} = qV_A - qV_B = qV_{AB}$$

or

$$V_{AB} = \frac{W_{B \to A}}{q} \text{ volts} \qquad \blacktriangleright (1.9) \blacktriangleleft$$

In general, there is a potential difference between charged objects and the difference in potential is equal to the work that must be done by external mechanical or other non-electrostatic forces in carrying a unit positive charge from the lower to the higher potential. The terminals of a battery, or the outlets on a d-c switchboard, are examples of such charged objects. The negatively charged terminal is at a lower potential, and the positively charged terminal is at a higher potential.

It follows from our previous definitions that all points on an isolated metal object must be at the same potential. If they were not, charge would move spontaneously along or through the conducting object from points of high to points of low potential until the postulated equality of potential was established. We can use this fact to devise an instrument

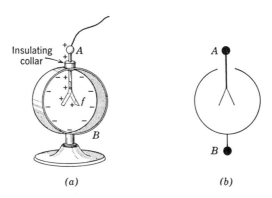

FIG. 1.6. (a) A gold-leaf electroscope. (b) Symbol for an electrostatic voltmeter.

for measuring the voltage or potential difference between two points. The electrostatic voltmeter based on the gold-leaf electroscope illustrates one simple way in which this can be done. See Figs. 1.6a and b.

The main features of a gold-leaf electroscope are shown in Fig. 1.6a. A cylindrical metallic cylinder with transparent ends has mounted in it a conducting rod A held by means of an insulating collar in B. At the end of the rod is a very thin gold foil f folded in the middle. When the instrument is uncharged, the two halves of the foil hang straight down. If now a certain amount of positive charge is removed from B and placed on A, a difference of potential will be established between A and B. The more charge transferred, the greater will be the difference of potential V_{AB}. But the positive charge on A will spread out, and part of it will be found on the foil f. The two halves of the foil will repel each other and will be attracted by the container B. The degree of separation of the two halves will be a measure of the amount of charge on A and B and therefore also of the potential difference V_{AB}. If the instrument is calibrated and provided with a scale, it becomes an electrostatic voltmeter. Its use as such is illustrated in Fig. 1.7.

Two parallel metal plates are connected to terminals a and b respectively. The plate connected to a has a charge $+Q$, and the plate connected to b a charge $-Q$. As a result, there is a difference of potential V_{ab} between the plates. These plates are connected through the dashed lines shown to the electroscope terminals A and B. The charge is now redistributed to include the electroscope, and, when equilibrium is established, the plate connected to a and the side of the electroscope A is at one potential throughout and the plate connected to b and the outer container of the electroscope B is at another. If the electroscope

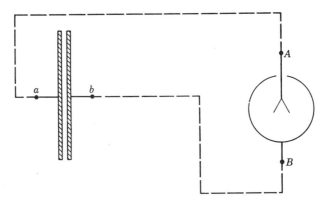

FIG. 1.7. A gold-leaf electroscope used as an electrostatic voltmeter to measure the potential difference between two charged plates.

is calibrated, it shows the potential difference $V_{AB} = V_{ab}$. This is, of course, the potential difference V_{ab} after the electroscope has been connected and is approximately the same as the potential difference originally present if only a small fraction of the charge originally on the parallel plates is taken up by the electroscope. We shall study this aspect of the problem in more detail in the next chapter.

Note about Units of Potential Difference

The potential difference between two points has the same units as the potential itself. According to the convention mentioned at the end of Section 1.1, large and small units of potential differences are:

The megavolt   (Mv) = 10^6 volts.
The kilovolt   (kv) = 10^3 volts.
The volt.
The millivolt   (mv) = 10^{-3} volt.
The microvolt   (μv) = 10^{-6} volt.

In the cgs electrostatic system of units the unit of potential is the *statvolt* = 1 erg/statcoulomb, which is approximately equal to 300 volts.

1.4 ELECTROMOTIVE FORCE

If two charged objects, such as the metal plates a and b of Fig. 1.7, are electrically connected to each other by means of a wire or other conductor, charge will flow through the conducting wire until the objects a and b are uncharged. The difference in potential will then be zero. The moving charge in the conductor is called an electric current. Two oppositely charged objects can maintain a current in a wire joining them only until the charge initially present has been dissipated.

A device capable of maintaining a current in a circuit is said to be a *source of electromotive force* (emf). It is a reservoir of energy, or a transformer of energy from one form into another. A source of emf is a device having electrical terminals between which a difference of potential is maintained even while a current is being delivered.

Among such devices are certain types of rotating machines called electric generators. Torque is applied to a shaft, and the work done by the forces exerting the torque is the source of electric energy supplied to a circuit connected to the generator.

Storage batteries are also sources of emf. The principles involved in their operation may be briefly described as follows: If two oppositely charged copper plates are dipped into a conducting solution, the free charges in the solution will move and a current will be established. The current will be such as to discharge the plates. If the plates are initially uncharged, there will be no force between them and therefore no current when they are put into the solution.

This is true only if the two plates are made of the same metal. If the plates are made of different metals, copper and zinc, for instance, the initially uncharged plates will be found to acquire a charge when placed in the solution. A difference of potential is produced by chemical forces. In the above example the copper is positive with respect to the zinc. The chemical action will be to remove positive charge from the zinc and transfer it to the copper and negative charge from the copper and transfer it to the zinc until equilibrium is established. Before equilibrium is established, chemical forces will act in such a way as to produce the charging process already described. As charge accumulates on the plates, electric forces will be set up in such a way as to oppose the continuation of the chemical process. Equilibrium is reached when the electrostatic forces are strong enough to stop the chemical processes from continuing, that is, when the work done by the chemical forces in carrying unit positive charge from the negative to the positive terminal is just equal and opposite in sign to the work done by the electrical forces. The total work done on a positive charge in being carried through a charged battery from the negative to the positive terminal is zero.

A further example of a source of emf is the thermocouple. A current will be generated in a loop of wire consisting of two pieces made of different metals, if the junctions are kept at different temperatures, T_1 and T_2. If one of the wires is cut, as in Fig. 1.8, a difference of poten-

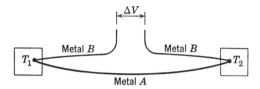

FIG. 1.8.   A thermocouple.

tial will be found between the two ends. The magnitude of this potential difference for any given combination of metals is a measure of the temperature difference between the junctions. At present this device is not used commercially to generate current, but it is important as an instrument for measuring temperature.

Most thermocouples produce only millivolts for differences in temperature of their junctions of the order of 100° centigrade, but even such small potential differences can be measured accurately. It is most convenient to be able to put a junction of two small wires in such widely

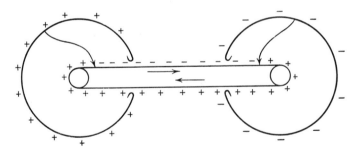

FIG. 1.9.   The Van de Graaff generator.   (See also Fig. 4.17 for a more modern version of a Van de Graaff generator.)

diverse and inaccessible places as, say, the low temperature chamber of a cryostat, or some muscle or organ of the human body, or a crucible of molten iron, and to be able to measure the temperature of this junction by maintaining the other at some fixed temperature, usually 0°C, and observing the voltage difference between two conveniently protruding bits of wire.

As a final source of emf we shall take up the Van de Graaff generator. The functioning of the instrument may be simply described in terms of the schematic diagram in Fig. 1.9. This is very much like the first large generator built about 20 years ago, consisting of two insulated spheres with an endless belt running from the inside of one to the inside of the other. Inside of each sphere there is a device for spraying charge of one sign onto the belt and transferring charge of opposite sign to the sphere itself, where it appears on the outer surface. The device for spraying charge onto the moving belt is not shown in the illustration,

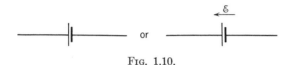

FIG. 1.10.

but is indicated by the arrowheads inside the spheres. In the left-hand sphere negative charge is being sprayed onto the belt, and in the right-hand sphere positive charge is being sprayed onto the belt. The potential difference between the spheres can be increased until electrical breakdown occurs. For instance, at sufficiently high voltage differences, a spark may jump through the air from one sphere to the other.

If the charges on the terminals of a source of emf are continuously replaced by some means, for example, by the moving belt of a Van de Graaff generator, the source becomes a continuously operable device for maintaining an electric current, and the device is said to have an emf designated by $\mathcal{E}$. The vector is considered to be in the direction that the device drives positive charges, or from the positive terminal through an external circuit to the negatively charged terminal. In general, the *emf of a generator is the terminal voltage when no current is being drawn.*

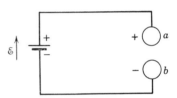

FIG. 1.11. Relationship between the emf of a battery and the current which it can produce.

A source of emf is designated in circuit diagrams by the symbols shown in Fig. 1.10. Of the two terminals the one on the long thin side of the symbol is positive, and the arrow indicates the direction in which positive charges are driven by the emf. Thus, in the case illustrated in Fig. 1.11, V_{ab} is a positive quantity and a positive charge released at a will go down in potential through the intervening space toward b. We may then think of the charge as being pushed back up to the higher potential by the battery or other source of emf represented by the symbol.

1.5   ELECTRIC CURRENTS AND MAGNETIC FORCES

The difficulties which Coulomb had to overcome to obtain reliable data on electrostatic forces were very considerable. In the first place, the forces produced by the quantity of charge that could be placed on a small object by available methods were small. In the second place, the charge on an object tends to leak off, particularly if there is considerable humidity in the air. It might seem that magnetic forces would be simpler to deal with. Anyone who has held two small permanent magnets is aware that the forces between them may be very appreciable. They are independent of such factors as atmospheric humidity. Further, since such forces had been known to exist for a long time, one might have expected the magnetic forces to have been analyzed much earlier in history. The magnetic compass, for example, was used as an aid to navigation before the twelfth century. Nevertheless, quantitative observations of both magnetic forces and electric currents were not made until the same period of history, namely, the end of the eighteenth century.

The magnetic force is quite different in character from the electrostatic or gravitational force. In the first place, it is not in general directed along a line joining two magnets and it is not inversely proportional to the square of the distance between them. If we were to examine the force between two magnetized objects, we should find that their orientation with respect to each other was an important variable. In other words, each magnet is to be described, not in terms of a scalar "quantity of magnetism," as was the mass in the gravitational case or the charge in the electrical case, but in terms of a directed vector quantity, describing its state of magnetization. Further, we should find that the force may be repulsive or attractive, depending on the mutual orientation of the two magnets, and need not be directed along the line joining them. For a fixed mutual orientation of the magnets, we should find that it varies inversely as the cube of the distance between the magnets when their separation is large compared to their dimensions. Finally, we should find that, in addition to the resultant force already described, each magnet may exert a torque on the other. The results, in other words, would be exceedingly complicated and hard to describe.

These difficulties are resolved by the introduction of a new concept which breaks the problem into two parts. This is the concept of a magnetic field. We consider a magnet as producing, or as being surrounded by, a magnetic field, and we then describe the forces in terms of the field of one magnet and the magnetization of the other. This field is perhaps best introduced through considering the interaction of the magnetized earth and the compass needle. We do not know what sort of thing the magnet inside the earth may be, but even without this knowledge we can describe the force. Actually we shall consider only the magnetic torque, or twist, which acts on the compass needle at any point on the earth's surface. The field may be thought of as exerting

FIG. 1.12.   The magnetic field surrounding (a) a bar magnet and (b) a horseshoe magnet, as revealed by iron filings.

forces which tend to make the compass needle point in the direction of the field.   A further well-known example is shown in Fig. 1.12, which shows the orientation of small magnetized iron fragments in the presence of a magnetic field.   The chains of magnetized particles serve as a graphic representation of the field surrounding the magnets.   In Fig. 1.12, it can be seen that the lines of the magnetic field extend from one part of a magnetized object to another.   These regions in which lines of force originate or terminate are called "poles."   When a piece of iron, for example, is polarized, or magnetized, it develops a north pole at one end and a south pole at the other.   In the illustration we cannot distinguish north poles from south poles, but by bringing up a compass needle whose poles have been marked we could tell whether the bar magnet in Fig. 1.12a had its north or south pole at the upper end, because, as in electrical phenomena, like magnetic poles repel each other whereas unlike poles attract each other.   We shall not here attempt to define magnetic poles more precisely, but it should be noted that isolated magnetic poles of one sign are not found in nature.   A magnetized object always contains both north and south poles.

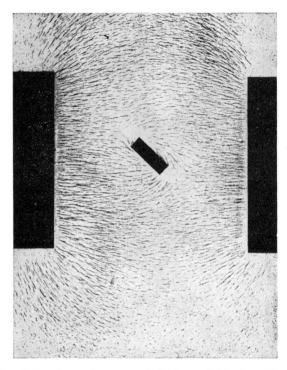

FIG. 1.13.   A complex magnetic field revealed by iron filings.

Figure 1.13 shows a complex magnetic field revealed by iron filings.

We now take up the problem of relating the electric and magnetic forces to each other, and shall show how these basic forces are related to phenomena that occur in electrical circuits.   Everyone is familiar with the words "ampere" and "volt" and with the meters which are used to measure these quantities, but there is often a certain amount of confusion regarding their precise significance.   We have already considered the concept of electrostatic potential energy and the related volt.   We shall now review the concepts associated with electrical currents and their measurement.

Let us return to our discussion of the historic sequence of events and consider how the concepts of current and ampere, on the one hand, and potential difference and volt, on the other hand, came to be developed.

At the end of the eighteenth century experimenters had only permanent magnets and electrostatic machines to experiment with. It was felt that somehow the phenomena which they produce must be related, but just how was not clear. In 1770 the Bavarian Academy sponsored a series of prize essays on "the identity of the two great mysterious forces, electricity and magnetism," but no connection was established. Regarding the functioning of an electrostatic generator, certain significant ideas were beginning to evolve. Henry Cavendish, the man who used an apparatus much like Coulomb's to measure the gravitational attraction between objects in his laboratory, described two ways of making electrical tests. One was to discharge charged objects through his own body and estimate the severity of the shock. The other was to observe the distance through which a spark would jump from one to the other of two charged objects. It was clear that these two tests measured different things, because the distance a spark could be made to jump from one object to another was by no means proportional to the severity of the shock felt when the two objects were grasped, one in each hand. The nature of the difference was, however, obscure. In order to clarify the issue, it was necessary to define electrical currents and electrical potential differences and find means of measuring them.

The series of events that led to this development took place during the first 30 years of the nineteenth century. Electrical batteries were produced. These made it possible not only to send pulses of charge through a wire but to drive charges around a metallic circuit in a continuous flow. The current so produced was observed to generate heat, to produce chemical changes if passed through a solution, and to give rise to light in an arc between electrodes.

Then in 1819 Hans Christian Oersted made the crucial discovery of a relation between electricity and magnetism. He showed that a compass needle was deflected by a current, that is, by electric charges in motion along a wire. In fact, a current produces a magnetic field, which can be demonstrated by means of iron filings, just as we demonstrated the field of a magnet. The filings, as shown in Fig. 1.14, form circles around the current-carrying wire. This qualitative fact is so familiar that its significance has often been underestimated. Its most obvious significance was that it made possible the construction of electrical meters. With the advent of these precise measuring instruments, the science of electricity and magnetism could begin to grow. But perhaps of even greater significance was the fact that the first step had been taken toward establishing a new set of laws of nature. The refinement of Oersted's ideas led, about 50 years later, to Maxwell's precise specification of the laws of electricity and magnetism, and enabled Maxwell to relate electrical phenomena to the transmission of energy through empty space.

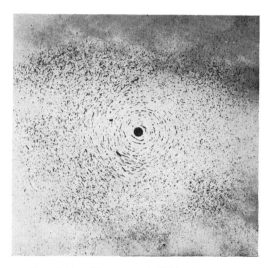

FIG. 1.14.   The magnetic field of a current.

Crude current-measuring devices were made soon after Oersted's discovery.   From the concept of quantity of charge q, responsible for electrostatic forces, was developed the concept of the rate of flow of charge.   *An ampere is a rate of flow of charge along a conductor at the rate of 1 coulomb per second.*

$$i = \frac{dq}{dt} \frac{\text{coulombs}}{\text{seconds}} \qquad \text{or amperes} \qquad \blacktriangleright(1.10)\blacktriangleleft$$

There is a certain ambiguity about the sign of the charge used in this expression for the current.   If we have two charged objects having equal and opposite charges, we can discharge them by moving all the positive charge to the negatively charged object, or all the negative charge to the positively charged object, or by moving some positive and some negative charge.   The electrical effects depend only on the total charge moved, not on which charge was moved.   The same is true of the magnetic effects due to moving charges.   Moving positive charge from left to right along a wire produces the same magnetic effects as the movement of negative charge at the same rate from right to left. In order to compute electrical changes, therefore, it is not necessary for us to know whether conductors actually carry moving positive or negative charge. The choice has been arbitrarily made that we consider the direction of a current as the direction of motion of positive charge producing the observed effects. Thus, if a wire is connected to the charged objects just discussed, the direction of the discharging current will be from the positively charged to the negatively charged object.

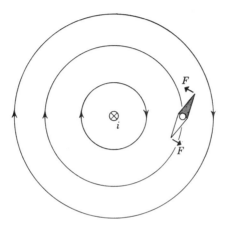

Fɪɢ. 1.15.   Torque on a compass needle near a conductor carrying a current.

It was eventually established that the torque on a compass needle held in some fixed place and orientation near a wire was proportional to the current flowing through the wire. For example, Fig. 1.15 represents a current flowing down into the paper along a conductor. Iron filings would form circular chains around the current, as shown in Fig. 1.15. A compass needle near such a conductor would have forces acting on it in the direction shown in the figure. The resulting torque would tend to make the needle align itself with the field. The magnitude of the torque in any position is proportional to the current. A very simple, though insensitive and clumsy, current-measuring device could be produced in this way.

Instead of measuring the forces acting on a magnetized compass needle near a conductor carrying a current, it is possible to determine a current in a conductor by measuring the forces on the conductor in the presence of a magnet. This is merely the reaction to the forces exerted on the compass needle. If the conductor exerts forces on a magnet, such as a compass needle, then the magnet must exert equal and opposite forces on the conductor. These forces are most easily described in terms of the field which the magnet produces at the conductor. A particularly simple case is shown in Fig. 1.16 in which current flows along a conductor at right angles to the uniform field between the poles of a magnet. The force acting on the conductor is proportional to the current and is at right angles to both current and field.

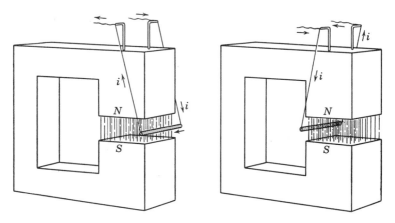

FIG. 1.16.   The electromagnetic force exerted by a magnetic field on a conductor carrying a current.

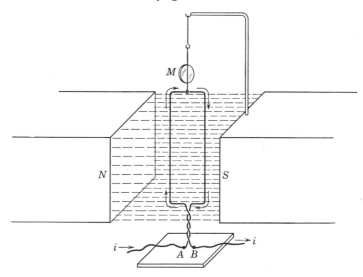

FIG. 1.17.   A simple form of galvanometer.

As shown in Fig. 1.16, reversing the current reverses the direction of the force.

This electromagnetic force is incorporated in a variety of ways in instruments called *galvanometers*. They contain either a fixed coil and a movable magnet or, more usually, a fixed magnet and a movable coil. The movable part is elastically suspended in such a way that it is rotated by an amount proportional to the torque, and therefore proportional to the current.

A simple form of galvanometer is shown in Fig. 1.17. A loop of wire is connected to terminals AB of a source of current between the poles of a magnet. The system is held taut from above and has a mirror M fastened to it. A light beam from a fixed source reflected onto a scale from the mirror shows the position of the system. When a current flows through the wire, a torque is exerted on the loop and the mirror is consequently rotated. The amount of rotation is a measure of the current. When an instrument of this sort is provided with a calibrated scale reading amperes, milliamperes, or microamperes, it is called an *ammeter*, a *milliammeter*, or a *microammeter*. The construction of actual instruments may be more complicated than the device shown in Fig. 1.17, but the fundamental principle involved is always the same.

Ballistic Galvanometers and the Measurement of Charge

Galvanometers may be used to measure not only current but also quantity of charge. To see how this can be done we must remember that the forces acting on the wires of the suspended coil of a galvanometer are proportional to the current. Symbolically, we may put

$$F = ki \qquad (1.11)$$

Suppose now that we pass a current i for some short time Δt through the galvanometer. The total charge Δq which has passed through the galvanometer will be

$$\Delta q = i \, \Delta t \qquad (1.12)$$

The forces will have given an impulse Ft to the coil. This impulse produces momentum. Actually the forces are so arranged that they tend to rotate the coil about its suspension. The impulse is an angular impulse and produces angular momentum about the suspension. This angular momentum will cause the galvanometer to swing, and if the impulsive force acts for a time short compared to a quarter period of the instrument then the subsequent total deflection, or maximum swing of the instrument, is proportional to the initially acquired momentum.

Going over the arguments again, we have:

1. A quantity of charge Δq flowing through a galvanometer is equivalent to a current pulse.

2. A current pulse through a galvanometer produces an impulsive torque whose magnitude is proportional to the charge Δq which passes through the galvanometer coil.

3. An impulsive torque will produce angular momentum. The angular momentum acquired by the coil, and therefore also its initial angular velocity ω_0, will be proportional to the charge Δq.

$$\Delta q \propto \omega_0 \qquad (1.13)$$

4. If the impulsive force is removed before the instrument is appreciably deflected, the total energy acquired is $\frac{1}{2}I\omega_0{}^2$.

5. The instrument, if left undisturbed, now swings to a maximum deflection, where it comes to rest. The kinetic energy is zero and has been converted into potential energy. The potential energy of a suspension twisted through an angle θ is equal to $\frac{1}{2}k\theta^2$, where k is the torsion constant of the suspension. We have therefore

$$\tfrac{1}{2}I\omega_0{}^2 = \tfrac{1}{2}k\theta^2$$

$$\omega_0 \propto \theta$$

and therefore, using Eq. 1.13, the maximum deflection θ is proportional to the charge sent through the instrument.

$$\Delta q \propto \theta \tag{1.14}$$

This instrument is the electrical analog of the ballistic pendulum used to measure the momentum of bullets.

1.6 RESISTORS, OHM'S LAW, JOULE'S LAW

A metallic wire is characterized by the fact that, if its temperature is kept constant, the current which it will pass is directly proportional to the voltage difference applied to its terminals. The proportionality

$$R$$

FIG. 1.18.

constant is called the resistance R of this wire. If the terminals A and B of a resistor R, as shown in Fig. 1.18, have across them a voltage V_{AB}, then the current i flowing through the resistor will be given the relation

$$iR = V_{AB} \qquad\blacktriangleright(1.15)\blacktriangleleft$$

$$i = V_{AB}/R$$

This is called *Ohm's law*. The resistance R has the dimensions of volts/ampere. The unit of resistance is called an *ohm*. A symbol commonly used to designate ohms is a Greek omega, ω (sometimes Ω). One ohm is equal to 1 volt per ampere. Thus a 5-ohm resistor carrying a current of 10 amp must necessarily have a potential difference of $10 \times 5 = 50$ volts appearing across its terminals. Conversely, if 50 volts are applied to its terminals, the resistor will pass a current $50/5 = 10$ amp. The direction of the current will always be from the terminal at the higher potential through the resistor to the terminal at the lower potential. These current-voltage relationships are graphically represented in Fig. 1.19. An electrical resistance may be computed from voltage and current measurements made with instruments connected as shown in Fig. 1.20.

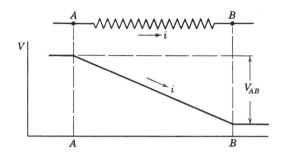

FIG. 1.19.   Voltage-current relationships in a resistor.

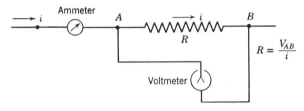

$$R = \frac{V_{AB}}{i}$$

FIG. 1.20.

Variable resistors are represented by one of the symbols shown in Fig. 1.21.   In the second designation the arrow represents a movable

FIG. 1.21.

sliding contact.   The resistance between this sliding contact and either one of the other terminals of the resistor depends on the position of the slider.

The Internal Resistance of a Source of EMF

As an example of the application of Ohm's law we shall consider the circuit shown in Fig. 1.22 involving a battery connected to a resistor.   A battery or other source of emf will in general have an internal resistance r.   This is often small compared to the external resistance and, if so, plays no part in limiting the current.   But, if we short-circuit the terminals of a battery, that is, connect them to the terminals of a conductor whose resistance is small compared to the internal resistance of the battery, the observed current will be entirely limited by the internal resistance.   This is the maximum current that the source of emf can deliver and is called the short-circuit current. Its magnitude is

$$i \text{ (short circuit)} = \mathcal{E}/r$$

The internal resistance of a battery must, in general, be included in the description of a circuit. If it is not explicitly given, it may be assumed to be negligible.

The total resistance of the circuit in Fig. 1.22 is $(R + r)$, and the current in this circuit will therefore be given by the equation

$$\mathcal{E} = i(R + r). \tag{1.16}$$

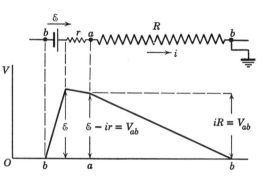

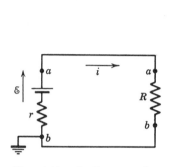

FIG. 1.22. A diagram of an electric circuit consisting of a battery whose emf is $\mathcal{E}$ and whole internal resistance is r, connected to an external resistance R and grounded at point b.

FIG. 1.23. Schematic diagram of the potential at various points of the circuit shown in FIG. 1.22.

Figure 1.23 represents the current-voltage relationships in this circuit. The circuit is here represented as a straight line for convenience, but the two end points are really one and the same point. Below the circuit diagram is a schematic plot of the potential at various points of the circuit. The terminal b is here assigned zero potential, since this point of the circuit is shown grounded, or connected to the earth, which is commonly used as a reference body at zero potential. In Fig. 1.23, there is a drop in potential, in going through any resistor in the direction of the current, equal to the current times the resistance.

It should be remembered as a universally applicable rule, already emphasized, that if a current i is passing through a resistance R there will necessarily be a potential difference of iR volts across its terminals, and that, conversely, if there is a potential difference of this magnitude across the terminals, there must be a current i flowing through it. Moreover, the current always flows through the resistor from high to low potential. Note that the potential difference between the battery terminals V_{ab} is no longer equal to the emf, but that when the battery is discharging

$$V_{ab} = \mathcal{E} - ir$$

The symbol $\mathcal{E}$ is reserved for the open-circuit potential difference across the terminals when no current is flowing through the battery.

Finally, in order for the voltage at the two ends of the diagram to be the same, the current must have such a value that the sum of the potential drops through the resistors is just equal to the emf of the battery. If, for example, a 6-volt battery having an internal resistance of 1 ohm is connected, as in Fig. 1.22, to a resistor having a resistance of 11 ohms, we have from Eq. 1.16,

$$6 \text{ volts} = i \text{ amp} \times (11 \text{ ohms} + 1 \text{ ohm})$$

or

$$i = 0.5 \text{ amp}$$

A variant of this situation is obtained by considering the same elements with which we have been dealing, but connected as shown in Fig. 1.24 at points b and c to some other circuit which will maintain a current i flowing from c to b. We again draw the voltage diagram, using the procedure described above, and arrive at the results shown in the figure. One of these results is

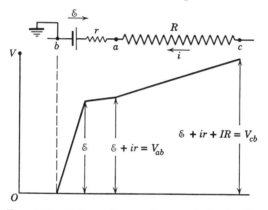

FIG. 1.24. Voltage diagram for a part of a circuit.

that the potential difference across the battery terminals is now greater than the open-circuit emf of the battery. This is generally true when a current is driven through a battery from its positive to its negative terminal, for example, when the battery is being charged.

Knowing the magnitude of the current in the circuit illustrated in Fig. 1.24, we can compute V_{cb}. We have, from Fig. 1.24,

$$V_{cb} = \mathcal{E} + ir + iR \tag{1.17}$$

Thus if we connect a 6-volt battery having an internal resistance of 1 ohm to a 114-volt line through an external resistor having a resistance of 11 ohms, and make the connection so that the positive terminal of the battery is connected to the positive terminal of the line, a charging current will be delivered to the battery. Its magnitude follows from Eq. 1.17.

$$114 = 6 + i(1) + i(11).$$

Solving for the current, we get $i = 9$ amp.

We shall now take up the energy and power relations in a simple circuit, for example, that shown in Fig. 1.25. In the circuit in question the battery is connected in series with a load CE and a switch ED. By a load we mean a device, such as a heater or a motor, which removes energy from the circuit when the battery drives a current through it. By a series connection we mean an arrangement in which the current flows successively through the units connected in series: that is, the current flows first through one; then without branching, the same

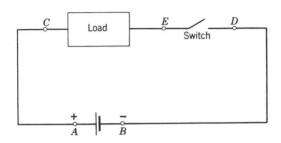

Fig. 1.25.   A simple circuit diagram.

current flows through the second; and then successively through any other units in the series connection.

Let us as an exercise first consider the potential differences between various points of the circuit when the switch is open. Suppose that the battery is a 6-volt storage battery. Then $V_{AB} = 6$ volts. A is at a potential 6 volts higher than B. B is at a potential 6 volts lower than A. We might also write $V_{BA} = -6$ volts, since V_{BA} is equivalent to $V_B - V_A$. The straight line connecting terminal A of the battery to terminal C of the load is assumed to involve no change of potential. Thus $V_{AC} = V_{CA} = 0$, and $V_{AB} = V_{CB}$. Similarly $V_{BD} = 0$, $V_{AB} = V_{AD} = V_{CD}$. If now the switch is closed, current will flow through the load. The switch again is assumed to carry the potential at D to E, so that $V_{ED} = 0$. Therefore the voltage across the load, or in other words the potential difference V_{CE} between its terminals, is equal to the potential difference between the battery terminals V_{AB}.

We have seen that the battery terminal voltage when we draw a current may be appreciably less than the open-circuit voltage, particularly if we draw large currents. We assume for the present, however, that the battery voltage remains 6 volts, and that when the switch is closed 6 volts appear across the load. This means that we should still have to do 6 joules of work on every coulomb of charge forced by some means from terminal E to terminal C, and, conversely, that every coulomb of charge flowing through the load from C to E loses 6 joules of energy. These 6 joules are converted into heat if the load is a heater, or into mechanical energy if the load is an efficient motor. The energy converted by q coulombs is qV_{CE} joules, and, if we have a current i amperes $= dq/dt$ coulombs per second, then we have iV_{CE} joules of energy per second or watts of power being converted. The power delivered by the battery is

$$W = iV_{AB} \text{ watts} \qquad (1.18)$$

The power converted by the load is

$$iV_{CE} \text{ watts}$$

Since the same current is flowing in both of these units, and the voltages across the two are equal, we conclude that the power delivered by the battery is consumed in the load. If the load draws 0.5 amp, the power delivered by the battery $iV_{AB} = 0.5 \times 6 = 3$ watts.

If the load is a resistor, the above considerations may be amplified. For example, in the resistor shown in Fig. 1.19, the power being converted to heat must be $W = iV_{AB}$. But from Ohm's law, as expressed in Eq. 1.15, we have $V_{AB} = iR$, or combining these results, we have

$$W = iV_{AB} = i^2R \text{ watts} \qquad \blacktriangleright (1.19) \blacktriangleleft$$

This is called *Joule's law*. For example, a 5-ohm resistor drawing 10 amp will generate $5 \times 10^2 = 500$ watts, or 500 joules/sec of heat.

Power Relations in a Charging or Discharging Battery

To illustrate the application of Joule's law, we consider first the battery connected to a resistor as in Fig. 1.22. The power delivered by the battery is $i\mathcal{E}$, and this is converted into heat in the resistor R and in the battery itself. We have

$$W = i\mathcal{E} = i^2R + i^2r = i(iR + ir)$$

This checks with Eq. 1.16, which states that the open-circuit emf of the battery must equal the sum of the voltage drops in all the resistances present.

If the battery is being charged by an externally applied voltage connected in series with a resistor R, as in Fig. 1.24, the power delivered by the external circuit iV_{cb} must equal the rate of generation of heat $i^2(r + R)$ plus the rate of storage of energy in the battery, $i\mathcal{E}$. Here the current i is opposed to the emf $\mathcal{E}$, and $i\mathcal{E}$ represents a rate of storage of energy in the battery.

If, as in the discussion of Fig. 1.24, a 6-volt battery having an internal resistance of 1 ohm is connected through an 11-ohm resistor to a 114-volt line, we find that the charging current will be 9 amp. The rate at which chemical energy is accumulated in the battery is 9×6 or 54 watts. The rate of evolution of heat in the battery is $i^2r = 81 \times 1 = 81$ watts. The total power supplied to the battery is $54 + 81 = 135$ watts. The heat generated in the resistor R is at the rate $i^2R = 81 \times 11 = 891$ watts. The total power supplied to the circuit is $135 + 891 = 1026$ watts or 1.026 kilowatts. This must check with the power delivered by the line $iV_{cb} = 114 \times 9 = 1026$ watts.

Wire Sizes and Current-Carrying Capacity

To give some idea of the magnitudes of the actual resistance of wires and the magnitude of the currents they can carry, we quote a few numbers which can be found in handbooks concerning copper wires. Wire sizes are conventionally given in B&S, or Brown and Sharpe, gage numbers. The diameters are given in mils, or thousandths of an inch. Areas are given in circular mils (cir mils). If the diameter of a wire having a circular cross section is D mils, its area in circular mils is D^2 cir mils. To convert to square inches we note that

$$\frac{\pi D^2}{4} \times 10^{-6} \text{ sq in.} = D^2 \text{ cir mils}$$

$$1 \text{ cir mil} = \frac{\pi}{4 \times 10^6} \text{ sq in.}$$

The "safe" current-carrying capacity of a wire is a fairly arbitrary quantity. What is permissible for a bare wire in an experiment in the laboratory would certainly be unsafe for an insulated wire in a conduit in a house. Approximate conservative values for confined insulated wires are given in Table 1.1.

TABLE 1.1   ALLOWABLE CARRYING CAPACITIES OF COPPER WIRE

(Regulation of the National Board of Fire Underwriters)

B&S Gage	Diameter, mils	Cross Section, cir mils	Amperes	
			Rubber Insulation	Other Insulation
0000	460.0	2,111,600	225	325
000	409.6	167,800	175	275
00	364.8	133,100	150	225
0	324.9	105,500	125	200
1	289.3	83,690	100	150
2	257.6	66,370	90	125
4	204.3	41,740	70	90
6	162.0	26,250	50	70
8	128.5	16,510	35	50
10	101.9	10,380	25	30
12	80.8	6,530	20	25
14	64.1	4,102	15	20
16	50.8	2,583	6	10
18	40.3	1,624	3	5

Note that, according to Table 1.1, to carry 1 or 2 amp a wire roughly $\frac{1}{32}$ in. in diameter is needed, whereas a wire $\frac{1}{8}$ in. in diameter will carry around 50 amp. For 500 amp something more like a copper bar around $\frac{1}{2}$ in. in diameter is necessary.

SUMMARY

Matter is composed of electric charges that exert forces on each other described by Coulomb's law

$$F = \frac{1}{4\pi\epsilon_0} \frac{qq'}{r^2}$$

The force F is in newtons if the charges q and q' are in coulombs, the distance r in meters, and

$$\epsilon_0 = 8.85 \times 10^{-12} \text{ coulomb}^2/\text{n-m}^2$$

Charges are of two kinds, positive and negative. Like charges repel each other; unlike charges attract each other.

Magnetized matter and electric currents are surrounded by magnetic fields which can be studied by means of iron filings.

An electric current is related to the movement of charge in a conductor or other conducting medium by the equation

$$i = \frac{dq}{dt} \frac{\text{coulombs}}{\text{second}} \quad \text{or amperes}$$

The current through a conductor in amperes is equal to the number of coulombs passing any cross section in 1 sec. The direction of the current is taken as the direction of motion of positive charge which would produce the same electrical effects as the observed current. If a current is due to the motion of negative charge, then the direction of motion of this negative charge is opposite to the direction of the current.

Currents are produced by potential differences. The terminals of a battery, for example, have a potential difference which is numerically equal to the work required to carry 1 positive coulomb from the negative to the positive terminal of the battery (along a path outside of the battery). Potential differences are expressed in volts, which have the dimensions of joules per coulomb. From this definition it follows that the power delivered by a battery to a load is

$$W = iV_{AB} \text{ watts}$$

where i is the current sent through the load by the battery and V_{AB} is the potential difference between the battery terminals while it is delivering the current i.

The current through a metallic conductor at any fixed temperature is proportional to the impressed voltage. The proportionality constant is called the resistance R in ohms, and the relation

$$iR = V_{AB}$$

where i is the current through the conductor in amperes and V_{AB} is the potential difference between its terminals, is called Ohm's law. The rate of generation of heat in a conductor having a resistance R, usually called a resistor, is

$$W = iV_{AB} = i^2R \text{ watts}$$

This is called Joule's law.

The voltage or potential difference between two points is measured by connecting the terminals of a voltmeter to the two points in question. Galvanometers are instruments which contain moving parts that produce observable deflections when currents are passed through them. Currents are measured by being passed through a calibrated galvanometer, or ammeter. Galvanometers may also be used ballistically to measure quantity of charge.

PROBLEMS

1. Two charges of 5 μc each are 0.01 meter apart. What is the force on each?

2. If two isolated charges of 1 coulomb each could be placed 1 meter apart, what would be the force between them expressed in tons?

3. A charge of 1 μc and one of 25 μc are 0.1 meter apart. Find the places where there would be no force on a third charge.

4. A charge of 1 μc and one of -25 μc are 0.1 meter apart. Find the place where there would be no force on a third charge.

5. From the value of $\epsilon_0 = 8.85 \times 10^{-12}$ coulomb^2/n-m^2, and the definition of the statcoulomb, prove that 1 coulomb $= 3 \times 10^9$ statcoulombs (approx.).

6. Positive charges of 1 μc are placed at two of the corners of an equilateral triangle 0.3 meter on a side, and a negative charge of 1 μc is placed on the third corner. (a) What are the magnitude and direction of the force on the negative charge? (b) What are the magnitude and direction of the forces on the positive charges?

7. Assume that it is possible to place a charge of 0.005 μc on each of three pith balls suspended from a common point by threads 0.3 meter long. What must the mass of the pith balls be if they hang at the corners of an equilateral triangle 0.03 meter on a side?

8. Two charges of 25 μc each are placed at the points $(-0.05$ meter, 0) and $(0.05$ meter, 0) in the x-y plane. (a) Find the force on a third charge of 1 μc placed at any point on the x axis; (b) at any point on the y axis.

9. Two charges of Q coulombs each are placed at two opposite corners of a square. What additional charges q placed at each of the other two corners will reduce the resultant electric force on each of the charges Q to zero? Is it possible to choose these charges so that the resultant forces on *all* of the charges is zero?

10. Make a sketch showing the distribution of poles in Fig. 1.13.

11. A storage battery delivers a current of 1.5 amp to a load for $\frac{1}{2}$ hour. (a) How many coulombs of charge have passed through the load? Make a sketch showing the polarity of the battery and the direction of the current. Show how an ammeter and a voltmeter should be connected to measure the current delivered by the battery and its terminal voltage. (b) If the current is actually carried by negatively charged electrons, the charge on each electron being -1.6×10^{-19} coulomb, how many

electrons would have passed through the load? In what direction would they have moved? What would then have been the direction of the current?

12. A 2-ohm resistor and a 10-ohm resistor are placed in series across a 6-volt battery having a negligible internal resistance. (a) Find the current through each resistor. (b) Find the potential across each resistor.

13. In Problem 12, how much power is delivered by the battery? How much heat is generated in each resistor?

14. (a) What is the resistance of a 100-watt lamp under ordinary operating conditions? (b) How much power would you expect to be drawn by each of the two 100-watt lamps connected across a 110-volt line in series?

15. A 10,000-ohm resistor and a 1000-ohm resistor are connected in series to a 200-volt power source. (a) What is the current drawn? (b) What is the voltage drop across each resistor?

16. The equation of motion of the moving coil of a galvanometer may be expressed in the form

$$\tau = \frac{d}{dt}(I\omega) = I\alpha = I\frac{d^2\theta}{dt^2}$$

stating that the torque τ applied to the moving coil is equal to the rate of change of angular momentum. If the system is given a deflection by some means and is then allowed to oscillate freely, the only torque acting will be that due to the suspension. This is proportional to the deflection θ of the system and is always in such a direction as to restore the system to its equilibrium position. The equation of motion of a freely swinging suspended system of this kind therefore is

$$I\frac{d^2\theta}{dt^2} = -k\theta$$

The solution of this equation will be a periodic function having an arbitrary amplitude but a given frequency.

(a) Assume that the solution has the form $\theta = A \sin 2\pi ft$, and find the equation for the frequency f with which the system will oscillate by substituting the expression suggested for θ into the equation of motion.

(b) Passing a steady current through this galvanometer produces a torque proportional to the current

$$\tau = ci$$

and this in turn produces a deflection which we have already defined

$$\tau = -k\theta$$

By observation, it is found that a particular ballistic galvanometer has a period of 10 sec, and that a steady current of 100 microamperes produces a steady deflection of 13 cm on a scale 1 meter away. The moment of inertia of the moving parts is 10^{-8} kg-m^2. How much torque is exerted on the moving coil when a current of 5 μa flows through it?

(c) When the instrument is used ballistically, how many coulombs must be discharged through it to produce a deflection of 10 cm on a scale 1 meter away?

★17. Show that the maximum possible rate at which a battery can deliver energy to an external resistor is realized when the external resistance is equal to the internal resistance of the battery

CHAPTER 2

Electric Fields

2.1 DEFINITION OF THE ELECTRIC FIELD

Electrostatic phenomena have been discussed so far in terms of charged particles and the forces between them. The forces act across empty space, to be sure, but the emphasis in the discussion has been very much on the particles, rather than on the intervening space. If we limit ourselves to electrostatic phenomena, this procedure is justified. The approach described is entirely correct and is well suited to the solution of many physical and engineering problems. There is, however, an alternative description of electrostatic phenomena in which the emphasis is put not so much on the charges but rather on the space between the charges. The space surrounding electric charges contains an electric field, and many electrical phenomena can best be described in terms of the properties of this field.

Alternative descriptions are not uncommon in science. When a theory has been developed to account for a group of observable phenomena (in our case the properties of electrically charged bodies), even though it may give completely correct results scientists are likely to look for alternative equivalent descriptions. The hope is that the alternative may deepen insight into the phenomena being studied and perhaps reveal unsuspected connections with other phenomena. Thus we shall derive some of the properties of the electric field, which, in so far as this chapter is concerned, will appear as rather difficult and complicated supplements to Coulomb's law, and the field itself will appear primarily as a mathematical fiction useful in making certain calculations, just as $\frac{1}{2}mv^2$ may at first have seemed a rather arbitrary mathematical fiction with no "reality." But just as the abstract concept of kinetic energy turns out to be a very fundamental attribute of matter, so the electric field turns out to be a very fundamental attribute of space. We shall find that energy and momentum, and also mass, can be moved from one particle to another distant particle through empty space, and that with the help of the concept of a field we can specify under given conditions just where in space and at what speed such transfers can take place. This is, of course, beyond the realm of electrostatics, but the importance of introducing the concept of the electric field at this point is to lay the groundwork for these other future considerations.

The *electric field* is a vector field specifying the magnitude and direction of the electric force that would act on unit positive charge placed at any point in space.

$$\mathbf{E} = \frac{\mathbf{F}}{q} \frac{\text{newtons}}{\text{coulomb}} \qquad \blacktriangleright (2.1) \blacktriangleleft$$

The electric field $\mathbf{E}$ at any point may be determined through placing a test charge q at that point, measuring the magnitude and direction of the electrical force action on q, and then dividing the observed force $\mathbf{F}$ by q.

The electric field at any point, or the electric intensity as it is also called, is determined by the existing charge distribution and can be computed by use of Coulomb's law. In making an experimental determination of the field by measuring the force $\mathbf{F}$ acting on a charge q at any given point, one must be careful not to disturb the existing distribution of charge by the introduction of the test charge q. The existing distribution can be preserved, in principle at least, if the test charge q is made sufficiently small, so that the force which the test charge exerts on the charges in the existing distribution may be neglected. A rigorous definition of the electric field is the limit of the ratio of the force $\Delta\mathbf{F}$ exerted on a charge Δq as Δq approaches zero, or

$$\mathbf{E} = \lim_{\Delta q \to 0} \frac{\Delta\mathbf{F}}{\Delta q}$$

Example of the Computation of the Electric Field Due to Point Charges

As an example of the application of the foregoing we compute the field at the origin due to the two charges not at the origin shown in Fig. 1.4. We have a charge of 3 μc on the positive x axis 0.1 meter from the origin and a charge of $-4\,\mu c$ on the positive y axis also 0.1 meter from the origin. The force on a charge of 1 μc at the origin was computed to be 4.5 newtons at an angle of 37° to the positive y axis. The force on unit charge, or 1 coulomb, would be a million times as large, or 4.5×10^6 newtons. But the electric field is the force per unit charge, or

$$E = 4.5 \times 10^6 \text{ newtons/coulomb}$$

in the direction of the resultant force $\mathbf{F}$ shown in Fig. 1.4.

The electric intensity due to a single charge can be computed from Coulomb's law. This procedure may be generalized. Let us compute the electric field at some arbitrary point in space due to charges $q_1, q_2, q_3, \cdots$, etc., at distances $r_1, r_2, r_3, \cdots$, etc., from the point in question, P. To do this we place a test charge q at the point P, and, using the previously derived relation,

$$\mathbf{F} = \frac{1}{4\pi\epsilon_0}\left[\frac{\vec{qq_1}}{r_1{}^2} + \frac{\vec{qq_2}}{r_2{}^2} + \cdots\right]$$

compute the force acting on q. Now, using the definition Eq. 2.1, we get

$$\mathbf{E} = \frac{\mathbf{F}}{q} = \frac{1}{4\pi\epsilon_0}\left[\frac{\vec{q_1}}{r_1{}^2} + \frac{\vec{q_2}}{r_2{}^2} + \cdots\right] \tag{2.2}$$

The terms on the right side of the above equation are the fields at the point P due to the separate charges. If these are designated by $\mathbf{E}_1, \mathbf{E}_2, \mathbf{E}_3$, etc., we may write

$$\mathbf{E} = \mathbf{E}_1 + \mathbf{E}_2 + \mathbf{E}_3 \cdots \tag{2.3}$$

The resultant electric field at any point in space is equal to the vector sum of the fields due to all the charges present. The field due to a positive charge is directed radially outward from the charge. The field due to a negative charge is directed radially inward toward the charge.

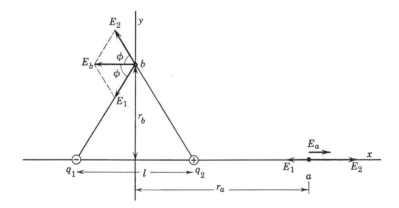

FIG. 2.1. Two equal and opposite charges a distance l apart.

The Field of an Electric Dipole

As a further example, we compute the field due to two charges q_1 and q_2 a distance l apart. We shall suppose that these charges have the same magnitude q, and that q_1 is negative whereas q_2 is positive. We choose the midpoint between the charges as the origin of coordinates, and compute first the field at point a on the x axis, as shown in Fig. 2.1. We have

$$E_a = E_2 - E_1 = \frac{1}{4\pi\epsilon_0}\left[\frac{q}{(r_a - l/2)^2} - \frac{q}{(r_a + l/2)^2}\right]$$

$$= \frac{q}{4\pi\epsilon_0}\frac{(r_a + l/2)^2 - (r_a - l/2)^2}{(r_a{}^2 - (l/2)^2)^2}$$

$$= \frac{q}{4\pi\epsilon_0}\frac{2r_a l}{[r_a{}^2 - (l/2)^2]^2} \tag{2.4}$$

Similarly, at point b we have for the magnitude of the electric intensity

$$E_b = E_1 \cos\phi + E_2 \cos\phi$$

$$= \frac{1}{4\pi\epsilon_0}\left[\frac{q}{r_b{}^2 + (l/2)^2} + \frac{q}{r_b{}^2 + (l/2)^2}\right]\frac{l/2}{\sqrt{r_b{}^2 + (l/2)^2}}$$

$$= \frac{q}{4\pi\epsilon_0}\frac{l}{(r_b{}^2 + (l/2)^2)^{3/2}} \tag{2.5}$$

These expressions assume a particularly simple form for distances from the origin that are large compared to the separation of the charges. In these circumstances the pair of charges is known as a dipole, and the quantity ql is called the electric moment, or electric dipole moment. Designating this by p, we have

$$E_a = \frac{1}{4\pi\epsilon_0}\frac{2p}{r_a{}^3} \qquad \text{if } r_a \gg l$$

and $\tag{2.6}$

$$E_b = \frac{1}{4\pi\epsilon_0}\frac{p}{r_b{}^3} \qquad \text{if } r_b \gg l$$

At points not too near a dipole it is impossible to tell just how the dipole is constructed, for example, whether it consists of charges q a distance l apart, or charges $2q$, a distance $l/2$ apart. At distant points the field depends only on the dipole moment p. We can use this fact to generalize the result, Eq. 2.6, to include points off the axis of the dipole. A dipole may be considered to be a vector

$$\mathbf{p} = q\mathbf{l}$$

where $\mathbf{l}$ is a vector whose magnitude is l, extending from the negative to the positive charge in Fig. 2.1. Any particular dipole may not be constructed in this way, but its field at distant points will be that of such a dipole. We can resolve a dipole into components, as in Fig. 2.2, and we find

$$\mathbf{p} = \mathbf{p}_x + \mathbf{p}_y \qquad q\mathbf{l} = q\mathbf{x} + q\mathbf{y}$$

The field at a point a distance r from a dipole in a direction making an angle θ with the dipole axis follows at once.

We imagine a rectangular coordinate system with the x axis in the direction of r, and the y axis at right angles. The field at r in the direction of r is due to p_x or $p \cos\theta$ only. The y component contributes nothing in the r direction. We have therefore

$$E_r = \frac{1}{4\pi\epsilon_0}\frac{2p \cos\theta}{r^3} \tag{2.7}$$

Similarly for the field at right angles to r in the direction of increasing θ

$$E_\theta = \frac{1}{4\pi\epsilon_0} \frac{p \sin \theta}{r^3} \tag{2.8}$$

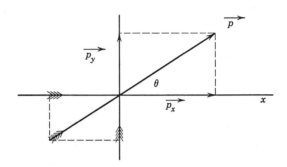

FIG. 2.2.   The resolution of a dipole into its components.

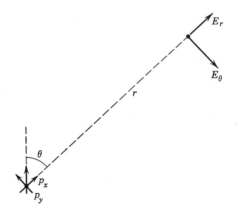

FIG. 2.3.   The field of a dipole at any point.

A further generalization of Coulomb's law concerns continuous charge distributions. We have seen that the electric field produced at any point in space by a series of point charges can be ascertained through computing the field at the point in question due to each of the charges acting alone, and then adding all these fields vectorially. The same process may be applied to continuous charge distributions. We shall consider now only surface distributions. The procedure for handling volume distributions is very similar.

The distribution of charge over a surface is characterized by its surface density σ or by the number of coulombs per unit area at any point. If the charge density is uniformly distributed over an area A, the total charge Q on this area is σA. If the charge is not uniformly distributed, it can nevertheless be stated that the charge dQ on an element of area dA is

$$dQ = \sigma \, dA$$

and that the total charge on a finite area is

$$Q = \int_A \sigma \, dA \qquad (2.9)$$

In order to evaluate this integral, it is necessary to express the elements of area dA in terms of suitable coordinates which can be integrated.

The Electric Field Due to Uniform Plane Charge Distributions

As an illustration of the computation of electric fields due to a continuous charge distribution rather than point charges, we shall first calculate the field for points along the axis of a uniformly charged ring, shown in Fig. 2.4. We

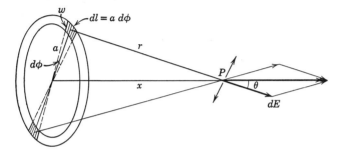

FIG. 2.4. The electric intensity at a point on the axis of a uniformly charged ring.

specify that the charge per unit area, or charge density on the ring, is σ, so that the charge within an area $dA = w \cdot a \, d\phi$ is $\sigma \, dA$. The electric field dE at the point P due to the charge dq within the element of area dA shown is

$$dE = \frac{1}{4\pi\epsilon_0} \frac{dq}{r^2}$$

It is clear that the axial components of the electric field due to all the elements of area around the ring will add, whereas the radial components will cancel in pairs because of the interaction of elements on opposite sides of the ring, as is illustrated in the figure. The resultant field will therefore be directed along the axis, and it is only the axial component of the field due to each element of area that will contribute to this resultant. The axial component due to the element of area shown in the illustration is

$$dE_x = dE \cos\theta = \frac{1}{4\pi\epsilon_0} \frac{dq}{r^2} \cdot \frac{x}{r}$$

But

$$dq = \sigma w \, dl = \sigma w \cdot a \, d\phi$$

and the resultant axial field due to the entire ring is

$$E_x = \int_0^{2\pi} \frac{1}{4\pi\epsilon_0} \frac{\sigma w a x \, d\phi}{r^3} \qquad (2.10)$$

If the total charge on the ring is

$$q_r = \sigma 2\pi a w$$

we may rewrite Eq. 2.10 in the form

$$E_x = \frac{1}{4\pi\epsilon_0} \frac{x}{r^3} q_r$$

$$= \frac{1}{4\pi\epsilon_0} \frac{x}{(a^2 + x^2)^{3/2}} q_r \qquad (2.11)$$

In order to find the field on the axis of a uniformly charged disk, we go back to Eq. 2.11, but we replace the charge q_r on a ring of finite width w by the differential charge dq_r on a ring of infinitesimal width da. In other words, we must put

$$dq_r = \sigma \cdot 2\pi a \cdot da$$

and finally rewrite Eq. 2.11 in the form

$$dE_x = \frac{1}{4\pi\epsilon_0} \frac{x}{(a^2 + x^2)^{3/2}} \sigma 2\pi a \, da$$

$$= \frac{\sigma x}{2\epsilon_0} \frac{a \, da}{(a^2 + x^2)^{3/2}}$$

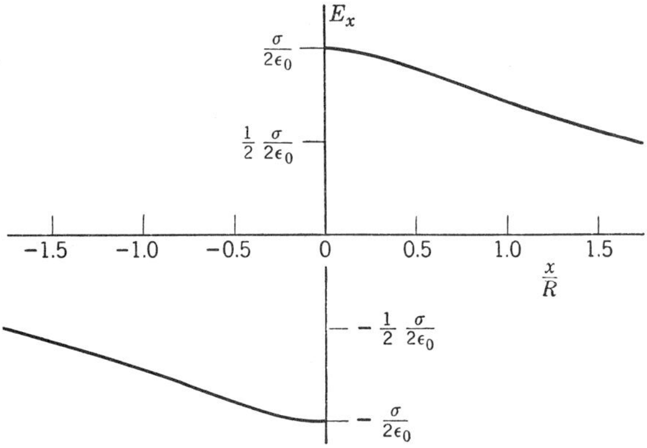

FIG. 2.5. The magnitude of the electric field along the axis of a uniform disk-shaped charge distribution of radius R at distances x from the center of the disk.

If the radius of the disk is R, we must integrate this expression from 0 to R.

$$E_x = \int_0^R dE_x = \frac{\sigma x}{2\epsilon_0} \int_0^R \frac{a \, da}{(a^2 + x^2)^{3/2}}$$

$$= \frac{\sigma x}{2\epsilon_0} \left[-\frac{1}{\sqrt{R^2 + x^2}} + \frac{1}{x} \right]$$

$$= \frac{\sigma}{2\epsilon_0} \left[1 - \frac{x}{\sqrt{R^2 + x^2}} \right]$$

$$= \frac{\sigma}{2\epsilon_0} \left[1 - \frac{1}{\sqrt{1 + (R/x)^2}} \right] \qquad (2.12)$$

This expression is plotted in Fig. 2.5. The field is directed away from the disk.

Since we have chosen the origin at the center of the disk, this means that E_x is positive to the right of the disk and negative to the left. Near the disk, for values of x small compared to R, $x \ll R$, the value of the electric field is $\sigma/2\epsilon_0$.

An important further development of this result is the computation of the field between uniformly but oppositely charged parallel plates separated by a distance small compared to their radii, as in Fig. 2.6. Midway between these plates the positive charges produce a field to the right whose magnitude is $\sigma/2\epsilon_0$. But at this same point the negative charges also produce a field of this magnitude to the right. The resultant field therefore is

$$E = \sigma/\epsilon_0 \qquad (2.13)$$

This result is applicable not only for the center point but throughout the region between the charges except near the edge of the plates.

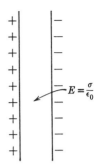

Fig. 2.6. The field between parallel plates carrying uniform charge distributions of equal magnitude but of opposite sign.

The general character of electric fields may be examined by a technique very similar to that employed for magnetic fields, but, instead of the iron filings which form chains in the direction of the magnetic field, small elongated insulating particles are used. In the fields shown in Fig. 2.7, hayseeds form the chains in the direction of the field.

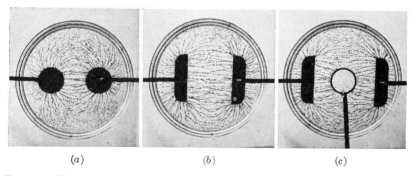

(a)   (b)   (c)

FIG. 2.7. Electrostatic fields as revealed by floating hayseeds. Note that the metallic ring in c shields from the external field the region which it encloses.

Pictorial representations, or maps of electric fields, may also be made by drawing *lines of force*. These lines of force are lines, usually curves, which are everywhere tangent to the local electric field. The lines of force around a single positive charge are shown in Fig. 2.8. From Coulomb's law we know that the force acting on another positive charge in the vicinity of the first will be in a direction radially outward.

The electric field will therefore be everywhere radially outward, and the lines of force will be straight lines radiating from the positive charge. Arrowheads along the lines of force are commonly used to designate the

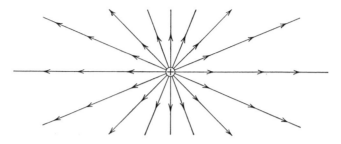

Fig. 2.8.   The radial field due to a single positive charge.

sense of the field.   The fields due to other charge distributions are shown in Fig. 2.9.   In (a) we have the field of a dipole, and in (b) the field between parallel plates.   Note that between the plates not too

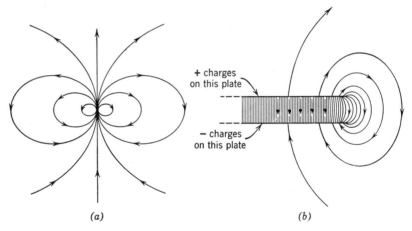

+ charges
on this plate

− charges
on this plate

(a)   (b)

Fig. 2.9.   (a) The field of a vertical dipole.   (b) The field between parallel charged plates.

near the edge the field is uniform.   It has the value computed in Eq. 2.13 for the central point.   Near the edges and in the region outside, the field has a more complicated form.

2.2   GAUSS'S LAW

Coulomb's law specifies the force at a distance which electric charges exert on each other.   In the previous section we introduced the electric field. It is a vector field which can be used to describe the force that a charge at any point in space would experience. The electric field, in this sense, is a mathematical tool. It is perhaps a little more than this, in that the pictures of electric fields in Figs. 2.7 to 2.9 are instructive as describing a physical situation. They are maps of conditions in space. We now take up a property of these maps summarized by Gauss's law.

If we integrate the normal component of the electric field, E_n, over any closed surface, S, then this integral multiplied by ϵ_0 will be numerically equal to the resultant charge inclosed by the surface S. Mathematically expressed, *Gauss's theorem*, which will be proved further on, has the form

$$\epsilon_0 \int_S E_n \, dA = \sum q_i \qquad \blacktriangleright (2.14) \blacktriangleleft$$

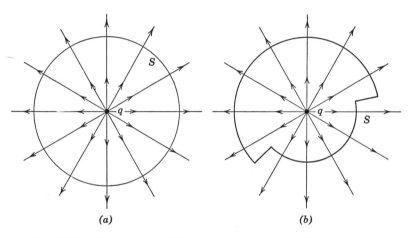

(a)   (b)

FIG. 2.10.   Two examples of Gaussian surfaces surrounding a charge q.

In this form, the theorem is applicable only to charges in a vacuum. We shall modify it further on to include insulating media. It will turn out to be a cornerstone of our attempts to describe the transmission of energy through space.

We shall first describe the application of Gauss's law to a point charge q whose field is directed radially outward from the charge. We shall choose as our Gaussian surface S a sphere with the charge at its center, as shown in Fig. 2.10a. The field at a distance r from a point charge q is, according to Coulomb's law,

$$E = \frac{1}{4\pi\epsilon_0} \frac{q}{r^2} \qquad (2.15)$$

If the radius of our surface is r, Eq. 2.15 gives the value of the field at any point of S. It is directed radially outward and is normal to S, so that in this particular case $E = E_n$. Further, it has the same value at every point of the surface. It is constant on S, and we may therefore take it out of the integral sign. We have

$$\epsilon_0 \int_S E_n \, dA = \epsilon_0 \frac{1}{4\pi\epsilon_0} \frac{q}{r^2} \int_S dA \qquad (2.16)$$

The integral dA over the surface of a sphere is $4\pi r^2$. Equation 2.16 therefore becomes

$$\epsilon_0 \int_S E_n \, dA = \frac{q}{4\pi r^2} 4\pi r^2 = q \qquad (2.17)$$

Gauss's law is satisfied for this particular case. Moreover, from the result, Eq. 2.17, we see that, since the radius r drops out, the theorem would be equally true for spheres of any radius. It is left as an exercise

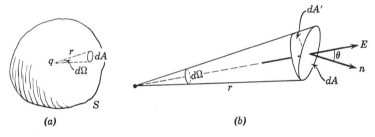

(a) (b)

Fig. 2.11.

to show that the above arguments hold for a Gaussian surface such as that in Fig. 2.10b, composed of radial and spherical segments. We proceed to prove the theorem quite generally.

Consider a point charge surrounded by a surface S of arbitrary shape, and construct an infinitesimal cone with its vertex at q intercepting the surface in an area dA, as in Fig. 2.11a. The solid angle subtended by dA at q is $d\Omega$. In Fig. 2.11b the relation between the electric field E, the normal to the surface n, and the projection dA' of dA on a plane normal to E is shown. We have

$$r^2 \, d\Omega = dA' = dA \cos \theta$$

Since the normal component of E is $E \cos \theta$, Gauss's law may be written

$$\epsilon_0 \int_S E \cos \theta \, dA = \epsilon_0 \int_S \frac{1}{4\pi\epsilon_0} \frac{q}{r^2} r^2 \, d\Omega = \frac{q}{4\pi} \int_S d\Omega$$

The integral of $d\Omega$ over the surface is 4π, and therefore Gauss's law is valid for a point charge. Since the fields due to several charges are additive, we can apply the above result to each charge separately and obtain

$$\epsilon_0 \int_S E_n \, dA = \epsilon_0 \int_S E_{n\,1} \, dA + \epsilon_0 \int_S E_{n\,2} \, dA + \cdots$$

$$= q_1 + q_2 + \cdots = \Sigma q_i$$

which is Gauss's law.

Gauss's law may be interpreted graphically, the electric fields being represented in terms of lines everywhere parallel to the field, as in Figs. 2.7–2.9. For example, let us return to the single point charge in Fig. 2.8. We shall assume that there are N lines drawn outward in all three space dimensions. The area of a spherical surface of radius r concentric with the charge q is $4\pi r^2$, and, if the lines are uniformly distributed, the density of lines per unit area is $N/4\pi r^2$, or numerically equal to the magnitude of the electric field $E = (1/4\pi\epsilon_0)(q/r^2)$ if $N = q/\epsilon_0$, or the number of lines per coulomb $N/q = 1/\epsilon_0$. The density of lines of force drawn parallel to the field will vary in just the same way that the electric field varies. This is true not only for a single point charge, but for any charge distribution. For example, in Fig. 2.9b the field between charged parallel plates is uniform, and in the graphic representation the spacing of the lines is uniform. In Fig. 2.9a the density of lines is greatest near the dipole where the field is greatest. This relation between line density and field is always quantitatively maintained, if the lines are continuous in space, originating on positive charges and terminating on negative charges. Gauss's theorem now becomes a matter of "counting lines." If there is an excess of N lines passing outward through a closed surface S, and if the number of lines originating on one coulomb is $1/\epsilon_0$, then the total charge within S must be $q = \epsilon_0 N$. The "number of lines" dN passing through an element of area dA normally is, in the notation of Fig. 2.11b, $dN = E \, dA' = E_n \, dA$. We therefore have

$$N = \int_S E_n \, dA = \Sigma q_i/\epsilon_0 \tag{2.18}$$

which is Gauss's law.

Gauss's law may be used to compute the electric field produced in space by charge distributions having a particular symmetry. If, because of this symmetry, we can choose our Gaussian surface so that E is normal to S and has the same value at every point, then we may take E

out of the integral in Eq. 2.14 and obtain

$$E = \frac{\Sigma q_i}{\epsilon_0 \int_S dA} \tag{2.19}$$

How this result is applied to spherical, cylindrical, and plane charge distributions is shown below.

The Fields Produced by Spherical, Cylindrical, and Plane Charge Distributions

There are three particular instances of symmetrical charge distributions whose fields may be calculated by means of Gauss's law much more simply than by the application of Coulomb's law. These charge distributions are of great practical interest, and we shall discuss them in some detail.

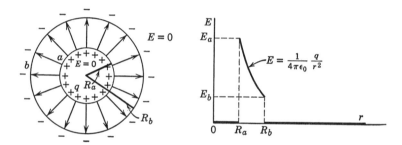

FIG. 2.12.   The field due to concentric spherical charge distributions.

Consider two concentric spheres whose radii are R_a and R_b, the inner sphere a having a charge $+q$ uniformly spread over its surface, and the outer sphere b having a charge $-q$ uniformly spread over its surface, as shown in Fig. 2.12. We propose to find the field due to this charge distribution. In applying Gauss's law, we are free to construct in any way we choose the surface over which the normal component of E is to be integrated. For the spherically symmetrical charge distribution we choose as the Gaussian surface a sphere concentric with the charge distribution. If this sphere has a radius less than R_a the total charge which it encloses is zero, and we are left with the result that, for

$$r < R_a$$

$$\epsilon_0 \int_S E_n \, da = 0 \tag{2.20}$$

For reasons of symmetry E_n must have the same value at every point of the Gaussian surface. In other words, Eq. 2.20 is satisfied not because positive values of E_n at some points cancel negative contributions to the integral at other points but because E_n, and also E, have the value zero at all points of the surface. But the surface is any sphere having any radius less than R_a. We have proved that E vanishes at every point within the inner of one or more uniformly charged spheres.

A similar argument applies to the region outside of the larger sphere. If the Gaussian surface is a sphere whose radius is larger than R_b, the total charge within it is $+q$ plus $-q$ which adds up to zero. We therefore conclude that E vanishes outside of the larger sphere.

In the region between the two spheres, however, the situation is different. The charge contained within the Gaussian surface having a radius r such that

$$R_a < r < R_b$$

is $+q$. As before, we conclude from symmetry that $E_n = E$ and that it has the same value at every point of the surface. Gauss's law then yields

$$\epsilon_0 \int_S E_n \, dA = \epsilon_0 E \int_S dA = \epsilon_0 E \cdot 4\pi r^2 = q$$

and finally, for $R_a < r < R_b$,

$$E = \frac{1}{4\pi\epsilon_0} \frac{q}{r^2} \tag{2.21}$$

The field *between* two spherical charge distributions is equal to that due to the charge on the inner sphere assumed concentrated at the origin and is independent of the magnitude of the radius of either sphere. The field due to this distribution of charge is shown in Fig. 2.12.

We now turn to uniform charge distributions on coaxial cylinders. In order to avoid complications at the ends of the cylinders, we shall assume that they are very long compared to their radii and we shall examine a central portion of length L far from the ends. In this case we may conclude from symmetry arguments that the field must be everywhere radially out from the axis. We choose cylinders of length L for our Gaussian surfaces. If the inner cylinder a of radius R_a has a charge $+q$ uniformly spread over its surface in a length L, and if the outer cylinder b of radius R_b has a charge $-q$ uniformly spread over a length L, we may conclude that the electric field within the inner cylinder and outside of the outer cylinder vanishes. The argument is similar to that used for the spherical charge distribution. If the Gaussian surface has either a radius smaller than R_a or greater than R_b, the total charge contained is zero, and we have

$$\epsilon_0 \int_S E_n \, dA = 0$$

where the integration extends over both ends as well as over the cylindrical portion of the surface S. The integration over the ends contributes nothing, since E does not have a component along the axis of the cylinders. As to the integration over the cylindrical portion of the surface, we conclude that E_n must have the same value at all points and, if this is true, then the only possible value of E_n or E that will make the integral vanish is zero.

If, however, we choose as our Gaussian surface a cylinder of length L whose radius is intermediate between R_a and R_b, we have

$$\epsilon_0 \int_S E_n \, dA = +q$$

Since E_n has the same value at all points of the cylindrical surface, and zero at the ends, this yields

$$\epsilon_0 \int_S E_n \, dA = \epsilon_0 E_n \cdot 2\pi r \cdot L = q$$

and, finally, since $E_n = E$, we have for $R_a < r < R_b$

$$E = \frac{1}{2\pi\epsilon_0} \frac{q/L}{r} \qquad (2.22)$$

The electric field between uniformly charged concentric cylinders varies inversely as the first power of the radius and vanishes elsewhere.

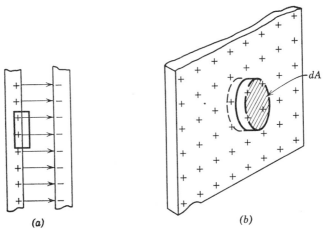

(a)   (b)

Fig. 2.13. (a) Cross-sectional view of the field between uniformly charged parallel plates. (b) Perspective of the Gaussian surface used in computing its magnitude.

Finally we come to the case of uniformly charged parallel plates. In order to avoid the discussion of end effects, we shall suppose that the separation between the plates is very small compared to their linear dimensions and we shall exclude from consideration points near the edges. We shall assume that our charged plates are made of metal and that the charge per unit area on the plates is σ. The situation is illustrated in Fig. 2.13. As our Gaussian surface, we choose a small pillbox having an area dA at each end and containing an amount of charge dq. For reasons of symmetry we conclude that the field must be uniform and perpendicular to the surface of the charged plates. Applying Gauss's law to the pillbox, we find that the contribution of the curved surfaces is zero since the field lies in these surfaces and so has no normal component. The contribution due to the flat face within the metal is zero, since the field in a metal in which there is no electric current vanishes. That leaves only the other flat face in the region between the plates to consider. Over this face the field is constant, and we get

$$\epsilon_0 \int_S E_n \, dA = \epsilon_0 E \, dA = dq$$

and therefore in the region between the plates

$$\epsilon_0 E = dq/dA = \sigma$$

$$E = \sigma/\epsilon_0 \qquad (2.23)$$

In the central region of equally but oppositely charged parallel plates, the electric intensity is equal to the surface charge density on the metallic plates divided by the permittivity of the medium between them. Notice that this is identical with the result, Eq. 2.13, previously arrived at through using Coulomb's law and integrating over the charge distributions.

2.3   THE ELECTROSTATIC POTENTIAL

The previous sections have introduced the concept of an electric field derivable from Coulomb's law of force. Whenever we have to do with force, we have also to do with energy. We shall now take up again and amplify what Chapter 1 had to say about electrostatic potential energy. The electrostatic potential at any point in space is defined as the potential energy of a unit charge at that point.

$$V = \frac{\text{Potential energy}}{q} \text{ joules/coulomb} \qquad \text{or volts} \qquad (2.24)$$

The potential energy of a charge q at any point in space is the work required to move this charge from a point where the potential energy is arbitrarily defined to be zero to the point in question. The difference of potential between two points is the work required to move unit charge from one to the other.

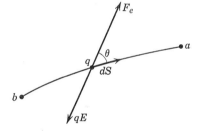

If F_e is the magnitude of an externally applied force shown in Fig. 2.14 which moves a charge q from point b to point a slowly and without giving it kinetic energy, then the work done by the force $\mathbf{F}_e$ is

Fig. 2.14.   Electric and mechanical forces involved in moving an electric charge q closely from a to b.

$$W = \int_b^a \mathbf{F}_e \cdot d\mathbf{s} = \int_b^a F_e \cos{(F_e, ds)} \, ds = \text{P.E.}_a - \text{P.E.}_b \qquad (2.25)$$

where P.E. is written for potential energy, and $\cos{(F_e, ds)}$ is the cosine of the angle θ between these two vectors. If the particle being moved slowly is a charge q in an electric field E, the force F_e must just balance the electric force qE. Thus we must have

$$F_e = qE$$

Since these forces are oppositely directed, we must have

$$\cos (F_e, ds) = - \cos (E, ds)$$

where $\cos (E, ds)$ is the angle between the field and the direction of motion and is the supplement of the angle θ shown in Fig. 2.14a. Substituting, and dividing both sides of Eq. 2.25 by q, we have

$$-\int_b^a E \cos (E, ds) \, ds = V_a - V_b$$

If we define the symbol V_{ab} to mean the difference in potential between a and b, or

$$V_{ab} = V_a - V_b = -V_{ba}$$

we have

$$V_{ab} = -\int_b^a E \cos (E, ds) \, ds \qquad\qquad \blacktriangleright(2.26)\blacktriangleleft$$

In this equation E and ds are the magnitudes of vectors and are therefore necessarily positive. Cos (E, ds) will be positive if the angle between the field and the direction of motion is less than 90° or if the motion has a component in the direction of the field. The path of integration in this expression is from b to a.

The electrostatic potential as defined in Eq. 2.26 depends only on the location of points a and b and is independent of the path along which the integral is evaluated. To prove this we consider first the field of a point charge and an arbitrary path between arbitrarily chosen points. If E_t is the tangential component of E in the direction ds, we have, from Eq. 2.26,

$$V_{ab} = -\int_b^a E_t \, ds = -\int_b^a E \cos \theta \, ds = -\int_b^a \frac{1}{4\pi\epsilon_0} \frac{q}{r^2} (ds \cos \theta)$$

But from the insert in Fig. 2.15 we see that $dr = ds \cos \theta$, and, therefore,

$$V_{ab} = -\frac{q}{4\pi\epsilon_0} \int_b^a \frac{dr}{r^2}$$

Notice that the angle θ which specifies the path of integration has dropped out of our expression for V_{ab}. Its magnitude depends only on the distance of points a and b from q. Now, making use of the fact that the fields of several charges are additive, we can conclude that, since V_{ab} for the field of each of several charges is independent of the path, then V_{ab} for the resultant field of any arbitrary charge distribution must also be. A concise statement of this result is that *the integral of the tangential component of E around any closed path vanishes.*

$$\oint E_t \, ds = 0 \qquad \blacktriangleright (2.27) \blacktriangleleft$$

The ring on the integral sign indicates that the integral is to be taken around a closed loop. That Eq. 2.27 follows from the above argument

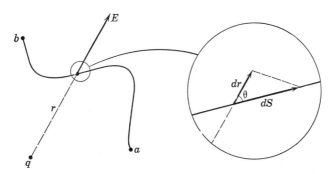

Fɪɢ. 2.15.

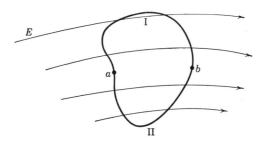

Fɪɢ. 2.16.

may be seen through reference to Fig. 2.16, showing a closed path along which the integral is to be taken. Choose any two points a and b on the loop. We have seen that V_{ab} computed through integrating along path I must be the same as V_{ab} computed through integrating along path II. But the contour integral, Eq. 2.27, may be written

$$\oint E_t \, ds = V_{ab} + V_{ba} = V_{ab} - V_{ab} = 0$$

which was to be proved.

It is to be emphasized here that Eq. 2.27 applies only in purely electrostatic problems. We shall see that when we come to consider time-dependent magnetic fields, certain modifications must be introduced.

The relation in Eq. 2.27 and Gauss's law, as expressed in Eq. 2.14, summarize the properties of electrostatic fields. They are the first steps in establishing Maxwell's equations describing the general electromagnetic character of space which we shall develop in succeeding chapters.

The Potential Difference between Charged
Spheres, Cylinders, and Flat Plates

As examples of the application of Eq. 2.26, we shall compute the potential difference between charged objects for the particular cases in which we know the electric field and can therefore carry out the required integration.

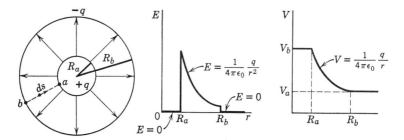

FIG. 2.17.   The electric field between concentric charged spheres.

It has been shown that the field between concentric spheres having equal and opposite charges is radial and that its magnitude is given by

$$E = \frac{1}{4\pi\epsilon_0}\frac{q}{r^2}$$

In order to find the difference in potential between two points a and b on the inner and outer spheres, as in Fig. 2.17, we apply Eq. 2.26 and find

$$V_{ab} = -\int_b^a \frac{1}{4\pi\epsilon_0}\frac{q}{r^2}\cos(E, ds)\,ds$$

Let us, to begin with, assume that both a and b lie at different distances from the origin along the same radius, and let us further assume that in the integration from b to a we are moving from negative charge at a distance R_b to positive charge on the smaller sphere of radius R_a.

$$R_a < R_b$$

It then follows that $\cos(E, ds) = -1$, since the motion is directed inward whereas the field is directed outward. Further, $ds = -dr$. We therefore have

$$V_{ab} = \frac{-q}{4\pi\epsilon_0}\int_b^a \frac{dr}{r^2} = \frac{-q}{4\pi\epsilon_0}\left[\frac{-1}{r}\right]_{R_b}^{R_a}$$

$$= \frac{q}{4\pi\epsilon_0}\left[\frac{1}{R_a} - \frac{1}{R_b}\right] = V_a - V_b \qquad (2.28)$$

We now note that along a path lying in a spherical surface with r constant, $\cos (E, ds) = 0$, no work is done, and there is consequently no change in potential. The previously imposed restriction that a and b lie along some one radius may therefore be removed, and Eq. 2.28 becomes a generally valid expression for the difference of potential between uniformly charged spheres.

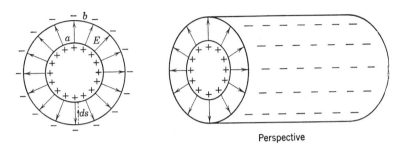

Perspective

FIG. 2.18.   The field between charged cylinders.

As a further example, we compute the potential difference between long oppositely charged concentric cylinders. In Eq. 2.22 we had arrived at an expression for the field between the cylinders. Its magnitude is

$$E = \frac{1}{2\pi\epsilon_0} \frac{q/L}{r} \tag{2.29}$$

Let us now assume that the outer cylinder b, having a radius R_b, shown in Fig. 2.18, is negatively charged. The field is again radially outward. If, now, we call the positively charged inner cylinder a and choose our path of integration from b to a, we have, since $-dr = ds$,

$$V_{ab} = -\int_b^a E \cos (E, ds)\, ds$$

$$= -\int_b^a \frac{1}{2\pi\epsilon_0} \frac{q/L}{r} (-1)(-dr)$$

$$V_{ab} = -\frac{q/L}{2\pi\epsilon_0} \ln \frac{R_a}{R_b} = \frac{q/L}{2\pi\epsilon_0} \ln \frac{R_b}{R_a} \tag{2.30}$$

By use of this result, the expression for the field, Eq. 2.29, may be rewritten as

$$E = \frac{1}{r} \frac{V_{ab}}{\ln (R_b/R_a)} \tag{2.31}$$

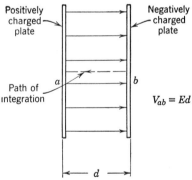

FIG. 2.19.   The field between parallel plates far from their edges.

Finally we come to the simplest example of all, the potential difference between uniformly charged plates. Let the distance between the plates be d, and let us choose a path of integration parallel to the field from plate b to plate a as shown in Fig. 2.19. The field as shown is in a direction opposite to the path of integration from the negatively charged plate b to the positively charged plate a. The quantity cos (E, ds) is therefore -1, and we have

$$V_{ab} = -\int_b^a E(-1)\, ds = Ed$$

or

$$V_{ab} = Ed \qquad\qquad (2.32)$$

The difference in potential between the two plates is equal to Ed, and the positively charged plate is at the higher potential. By using Eq. 2.23 relating the field to the charge density σ, we may put Eq. 2.32 in the form

$$V_{ab} = \sigma d/\epsilon_0$$

In the above examples we have made use of Eq. 2.26 to compute the difference in potential between charged objects. Exactly the same procedure may be used to compute the potential at any point in space. In such problems it is conventional to assign zero potential to infinitely remote points. By applying Eq. 2.26 to a point charge q, we get, as in deriving Eq. 2.28

$$V_r = +\int_r^\infty \frac{1}{4\pi\epsilon_0}\frac{q}{r^2}\, dr$$

$$V_r = \frac{1}{4\pi\epsilon_0}\frac{q}{r} \qquad\qquad \blacktriangleright(2.33)\blacktriangleleft$$

The electrostatic potential at a distance r from a charge q is inversely proportional to the first power of the distance from the charge. It is assumed to be zero for $r = \infty$ and is proportional to q, being positive for positive charges and negative for negative charges.

The above result for one charge may be generalized to many charges through noting that, if the fields due to many charges $q_1, q_2, q_3 \cdots$ at any point in space are $E_1, E_2, E_3 \cdots$, then

$$V_r = -\int_r^\infty E \cos (E, ds)\, ds$$

$$= -\int_r^\infty [E_1 \cos (E_1, ds) + E_2 \cos (E_2, ds) + \cdots]\, ds$$

$$V_r = \frac{1}{4\pi\epsilon_0}\left[\frac{q_1}{r_1} + \frac{q_2}{r_2} + \cdots\right] = \frac{1}{4\pi\epsilon_0}\sum \frac{q}{r} \qquad\qquad \blacktriangleright(2.34)\blacktriangleleft$$

Note that the terms in Eq. 2.34 are scalars, and that the sum is a scalar sum. The potential due to many charges is therefore much easier to find than is the electric field due to many charges, determining which requires a vector addition. If charges are continuously distributed in space with a density ρ, it follows from the above discussion that the potential at any point is given by

$$V = \frac{1}{4\pi\epsilon_0} \int \frac{\rho \, dv}{r}$$ ▶(2.35)◀

where r is a radius from the point at which the potential is to be evaluated to the volume element dv. The integration is to be extended over all those parts of space where charges are located.

The Potential Due to Several Charges

To illustrate these matters, we compute the potentials at the points a, b, and c, in Fig. 2.20, assuming that $q_1 = 10^{-8}$ coulomb, and that $q_2 = -10^{-8}$ coulomb.

At point a we have for the potential due to q_1

$$\frac{1}{4\pi\epsilon_0} \frac{q_1}{r_1} = 9 \times 10^9 \times \frac{10^{-8}}{0.05} = 1800 \text{ volts}$$

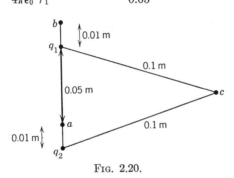

FIG. 2.20.

At point a the potential due to q_2 is

$$\frac{1}{4\pi\epsilon_0} \frac{q_2}{r_2} = \frac{9 \times 10^9 \times (-1) \times 10^{-8}}{0.01} = -9000 \text{ volts}$$

The potential at a due to both charges is therefore

$$V_a = 1800 - 9000 = -7200 \text{ volts}$$

Similarly one finds

$$V_b = 7710 \text{ volts}$$

$$V_c = 0$$

The difference in potential between a and b is

$$V_{ab} = V_a - V_b = -7200 - 7710 = -14{,}910 \text{ volts}$$

Point b is at a potential 14,910 volts higher than a and 7710 volts higher than c.

We have shown above how to compute electrostatic potential differences between two points in space if we know the field along some path.

It is possible, conversely, to calculate the field if we know the way in which the potential changes in the vicinity of a point. Through considering an infinitesimal element of motion, Eq. 2.26 may be written

$$-E \cos (E, ds) \, ds = dV$$

Since by $E \cos (E, ds)$ we mean the magnitude of the component of E in the direction ds, we may put

$$E_x = -\frac{\partial V}{\partial x} \qquad E_y = -\frac{\partial V}{\partial y} \qquad E_z = -\frac{\partial V}{\partial z} \qquad \blacktriangleright(2.36)\blacktriangleleft$$

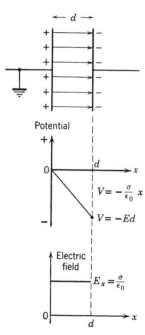

Potential

$V = -\frac{\sigma}{\epsilon_0} x$

$V = -Ed$

Electric field

$E_x = \frac{\sigma}{\epsilon_0}$

FIG. 2.21. The field and potential between charged plates.

where the ∂'s signify that in the differentiation we are in each case considering motion in the direction of one axis only, with no components of motion in the direction of the other axes. Notice that according to Eq. 2.36, E has the dimensions volts/meter, and that this is equivalent to the previously used unit newtons/coulomb.

To apply this result to the parallel plates discussed above, we must compute the potential at some arbitrary point between the plates. In the region between the plates at a distance x from the positively charged plate in Fig. 2.21 the potential is lower than at the positively charged plate. If this is grounded the potential at x is

$$V(x) = -E_x x = -(\sigma/\epsilon_0)x$$

By applying Eq. 2.36, we get

$$E_x = -\frac{\partial V}{\partial x} = \frac{\sigma}{\epsilon_0}$$

This is the result previously found in Eq. 2.23. Similarly the field at a distance r from a point charge, by Eqs. 2.33 and 2.36, becomes

$$E_r = -\frac{\partial V}{\partial r} = -\frac{\partial}{\partial r}\left(\frac{1}{4\pi\epsilon_0}\frac{q}{r}\right) = \frac{1}{4\pi\epsilon_0}\frac{q}{r^2}$$

which is, of course, in agreement with Coulomb's law.

The Computation of the Field of a Dipole from its Potential

To illustrate the advantages of this procedure, let us use it to compute the field of a dipole. The symbols to be used are defined in Fig. 2.22. From the figure it is clear that the potential due to the dipole, being the sum of the potentials due to the two point charges of which it is made up, is

$$V = \frac{1}{4\pi\epsilon_0} \left(\frac{q}{r - (d/2)\cos\theta} + \frac{-q}{r + (d/2)\cos\theta} \right)$$

$$= \frac{q}{4\pi\epsilon_0} \frac{d\cos\theta}{r^2 - (d^2/4)\cos^2\theta}$$

If we limit ourselves to distant points (and it is only in this approximation that the expression "field of a dipole" is actually used) we may neglect the quantity

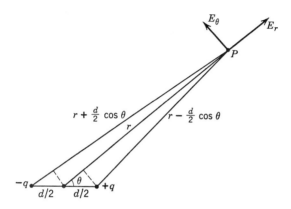

FIG. 2.22. Symbols used in specifying the field and potential of a dipole.

$(d^2/4)\cos^2\theta$ in comparison with r^2 in the denominator, and the above expression becomes

$$V = \frac{1}{4\pi\epsilon_0} \frac{(qd)}{r^2} \cos\theta$$

$$= \frac{1}{4\pi\epsilon_0} \frac{p}{r^2} \cos\theta \tag{2.37}$$

The quantity $p = qd$ is the dipole moment already defined in Section 2.1. We now proceed to calculate the field at any point.

In polar coordinates, a distance ds in a radial direction is simply dr; a distance ds at right angles to r and in the direction of increasing θ is $r\,d\theta$. We can therefore apply the result, Eq. 2.36, without transforming to rectangular coordinates. The results are

$$E_r = -\frac{\partial V}{\partial r} = \frac{1}{4\pi\epsilon_0} \frac{2p}{r^3} \cos\theta \tag{2.38}$$

$$E_\theta = -\frac{1}{r}\frac{\partial V}{\partial\theta} = \frac{1}{4\pi\epsilon_0} \frac{p}{r^3} \sin\theta$$

It is to be noted that at distant points the field of a dipole falls off more rapidly than the field of a pole, namely, as the inverse cube of the distance rather than as the inverse square. These results check with Eqs. 2.7 and 2.8, computed by means of Coulomb's law.

_____

We have shown that fields may be represented graphically by means of lines of force, as in Figs. 2.7, 2.8, and 2.9. Surfaces of constant potential are also useful in such diagrams. The electric field at any

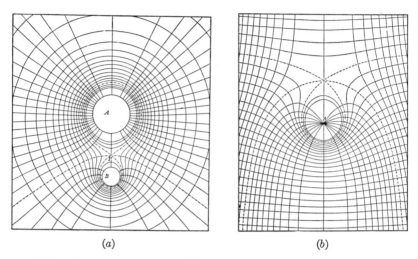

(a)   (b)

FIG. 2.23. (a) Some of the lines of force and equipotentials due to two electric charges of the same sign, the charge A being four times as great as B. (b) Some of the lines of force and equipotentials due to a charge in a field which was homogeneous before the introduction of the charge. These drawings were made by Maxwell, and are reproduced from his book, *Electricity and Magnetism*, first published in 1873.

point in space is necessarily perpendicular to the *equipotential surface* passing through that point because it is only when cos (E, ds) is zero, or when E is perpendicular to ds, that

$$dV = -E \cos (E, ds) \, ds = 0$$

Lines of force and equipotential surfaces due to two unequal charges of the same sign, and those due to a change in an electric field, are shown in Fig. 2.23a and b.

The conclusion that electric fields within metals must vanish, reached in Chapter 1, takes on added significance when we consider potentials. From the definition of a metal as a substance containing free electrons, so that any electric force, and therefore any electric field, will produce a current, we showed that the field inside a metal must always be zero in an electrostatic problem. If a piece of metal is charged, the charge will so distribute itself over the surface that the field within the metal is zero, as shown in Fig. 2.24a. If an uncharged piece of metal is placed in an electric field, charges will be induced on its surface in precisely such a way that the resultant total field inside the metal will vanish, as shown in Fig. 2.24b. It should be noted that there can be no excess charge within the body of the metal, since this would require an electric field around the charge. Excess charge must necessarily be confined to the surface of the metal. Further, the electric field just outside the metal must be normal to the surface. If there were a tangential component the surface charges would move along the surface, and we should not have a stable electrostatic distribution. A piece of metal within which there is no current is everywhere at the same potential, and its surface is therefore an equipotential surface.

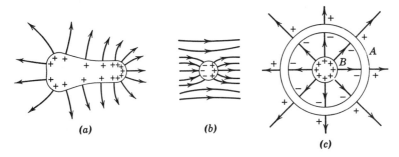

(a)   *(b)*

(c)

FIG. 2.24. The electrostatic field always vanishes inside a metallic object.

If the conductor is not solid, but is hollow as in Fig. 2.24c, the same result holds true. The charges must be confined to its surfaces. The illustration represents a hollow uncharged conductor A surrounding a solid charged conductor B. Lines of force originate on the positive charges on the inner conductor. These lines cannot extend through conductor A. They terminate on negative charges induced on the inner wall of the hollow conductor, and an equal number of new lines originate on the positive charges induced on its outer surface.

2.4 THE STORAGE OF ELECTROSTATIC ENERGY; CAPACITORS

We now turn from the rather abstract discussion of electrostatic potential and the properties of electric fields to certain important components of electrical circuits called *capacitors*, or sometimes *condensers*, which illustrate the application of the previous train of thought to concrete problems.

A capacitor is a circuit element which may be used for storing electric charge or electrostatic energy. A common form of capacitor consists of two thin sheets of metal separated by a sheet of insulation, usually folded and rolled up to save space. The metallic sheets are connected to protruding leads which form the terminals. A capacitor connected to a storage battery will not pass a steady current, but charge will accumulate on the plates, positive and negative in equal amounts.

When charge is removed from one of the plates of a capacitor and supplied to the other, a potential difference will appear. This potential difference is proportional to the charge on the plates. Thus if a quantity of charge Q is removed from one side of a capacitor and placed on the other side, a difference of potential V_{ab} will be established between the two parts such that

$$Q = CV_{ab}$$

where C is a constant whose magnitude is determined by the shape and separation of the component parts. The quantity C is called the *capacitance* of the *capacitor*. The mks unit of capacitance is the *farad*. We have then

$$C = \frac{Q \text{ coulombs}}{V_{ab} \text{ volts}} = \frac{Q}{V_{ab}} \text{ farads} \qquad \blacktriangleright (2.39) \blacktriangleleft$$

Microfarads, and *micromicrofarads*, designated by the symbols μf and $\mu\mu f$, have the magnitudes 10^{-6} and 10^{-12} farads, respectively. In the electrostatic cgs system of units, capacitance is measured in statcoulombs per statvolt, or statfarads. Statfarads have the dimension of centimeters.

$$1 \text{ farad} = 9 \times 10^{11} \text{ statfarads}$$

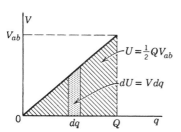

FIG. 2.25. A plot of the charge and the potential difference between the two parts of a capacitor.

A charged capacitor necessarily has associated with it a certain amount of electrostatic energy. If an amount of positive charge dq is taken from the negative part of a capacitor to the positive part, which is V volts higher in potential, the work done, and therefore also the increase in energy, is $dU = V\,dq$, as shown in the darker dotted region of Fig. 2.25. The total energy in the capacitor when it is charged to a potential difference V_{ab} by the transfer of a total amount of charge Q is found by integration to be

$$U = \int_0^Q V\,dQ = \int_0^{V_{ab}} CV\,dV = \tfrac{1}{2}CV_{ab}{}^2 \text{ joules} \qquad (2.40)$$

This also may be expressed in the following equivalent ways:

$$U = \tfrac{1}{2}QV_{ab} = \tfrac{1}{2}CV_{ab}{}^2 = \tfrac{1}{2}\frac{Q^2}{C} \text{ joules} \qquad \blacktriangleright(2.41)\blacktriangleleft$$

Note that $U = \tfrac{1}{2}QV_{ab}$ is an area in a q-V diagram just equal to the shaded area in Fig. 2.25.

Capacitors may be thought of as containers for the storage of electrostatic potential energy. Work must be done in charging a capacitor. The energy equivalent of this work can be recovered at a later time from the charged capacitor. If, for example, electrons were released by some means from the negative element of a capacitor, they would be attracted by the positive element, and the total kinetic energy acquired by all the electrons constituting the negative charge of the capacitor, if they were free to move, would be exactly that specified in Eq. 2.41. The electrostatic energy stored in a capacitor can also be fed back to an electric circuit connected to its terminals.

Capacitance may be thought of as an experimentally determinable coefficient characteristic of a particular pair of metallic objects separated by a non-conducting medium. Perhaps the physically most significant aspect of this coefficient is its role in the energy equation, Eq. 2.41, although its definition is usually given in terms of the voltage-charge relation, Eq. 2.39. We shall see that capacitance can also be computed from the known shape and construction of a capacitor. The conventional symbol for a capacitor is

$$\dashv\vdash \quad \text{or} \quad \dashv\Vdash \quad \text{or} \quad \dashv\!\!\!/\!\!\vdash$$

The Capacitance of Parallel Plates,
Concentric Spheres, and Coaxial Cylinders

Since charges of opposite sign attract each other, the charges on oppositely charged objects will crowd into portions of these objects that are as near together as possible. There will, therefore, also be a tendency for the electric field to be concentrated in the region of space between the objects. A particular case of interest is that of two flat parallel plates whose separation is small compared to their linear dimensions. The plates are assumed to have equal charges of opposite sign. See Fig. 2.9b. The electric field is shown as uniform in the region between the plates except near the edges, where it falls off in magnitude. The electric charges are likewise almost all uniformly distributed on the inside surface of the plates. When the distance between the plates is small compared to their linear dimensions, it is customary to neglect the edge effects and to treat the entire charge distribution and all the field as uniform. This simplification makes the computation of the properties of this capacitor very direct.

Let us designate the area of one side of one of these plates by A and the separation of the inside surfaces by d. Now, starting with any one of the variables E, V, Q, or σ as given, we can compute all the others. The following equations, which are simply a restatement of previous definitions put into the form required by the above geometry, are sufficient. For example, let us suppose that, in addition to the dimensions of the capacitor, we are given its charge Q. The charge density on the plates is therefore

$$\sigma = Q/A$$

But, from Gauss's law, we have computed the electric field in terms of the charge density, Eq. 2.23. From this, if the medium between the plates is a vacuum, or air, we find that the electric intensity E is

$$E = \frac{\sigma}{\epsilon_0} = \frac{Q}{\epsilon_0 A}$$

Finally, the difference in potential between the plates is equal to the work done in carrying unit positive charge from the negative to the positive plate. But, since the field is uniform, this is simply

$$V_{ab} = Ed = \frac{Qd}{\epsilon_0 A} \tag{2.42}$$

The capacitance of this capacitor in terms of its dimensions follows at once from the definition

$$C = \frac{Q}{V_{ab}} = \epsilon_0 \frac{A}{d} \quad \text{(parallel plate capacitor)} \qquad \blacktriangleright(2.43)\blacktriangleleft$$

A similar computation for spheres and cylinders is given below to illustrate further the application of the above ideas for cases in which the field is not uniform.

In a capacitor consisting of concentric spheres, the lines of force are confined to the region between the spheres. The density of charge on the inner and outer surfaces and the electric field between the two surfaces are given by

$$\sigma_a = \frac{Q}{4\pi R_a{}^2} \qquad \sigma_b = -\frac{Q}{4\pi R_b{}^2} \qquad E = \frac{1}{4\pi\epsilon_0} \frac{Q}{r^2} \tag{2.44}$$

The difference in potential between the two spheres must be found by integration, since E is not constant. We have, from Eq. 2.28,

$$V_{ab} = \frac{Q}{4\pi\epsilon_0} \left[\frac{1}{R_a} - \frac{1}{R_b} \right] \tag{2.45}$$

The capacity of the system follows at once from Eq. 2.45. We see that

$$C = \frac{Q}{V_{ba}} = 4\pi\epsilon_0 \left[\frac{R_a R_b}{R_b - R_a} \right] \quad \text{(concentric spheres)} \qquad \blacktriangleright(2.46)\blacktriangleleft$$

which, for $R_b \gg R_a$, reduces to

$$C = 4\pi\epsilon_0 R_a \quad \text{(a single sphere)} \qquad \blacktriangleright(2.47)\blacktriangleleft$$

A similar procedure leads to similar results for coaxial cylinders. The only different feature is that we have a different expression for the electric field between the cylinders. This we have already derived under the assumption that we may neglect end effects, which is allowable if the distance between the cylinders is small compared to their lengths. Figure 2.26 represents a central portion of such a system. The electric field is radially outward from the inner cylinder to the outer cylinder.

The previously obtained result, Eq. 2.22, is

$$E = \frac{Q}{2\pi\epsilon_0 rL} \tag{2.48}$$

and the expression for the capacitance follows from Eq. 2.30

$$V_{ab} = \frac{Q}{2\pi\epsilon_0 L} \ln \frac{R_b}{R_a} \tag{2.49}$$

$$C = \frac{Q}{V_{ab}} = \frac{2\pi\epsilon_0 L}{\ln (R_b/R_a)} \quad \text{(coaxial cylinders)} \qquad \blacktriangleright(2.50)\blacktriangleleft$$

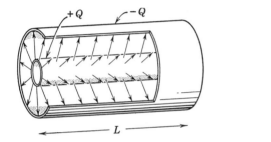
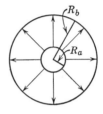

Fig. 2.26.   A capacitor made of coaxial cylinders.

Numerical Examples of the Magnitudes of Practical Capacitances

Let us compute the capacitance of 20 metal sheets having an area of 10 cm², alternately connected together, and 0.5 mm apart. The capacitance of any pair of plates is, according to Eq. 2.43,

$$C = \epsilon_0 \frac{A}{d} = \frac{8.85 \times 10^{-12} \times 10^{-3}}{0.5 \times 10^{-3}} = 17.7 \times 10^{-12} \text{ farad}$$

$$= 17.7 \ \mu\mu\text{f}$$

Between 20 such plates there are 19 air gaps, and the capacity is just 19 times the above. For proof of this, we return to the definition of capacitance as the charge per unit potential difference. If a potential difference V_{ab} is applied, the field between adjacent plates is $E = V_{ab}/d$, and the surface charge density which terminates the lines of force of this field is $Q/A = \epsilon_0 E$. Let us consider the positively charged plates only. There are 10 of these. Nine are charged on both sides. One positively charged plate, the end one, is charged on one side only. The total charge on the 10 positively charged plates is therefore $2 \times 9Q + Q = 19Q$, and the capacitance, as stated, is

$$19 \times 17.7 \times 10^{-12} \text{ farad} = 337 \ \mu\mu\text{f}$$

If this capacitor is connected to a 100-volt battery, the total charge drawn is

$$CV = 3.37 \times 10^{-10} \times 10^2 = 3.37 \times 10^{-8} \text{ coulomb}$$

$$= 0.0337 \ \mu\text{c}$$

The energy stored is

$$U = \tfrac{1}{2}(QV) = \tfrac{1}{2}(3.37 \times 10^{-8} \times 10^2) = 1.68 \times 10^{-6} \text{ joule}$$

The electric intensity between the plates is

$$E = \frac{V}{d} = \frac{100}{0.5 \times 10^{-3}} = 2 \times 10^5 \text{ volts/meter}$$

The above capacitor has not a very large capacitance. If instead of the above dimensions we had chosen 20 metal foils having an area of 1 meter^2 and separated by thin sheets of paper 0.001 in. or 0.025 mm thick, the corresponding results would have been

$$C = 6.73 \,\mu\text{f} \qquad U = 0.0337 \text{ joule}$$

$$Q = 673 \,\mu\text{c} \qquad E = 4 \times 10^6 \text{ volts/meter}$$

In the beginning of this section the electrostatic energy of a capacitor across which there is a potential difference V_{ab} and on which there is a charge Q was shown to be

$$U = \tfrac{1}{2}QV_{ab} \text{ joules} \tag{2.51}$$

We shall now present arguments that make it appear plausible that this energy is located in the electric field itself, with an energy density u at any point given by

$$u = \tfrac{1}{2}\epsilon_0 E^2 \text{ joules/meter}^3 \qquad\qquad \blacktriangleright(2.52)\blacktriangleleft$$

That this relation is at least dimensionally correct follows from the fact that

$$\epsilon_0 E^2 = \frac{\text{coulombs}^2}{\text{n-m}^2} \cdot \frac{\text{newtons}^2}{\text{coulombs}^2} = \frac{\text{newtons}}{\text{meters}^2} = \frac{\text{joules}}{\text{meters}^3}$$

Moreover, the use of Eq. 2.52 can be shown to give correct results for the three particular capacitors which we have considered. We shall go through the computations only for the parallel plate capacitor. Experience has shown that Eq. 2.52 is a generally applicable result, and that its validity is not limited to the special cases for which we can demonstrate its correctness by simple calculations.

The quantity Q in Eq. 2.51 is the charge on the capacitor. From this we can compute that the electric field between the plates is

$$E = \sigma/\epsilon_0 = Q/\epsilon_0 A$$

where A, as above, is the area of one side of one of the plates of the capacitor. Further, since in a uniform electric field the potential difference between two points separated by a distance d in the direction of the field is Ed, we can express the total energy U as follows:

$$U = \tfrac{1}{2}QV_{ab} = \tfrac{1}{2}(\epsilon_0 EA)(E \cdot d) = \tfrac{1}{2}\epsilon_0 E^2 \times (\text{volume of capacitor})$$

or, as was to be shown,

$$u = \frac{U}{\text{volume}} = \tfrac{1}{2}\epsilon_0 E^2$$

Another approach to the problem is in terms of the mechanical forces which the two plates of the capacitor exert on each other. Figure 2.27 illustrates the capacitor with which we propose to deal. For simplicity, we consider that the space between the plates is empty and that the negative plate is fixed. We assume an externally applied mechanical force F_{ext} on the positive plate which balances the electrical force F_{el} at every instant. The work dW done by the external forces in increasing the separation of the plates by dx is converted to an amount of electrostatic energy dU. We have

$$dW = dU = F_{ext} \cdot dx \qquad (2.53)$$

But, from previous arguments, we have

$$U = Q^2/2C$$

and

$$C = \epsilon_0 A/x$$

We can therefore put

$$U = \frac{Q^2 x}{2\epsilon_0 A} \qquad dU = \left(\frac{Q^2}{2\epsilon_0 A}\right) dx$$

or, since

$$\frac{Q}{\epsilon_0 A} = E$$

we get

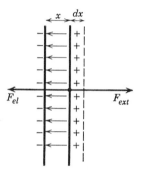

Fig. 2.27. The work done in separating the plates of a capacitor.

$$dU = \frac{\epsilon_0 E^2}{2} A \cdot dx = \frac{\epsilon_0 E^2}{2} dv$$

The change in energy of the capacitor when the separation between the plates, and therefore also the volume, is increased is the energy density $\tfrac{1}{2}\epsilon_0 E^2$ multiplied by the increase in volume dv. We may also put the above expression in the form

$$dU = \frac{EQ}{2} dx$$

which, by comparison with Eq. 2.53, yields for the magnitude of the electrical force acting on one plate of the capacitor

$$F_{el} = EQ/2 \qquad (2.54)$$

This result at first glance seems incompatible with Fig. 2.27, in which the entire charge Q seems exposed to the resultant electrical field E. One might consequently expect twice the force which was derived above. The difficulty lies in the assumption that the field E which exists between the plates of the charged capacitor is, in fact, the field to be used in computing the force on the charges. The convention which was originally adopted stated that the force exerted on unit charge at some point was equal to the electric field at that point (before the test charge was put there).

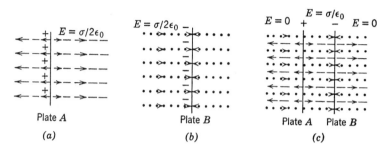

FIG. 2.28.   The fields due to infinite uniformly charged plates.

A simple and correct argument is illustrated in Fig. 2.28. In part a we see the field of a single infinite uniformly charged plate carrying a positive charge. In b we see a corresponding negatively charged plate, and in c we see the field of the two combined. The electric field of either one alone is only half as intense as the field between the two when they are placed side by side. The force which is exerted on a part of either plate carrying a total charge Q is therefore $\frac{1}{2}EQ$, E being the field between a pair.

2.5   INTERCONNECTED CAPACITORS

When several capacitors are connected together, the circuit which they form will have properties which we shall now examine to illustrate the application of the ideas that have been developed about charge and potential. The criteria to be satisfied are that in general for each capacitor we expect equal and opposite charges on the two halves, that for each capacitor

$$Q = CV_{ab}$$

and that the potential difference between two points must be equal to the sum of all the intermediate potential differences involved in going from one of these points to the other by any path whatever. In addition, we shall have to keep track of all the charges present as connections are altered by the closing and opening of switches.

If a capacitor whose capacitance is C is charged by having its terminals connected to the terminals of a battery, the battery voltage V will appear across the capacitor and a charge $q = CV$ will be transferred to the capacitor, a $+$ charge to that side of the capacitor connected to the $+$ terminal of the battery, and an equal minus charge to the other side. The capacitor may now be disconnected from the battery without altering its charge or the potential difference between its terminals, provided that in the disconnecting no conducting path from one terminal to the other is set up. If such a conducting path does appear, the potential differences between the terminals are reduced to zero and the plus and minus charges cancel each other. A discharge current from the + terminal through the conducting path to the minus terminal flows until the charge is removed and the terminals are at the same potential.

Capacitors connected in *parallel*, or side by side, are shown in Fig. 2.29. The total charge Q supplied by the circuit at a is equal to the sum of the charges on the two capacitors,

$$Q = Q_1 + Q_2$$

But

$$Q_1 = V_{ab}C_1$$

and

$$Q_2 = V_{ab}C_2$$

and consequently

$$\frac{Q_1}{Q_2} = \frac{C_1}{C_2}$$

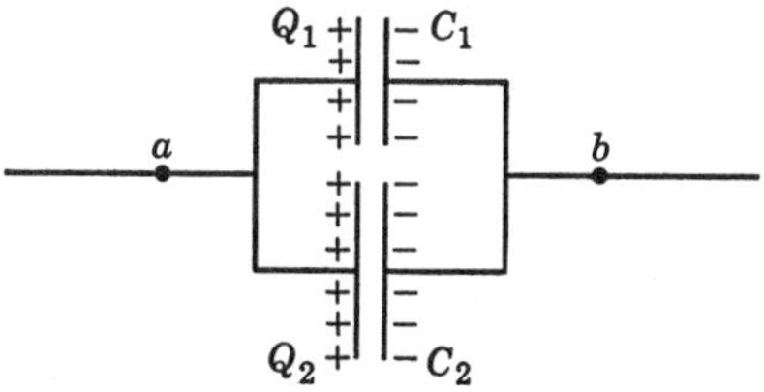

Fig. 2.29.   Capacitors in parallel.

The ratio of the charges on the two capacitors connected in parallel is equal to the ratio of their capacitances.

A useful concept in describing a circuit of this kind is the *equivalent capacitance*. By this we mean the single capacitance which could replace the parallel arrangement above between the terminals a and b and produce identical electrical effects. The equivalent capacitance of the parallel capacitors shown in Fig. 2.29 would be that capacitance which would contain a charge $Q = Q_1 + Q_2$ when the potential difference between its terminals was V_{ab}, as above, or

$$C = Q/V_{ab}$$

which, according to the above discussion is

$$C = \frac{Q_1 + Q_2}{V_{ab}} = \frac{Q_1}{V_{ab}} + \frac{Q_2}{V_{ab}}$$

or

$$C = C_1 + C_2 \tag{2.55}$$

The equivalent capacitance of two (or more) capacitors connected in parallel is equal to the sum of the separate capacitances.

Capacitors connected in series, as in Fig. 2.30, may be used as voltage dividers. Whatever voltage is applied to the combination, the ratio of the voltage drops across the two capacitors is constant and the voltage across either one is a fixed fraction of the total. To see this, let us consider what happens when the terminals ab above are maintained at a constant difference of potential, the potential at a being higher than that at b. We must have, first of all,

$$V_{ab} = V_{ac} + V_{cb}$$

But

$$V_{ab} = Q_1/C_1$$

$$V_{cb} = Q_2/C_2$$

Also, since the resultant charge in the section between the capacitors, marked c in Fig. 2.30, was zero before a difference of potential V_{ab} was applied, and since no charge was brought into this insulated section, the resultant charge must still be zero and the magnitude of the charge on the two capacitors must be the same.

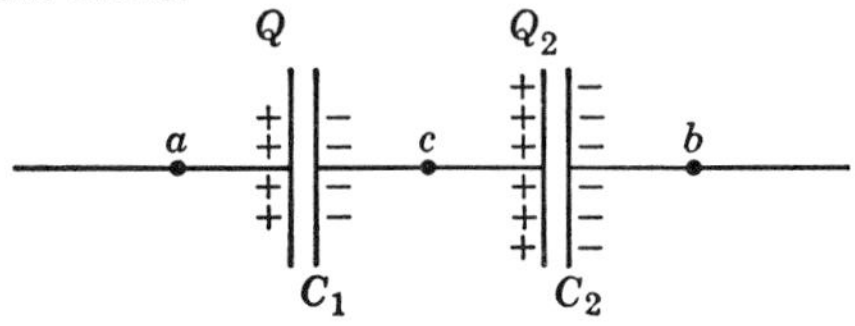

$$Q_1 = Q_2$$

Calling this Q, we have

$$\frac{V_{ac}}{V_{cb}} = \frac{Q/C_1}{Q/C_2} = \frac{C_2}{C_1}$$

Fig. 2.30.   Capacitors in series.

which was to be shown.

The series combination shown in Fig. 2.30 has an equivalent capacitance C, which is just the magnitude of the charge delivered to the combination, Q, when a potential difference V_{ab} is applied, divided by V_{ab}.

$$C = Q/V_{ab}$$

or

$$\frac{1}{C} = \frac{V_{ab}}{Q} = \frac{V_{ac} + V_{cb}}{Q} = \frac{V_{ac}}{Q_1} + \frac{V_{cb}}{Q_2}$$

which may be written

$$\frac{1}{C} = \frac{1}{C_1} + \frac{1}{C_2} \tag{2.56}$$

The reciprocal of the equivalent capacitance of two (or more) capacitors connected in series is the sum of the reciprocals of the separate capacitances.

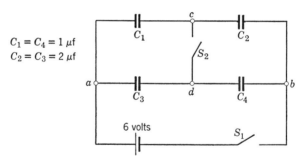

$C_1 = C_4 = 1\ \mu\text{f}$
$C_2 = C_3 = 2\ \mu\text{f}$

Fig. 2.31.   Circuit diagram.

A Circuit Involving Capacitances, Batteries, and Switches

Consider the circuit shown in Fig. 2.31.   Initially both switches are open, and the capacitors are all discharged.   Switch S_1 is closed.   What is then the equilibrium charge on each capacitor and the voltage across it?

A possible approach to the solution of this problem is to note that, as long as S_2 is open, we may consider C_1 and C_2 as a simple series connection.   From the above analysis it follows that $V_{ac}/V_{cb} = C_2/C_1 = 2/1$.   But since $V_{ab} = 6$

volts, it follows that $V_{ac} = 4$ volts and $V_{cb} = 2$ volts. The charges then follow from the properties of capacitors. $Q_1 = C_1 V_{ac} = 10^{-6} \times 4 = 4 \times 10^{-6}$ coulomb, and $Q_2 = C_2 V_{cb} = 2 \times 10^{-6} \times 2 = 4 \times 10^{-6}$ coulomb.

An equivalent argument involving equivalent capacitances may be used. We apply it to the other two capacitors, C_3 and C_4. The equivalent capacitance of this pair is

$$\frac{1}{C} = \frac{1}{C_3} + \frac{1}{C_4} = \frac{1}{2 \times 10^{-6}} + \frac{1}{10^{-6}} = \frac{3}{2 \times 10^{-6}}$$

$$C = \tfrac{2}{3} \times 10^{-6} \text{ farad}$$

The charge which this equivalent capacitance will draw when connected to the 6-volt battery will be

$$Q = CV = \tfrac{2}{3} \times 10^{-6} \times 6 = 4 \times 10^{-6} \text{ coulomb}$$

But, since this charge appears on C_3, it must also appear on C_4, as the total charge on the isolated section between them must add up to zero, and this is possible only if $Q = Q_3 = Q_4 = 4 \times 10^{-6}$ coulomb. The voltages across these capacitors are

$$V_{ad} = \frac{Q}{C_3} = \frac{4 \times 10^{-6}}{2 \times 10^{-6}} = 2 \text{ volts}$$

$$V_{db} = \frac{Q}{C_4} = \frac{4 \times 10^{-6}}{10^{-6}} = 4 \text{ volts}$$

If now the switch S_2 is closed, what will be the charge on each capacitor and the voltage across it? By closing the switch S_2, we assure that points c and d are at the same potential. In order to produce this condition, charge in the central isolated section containing the switch will have to redistribute itself. The problem is greatly simplified, as is so often the case, if we notice its symmetry. C_1 and C_3 may now be considered in parallel, and their equivalent capacitance is 3 μf. Likewise C_2 and C_4 are in parallel and have the same equivalent capacitance. The 6 volts of the battery will therefore be equally divided between them. $V_{ac} = V_{ad} = 3$ volts. $V_{cb} = V_{db} = 3$ volts. We can then get the charges on each capacitor directly.

$$Q_1 = C_1 V_{ac} = 10^{-6} \times 3 = 3 \ \mu\text{c}$$

$$Q_2 = C_2 V_{cb} = 2 \times 10^{-6} \times 3 = 6 \ \mu\text{c}$$

$$Q_3 = C_3 V_{ad} = 2 \times 10^{-6} \times 3 = 6 \ \mu\text{c}$$

$$Q_4 = C_4 V_{db} = 10^{-6} \times 3 = 3 \ \mu\text{c}$$

Charged Spheres

A quite different sort of problem, but one involving the same principles is that of interconnected spheres. We have shown that the potential at a distance r from a point charge q was $\dfrac{1}{4\pi\epsilon_0} \dfrac{q}{r}$, and that this was also the potential due to a uniformly charged sphere at points outside the sphere. On and inside a sphere of radius R the potential is $\dfrac{1}{4\pi\epsilon_0} \dfrac{q}{R}$ if the charge q is uniformly distributed. The procedures outlined for computing the potential at any point in space due to arbitrary charge distributions permit us to calculate the potentials due to two charged spheres, provided we are justified in assuming that the charge distributions on each are uniform so that the above considerations apply. This will in general be true if the distances between the spheres are large compared to their radii. We then have for the potential at any point outside the two spheres

$$V = \frac{1}{4\pi\epsilon_0}\left(\frac{q_1}{r_1} + \frac{q_2}{r_2}\right) \tag{2.57}$$

where r_1 and r_2 are the distances from the point at which the potential V is measured to the spheres. These ideas are useful in a variety of ways illustrated by the following problems.

The fields and potentials between two equal spheres

Let us assume that we have two spheres in a vacuum. Each sphere has, uniformly distributed over its surface, a charge Q. One sphere is positive, and the other is negative. We shall designate the radius of the spheres by R and their separation by d. We shall further assume that R is very small compared to d. In this case the surfaces of the uniformly charged spheres are equipotential surfaces. The potential along a line joining their centers is

$$V = \frac{Q}{4\pi\epsilon_0}\left[\frac{1}{d + x} - \frac{1}{d - x}\right] \tag{2.58}$$

for points outside the spheres. Inside the spheres the local charges produce no force and so no field. The charges on the distant sphere are assumed too far away to be effective. The electric field is, therefore, zero inside the sphere, and the electric potential must be constant.

The electric field, which is in the x direction for points on the line of centers, is given by

$$E = E_x = -\frac{\partial V}{\partial x} = \frac{Q}{4\pi\epsilon_0}\left[\frac{1}{(d + x)^2} + \frac{1}{(d - x)^2}\right] \tag{2.59}$$

These results are shown graphically in Fig. 2.32. Corresponding quantities for points off the axis are much more difficult to compute.

If, by some mechanism, positive charge is released from the positive sphere and moves along the line of centers toward the negative sphere, we have an electric circuit. The above equations suffice to compute the motion of any particular charge released in any particular way. The charge will be accelerated by the electric forces. Its terminal velocity, if it started from rest, is given by the following equation expressing the law of conservation of energy,

$$\tfrac{1}{2}mv^2 = qV_{ab} \text{ joules}$$

When the positive charge strikes the negative sphere with the above velocity, its kinetic energy is transformed into heat.

What if the charge q is ejected in some other direction? We cannot then draw a figure such as Fig. 2.32 from which the potential and kinetic energies at every instant are immediately derivable; at least, we cannot, without going through a much longer computation. But the energy lost and heat liberated are the same as before. These quantities are independent of the path by which the charge travels.

What if we release q coulombs per second? As long as the total charge on the spheres remains undiminished, so that V_{ab} remains unchanged, we shall have energy released per unit charge just as calculated above. Or, since the electric current i is the number of coulombs released per second,

$$i = \frac{dq}{dt} \text{ coulombs/sec} \qquad \text{or amperes} \qquad (2.60)$$

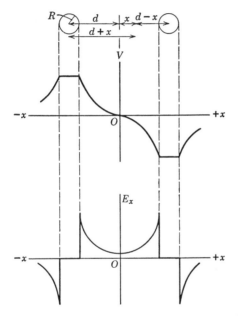

FIG. 2.32. The electric field and potential along the line of centers of two charged spheres.

we get for the rate of conversion of electric potential energy into heat

$$W = iV_{ab} \text{ joules/sec} \qquad \text{or watts} \qquad (2.61)$$

as discussed in Chapter 1.

The sharing of charge by unequal spheres

A sphere of radius R_1 is given an initial charge Q_0. A second sphere of radius R_2 is brought to a distance r from the first and is connected to it by a thin wire, as shown in Fig. 2.33. How is the charge Q_0 then distributed between the spheres, if we assume the separation sufficiently great for the charges to be considered uniformly spread over each sphere?

After the connection has been made, we assume the initial charge Q_0 to be so distributed that an amount Q_1 is on the sphere of radius R_1, and an amount Q_2 on the sphere of radius R_2. When they are connected, the two spheres must be at the same potential. But from Eq. 2.57 we have for the potential at the center of the first sphere

$$V_1 = \frac{1}{4\pi\epsilon_0} \left(\frac{Q_1}{R_1} + \frac{Q_2}{r} \right)$$

and for the potential at the center of the second,

$$V_2 = \frac{1}{4\pi\epsilon_0} \left(\frac{Q_2}{R_2} + \frac{Q_1}{r} \right)$$

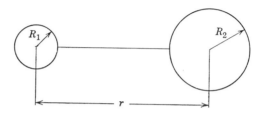

FIG. 2.33.   Interconnected charged spheres.

Equating these two expressions we get

$$\frac{Q_1}{R_1} + \frac{Q_2}{r} = \frac{Q_2}{R_2} + \frac{Q_1}{r}$$

$$\frac{Q_1}{Q_2} = \frac{1/R_2 - 1/r}{1/R_1 - 1/r} = \frac{R_1}{R_2} \cdot \frac{r - R_2}{r - R_1}$$

An interesting further variation in this problem is to consider grounds, or connections to the earth, whose potential may be considered zero since its radius is so large. If we connect the spheres in the above problem to ground, what will the charge distribution be?   We must expect $V_1 = V_2 = 0$.   In order for this to be true we must have

$$\frac{Q_1}{R_1} + \frac{Q_2}{r} = 0 \qquad \text{and} \qquad \frac{Q_2}{R_2} + \frac{Q_1}{r} = 0$$

This is possible only if Q_1 and Q_2 are zero, but this is what we should expect. The charge Q_0 has leaked off to the ground through the connection.

If the spheres are concentric, still other arguments apply.   Let us consider the arrangement shown in Fig. 2.34.   We must consider three surfaces: (1) The surface of the inner sphere with a charge Q_1 and at a potential V_1.   (2) The inner surface of the outer sphere with a charge Q_2 and at a potential V_2. (3) The outer surface of the outer sphere with a charge Q_3 and at a potential V_3.   We have shown the outer sphere with a small hole to allow altering conditions on the inner sphere.   There are in this problem just two independent variables: for example, the total charge on the inner sphere, and the total charge on the outer sphere.   If these are fixed, the remaining charge distributions and potentials can be calculated. The relations wanted are the following:

$$V_3 = \frac{1}{4\pi\epsilon_0} \frac{Q_3}{r_0} \qquad \text{from Coulomb's law} \qquad (2.62)$$

$$V_3 = V_2 \qquad (2.63)$$

because 3 and 2 are part of the same metallic surface.

$$Q_1 = -Q_2 \qquad (2.64)$$

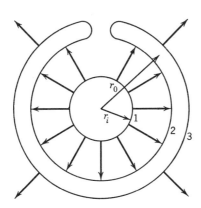

FIG. 2.34. Concentric spheres.

because the field between the spheres originates and terminates on the same quantity of charge.

$$V_1 - V_2 = \frac{1}{4\pi\epsilon_0} Q_1 \left[\frac{1}{r_i} - \frac{1}{r_0} \right] \qquad \text{from Coulomb's law} \qquad (2.65)$$

$$Q_2 + Q_3 = Q_0 \qquad \text{the total charge on the outer sphere} \qquad (2.66)$$

As an example, let us compute the desired quantities if the inner sphere is grounded, if $V_1 = 0$, and if the outer sphere is given a charge of 2×10^{-10} coulomb, assuming $r_i = 10^{-2}$ meter, $r_0 = 3 \times 10^{-2}$ meter. From Eq. 2.65

$$0 - V_2 = 9 \times 10^9 Q_1 \left[\frac{1}{10^{-2}} - \frac{1}{3 \times 10^{-2}} \right] = 6 \times 10^{11} Q_1$$

Using this and Eqs. 2.62 and 2.63 we get

$$V_3 = V_2 = -6 \times 10^{11} Q_1 = +6 \times 10^{11} Q_2 = +6 \times 10^{11} (Q_0 - Q_3)$$

and now combining this with Eq. 2.62

$$V_3 = \frac{1}{2\pi\epsilon_0} \frac{Q_3}{r_0} = 9 \times 10^9 \frac{Q_3}{3 \times 10^{-2}} = +6 \times 10^{11} (2 \times 10^{-10} - Q_3)$$

$$3 \times 10^{11} Q_3 = +120 - 6 \times 10^{11} Q_3$$

$$Q_3 = 1.32 \times 10^{-10} \text{ coulomb}$$

$$Q_2 = Q_0 - Q_3 = (2 - 1.32) \times 10^{-10} = +0.68 \times 10^{-10} \text{ coulomb}$$

$$Q_1 = -0.68 \times 10^{-10} \text{ coulomb}$$

$$V_3 = 9 \times 10^9 \times \frac{1.32 \times 10^{-10}}{3 \times 10^{-2}} = 40 \text{ volts}$$

As a check, we use Eq. 2.65

$$0 - 40 = 9 \times 10^9 \times (-0.68) \times 10^{-10} \left[\frac{1}{10^{-2}} - \frac{1}{3 \times 10^{-2}} \right]$$

$$= 60 \times (-0.68) = -40.5$$

which, within the limits of the accuracy used, checks.

SUMMARY

Coulomb's law of force is supplemented by the introduction of a new concept. The new concept is that of an electric field, also called the electric intensity, around charged bodies. The electric field E at any point in space specifies the magnitude of the electric force F which would act on a charge q placed at that point.

$$\mathbf{F} = q\mathbf{E}$$

The electric field at any point in space may be calculated from data on the location of all existing electric charges by means of Coulomb's law. The dimensions of E are either newtons/coulomb, or the equivalent, volts/meter.

The electric field has certain important properties to which we shall return repeatedly. The first property is that Gauss's law is satisfied. In a vacuum, or in air, it has the form

$$\int_S E_n \, dA = \frac{\sum q_i}{\epsilon_0}$$

The integral of the outward normal component of the electric field over any closed surface in an electric field is equal to the resultant charge within the surface divided by ϵ_0.

The second important property is specifically limited to electrostatic fields. The electrostatic field has a potential. The difference in potential between any two points is given by

$$V_a - V_b = -\int_b^a E_t \, ds = V_{ab} = -V_{ba}$$

The potential may be computed from a knowledge of the field, or conversely, it may be computed directly from a knowledge of the location of all charges,

$$V = \sum \frac{1}{4\pi\epsilon_0} \frac{q}{r}$$

and then the electric field may be computed from the potential

$$E_x = -\frac{\partial V}{\partial x}$$

$$E_y = -\frac{\partial V}{\partial y}$$

$$E_z = -\frac{\partial V}{\partial z}$$

A particular property of fields that have a potential is that

$$\oint E_t \, ds = 0$$

The integral of the tangential component of E around any closed path in an electrostatic field vanishes.

The electrostatic potential energy between charges may be thought of as located in space with a density

$$u = \tfrac{1}{2}\epsilon_0 E^2 \text{ joules/meter}^3$$

A capacitor may then be considered as a device for storing electrostatic energy. It can have various forms, but a most simple and useful one is the parallel plate capacitor. The capacitance of a capacitor is defined as the charge on it per unit of potential difference between its parts,

$$C = \frac{Q}{V_{ab}} \frac{\text{coulombs}}{\text{volt}} \quad \text{or farads}$$

The capacitance of a capacitor may also be given in terms of its dimensions. A parallel plate capacitor, consisting of two plates whose superficial area is A, separated by a distance d, and with air between the plates, has a capacitance C given by

$$C = \frac{\epsilon_0 A}{d} \text{ farads}$$

The total electrostatic energy U stored in a capacitor carrying a total charge Q which produces a potential difference V_{ab} between its terminals is

$$U = \tfrac{1}{2}QV_{ab} = \tfrac{1}{2}CV_{ab}^2 = \tfrac{1}{2}\frac{Q^2}{C}$$

PROBLEMS

1. Positive point charges of 1 μc are located at the points $x = 1$ meter, $y = 0$, and $x = -1$ meter, $y = 0$ of a rectangular coordinate system. Find the electric field at the following points: (a) $x = 0$, $y = 0$; (b) $x = 0$, $y = 1$; (c) $x = 2$, $y = 0$.

2. Same as Problem 1, except that the charge at $x = -1$, $y = 0$ is negative.

3. Sketch the electric field lines of force around two positive charges separated by a distance d. Do the same for two charges equal in magnitude but opposite in sign.

4. Make a rough plot of the electric field in Problem 3 for points along the line joining the charges (x axis), and along the perpendicular bisector (y axis).

5. A straight wire L meters long is uniformly charged so that there are t coulombs/meter. (a) Find an expression for the electric field at any point along the axis of the wire. (b) If $L = 1$ meter, and $t = 25$ μc/meter, find the numerical value of the field 1 meter from the center of the wire. (c) Find the electric field at points on the perpendicular bisector of the wire.

6. A circular ring of radius R is uniformly charged over one half of its length with a charge Q_1 and uniformly over the other half with Q_2. (a) Find the component of the electric field directed along the axis, at any point on the axis of the ring. (b) How would this result be changed if the total charge ($Q_1 + Q_2$) were distributed uniformly on the ring? (c) What would be the components of E perpendicular to the axis in each of the two cases?

7. A segment of a circle of radius R subtending an angle ψ at the center, carries a uniformly distributed charge Q. The remainder of the ring carries a uniformly distributed charge $-Q$. Prove that the electric field strength at the center is given by the expression

$$E = 4\pi kQ \frac{\sin \psi/2}{\psi(2\pi - \psi)R^2}$$

8. A straight wire L meters long is charged uniformly over one half of its length with a charge Q, and over the other half with $-Q$. (a) Find the electric field at points along the axis of the wire; (b) along the perpendicular bisector of the wire.

9. Find the electric field of a uniform spherical charge distribution of radius R for points outside of the sphere by integrating Coulomb's law.

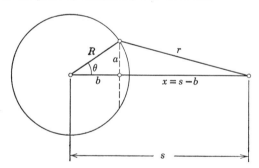

Fig. 2.35.   Illustration for problem 9.

To do this, make use of the expression, Eq. 2.11, for the field on the axis of a ring-shaped charge distribution and set up a new system of coordinates which will facilitate the integration, as indicated in Fig. 2.35. Note that q_r now becomes dq, where, if Q is the total charge on the sphere, and $Q/4\pi R^2 = \sigma$,

$$dq = \sigma \cdot 2\pi aR \, d\theta$$

$$b = R \cos \theta$$

$$x = s - R \cos \theta$$

$$a = R \sin \theta$$

10. A very long straight wire is uniformly charged so that there are t coulombs/meter. (a) Using Gauss's law, find an expression for the electric field at any point. (b) Find the values of the field at points 0.1, 1, and 100 meters from the wire when $t = 20$ μc/meter.

11. A Gaussian surface consisting of a sphere 24 cm in diameter is placed with its center on the axis of the wire of Problem 10. Using the expression already obtained, evaluate $\epsilon_0 \int_S E_n \, dA$ and show that it does equal $\sum q = 20(0.24) = 4.8$ μc.

12. Prove that $\sigma = \epsilon_0 E$ at any electrostatically charged metal surface.

★13. Derive an equation for the lines of force in the field of a dipole. *Hint:* Notice that if the dipole is at the origin and pointing along the axis of a spherical coordinate system, $dr/rd\theta = E_r/E_\theta$ along a line of force at the point r, θ. This now provides a differential equation which must be integrated in order to express r as a function of θ. There will be a constant of integration in this expression, r_0, which determines the particular line being described.

14. Given an isolated charge of 5 μc, show that $\oint E_t \, ds = 0$ around the following closed path: From $\theta = 0°$, $r = 1$ meter, to $\theta = 0°$, $r = 5$ meters; then, at $r = 5$ meters, from $\theta = 0°$, to $\theta = \pi/2$; then, at $\theta = \pi/2$, from $r = 5$ meters to $r = 1$ meter; then, at $r = 1$ meter, from $\theta = \pi/2$ to $\theta = 0°$, the starting point.

15. Compute the potential along the x axis due to a charge $+q$ at $x = l/2$, $y = 0$ and a charge $-q$ at $x = -l/2$, $y = 0$. See Fig. 2.1. Find the electric field at the point $x = r_a$, $y = 0$ by differentiating the expression for the potential, and show that it agrees with Eq. 2.4.

16. Given a charge q distributed uniformly throughout a sphere of radius R with charge density ρ: (a) Using Gauss's law, derive a formula for the electric field at points inside and outside the sphere. (b) Make a plot of the magnitude of the electric field vs. distance from the center of the sphere. (c) Calculate the potential as a function of distance from the center of the sphere for points both outside and inside the sphere. (d) Plot the potential as a function of distance from the center of the sphere.

17. A flat metal plate in a vacuum tube has an area of 1 cm^2, and has a charge 8 $\mu\mu c$ uniformly distributed over one face. Immediately above this plate is an equal and opposite charge uniformly distributed in a layer 1 mm thick. (a) What is the electric field at any point in this layer? Neglect edge effect, so that the field will be everywhere perpendicular to the plate. (b) What is the potential difference between the plate and any point in the layer? (c) Show that if the x axis is normal to the face of the plate, $E_x = -\partial V/\partial x$.

18. In Fig. 2.23a what is the charge distribution? Which are the lines of force and which are the equipotentials? Discuss the vicinity of P. Discuss b in a similar fashion.

19. Capacitors, batteries, and switches are connected together as shown in Fig. 2.36. (a) What is the charge on each capacitor when S_1 is closed? (b) When S_2 also is closed?

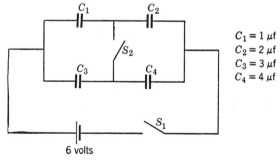

$C_1 = 1$ μf
$C_2 = 2$ μf
$C_3 = 3$ μf
$C_4 = 4$ μf

6 volts

FIG. 2.36. Illustration for problem 19.

20. A capacitor of 2 μf and one of 5 μf are each charged separately from a 100-volt battery. (a) If they are now connected so that their two positive terminals are together and their two negative terminals are together, what is the charge and potential on each? (b) If instead they had been connected so that the positive terminal of each had been connected to the negative terminal of the other, what would be the charge and the potential on each? (c) How much energy is stored before they are connected? (d) How much energy is stored after they are connected as in a? (e) How much energy is stored after tney are connected as in b? (f) How might we reconcile d and e?

21. The two capacitors in Problem 20 are connected in series, and then the combination is charged from a 100-volt battery. The capacitors are then disconnected. Answer the same questions as in Problem 20.

22. Three capacitors of 2, 4, and 6 μf, respectively, are connected in series, and the whole combination charged from a 200-volt battery. (a) Find the charge on each. (b) Find the potential difference across each. (c) Find the energy stored in each.

23. A 4 μf capacitor and a 6 μf capacitor are connected in parallel, and this combination is connected in series with a 2 μf capacitor. This whole combination is then connected to a 200-volt battery. (a) Find the charge on each capacitor. (b) Find the total energy stored.

24. Two capacitors, one charged and the other uncharged, are connected together in parallel. Prove that, when equilibrium is reached, each capacitor carries a fraction of the initial charge equal to the ratio of its capacity to the sum of the two capacities. Show that the final energy stored is always less than the initial energy, and show that the difference is $Q^2 C_2 / C_1 (C_1 + C_2)$.

25. A parallel plate capacitor of 5 μμf with square plates 10 cm on a side is connected to a 100-volt battery and then disconnected. (a) Find the charge on each plate. (b) Find the electric field between the plates. (c) Find the force between the plates. (d) Find the energy stored. If the spacing of the plates is now doubled, (e) find the charge on each plate. (f) Find the electric field between the plates. (g) Find the force between the plates. (h) Find the energy stored. (i) Find the potential between the plates.

★26. Wires are connected together along the edges of a cube, and in each one a capacitor having a capacitance of 1 μμf is inserted. (a) What is the equivalent capacitance between terminals at adjacent corners? (b) What is the equivalent capacitance between terminals at opposite corners?

27. What is the approximate capacity of the earth? Consider it to be a conducting sphere of radius 4000 mi.

28. A spherical drop of water 1 cm in diameter carries a charge of 10^{-9} coulomb. (a) What is the potential at the surface of the drop? (b) If two such drops, similarly charged, coalesce to form a single drop, what is the potential at the surface of the drop thus formed?

29. The greatest electric field which air can support without breakdown is 3×10^6 volts/meter. What is the smallest sphere that can be charged to 1,000,000 volts in air?

30. The spherical electrode of a Van de Graaff generator, 2 meters in diameter, is charged by a moving belt. The charging current is 10 μamp. How long does it take to charge the sphere to its sparking potential, assuming that this is given when the field at the surface of the sphere is 3×10^6 volts/meter?

31. Two concentric conducting spheres of radii 10 and 20 cm are initially at zero potential and are insulated from each other and from ground. Give the potential of each sphere and the charge on each surface under the following conditions. (a) A

charge of 10^{-9} coulomb is placed on the inner sphere, and the outer one is insulated and carries no net charge. (b) Same as a, but with the outer sphere grounded. (c) A charge of 10^{-9} coulomb is placed on the outer sphere with no charge on the inner sphere. (d) A charge of 10^{-9} coulomb is placed on the outer sphere, and the inner sphere is grounded.

32. A sphere 10 cm in radius is charged so that its potential is 1000 volts above ground. (a) What is the charge on the sphere? Another sphere having a radius of 3 cm, and connected to ground by a thin wire, is brought to a point 1 meter from the center of the first sphere. (b) What will be the charge on the smaller sphere?

33. A No. 16 B&S gage wire is raised to an increasing potential until the surrounding air breaks down. Assume that this occurs when the electric field at the surface of the wire is 3×10^6 volts/meter. What is the charge per unit length? What would it have been if No. 000 wire had been used?

34. Prove by integrating Eq. 2.52 that the energy in the electric field between charged concentric spheres is equal to that computed from their capacitance, given in Eq. 2.46.

35. Prove by integrating Eq. 2.52 that the energy in the field between coaxial charged cylinders is equal to that computed from their capacitance given in Eq. 2.50.

★36. Our concept of the physical significance of an electric field may be considerably altered as a result of considerations regarding the energy density in space. If we find that $u = \frac{1}{2}\epsilon_0 E^2$ is always valid, then we may take this as the definition of E. The electric field becomes a "field of energy," and the concept of an electric "field of force" must be derived as a special property of this field. The electric force qE then may be considered a consequence of the fact that, when q is moved in a direction opposite to E, electrostatic potential energy is accumulated, or "pushed out" into space. In our present *electrostatic* considerations, this cannot be demonstrated. The energy is "pushed out" when q is moved in a direction opposite to E, it is stored when Q is at rest, and it is given up by the field to q when q moves in the direction of E. Later, when we take up *electrodynamics*, we shall find that, if we suddenly jerk the charge q, we can push energy out into space and "snap it loose" from q. Energy is radiated. This can be demonstrated to take place and can be calculated in detail by means of various new concepts, including $u = \frac{1}{2}\epsilon_0 E^2$. There is, then, real evidence that electrostatic forces are consequences of the fact that, when charges are moved about, energy is stored in or removed from space. In this problem and the next we show how the electric "field of force" can be derived from the more fundamental "field of energy."

Set up an expression for the energy density at any point in space due to a single point charge q and for additional $+$ and $-$ charges spread uniformly with a density σ over infinite parallel planes a distance d apart. If U is the total electrostatic energy in space, then the force F acting on Q is

$$F = -\, dU/da$$

where a is the distance from q to the positively charged plane. Show that this equation for F reduces to

$$F = qE = q\,\frac{\sigma}{\epsilon_0}$$

when q is between the charged planes, and

$$F = 0$$

when q is outside the region between the planes. The integrations involved in this calculation are particularly simple if the origin of coordinates is chosen at the charge q.

Notice that the square roots occurring here must always be positive, as they represent distances which are necessarily positive. Thus $\sqrt{(a - x)^2} = a - x$ for $x < a$, and $x - a$ for $x > a$. For example, under these conditions

$$\int_0^\infty \frac{dx}{\sqrt{(x - a)^2}} = \int_0^a \frac{dx}{a - x} + \int_a^\infty \frac{dx}{x - a}$$

★37. This problem follows Problem 36, which should be studied first. By differentiating the expression for the total energy in space due to a charge Q spread uniformly over a sphere of radius R and a point charge q, show that, if the distance from the center of the sphere to q is s,

$$F = \frac{1}{4\pi\epsilon_0} \cdot \frac{qQ}{s^2} \quad \text{if } s > R$$

$$= 0 \quad \text{if } s < R$$

The expressions to be integrated are listed in tables of integrals if the energy density is described in spherical coordinates, r, θ, ϕ, with the origin at the center of the sphere, and the polar axis passing through q. The order of integration should be first ϕ, then θ, and finally r.

Note that this result establishes Coulomb's law on the basis of the energy density concept, and that it can be generalized to include any number of changes.

CHAPTER 3

The Electrical Properties
of Matter

3.1 ELECTRONS AND PROTONS

We now turn to the nature of the charges whose fields were discussed in the previous chapter. During the first years of this century, it was known that matter was made up of atoms and that knocking electrons out of them would ionize atoms. Atomic masses and sizes were known. From the chemical atomic weights and Avogadro's number, the mass of the lightest atom, hydrogen, was found to be

$$\text{Mass of hydrogen atom} = \frac{1 \text{ gm/mole}}{6.02 \times 10^{23} \text{ atoms/mole}}$$

$$1.66 \times 10^{-24} \text{ grams} = 1.66 \times 10^{-27} \text{ kg}$$

From atomic and molecular weights, and from the densities of solids and liquids in which atoms and molecules may be assumed to be tightly packed, atomic radii were found to lie roughly between 1 and 2×10^{-10} meter. The electrons which could be knocked out of atoms were found to have much smaller masses than atoms. The mass of an electron m is approximately 9.1×10^{-31} kg. The charge on an electron was found to be negative, and the electron was recognized as a single entity in nature, whereas the positively charged atoms, or positive ions, are of many different kinds. The structure of ions and atoms and the nature of the positive charge in matter were discovered shortly after 1910 by experiments to be described in the next section.

At about this time, Millikan undertook the precise determination of the electronic charge e. We shall adopt for this quantity the approximately correct value $e = 1.6 \times 10^{-19}$ coulomb. His experiments were extremely simple in principle but difficult to carry out successfully. Very small oil drops were sprayed by an atomizer into the region between horizontal metal plates, as shown in Fig. 3.1. Here a vertical electric field was produced through giving the plates equal charges of opposite sign. The oil drops could be charged by being subjected for a time to

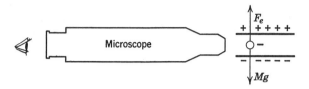

FIG. 3.1. Millikan's oil drop experiment to determine the electronic charge e.

ionizing radiation of some sort, and their movements could then be observed by means of a microscope. For any given charge on a drop the field required to support it against the force of gravity could be measured. If this field is E, we must have

$$QE = Mg$$

where E can be computed from the potential difference between the plates and their separation. Q can then be determined if the mass M of the drop is known, or changes in Q can be measured directly. In Millikan's experiments the observed charges were always integral multiples of a smallest unit, which must be the electronic charge itself. This is one of the fundamental constants of nature, and its determination was an important step in the development of atomic theory.

The hydrogen + ion is called a proton. It must have the same charge as an electron, since the combination of the two forms an electrically neutral atom. Its mass M_P is very nearly equal to that of the neutral atom since the electron's proportion of the total mass is very small. The ratio of the mass of the proton to that of the electron is, approximately, 1837. To summarize, then, we have

$$m = 9.1 \times 10^{-31} \text{ kg} \qquad \blacktriangleright(3.1)\blacktriangleleft$$

$$\frac{M_P}{m} = 1837$$

$$e = 1.6 \times 10^{-19} \text{ coulomb}$$

A knowledge of the electronic charge and the sizes of atoms makes it possible to infer certain important facts about atomic energies and to specify suitable energy units for atomic problems. For example, the potential energy of an electron in the field of a proton at a distance of

10^{-10} meter, which is of the order of atomic dimensions, is

$$\text{P.E.} = -\frac{9 \times 10^9 \times (1.6 \times 10^{-19})^2}{10^{-10}} = -23 \times 10^{-19} \text{ joule}$$

The joule is apparently a very large unit compared to atomic energies. A much more convenient unit is the *electron volt* (ev), which is the amount of work required to raise the potential of an electron by 1 volt, or conversely, the amount of kinetic energy which an electron would acquire in falling through 1 volt. From this definition it follows that

$$1 \text{ ev} = 1.6 \times 10^{-19} \text{ joule} \qquad \blacktriangleright(3.2)\blacktriangleleft$$

The potential energy of the electron at a distance of 10^{-10} meter from a proton now turns out to be -14.4 ev. The work required to remove this electron, assumed at rest, from the proton is 14.4 ev. In other words, suppose we have two metal plates in an evacuated space and connect them to a 6-volt storage battery. An electron released from the negative electrode or a proton released from the positive electrode would acquire a kinetic energy of only 6 ev in traversing the space between the electrodes, and could not ionize a hydrogen atom in a collision. If, on the other hand, the plates were connected to a potential difference of 110 volts, ionization could result from a collision after the electron or proton had moved only part way across the gap between the plates. We conclude that, since 110 volts are easily available, the ionization of a hydrogen atom can be achieved without difficulty. This conclusion can be extended to any atom, since all atoms have about the same size, and since the force acting on an electron being removed is that of the remaining singly charged positive ion.

The potential energy of an electron in the field of a proton or other singly charged positive ion is shown in Fig. 3.2*a*. This is a plot of the expression $-ke/r$, which is the energy in electron volts. This assumes that charges may be treated as non-overlapping spherical distributions and will be valid for separations greater than atomic dimensions.

A similar plot for two protons is shown in Fig. 3.2*b* and illustrates the difficulty of producing a proton-proton collision if protons turn out to have radii very much smaller than atoms, as in fact they do. Suppose, for instance, that we wish to bring two protons to within a distance of 0.5×10^{-14} meter of each other. The mutual potential energy at this separation is 2.88×10^5 ev, or 0.288 million electron volts, usually written Mev. If we wish to achieve this result by bombarding protons, assumed held at rest, with high-speed protons, then the initial kinetic energy of the bombarding particles must have been 0.288 Mev at least. As the particles approach each other in a head-on collision, the total energy remains constant at 0.288 Mev, if this is the initial kinetic energy, but the kinetic energy decreases as the potential energy increases. For example, at a separation of 10^{-14} meter half of the initial kinetic energy

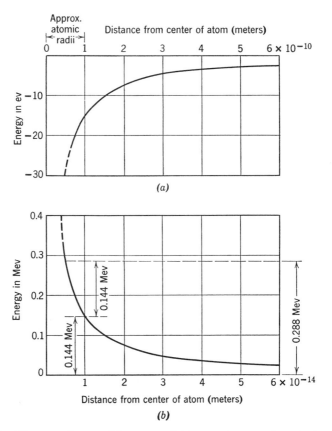

Fig. 3.2.   The mutual potential energy of (a) a proton or other singly charged positive ion and an electron, and (b) two protons.

has been converted to potential energy. We see that the coulomb repulsive force keeps subatomic particles of like charge apart very effectively unless they have exceedingly high energies.

3.2   RUTHERFORD AND THE NUCLEAR ATOM

Although, at the turn of the century, there were various hypotheses as to how positive and negative charges were combined to form neutral atoms, experimenters had been unable to devise conclusive tests of any of the proposals. Rutherford set out to prove or disprove one of these hypotheses, namely, that the atom consists of a small positive nucleus containing most of the mass, surrounded by negative electrons. The fundamental idea behind his experiments is easily described. He proposed to shoot high-energy charged particles into an atom where the forces would depend on just how charges within the atom were distributed. These forces would deflect the projectiles, and by observing these deflections he would try to infer how the atomic charges must have been distributed. This experiment was so significant in the development of physics that we shall consider it in detail. It illustrates both how physical principles can be applied to particular situations and how an experiment must be analyzed. The method is still in use for the study of nuclear structure.

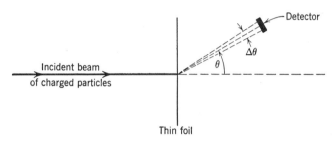

FIG. 3.3. A diagram illustrating the main components of Rutherford's scattering experiment (1911).

We shall first consider the practical and theoretical difficulties that had to be overcome to make the experiment possible. In Fig. 3.3 is a diagram showing schematically how such an experiment might be carried out. A beam of charged particles is shot at a thin film. Here some of the particles will penetrate atoms and will consequently not emerge in the direction of incidence, or $\theta = 0$, but will be scattered. Some means of observing the fraction of the incident particles that are scattered through an angle θ in an angular range $\Delta\theta$ must be provided. Then, after observing the number of particles scattered through various angles, one must find some means of calculating what the forces within the scattering atom must have been.

As a source of particles Rutherford chose various naturally occurring radioactive substances which emit alpha rays. These rays had been shown to consist of positively charged particles having a charge equal in magnitude to two electronic charges, and were known to have ranges of several centimeters in air. The paths of alpha particles in air are shown in Fig. 3.4. They can be made to leave behind a vapor trail, much as jet planes do in the upper atmosphere. In their passage through the air, the alpha particles occasionally penetrate an atom, knock out one or more electrons, and thus ionize the atom. In the presence of supersaturated water vapor, drops of water condense preferentially around ions and these condensed droplets reveal the paths of the ionizing particles. It is apparent from the number of droplets generated by each alpha particle that the particles are capable of pene-

Fig. 3.4.   Cloud chamber photograph of alpha-particle tracks. From *Radiations from Radioactive Substances*, Ernest Rutherford, James Chadwick, and C. D. Ellis, Cambridge University Press, 1930. Used by permission.

trating very many atoms. Furthermore, since the ranges are all very nearly the same, we may assume that the original kinetic energies of all the particles were the same, and that the small differences in path length are due to accidental fluctuations in the numbers of atoms encountered. The alpha particles are therefore well suited for use as projectiles.

In such an experiment, it is important that the scattering film be suitably chosen. It must be strong and durable to last through long periods of observation. The interpretation of results will be much simplified if scattering is due primarily to single atoms or, in other words, if the film is thin enough so that the chance of two scattering processes is small. Rutherford chose very thin metal foils for his experiment.

Then, there was the question of detection. It was found that high-speed particles produce momentary scintillations when they strike certain fluorescent materials. Rutherford made use of this effect to count the number of particles arriving per second at any given angle of deviation θ. A microscope was focused on the fluorescent material at the detector position in Fig. 3.3, and, after the eye of the observer was dark-adapted so that the scintillations were clearly visible, many long hours had to be spent in counting the number observed per second.

There remained finally the matter of theoretical interpretation of the results. The procedure here was to make a theoretical prediction based on the assumption of a nuclear atom and to determine whether the observed data could be fitted to the predictions. The detailed mathematical steps are described at the end of this section. The results, briefly, are these. If a particle of mass m and charge Q_p is fired with an initial velocity v_0 at a nucleus of charge Q_N so that its undeviated path would pass at a distance p from the nucleus (see Fig. 3.9), it will be deviated by the Coulomb force of repulsion exerted by the nucleus so that it will recede at an angle θ to the initial path where θ is such that

$$\tan \frac{\theta}{2} = \frac{Q_p Q_N}{4\pi\epsilon_0 m v_0^2 p} \tag{3.3}$$

This expression may be further simplified if we designate by s the closest possible distance of approach of a particle having a charge Q_p approaching a nucleus with an initial velocity v_0. The initial kinetic energy must all be transformed to potential energy when the particle comes to rest at a distance s from the nucleus, or

$$\tfrac{1}{2}m v_0^2 = \frac{1}{4\pi\epsilon_0} \frac{Q_p Q_N}{s}$$

and therefore

$$\tan \frac{\theta}{2} = \frac{s}{2p} \tag{3.4}$$

This result is illustrated in Fig. 3.5. Here the center of the figure locates the bombarded nucleus, and the radial distance from the nucleus represents the perpendicular distance p to an incoming particle. The angles are the angles of deviation for various values of p. The areas between successive circles are equal, so that, if the nucleus in question is being bombarded by uniformly distributed particles, there will be equal numbers scattered into the range between 131.5° and 180°, or 115.5° and 131.5°, or 104.5° and 155.5°, etc. Incident particles aimed directly at the nucleus will be scattered through 180°. Particles aimed farther and farther from the nucleus are scattered through smaller angles.

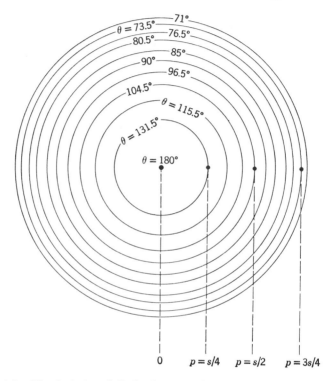

FIG. 3.5.   The deviation of Coulomb-scattered particles according to Eq. 3.4.

Although this result cannot be compared directly with experiment, it leads to another that can. Suppose we bombard a foil of thickness t containing n atoms per unit volume. If an area A of the film is being bombarded, the number of atoms in the bombarded area is nAt. A part of the bombarded area is shown in Fig. 3.6. The nuclei are represented as points, and all the nuclei in the film within the area selected are shown. If there are N bombarding particles impinging on the film per second, the fraction of these moving toward a nucleus with a distance between p and $p + dp$ is the ratio of the area of the shaded rings shown in Fig. 3.6 to the area A, or

$$\frac{\Delta N}{N} = (nAt)\frac{2\pi p \, \Delta p}{A} \tag{3.5}$$

provided the film is thin enough and the rings are small enough so that neighboring rings do not overlap. But if

$$p = \frac{s}{2} \cot \frac{\theta}{2} \quad \text{then} \quad \Delta p = \frac{s}{4} \frac{\Delta \theta}{\sin^2 \theta/2}$$

Substituting into Eq. 3.5 yields

$$\frac{\Delta N}{N} = \frac{\pi n t s^2}{4} \frac{\cos (\theta/2) \, \Delta \theta}{\sin^3 \theta/2} \tag{3.6}$$

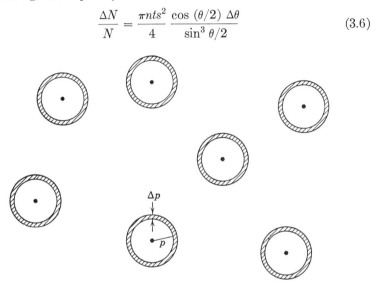

FIG. 3.6.   Nuclear distribution within a film as seen by an incoming alpha particle.

as the fraction of the incident particles scattered through an angle between θ and $\theta + \Delta \theta$. In order to find the fraction scattered onto a scintillating screen of area A_s at a distance r from the scatterer, we must multiply Eq. 3.6 by the ratio of A_s to the area subtending an angle between θ and $\theta + \Delta \theta$, or $A_s/(2\pi r \sin \theta \cdot r \, \Delta \theta)$. But since

$$\sin \theta = 2 \sin \frac{\theta}{2} \cos \frac{\theta}{2}$$

our final result for the fraction f scattered onto A_s is

$$f = \frac{n t s^2}{16 r^2} \frac{A_s}{\sin^4 \theta/2} \tag{3.7}$$

$$s = \frac{Q_p Q_N}{2\pi \epsilon_0 m v_0^2}$$

The fraction to be expected scattered back into the direction of incidence is very small compared to the fraction scattered in a forward direction. Further, for films containing the same number of atoms per unit area and bombarded with alpha particles of the same energy the fraction scattered should be proportional to the square of the nuclear charge, Q_N.

Exhaustive experiments to check Eq. 3.7 were undertaken by Geiger and Marsden. Representative results published by them in 1913 are reproduced below. Since plots of quantities varying over several orders

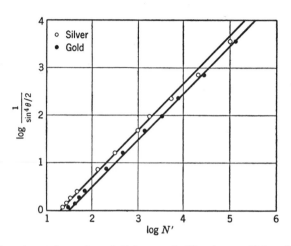

FIG. 3.7. Experimental results of Geiger and Marsden verifying Rutherford's analysis of a nuclear atom.

of magnitude are inconvenient, they took the logarithm of both sides of Eq. 3.7. Since $f = N'/N$, or the ratio of the number of scintillations counted per unit time to the number of incident particles per unit time, we get

$$\log N' = \log \frac{1}{\sin^4 \theta/2} + \log \frac{nts^2 A_s N}{16r^2} \qquad (3.8)$$

If $\log N'$ is plotted as a function of $\log \dfrac{1}{\sin^4 \theta/2}$, a straight line having a 45° slope is to be expected if Eq. 3.8 is satisfied. The experimental points shown in Fig. 3.7 do fall on such a line.

Further, we see that the results for gold and silver are displaced from each other. This is because the second constant term on the right side of Eq. 3.8 has different values. Geiger and Marsden concluded from their work that, if the nuclear charge is expressed in units having an electronic charge, so that

$$Q_N = Ze$$

then the quantity Z, called the atomic number, is approximately one-half of the atomic weight for the elements investigated. The agreement between theory and experiment was strikingly good, but there were certain deviations both at very small and at very large scattering angles. The former were found to be due to multiple scattering of particles which did not come near some one nucleus but were slightly scattered by several. This small angle scattering is beyond the limits set for the experiment and need not concern us farther. The deviations at large angles are more interesting. It was found that, when large bombarding energies were used so that the distance of closest approach $s < 10^{-14}$ meter, then the back-scattered particles which actually came as close as this to the scattering nucleus were subject to a new force in addition to the electric or Coulomb force. This then, was the first evidence concerning nuclear sizes,

$$R \simeq 10^{-14} \text{ meter}$$

and showed that the atomic nucleus was very small indeed compared to an atom.

The Derivation of Equation 3.3 for the Scattering of α Particles within a Nuclear Atom

In order to derive Eq. 3.3 for the scattering of alpha particles, we must consider the electrostatic forces within a nuclear atom. There is, first of all, the Coulomb force exerted by the charge Q_N of the nucleus on the charge Q_p of the projectile.

$$F = k \frac{Q_N Q_p}{r^2} \tag{3.9}$$

which is valid as long as the projectile does not penetrate into the nucleus, or for $r > R$, where R is the nuclear radius. We must, however, also consider the forces due to the electrons. The fact that the rays in Fig. 3.4 are so nearly straight indicates that the alpha particles are not appreciably deflected in an encounter with an electron in an atom. We conclude that the electrons must have a much smaller mass than an alpha particle. Actually, the alpha particle has almost 10,000 times the mass of an electron, and it is therefore not appreciably deflected in an encounter with an electron, just as a billiard ball will not be deflected in an encounter with a ping-pong ball. It may, however, be argued that the electrons in an atom constitute, on the average, some sort of more or less rigid jelly, and that we must consider not only the forces due to a single electron but also those due to the entire electronic charge, equal in magnitude, but opposite in sign, to the nuclear charge Q_N. From Gauss's law, we can compute the field at any point due to both nucleus and electrons. If we assume the electrons to be distributed uniformly over the atomic volume, say a sphere of radius r_0, the electric field between the surface of the nucleus and the surface of the atom will be

$$E = k \frac{Q_N}{r^2} - k \frac{Q_N r}{r_0^3} \tag{3.10}$$

The nuclear field is large only near the nucleus, and in this range of small r the field due to the electrons is small. Thus, if the nucleus is very small compared to the atom, the nuclear field will predominate for $r \simeq R$. For $r \simeq r_0$ the electrons will modify the field, but here it is so small as to be negligible. The magnitude of the forces and corrections is shown in Fig. 3.8 for the case

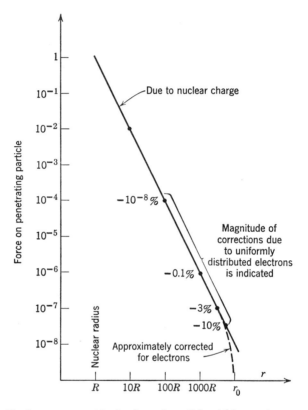

FIG. 3.8.   The force on a positively charged particle within an atom assuming that the atomic radius is 10^4 times the nuclear radius.

$R = 10^{-4}r_0$. If the nucleus is small compared to the atom, we may expect that any rays that penetrate deeply enough to be deflected at all will be deflected by the Coulomb field of the nucleus alone.

It remains, now, to compute the trajectory of an incident particle under the influence of Coulomb's law. The relevant quantities are shown in Fig. 3.9. The first condition to be satisfied is the conservation of energy.

$$\tfrac{1}{2}mv^2 + \frac{kQ_NQ_p}{r} = \tfrac{1}{2}mv_0{}^2 \tag{3.11}$$

The sum of the kinetic and potential energies must be constant, and equal to the initial kinetic energy at great separations for which the potential energy is zero. The second condition to be satisfied is the conservation of angular momentum

$$mr^2\omega = mr^2\frac{d\phi}{dt} = pmv_0 \tag{3.12}$$

The angular momentum must be constant and equal to the initial angular momentum. From Eq. 3.12 we obtain

$$\frac{d\phi}{dt} = \frac{pv_0}{r^2} \tag{3.13}$$

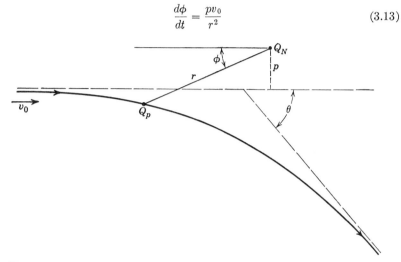

FIG. 3.9. The orbit of a positively charged particle in the field of a nucleus.

From the relation
$$v^2 = \left(\frac{dr}{dt}\right)^2 + \left(r\frac{d\phi}{dt}\right)^2$$

and using Eq. 3.13 and the relation

$$\frac{dr}{dt} = \frac{dr}{d\phi}\frac{d\phi}{dt} = \frac{pv_0}{r^2}\frac{dr}{d\phi}$$

we get
$$v^2 = \left(\frac{pv_0}{r^2}\right)^2\left(\frac{dr}{d\phi}\right)^2 + \left(\frac{pv_0}{r}\right)^2$$

Substituting this into Eq. 3.11 and solving for $dr/d\phi$, results in

$$\frac{dr}{d\phi} = \frac{r}{p}\sqrt{r^2 - sr - p^2}$$

where, as before, s is the distance of closest approach defined in Eq. 3.7. The resulting expressions can be integrated.

$$p\int\frac{dr}{r\sqrt{r^2 - sr - p^2}} = \int d\phi$$

$$\sin^{-1}\frac{-(sr + 2p^2)}{r\sqrt{s^2 + 4p^2}} = \phi + C \tag{3.14}$$

where C is a constant of integration. If, as in Fig. 3.9, we chose coordinates such that $\phi = 0$ for $r = \infty$, then

$$C = \sin^{-1} \frac{-s}{\sqrt{s^2 + 4p^2}} \tag{3.15}$$

In order to find the angle θ by which the particle is deviated we must find another value of ϕ satisfying Eq. 3.14 for $r = \infty$. Calling this $\phi_d = \pi - \theta$, and substituting into Eq. 3.14, we get

$$\sin(\pi - \theta + C) = \frac{-s}{\sqrt{s^2 + 4p^2}}$$

This requires some elementary manipulation to get an explicit expression for θ. We have

$$\sin C = \frac{-s}{\sqrt{s^2 + 4p^2}}$$

and therefore

$$\sin(\pi + C) = -\sin C = \frac{s}{\sqrt{s^2 + 4p^2}}$$

$$\cos(\pi + C) = -\cos C = \frac{2p}{\sqrt{s^2 + 4p^2}}$$

$$\sin(\pi + C - \theta) = \sin(\pi + C)\cos\theta - \cos(\pi + C)\sin\theta$$
$$= -\sin C \cos\theta + \cos C \sin\theta = -\sin C$$

$$\frac{\sin\theta}{1 + \cos\theta} = \tan\frac{\theta}{2} = \tan C = \frac{s}{2p}$$

which is tne result to be proved

$$\tan\frac{\theta}{2} = \frac{s}{2p} = \frac{kQ_pQ_N}{mv_0^2 p} \tag{3.16}$$

3.3 EXCITATION AND IONIZATION; CONDUCTION IN GASES AND SOLUTIONS

In a gas in equilibrium at a temperature $T°$ absolute, the average translational kinetic energy is $\frac{3}{2}kT$. Here k is the Boltzmann gas constant. $k = 1.38 \times 10^{-23}$ joule per degree. We find that, at room temperature, where $T \simeq 300°$, the average kinetic energy is 6.2×10^{-21} joule or 0.04 ev.

Atoms at room temperature appear to be stable. Collisions between atoms having kinetic energies of the order of a few hundredths of an electron volt do not, in general, disturb the atoms. They are *elastic collisions* in which the kinetic energies of the particles before the collision are equal to their kinetic energies after the collision. As the kinetic energy of the particles involved in the collision is increased, two important phenomena occur. There are two kinds of *inelastic collision* in which the kinetic energy of the colliding particles is decreased and converted into another form. The first of these is the emission of light. If we hit an atom hard enough with a projectile, it will emit light. The energy lost in the collision is radiated as light. In mercury vapor, for instance, the mercury atom must be hit with a particle having an energy of about 5 ev in order to be made to radiate. We shall examine the radiation process in detail farther on. For the present we must consider this kind of inelastic collision as an unexplained fact. The second kind of inelastic collision produces ionization. It breaks the atom, in a sense, by removing one electron. A mercury atom must be hit by a particle having a kinetic energy of about 10 ev if it is to be ionized.

A gas made up of neutral atoms is normally an insulator. Even in the presence of an electric field between charged electrodes it will pass no current, as there are no charges to be forced into motion by the field. In general, however, there are a few charges present. Because of the action of cosmic rays, or of neighboring radioactive elements, or even of light (particularly ultraviolet light), on gas molecules or metal surfaces, electrons and ions are produced. The ions may be positive or negative. In the absence of any fields, the electrons and ions move about until they come under the influence of charges of the opposite sign. If an electric field is present, positive ions will drift in the direction of the field, and negative ions and electrons in a direction opposite to the field.

Gases, such as air at atmospheric pressure, conduct a very small current at low field strengths because of the drift of the very few ions present. This, for example, is the current that discharges a well-insulated electroscope. If, however, the electric field strength in the gas is sufficiently increased, a point is reached at which a breakdown occurs. Lightning flashes are produced in this way. In such a flash, the free electrons are sufficiently accelerated between collisions to break up or ionize the atoms which they hit, and the newly created free electrons produce more ions by further impacts. The gas becomes highly conducting along the path of the flash. If the spark reduces the potential difference between the electrodes (in the case of lightning, a cloud and the earth), the discharge stops. If the potential between electrodes is maintained, the ionized path continues to conduct.

A point of great practical importance is that it is technically relatively easy to emit electrons into a vacuum or low-pressure gas and there to control their motion. There is a binding force which holds electrons in metals. But when a metal is sufficiently heated, for example an incandescent filament, some of the electrons in the metal are boiled off. It has been found that certain oxides emit electrons much more readily than pure metals, and these are used as electron sources at much lower temperatures, around 750°C, on a dull red heat.

An evacuated vessel with two metallic connections in it, called electrodes, will pass a current if the heated electron-emitting electrode is negatively charged so that the negatively charged electrons are repelled from it and attracted to the positively charged electrode. This result may be accomplished through connecting the heated electrode to the negative terminal of a battery and the other electrode to the positive terminals. The electron-emitting negative terminal is called the *cathode*, and the positive terminal is called the *anode*. An electric field is thus maintained in the region between the electrodes. If the tube is sufficiently well evacuated so that the electrons make no collisions on the way from the heated cathode to the anode, then the kinetic energy which they acquire is just equal to the potential energy which they lose in moving from cathode to anode. If the voltage on the tube is V_{ab}, we have that $eV_{ab} = \frac{1}{2}mv^2$.

The phenomena that take place in a gas-filled tube in which a current is maintained between electrodes are very complicated indeed. Light is produced as a result of inelastic collisions. Heat is produced in elastic collisions between the ions and electrons that have been accelerated by the field and the slower gas atoms. Ions and electrons are formed and recombine. The detailed investigation of these phenomena is an important task for engineers and applied physicists. We shall consider only one aspect, namely, how a steady current is maintained in an ionized gas having a uniform charge density.

In the long thin discharge tube shown in Fig. 3.10 there are a neutral gas and in addition positive and negative ions or electrons with a density n per unit volume. Gas atoms and ions are to be thought of as in random motion. Because of the electric field, however, there is superimposed on the random motion of the individual particles a drift of the "clouds" of charge, the positive charge drifting toward the cathode and the negative charge toward the anode.

Let us first consider the positive charge, shown separately in Fig. 3.10*b*. We designate the average drift velocity of the positive charge v_{dr+}. Its contribution to the current will be the total quantity of charge crossing any cross section of the tube per second.

$$i_+ = \frac{Q_+}{t}$$

But the charges move a distance $v_{dr+}t$ in a time t, so that

$$Q_+ = (v_{dr+}At)n \cdot e \tag{3.17}$$

where e is the charge per positive ion. Similarly, the negative charges will drift to the left and their contribution will add to the current i.

$$i = i_+ + i_- = \frac{Q_+ + Q_-}{t} = ne(v_{dr+} + v_{dr-})A \qquad (3.18)$$

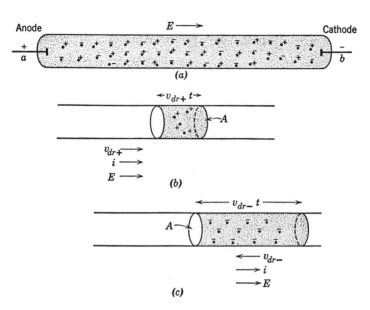

FIG. 3.10.   The contributions of the positive and negative charges in a discharge to the current.

If the drift velocity is proportional to the field, we may put

$$v_{dr+} = \mu_+ E$$

$$v_{dr-} = \mu_- E$$

where the quantities μ are called the *mobilities* of the positive and negative charges. If the difference in potential across a tube of length L is V_{ab}, we have, if the field is uniform,

$$V_{ab} = EL$$

$$i = \frac{ne(\mu_+ + \mu_-)A}{L} V_{ab}$$

which may be rewritten

$$V_{ab} = i \cdot \frac{L}{ne(\mu_+ + \mu_-)A} \qquad (3.19)$$

This is Ohm's law if n and μ are independent of current. In gas discharges they generally are not, and Ohm's law is not satisfied. The correct computation of ion and electron mobilities is too complex for us to undertake. We shall show below, however, how their orders of magnitude may be estimated.

Estimate of the Magnitude of Ion and Electron Mobilities

Let us consider first a gas containing n_a atoms of radius R_a in which we wish to compute the drift velocity v_{dr} of a cloud of ions of radius R_i, each ion having

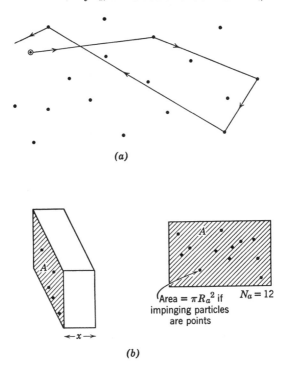

(a)

(b)

Fig. 3.11.   The mean free path of a particle is the average distance traveled between collisions.

an average velocity v_i. It is shown below that the average distance traveled by the ion between collisions is

$$\lambda = \frac{1}{n_a \pi (R_a + R_i)^2} \tag{3.20}$$

λ is called the mean free path of the ions, and is illustrated in Fig. 3.11a. In order to see this, consider a box of cross-sectional area A and thickness x containing N_a atoms, illustrated in Fig. 3.11b. We wish to know the probability that a point particle will make a collision in the box when traversing it at right angles to A. The N_a atoms block out an area $N_a\pi R_a^2$, and the required probability is $N_a\pi R_a^2/A$, if N_a is small enough so that no atoms are "behind each other" from the point of view of impinging point particle. If we express the number of particles in the box in terms of the number of particles per unit volume n_a, we get for the required probability $n_a\pi R_a^2 x$. Without going into detail about this question of overlap, it is clear that if $x \gg \dfrac{1}{n_a\pi R_a^2}$ the particle is almost certain to make a collision, whereas if $x \ll \dfrac{1}{n_a\pi R_a^2}$ the probability of making a collision is small. The average distance of penetration into a gas containing n_a atoms per unit volume turns out to be equal to the thickness of box for which $n_a\pi R_a^2 x = 1$. The value of x for which this is satisfied is called the mean free path λ, as it is also the average distance between collisions for a point particle moving in a random direction through the gas. If the impinging particle is an ion of radius R_i, it will collide with a gas atom if its center comes within a distance $R_a + R_i$ of a gas atom. In a discussion of this case analogous to the above discussion we may consider the blocked out area by each atom to be $\pi(R_a + R_i)^2$, and the final result is then that given by Eq. 3.20 above.

From this result we can proceed to our estimate of the drift velocity. If t is the average time between collisions, then the mean drift distance of the cloud of electrons being acted on by a constant acceleration a for a time t is $\frac{1}{2}at^2$. For a singly charged ion we have

$$a = F/M_i = eE/M_i \tag{3.21}$$

The drift velocity is the mean distance of drift between collisions divided by the mean time between collisions, or

$$v_{dr} = \frac{\frac{1}{2}at^2}{t} = \frac{t}{2}\frac{eE}{M_i} \tag{3.22}$$

But the time between collisions is related to the mean free path and the ionic velocity by the equation

$$t = \lambda/v_i$$

where v_i is the average velocity of the ion. We therefore get

$$v_{dr} = \frac{1}{2}\frac{e\lambda}{M_i v_i}E \tag{3.23}$$

$$\mu = \frac{v_{dr}}{E} = \frac{1}{2}\frac{e\lambda}{M_i v_i} \tag{3.24}$$

In this expression v_i, the linear velocity of the ions is very nearly equal to its thermal velocity. It is true that the ions are being accelerated by the field. But the ions have masses comparable to those of the gas atoms with which they collide. In collisions between particles of comparable mass, as between billiard balls, for instance, there is a tendency for the colliding particles to share their energy. The ions therefore continually lose the excess energy which they acquire. This turns up in the gas in the form of heat.

A similar calculation leads to a similar result for electrons, but its interpretation is more difficult. In the first place the electrons are much lighter than atoms and therefore do not share the energy which they acquire from the field as readily in a collision as did the ions. The average velocity of the electrons in a discharge turns out not to correspond to a temperature of 300° absolute, but often more nearly to an electron temperature of 10,000° absolute, and this is the value that must be substituted into the formula for the mobility. Further, the mean free path of electrons in a gas is unexpectedly complicated. It turns out to be strongly dependent on the electron velocity for reasons that will not be apparent until we take up atomic theory in detail. However, the use of Eq. 3.20 with $R_i = 0$ for the electron gives at least a correct order of magnitude for its mean free path.

Conduction in Solutions

Conduction of current in ionized liquid solution proceeds much as in gases, except that there are no free electrons present. Currents in solutions are of particular interest because of the chemical changes which they produce.

Certain salts, such as copper sulphate, $CuSO_4$, break up into ions when dissolved in water. In this particular case, the ions are both doubly charged, being

$$Cu^{++} \quad \text{and} \quad SO_4^{--}$$

ions. The chloride $CuCl_2$, on the other hand, breaks up into

$$\text{one } Cu^{++} \quad \text{and} \quad \text{two } Cl^-$$

ions. The former are again doubly charged, but the latter are only singly charged.

The ions in such ionized solutions, when placed between charged electrodes, tend to drift toward the oppositely charged electrode because of the Coulomb forces of attraction and repulsion. When an ion reaches the oppositely charged electrode, it loses its charge and may adhere to the electrode, as, for example, in the case of the copper ions above. This is the electroplating process and may be used to measure the quantity of charge that has passed through a solution. For example, 1 mole of copper, weighing 63 grams, contains 6.02×10^{23} atoms. The charge on this number of doubly ionized copper ions is

$$2 \times 1.6 \times 10^{-19} \times 6.02 \times 10^{23} \text{ coulombs}$$

or

$$2 \times 96,000 \text{ coulombs}$$

The number of grams of copper deposited on the cathode for every coulomb that has passed through the solution is therefore

$$\frac{63}{2 \times 96,000} = 0.00033 \text{ gram/coulomb}$$

The number of coulombs per mole of singly charged ions is called a *faraday*, whose value is approximately

$$1 \text{ faraday} = 96,000 \text{ coulombs/mole of singly charged ions}$$

3.4 METALS AND SEMICONDUCTORS; RESISTIVITY

Metals are characterized by the fact that they contain free electrons. Insulators contain many electrons, but these cannot move under the influence of an electric field. To say that they are bound to their own atoms would not be quite correct. In general, the electrons in an insulator can perform one kind of motion: they can change places. But this kind of motion cannot be used to conduct a current. We require net transport of charge, and this can never be achieved by means of exchanges of this kind. But this concept of electrons changing places gives us a clue as to how electrons in a metal can be free. It is not that a metal has some inherently different structure which does not interfere with the free motion of the electrons, whereas insulator atoms hold the electrons and do not allow them to move. The situation is rather that in both cases the electrons can move from one atom to a neighbor if by doing so they do not create a negative charge separated from a positive charge. If the motion of an electron involves this separation of charges, it does not occur because of the large energies required. Even in an insulator electrons can change places without creating such free charges, and consequently they do. The outer electrons of adjacent atoms are very likely to change places rapidly.

In a metal we have a peculiar situation which can best be described by saying that, for reasons which we need not go into, there are electrons in the lattice over and above the electrons which would be present in an insulator. These electrons do not constitute an excess charge in the metal as a whole. The total charge of all the nuclei in the metal is equal to the total charge of all the electrons. We might think of a metal as containing ionized atoms from which electrons have been removed spontaneously by forces which we cannot here describe. We shall return to this situation in later chapters when we take up a more detailed wave-mechanical description of electrons.

In a metal a free electron may exist on one atom as readily as another. It has no preference, except that it cannot move to another atom in which a free electron already exists. The fact that these electrons are free is simply due to there not being too many of them. With one free electron per atom, we might expect to have an insulator again. The situation is illustrated in Fig. 3.12a. Although such a picture does violence to the facts in that free electrons cannot be localized on partic- ular atoms, as shown, it nevertheless has a statistical validity and may be helpful in describing the situation. In the illustration, the crystal is symbolized by the rectangular arrangement of squares representing atoms and the free electrons are designated by an f. These free electrons are free to wander about the crystal, the only restriction on their motion being that they are excluded from an atom in which there already is a free electron.

In a good conductor we want lots of free electrons, but not too many.

If we approach the situation shown in Fig. 3.12*b*, in which almost every atom has a free electron, only very few of the free electrons can move because only very few are adjacent to a "hole" in the free electron distribution into which they are allowed to move. In such a distribution most of the electrons are held fixed as in an insulator, and we may think of the holes as moving around freely in the distribution. They, like free electrons in a less-filled crystal, can move anywhere except into an atom in which there already is a hole. If electrical forces tending to push electrons to the left are applied to the crystal, the holes will

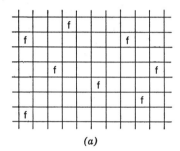
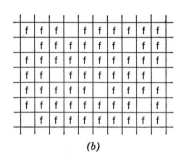

(a)   (b)

FIG. 3.12.   Model of a conducting solid.

move to the right.   When a hole has moved from a positive terminal to a negative terminal, the net effect is just the same as would have been achieved by having a positive electron move through the crystal.

We must now consider the electrical resistance of metallic conductors. It is found that in the most perfect metallic single crystals that can be made the electrical resistance is exceedingly small.   The electrons seem to be able to jump from atom to atom without loss of energy.   Such things as collisions, in the sense used in the study of gas discharges, seem to be negligible.   Any imperfections in the crystal structure, however, impede the motion of the electrons, even the random vibrational motion of the atoms.   Thus perfect single crystals near the absolute zero of temperature have a resistance approaching zero.   Raising the temperature increases the resistance.   Adding impurities, or alloying, or the introduction of imperfections as the result of breaking up a single crystal into many small crystallites by plastic deformation, will also increase the resistance.

These effects can be treated much as we treated electrons and ions in a vacuum, if we assume that the electron in a pure metal is accelerated by the field so that it moves a distance x between collisions, the "collisions" being with the crystal imperfections.   We have, if the mean time between collisions is t,

$$x = \tfrac{1}{2}at^2 = \tfrac{1}{2}\frac{eE}{m}t^2$$

and a drift velocity of the electron gas

$$v_{dr} = \frac{x}{t} = \tfrac{1}{2}\frac{eE}{m}t \tag{3.25}$$

In this expression the time between "collisions" is a parameter to be determined by observations on actual drift velocities.

The Drift Velocity of Free Electrons in a Metal

Let us compute the average drift velocity of the free electrons in a wire carrying a current, much as we did for the ions and electrons in a gas discharge. If there are n free electrons per unit volume moving with a velocity v_{dr} in a wire of cross-sectional area A, we can compute the total charge passing through a cross section of the wire per second. We find, as above for a gas discharge,

$$i = nev_{dr}A \tag{3.26}$$

A copper wire having a cross-sectional area of 1 mm^2 is about a B&S No. 18 wire, and, from Table 1.1, we conclude that a large current for such a wire would be 5 amp. For such a current, the drift velocity is

$$v_{dr} = \frac{i}{neA} = \frac{5}{n1.6 \times 10^{-19} \times 10^{-6}} = \frac{3.1 \times 10^{25}}{n}$$

To estimate n we observe that 1 mole of copper weighing 63 grams contains 6.03×10^{23} atoms. Since the density of copper is 8.8 grams/cc, and since the number of atoms per gram is $6.02 \times 10^{23}/63$, we have for the number of copper atoms per cubic centimeter

$$\frac{8.8 \times 6.02 \times 10^{23}}{63} = 0.84 \times 10^{23}$$

or

$$0.84 \times 10^{29} \text{ atoms per meter}^3$$

The number of free electrons per unit volume in copper is certainly less than the number of atoms, but it is of this order of magnitude. Neglecting the difference, we get for the velocity of the electron gas

$$v_{dr} = 3.7 \times 10^{-4} \text{ meter/sec}$$

The drift velocity of electrons in metals under normal conditions is very small.

If we combine Eq. 3.25 with Eq. 3.26, we get

$$i = ne\tfrac{1}{2}\frac{eE}{m}tA = \left(\frac{ne^2}{2m}t\right)\left(\frac{A}{L}\right)V_{ab} \tag{3.27}$$

This is Ohm's law

$$V_{ab} = iR$$

if we put

$$R = \left(\frac{2m}{ne^2t}\right)\frac{L}{A}$$

In this form, the resistance of the wire being considered consists of two terms. One depends only on the properties of the material being used. We call this the *resistivity*

$$\rho = \frac{2m}{ne^2t} \text{ ohm-meters} \tag{3.28}$$

The second term depends on the shape of the conductor. For cylindrical conductors, it is proportional to the length of the conductor and inversely proportional to the area. The reciprocal of the resistivity is called the *conductivity* σ.

$$R = \rho\frac{L}{A} \qquad \blacktriangleright(3.29)\blacktriangleleft$$

$$\rho = \frac{1}{\sigma}$$

The resistivity of metals varies with temperature. Typical curves for metals are shown in Fig. 3.13. Near the absolute zero the resistance approaches very small values. At higher temperatures there is a region where resistivity is very closely a linear function of temperature. In this region, which includes room temperature, usually taken as 20°C, the resistivity may be written

$$\rho_T = \rho_{20} + \text{constant } (T - 20) \tag{3.30}$$

where T is the temperature in degrees centigrade. The constant is determined by the slope of the resistivity versus temperature curve. This constant is usually put into the form $\alpha\rho_{20}$ so that Eq. 3.30 becomes

$$\rho_T = \rho_{20}[1 + \alpha(T - 20)] \tag{3.31}$$

Because changes in physical dimensions due to thermal expansion produce negligibly small changes in resistivity, we may also write of a conductor having a resistance R_{20} at 20°C

$$R_T = R_{20}[1 + \alpha(T - 20)] \tag{3.32}$$

The resistivities and temperature coefficient of resistivity of some metals and alloys are given in Table 3.1.

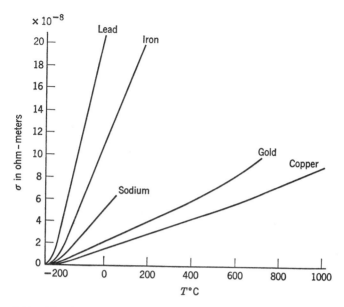

FIG. 3.13.   The dependence of resistivity on temperature for various metals.

TABLE 3.1   APPROXIMATE VALUES OF THE RESISTIVITY ρ_{20} IN OHM-METERS
AT 20°C, AND TEMPERATURE COEFFICIENT OF RESISTIVITY α OF
VARIOUS METALS AND ALLOYS

	$\rho_{20} \times 10^8$	$\alpha \times 10^3$
Copper	1.7	4
Aluminum	2.8	4
Silver	1.6	3.7
Gold	2.4	3.5
Platinum	10.6	3.6
Tungsten	3.5	4.7
Steel	20 to 60	4
Nichrome, 60% Ni, 15% Cr, 25% Fe	112	0.16
Manganin, 4% Ni, 12% Mn, 84% Cu	48	0.01
Constantan, 45% Ni, 55% Cu	49	0.01

Some metals and alloys show the phenomenon of *superconductivity*.
At a critical temperature they lose essentially all signs of resistance.
In lead, for example, this occurs just above 7° absolute.   A current
started in a ring of superconducting lead will continue of itself for days,
provided the temperature is kept sufficiently low.   This curious phenomenon was once thought to offer a possibility of conducting large currents
in small wires without loss of energy due to heating the wire.   Further
investigation, however, proved this to be impossible.   Superconductivity
exists only at low current densities.

Solids may be roughly classified into three groups in so far as their resistivities are concerned. On the one hand, we have most of the metallic elements and alloys of such elements with each other. These have low resistivities, of the order of 10^{-8} to 10^{-6} ohm-meter at room temperature. The resistivity of these metallic conductors decreases markedly as the temperature goes down.

Second, we have insulators, such as amber, Bakelite, mica, paper, glass, or quartz. These substances have resistivities of the order of 10^{12} to 10^{14} ohm-meters, or 10^{20} times the resistivities of metals. For most purposes, such insulators may be said to pass no current at all.

Finally, between metallic conductors and insulators, there are the so-called semiconductors. These are characterized by their intermediate resistivity, between that of conductors and insulators, by their temperature coefficient of resistivity which is typically negative, and by their great electrical sensitiveness to impurities. Their high resistivity is due to the presence of very few conduction electrons or, what amounts to the same thing, very many so that there are very few holes in such a structure as is shown in Fig. 3.11 for the free electrons to move into. Semiconductors in which there are very few free electrons are called N-type semiconductors, because the current is carried by negative charges. Semiconductors in which there are very few holes in the free electron structure are called P-type semiconductors, because they behave as though the current were carried by the motion of positive charges. At this point we have no means of distinguishing between the two, but we shall see in Chapter 6 that, by making use of magnetic effects, we can tell whether a semiconductor is N or P type. The negative temperature coefficient of the resistivity of semiconductors indicates that they become better conductors as the temperature is increased. This is due to an increase in the number of conducting electrons or holes. Even slight changes in the number of current carriers become important when there are very few present in the first place. The importance of slight impurities likewise is due to the fact that impurity atoms may contribute current-carrying charges, or may remove such charges, and, if there are few such charges present, the changes brought about may be considerable.

Semiconductors are proving to be of great importance because the few current carriers present can be controlled or influenced in a variety of ways. There are also other effects than the control of the current which a given unit will pass when a fixed voltage is applied. For example, some show photoconductivity, or a change in resistivity when illuminated, particularly by ultraviolet light. Related effects are to be found in phosphors, which are impurity-activated solids which can be made to give off light in much the same way that vapors in a gas discharge do. Examples are the phosphors in TV tubes which give off light when struck by electrons, or the phosphors in fluorescent lamps which give off visible light when stimulated by invisible ultraviolet light generated in the discharge.

Resistances in Series and in Parallel

From the relation between resistance and resistivity

$$R = \rho \frac{L}{A}$$

we can conclude that n wires of length L_1, area A, and resistivity ρ, when connected together end to end forming a new wire of length nL_1, will have a resistance

$$R = \frac{\rho n L_1}{a_1} = R_1 + R_1 + R_1 \cdots n \text{ terms}$$

This result can be generalized to give the equivalent resistance of any arbitrary resistances connected in series, as in Fig. 3.14. We find that, if there is a poten-

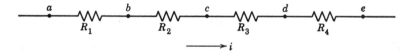

FIG. 3.14. Resistors connected in series.

tial difference V_{ae} between the outer terminals, this must be the sum of the individual potential differences across the several units connected in series.

$$V_{ae} = V_{ab} + V_{bc} + V_{cd} + V_{de}$$

Since no charge accumulates at the junctions, the same current i flows through each resistor. We therefore have

$$V_{ab} = iR_1$$
$$V_{bc} = iR_2$$
$$V_{cd} = iR_3$$
$$V_{de} = iR_4$$

or, adding,

$$V_{ae} = i(R_1 + R_2 + R_3 + R_4)$$

By definition the equivalent resistance of the combination is

$$R = V_{ae}/i$$

and therefore

$$R = R_1 + R_2 + R_3 + R_4 \tag{3.33}$$

for resistances in series.

Similarly, if we place n equal wires of area A_1 side by side, or in parallel, as in Fig. 3.15, they will form a new wire whose cross-sectional area is nA_1, and whose resistance is

$$R = \frac{\rho L}{nA_1}$$

this may be written

$$\frac{1}{R} = \frac{n}{R_1} = \frac{1}{R_1} + \frac{1}{R_1} + \frac{1}{R_1} + \cdots n \text{ terms}$$

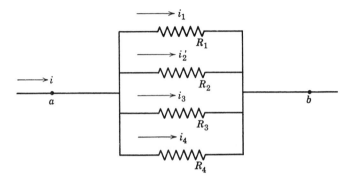

FIG. 3.15.   Resistors connected in parallel.

This result may be generalized for arbitrary resistances in parallel.   It is clear that the sum of the currents through the separate resistors must equal the line current i, or

$$i = i_1 + i_2 + i_3 + i_4$$

The voltage drop through each resistor is V_{ab}.   We therefore have

$$V_{ab} = i_1 R_1 = i_2 R_2 = i_3 R_3 = i_4 R_4$$

or

$$i = \frac{V_{ab}}{R_1} + \frac{V_{ab}}{R_2} + \frac{V_{ab}}{R_3} + \frac{V_{ab}}{R_4} \tag{3.34}$$

By definition the equivalent resistance of the circuit is

$$R = V_{ab}/i$$

Substituting into Eq. 3.34 we get

$$\frac{1}{R} = \frac{1}{R_1} + \frac{1}{R_2} + \frac{1}{R_3} + \frac{1}{R_4} \tag{3.35}$$

for the equivalent resistance of resistances connected in parallel.

Non-Uniform Current Distributions

If the resistance of a piece of metal in which the current flow is not uniform is to be calculated, we must compute the voltage drop across small volume elements in which the current density, or current per unit of area, is uniform, and then sum over a series of such elements. A differential volume element through which a current is flowing in the direction of an edge of length ds is shown in Fig. 3.16. Within this differential volume element we may consider the current uniformly distributed, and Eq. 3.29 is applicable.

$$di \cdot \frac{\rho \, ds}{dA} = E \, ds$$

$$di = \frac{dA}{\rho} \left(-\frac{dV}{ds} \right) = -\sigma \, dA \, \frac{dV}{ds} \tag{3.36}$$

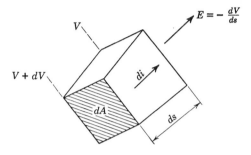

FIG. 3.16. A current in a differential volume element.

Let us apply this to the case of radial flow of current in a thin sheet, as shown in Fig. 3.17. Heavy copper electrodes in the form of rings form equipotentials V_a and V_b having radii R_a and R_b. The current flows radially outward through

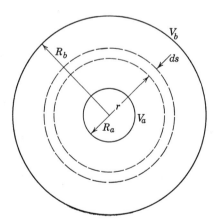

FIG. 3.17. Radial flow of current in a thin sheet.

a sheet of thickness t and resistivity ρ. What is the resistance of this sheet between a and b? If we chose our volume element so that $ds = dr$, and $dA = t \cdot rd\,\theta$, we see that the current is the same at every point around a ring of radius r, and therefore the total current i through any ring-shaped section is

$$i = \int di = -\int_0^{2\pi} \sigma t r \, d\theta \, \frac{dV}{dr} = -2\pi\sigma t r \frac{dV}{dr}$$

$$-\frac{i\rho}{2\pi t} \cdot \frac{dr}{r} = dV$$

We must now integrate from the inside electrode to the outside electrode.

$$-\frac{i\rho}{2\pi t} \int_{R_b}^{R_a} \frac{dr}{r} = \int_b^a dV = V_a - V_b = V_{ab}$$

$$-\frac{i\rho}{2\pi t} \ln \frac{R_a}{R_b} = V_{ab}$$

$$i \cdot \rho \, \frac{\ln R_b/R_a}{2\pi t} = V_{ab}$$

$$R = \frac{V_{ab}}{i} = \rho \, \frac{\ln R_b/R_a}{2\pi t} \tag{3.37}$$

3.5   POLARIZATION

Although the charges in an insulator are not able to move about freely, they are certainly not rigidly bound. When an electric field is applied to an insulator, therefore, the negative charges will be pulled, and may be expected to move very slightly, in one direction, whereas the positive charges will be pulled, and may be expected to move very slightly, in the other. The charges are bound by finite forces, and we may therefore expect a displacement. This displacement leads to a polarization. The atoms are polarized by the field. The field induces an electric moment in each atom. Suppose, for example, that an atom in the absence of a field is a spherical shell of electrons surrounding its nucleus. The field will then exert a force in one direction on the nucleus and in the opposite direction on the electrons. The electrons will be slightly displaced, and the atom will be polarized. It will acquire a dipole moment. The degree and manner of this polarization are an important problem in atomic physics. In addition to the kind of polarization described above in which spherically symmetrical atoms may be distorted by an electric field, there is a different kind of polarization in substances, such as water, shown in Fig. 3.18, in which each molecule has a permanent dipole moment. The effect of the electric field is to produce an orientation in opposition to the disorienting tendency of the thermal agitation within the insulator, or *dielectric*, as it is also called. Substances composed of such polar molecules show particularly strong polarization due to the action of electric fields, and more so at low temperatures than high because the thermal agitation is less.

We shall proceed with an analysis of the polarizability of dielectrics, in order to isolate the parameters of importance and so gain insight into the response of insulators to electric fields.

It is interesting to note that even the very crude model of an atom or molecule which we have used suffices to estimate the order of magnitude of their polarizabilities. We distinguish the two cases mentioned earlier in

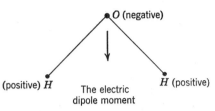

FIG. 3.18. The water molecule.

the text, in which we have (*a*) spherical uncharged atoms and (*b*) molecules with a permanent electric dipole moment.

For the first case we consider the relative displacement of the positive and negative charges in a spherical atom due to an electric field, as shown in Fig. 3.19. The spherical atom of radius R is shown in (*a*) with-

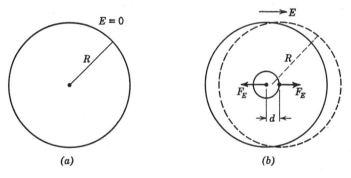

FIG. 3.19. The polarizability of a spherical atom.

out an applied field and in (*b*) with an applied field. The nucleus is shown displaced slightly to the right, and the center of the electronic charge distribution slightly to the left. The electronic cloud will no longer be spherical, but we shall neglect this effect. If we can compute the displacement d between the center of the electron cloud and the nucleus, our task is essentially done. If the nucleus has a charge Ze, the induced dipole moment will be

$$p = Zed \qquad (3.38)$$

because, at points outside of the atom, the field due to the electrons will be identical with that of Z electrons at the center of the electronic charge distribution, at a distance d from the positively charged nucleus. The sum of these two fields at points outside of the atom will then be that of a dipole whose moment is $p = Zed$.

The forces F_E exerted by the external field on the nucleus and on the electrons are

$$F_E = ZeE \tag{3.39}$$

These must be just balanced by the attractive forces between the displaced charges. To estimate this attraction we assume that the electrons are uniformly distributed within the atom. We have seen that the force on a charge inside of a uniform spherical shell is zero, and that the force on a charge outside of a spherical shell is just that which would be exerted by the total charge concentrated at the center. The force exerted on the nucleus is therefore

$$F_N = \frac{1}{4\pi\epsilon_0} \frac{Ze \cdot Q}{d^2} \tag{3.40}$$

where Q is the charge of all the electrons within a sphere of radius d. But this is given by

$$Q = Ze \frac{\frac{4}{3}\pi d^3}{\frac{4}{3}\pi R^3} \tag{3.41}$$

and on substituting into Eq. 3.40 we have

$$F_N = \frac{1}{4\pi\epsilon_0} \frac{(Ze)^2}{R^3} d \tag{3.42}$$

For equilibrium the attractive force given by Eq. 3.42 must just balance the force given by Eq. 3.39 pulling the charges apart.

$$ZeE = \frac{1}{4\pi\epsilon_0} \frac{(Ze)^2}{R^3} d \tag{3.43}$$

Solving for the desired dipole moment $p = Zed$, we get

$$p = Zed = 4\pi\epsilon_0 R^3 E \tag{3.44}$$

The induced dipole moment is proportional to the applied field.

The existence of polarizable matter is of great importance in modifying the properties of capacitors. We must consider the effect of inducing a dipole moment in all the atoms in a slab of dielectric such as is shown in Fig. 3.20. In computing the electric fields due to the polarized atoms, it is their dipole moments that will be important, and the description of the polarization of macroscopic matter will be given by a new vector quantity, the *dipole moment per unit volume, designated by P.* In Fig. 3.20 we have represented the atoms as cubes with the induced charges spread over their faces. This scheme is permissible so long as the dipole moment is correct. Whether we describe it as $p = qd$ or $(2q)(d/2)$, for example, is irrelevant to the present discussion. For the elements of the dielectric shown in Fig. 3.20 we have

$$p = q_i \delta$$

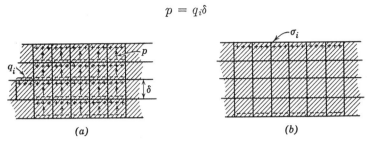

(a)   (b)

FIG. 3.20.   The polarization of a dielectric.

where q_i is the induced charge on two of the surfaces of each atomic cube, and δ is the distance between the induced positive and negative charged faces.

It is apparent that the polarized dielectric shown in Fig. 3.20a, in which every atom has a moment p, is electrically equivalent to the slab shown in Fig. 3.20b, in which it is assumed that the opposite charges on adjacent faces cancel, and we are left with just the surface charges on the two end surfaces. The number of atoms per unit volume n is

$$n = \frac{1}{\delta^3}$$

and the dipole moment per unit volume P is pn. The induced surface charge density σ_i is q_i/δ^2, and in terms of the polarization we have

$$P = pn = q_i\delta \cdot n = \frac{q_i\delta}{\delta^3} = \frac{q}{\delta^2} = \sigma_i \qquad (3.45)$$

The induced polarization, or the induced dipole moment per unit volume, is numerically equal to the induced surface charge density.

If the induced dipole moment of an atom is proportional to the applied field, then we may conclude that the induced surface density of charge is also proportional to the applied field. The proportionality constant between the polarization and the field is called the *electric susceptibility*, k, so that

$$P = kE = \sigma_i \qquad \blacktriangleright(3.46)\blacktriangleleft$$

As a result of the polarization of the dielectric in the capacitor shown, in part, in Fig. 3.21a, the surface charge density that must be used in computing the electric field between the plates of the capacitor is no longer the free charge density σ_f but rather this diminished by σ_i, the charge density induced on the surface of the dielectric. We have

$$E = \frac{1}{\epsilon_0}(\sigma_f - \sigma_i) \qquad (3.47)$$

The electric field is determined by all the charges present.

We are now in a position to compute the effect of the dielectric on the capacitance of a capacitor. This is defined as the free charges on its plates per unit potential difference

$$C = \frac{Q_f}{V_{ab}} \qquad (3.48)$$

From the point of view of the circuit in which the capacitor is to be used, only the free charges which flow out of the circuit onto the plates are

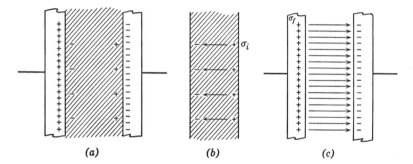

(a)   *(b)*   *(c)*

FIG. 3.21. The induced and free charges on a capacitor containing a dielectric.

of significance, and it is only these which must be used in Eq. 3.48. In a capacitor of area A with a separation d between the plates

$$Q_f = \sigma_f A$$

$$V_{ab} = Ed$$

so that Eq. 3.48 becomes

$$C = \frac{\sigma_f A}{Ed}$$

But from Eqs. 3.46 and 3.47 we have that

$$\sigma_f = \epsilon_0 E + \sigma_i = \epsilon_0 E + P \qquad (3.49)$$
$$= \epsilon_0 E + kE$$
$$= (\epsilon_0 + k)E$$

and therefore

$$C = (\epsilon_0 + k) \frac{A}{d} \qquad (3.50)$$

When a dielectric is added to a capacitor, a new term proportional to the susceptibility of the dielectric is added. It is customary to write

$$\epsilon_0 + k = \epsilon \qquad (3.51)$$

where ϵ is called the *permittivity* of the dielectric, and then to introduce a *dielectric coefficient* K_e defined by

$$K_e = \frac{\epsilon}{\epsilon_0} = 1 + \frac{k}{\epsilon_0} \qquad (3.52)$$

The capacitance of a capacitor may then be written

$$C = K_e \frac{\epsilon_0 A}{d} \qquad (3.53)$$

which is just K_e times its capacitance without a dielectric. This equation offers a convenient way to measure the dielectric coefficient and, through it, the related electric susceptibility. Measure the capacitance with and without the dielectric. The ratio of the two results is the dielectric coefficient of the insulator.

We can now combine this result with our analysis of the polarizability of spherical atoms and determine the effect of substances containing polarized atoms on capacitance. If there are n atoms per unit volume, each of which has a dipole moment p, we have for the polarization vector

$$P = np$$

and using Eqs. 3.44 and 3.46

$$P = 4\pi\epsilon_0 n R^3 E$$

$$k = \frac{P}{E} = 4\pi\epsilon_0 n R^3$$

and, finally, from the definition of the dielectric coefficient in Eq. 3.52

$$K_e = 1 + n4\pi R^3 \qquad (3.54)$$

We apply this first to gases. Under atmospheric conditions a gas contains 3×10^{25} atoms per cubic meter. If we take for the radius of an atom 10^{-10} meter, we get about

$$K_e = 1.0004$$

which is the order of magnitude actually found. A gas at atmospheric pressure will have only a very slight effect on capacitance.

For dielectrics in condensed phases, we must increase n, the number of atoms per unit volume. If we assume atoms of the same size as above, packed tightly, we see that the number per unit volume will be

$$1/(2R)^3 = 1/8 \times 10^{-30} \simeq 10^{29}/\text{meter}^3$$

This is about 3000 times the number in the gas. Using Eq. 3.54, we get

$$K_e = 1 + (4 \times 10^{-4})(3 \times 10^3)$$

$$K_e = 2.2$$

which is the order of magnitude observed for non-polar substances.

The dielectric coefficient for polar molecules is too difficult for us to estimate, as it involves a considerable knowledge of statistical mechanics. At least, however, we can give the answer and show that it is reasonable. A polar molecule is characterized by a permanent dipole moment p_0 due to an unequal distribution of charge. We might guess that the order of magnitude of this dipole moment, due to a tendency for an electron to leave its atom in favor of a neighboring atom in a molecule, might usually be less than that corresponding to an electron leaving one of a pair of atoms completely, but perhaps of this general order of magnitude.

$$p_0 \simeq 1.6 \times 10^{-19} \text{ coulomb} \cdot 10^{-10} \text{ meter} = 1.6 \times 10^{-29} \text{ coulomb-meter}$$

In the presence of a field a torque would act on each dipole to orient it in the field. Thermal collisions would tend to disorient the dipoles. The stronger the field E, the greater the tendency to alignment, and the greater the induced polarization. We might expect, again

$$P \propto E$$

The more violent the thermal collisions, the greater the tendency to disorientation. We might expect

$$P \propto \frac{1}{T}$$

The induced polarization will also be proportional to n, the number of dipoles per unit volume. We might expect

$$P \propto \frac{E}{T} n$$

The expression deduced from kinetic theory is

$$P = \frac{p_0^2 E}{3kT}\, n$$

$$K_e = 1 + \frac{p_0^2 n}{3\epsilon_0 kT} \tag{3.55}$$

where k is the Boltzmann constant. The dielectric coefficients predicted by this expression are of the order of magnitude of several hundred, which is the order of magnitude observed for substances, like water, containing polar molecules, in which the electric properties are markedly dependent on temperature.

Table 3.2 lists the dielectric coefficient of various substances, as well as the dielectric strength, or the maximum electric field which can be applied without breakdown.

TABLE 3.2   THE DIELECTRIC COEFFICIENT, $K_e = \epsilon/\epsilon_0$, AND THE
DIELECTRIC STRENGTH OF VARIOUS SUBSTANCES

Substance	K_e	Dielectric Strength
Glass	5–10	14×10^6 volts/meter
Mica	3–6	$10\text{–}100 \times 10^6$
Paper	7	12×10^6
Quartz	4	8×10^6
Water	81	
Air (1 atmosphere)	1.0006	3×10^6

The dielectric coefficient or susceptibility of a dielectric need not be a constant, independent of field strength, although it usually is. An interesting example of the more complex properties of dielectrics is the *electret*. This is the name given to certain substances, as for instance certain waxes, in which permanent electric dipole moments can be induced. The procedure is to place the wax between two flat electrodes, heat it, and apply a high voltage, or, in other words, create a strong field in the wax. This will induce a strong polarization. Then, without removing the field, cool the wax. On removal of the electrodes, the wax will be found permanently polarized. Although complex changes do take place with time, especially if the wax is slightly heated, these surely are caused by the fields present in the wax as a result of the initial polarization. Such an electret if placed in an ionized gas will acquire free surface charges which may completely cancel the field due to the polarization, but one can show the presence of continued polarization by removing the surface charges and thus restoring the field due to the permanent polarization. If heated sufficiently so that the molecules can reorient themselves, an electret loses its polarization.

3.6 DISPLACEMENT CURRENTS AND DISPLACEMENT

Metals can conduct a constant or direct current, but insulators cannot. The situation is entirely changed, however, when we come to consider alternating currents. Let us consider the current in a line terminated by a capacitor C when the line is connected to a potential difference oscillating at the frequency f with an amplitude V_0.

$$V_{ab} = V_0 \sin 2\pi ft \qquad (3.56)$$

If this represents the voltage across the capacitor, and if the capacitor has the property that the charge on its plates is related to the voltage between them by the expression

$$Q = CV_{ab} \qquad (3.57)$$

then the charge must be a periodic function of the time,

$$Q = CV_0 \sin 2\pi ft \qquad (3.58)$$

But if the charge is flowing in and out of the terminals of the capacitor, there must be a charging current flowing from the line to the plates.

$$i = \frac{dQ}{dt} = (2\pi fC)V_0 \cos 2\pi ft$$

$$= I_0 \cos 2\pi ft$$

$$I_0 \left(\frac{1}{2\pi fC} \right) = V_0 \qquad (3.59)$$

The amplitude of the charging current is proportional to the amplitude of the applied voltage. The quantity

$$X_C = \frac{1}{2\pi fC} \text{ ohms} \qquad \blacktriangleright(3.60)\blacktriangleleft$$

is called the *reactance* of the capacitor and has the dimensions of ohms. Note, however, that the instantaneous current is not proportional to the instantaneous voltage. These quantities are plotted in Fig. 3.22. The voltage reaches its positive maximum one-quarter of a cycle after the current. One speaks of a cycle as representing 360°, and therefore the current wave is said to lead the voltage wave by 90°.

In a conductor carrying a current the charges do not move steadily in one direction. They oscillate to and fro with an amplitude determined by the current amplitude. But in the insulator in a capacitor

carrying alternating current the charges also oscillate to and fro. They
are periodically displaced. Clerk Maxwell proposed that the current in
the insulator be called the *displacement current*, and that its magnitude
be so defined that the displacement current in the insulator be equal to
the conduction current to the plates,

$$i \text{ (displacement)} = i \text{ (conduction)} \qquad (3.61)$$

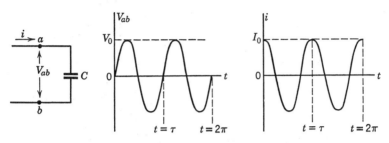

FIG. 3.22.   Alternating current and voltage in a capacitor.

or, in other words, so that the current in a series circuit containing a
capacitor is continuous, and at any given instant has the same value
at every point.   Following this specification we have

$$i \text{ (conduction)} = dQ/dt$$

But the free charge Q is equal to the free charge density σ_f multiplied
by the area of the capacitor, or from Eq. (3.49)

$$i \text{ (conduction)} = \frac{d}{dt} (\epsilon_0 E + P)A$$

The quantity $\epsilon_0 E + P$ Maxwell called the displacement, D, and a new
vector field was introduced

$$D = \epsilon_0 E + P \qquad (3.62)$$

From our definition of permittivity in Eq. 3.51

$$\epsilon = \epsilon_0 + k$$

and our definition of displacement

$$D = \epsilon_0 E + P = \epsilon_0 E + kE = (\epsilon_0 + k)E$$

we see that

$$D = \epsilon E = K_e \epsilon_0 E \qquad (3.63)$$

Wherever there is an electric field, there is also a displacement, but
there is a displacement current only if the displacement is changing.
The displacement current density in the presence of a changing polar-

ization is defined as

$$J_D = \frac{dD}{dt} \text{ amperes/meter}^2 \qquad \blacktriangleright(3.64)\blacktriangleleft$$

and the displacement current in a capacitor as

$$i_D = \frac{dD}{dt} A \qquad \blacktriangleright(3.65)\blacktriangleleft$$

The remarkable aspect about this result is that in order to maintain the idea of a continuous current it is necessary to have the displacement consist of two parts, one, the polarization P of the dielectric, and the second, a part due to the electric field irrespective of whether a physical dielectric is present or not. It is as though a vacuum in a field E were polarized to an extent given by $\epsilon_0 E$, and, if matter were present, there would be an additional polarization P. The total polarization, or displacement, as Maxwell called it, is the sum of the polarization of the vacuum and the polarization of the matter in it. This strange idea will have additional confirmation when we come farther on to discuss the magnetic effects due to currents.

Conduction and Displacement Currents in Solids

We have so far discussed circuit elements as though they were necessarily pure resistors or pure capacitors, and have tacitly assumed that the electric field required to maintain a current on a conductor produced no polarization, and that the electric field required to maintain a polarization in a dielectric produced no current.

In typical non-polar dielectrics, the dielectric coefficient is of the order of 2 or 3 and may be as high as 10. The resistivity is of the order of 10^{15} ohm-meters. Let us compute the conduction and displacement currents in a parallel plate capacitor in which the insulating medium has the above properties. If the applied voltage is $V_0 \sin 2\pi f t$, we have for the amplitude of the conduction current

$$I_{0\,c} = \frac{V_0}{R} = \frac{V_0}{\rho L} A$$

and for the amplitude of the displacement current

$$I_{0\,D} = \frac{V_0}{X_0} = 2\pi f C V_0 = \frac{2\pi f K_e \epsilon_0 A}{L} V_0$$

The ratio of the conduction current to the displacement current is

$$\frac{I_{0\,c}}{I_{0\,D}} = \frac{1}{\rho K_e \epsilon_0 \cdot 2\pi f} = \frac{1}{10^{15} \times 3 \times 8.85 \times 10^{-12} \times 2\pi f} = \frac{6 \times 10^{-6}}{f} \qquad (3.66)$$

Clearly, for any frequency of practical interest, the conduction current is entirely negligible compared to the displacement current, and we are justified in treating the dielectric in terms of capacitance only.

The resistivity of metallic conductors is of the order of 10^{-7} ohm-meter. Although the free electrons give rise to conduction currents, there are also bound electrons in the atomic cores. These cores must be polarizable. Let us assume a dielectric coefficient of the same order of magnitude as for dielectrics. For a short cylindrical conductor we can compute the conduction and displacement currents as above. We get

$$\frac{I_{0\,c}}{I_{0\,D}} = \frac{1}{\rho K_e \epsilon_0 2\pi f} = \frac{6 \times 10^{16}}{f} \tag{3.67}$$

We see that for the highest frequencies which can be handled by electric circuits, of the order of thousands of megacycles per second, the displacement current is negligible compared to the conduction current. This then is the justification for treating metallic conductors as pure resistances.

However, it is clear that there is a range of resistivities for which both properties, the conduction and polarization of a substance, must be taken into account. In such a substance we must have $I_{0\,c} \simeq I_{0\,D}$, or, according to Eq. 3.66

$$\rho \simeq \frac{1}{K_e \epsilon_0 2\pi f} = \frac{6 \times 10^9}{f}$$

For frequencies such as are actually important, between a few cycles per second and thousands of megacycles per second, the range of resistivities is from a few ohm-meters to a few thousands of megohm-meters. Semiconductors have resistivities in this range. In such substances, both conduction and displacement currents may be important.

———

We must now consider how Coulomb's law of force and Gauss's law are modified by the presence of a dielectric. If the dielectric fills all space, the force between charges in it is found through replacing ϵ_0 of Eq. 1.6 by the permittivity ϵ of the medium in which the charges are embedded. We get

$$F = \frac{1}{4\pi\epsilon} \frac{qq'}{r^2} \; ; \qquad E = \frac{1}{4\pi\epsilon} \frac{q}{r^2} \tag{3.68}$$

It follows then that the displacement is a vector field depending only on the free charges present and independent of the permittivity of the surrounding medium.

$$D = \frac{1}{4\pi} \frac{q}{r^2} \tag{3.69}$$

But if this is so, then we can rewrite Gauss's law replacing the quantity $\epsilon_0 E$ by the displacement $\epsilon E = D$. We have, then,

$$\int_S D_n \, dA = \Sigma q \qquad \blacktriangleright(3.70)\blacktriangleleft$$

where q represents the free or excess charge attached to neutral polarized atoms in the volume bounded by the surface of integration S.

It can be shown that Eq. 3.70 is valid even when several dielectrics are present. We shall therefore adopt this as the final form of Gauss's law, and shall illustrate its application to the formulation of boundary conditions below. The following example may serve to make these boundary conditions plausible.

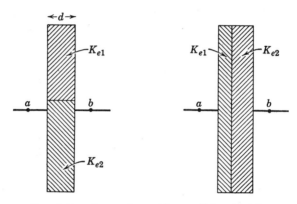

Fɪɢ. 3.23.   A capacitor with two dielectric slabs.

A Capacitor Containing Two Different Dielectrics

From the above discussion we see that in a capacitor with two different dielectrics filling different portions of the capacitor, as in Fig. 3.23a, the electric field is the same in both dielectrics. That is because, as was pointed out, the potential is constant over both metal surfaces and the distance between them is constant, and therefore E, which must satisfy the relation

$$Ed = V_{ab}$$

must be the same at all points not too near the edges. Notice that here E is tangent to the surface separating the two dielectrics. Calling the magnitude of the tangential component of the field on the two sides of this surface $E_{t\,1}$ and $E_{t\,2}$, we see that the relation

$$E_{t\,1} = E_{t\,2} \tag{3.71}$$

is satisfied. The displacement in the two dielectrics is, however, different.

$$D_1 = K_{e\,1}\epsilon_0 E$$

$$D_2 = K_{e\,2}\epsilon_0 E$$

If on the other hand the two dielectrics are arranged in layers as shown in

Fig. 3.23b, the fields will be different. On the other hand, since the free surface charge density will be uniform, and since the lines of displacement will be determined by these free charges only, the displacement will be the same in both media. Notice that here D is perpendicular to, or normal to, the surface separating the two dielectrics. Calling the magnitude of the normal component of D on the two sides of this surface $D_{n\ 1}$ and $D_{n\ 2}$, we see that the relation

$$D_{n\ 1} = D_{n\ 2} \qquad (3.72)$$

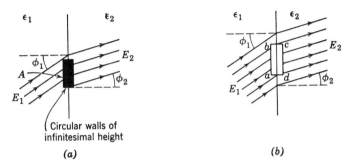

FIG. 3.24. The electric field at the interface between two dielectrics.

is satisfied. The field E, however, will now be different in the two media because of the induced charges on the interface between the two dielectrics

$$E_1 = \frac{D}{K_1 \epsilon_0}$$

$$E_2 = \frac{D}{K_2 \epsilon_0}$$

The relations 3.71 and 3.72 may be shown by the application of Gauss's law to be quite generally applicable, and may be used to compute the change in electric field at the boundary between two dielectric media for fields incident at oblique angles, as illustrated in Fig. 3.24 below.

Boundary Conditions at the Interface between Two Dielectric Media

In order to determine the boundary conditions which specify how the electric field behaves at the interface between two dielectrics, such as are shown in Fig. 3.24, we shall apply the two fundamental relationships which summarize the properties of electrostatic fields.

The first of these is Gauss's law,

$$\int_S D_n \, dA = \sum q_i$$

Consider the application of this law to a Gaussian surface shaped like a pillbox. A cross section is shown in black in Fig. 3.24a. Its height is to be considered infinitesimal, and the area of its ends is A. The curved walls are perpendicular to the boundary. Since there is no free charge within the box, the right-hand side of the above equation vanishes and the integral of the normal component of D over the surface is zero. Since the curved walls of the Gaussian surface have an infinitesimal area, they contribute nothing to the integral. Since the field enters the box through the left surface, its contribution to the integral of the outward normal component of D is negative. We have for the two surfaces

$$-AD_1 \cos \phi_1 = -AD_{n\,1}$$
$$AD_2 \cos \phi_2 = AD_{n\,2}$$

The result for the entire Gaussian surface then is

$$-AD_{n\,1} + AD_{n\,2} = 0$$
$$D_{n\,1} = D_{n\,2} \qquad \blacktriangleright (3.73) \blacktriangleleft$$

The normal component of the displacement has the same value at the two sides of the boundary between two dielectrics.

We now apply the second relationship describing the fundamental properties of electrostatic fields,

$$\oint E_t \, ds = 0$$

to the path a, b, c, d in Fig. 3.24b. Sides bc and ad are to be considered infinitesimal, so that their contributions to the line integral are negligible. If the lengths ab and cd are L, we have for the contributions from these two sides to the contour integral

$$LE_1 \sin \phi_1 \text{ or } LE_{t\,1}, \text{ and } -LE_2 \sin \phi_2 \text{ or } -LE_{t\,2}$$

and for the entire integral

$$LE_{t\,1} - LE_{t\,2} = 0$$
$$E_{t\,1} = E_{t\,2} \qquad \blacktriangleright (3.74) \blacktriangleleft$$

The tangential components of the electric field have the same values on the two sides of the interface between two dielectrics. Equations 3.73 and 3.74 suffice to compute the magnitude and direction of the fields on one side of such a boundary if the values on the other side are known. We shall find these results of particular importance when we come to a discussion of the reflection and refraction of electromagnetic waves.

3.7 THE ENERGY IN POLARIZED DIELECTRICS

We have shown that the energy in a polarized capacitor is necessarily

$$U = \tfrac{1}{2}Q_f V_{ab} \qquad (3.75)$$

where Q_f has been written for the charge to emphasize that we are here dealing with the free charge on the surface of metallic parts of the capacitor. Since the D field has been shown to be due to free charges alone,

$$\frac{Q_f}{A} = \sigma_f = D \qquad (3.76)$$

and since, for a parallel plate capacitor,

$$V_{ab} = Ed \qquad (3.77)$$

Eq. 3.75 may be put into the form

$$U = \tfrac{1}{2}Q_f V_{ab} = \tfrac{1}{2}DE(Ad)$$

But, since (Ad) is the volume of the dielectric, we may write, for the energy density in the dielectric, a quantity analogous to that appropriate to the air-filled capacitor,

$$u = \tfrac{1}{2}DE \qquad \blacktriangleright(3.78)\blacktriangleleft$$

The displacement D is made up of the two terms

$$D = \epsilon_0 E + P$$

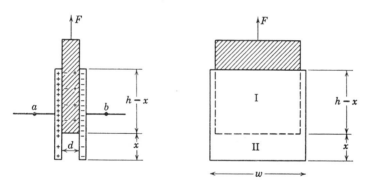

Fig. 3.25.   A dielectric slab being removed from a capacitor.

and substituting this into Eq. 3.78 gives

$$u = \frac{\epsilon_0 E^2}{2} + \frac{PE}{2} \qquad (3.79)$$

The first term represents the energy density in the region between the plates of the capacitor whether the dielectric is present or not. The second term represents the additional energy due to the polarized medium. An amount of work $PE/2$ joules per unit volume must be done in polarizing a dielectric in which the polarization is proportional to the applied field.

To illustrate this result we discuss the forces exerted on flat slabs of dielectrics being withdrawn from the region between the fixed plates of a capacitor, as shown in Fig. 3.25. We neglect frictional forces, and, if the plates are being drawn out vertically as shown, we neglect the constant force of gravity. The reason for the attraction of the capacitor for the dielectric so that the force F

shown is required to withdraw it may be found in considering the Coulomb forces on the induced charges of the dielectric. Because of symmetry the forces due to free charges on the portion of the conductor adjacent to the dielectric will cancel. However, the charges in the part from which the dielectric has already been withdrawn will attract the adjacent induced charges, thus giving rise to an attractive force between capacitor and dielectric.

Instead of computing this force from Coulomb's law, we shall compute it from energy considerations. If there is an attractive electrical force present, then the externally applied force F must do an amount of work $F\,dx$ in removing the dielectric by an amount dx. The work done must then go to increasing the potential energy of the capacitor, dU.

$$F\,dx = dU \qquad \text{or} \qquad F = dU/dx \qquad (3.80)$$

This increase in the electrostatic potential energy we can calculate.

We shall assume that the distance d between plates is small compared to x, $h - x$, and w, so that end effects may be neglected. E, P, and D are considered to be uniform and everywhere normal to the outer surfaces.

The electric field must be the same at all points of the capacitor, $E = V_{ab}/d$. The charge density in region I is, however, different from that in region II. We have

$$E = \frac{\sigma_I}{\epsilon} = \frac{\sigma_{II}}{\epsilon_0} \qquad (3.81)$$

$$\frac{Q_1}{\epsilon w(h - x)} = \frac{Q_2}{\epsilon_0 w x}$$

Since we are considering an isolated capacitor, the total charge Q is constant,

$$Q = Q_1 + Q_2 \qquad (3.82)$$

Solving these two equations we get

$$Q_1 = \frac{Q K_e(h - x)}{x + K_e(h - x)}$$

$$Q_2 = \frac{Qx}{x + K_e(h - x)}$$

$$E = \frac{Q}{\epsilon_0 w[x + K_e(h - x)]} \qquad (3.83)$$

The electric field in the capacitor increases as the dielectric is removed. The energy U in the charged capacitor will be the sum of two terms

$$U = \tfrac{1}{2}\epsilon E^2 wd(h - x) + \tfrac{1}{2}\epsilon_0 E^2 wdx \qquad (3.84)$$

$$= \frac{1}{2}\frac{Q^2 d}{\epsilon_0 w}\frac{1}{x + K_e(h - x)}$$

and by differentiating this expression we find, using Eq. 3.80,

$$F = \frac{1}{2}\frac{Q^2 d}{\epsilon_0 w}\frac{K_e - 1}{[x + K_e(h - x)]^2}$$

or, substituting the value of E from Eq. 3.83, and noting that

$$P = kE = (K_e - 1)\epsilon_0 E,$$

$$F/wd = \tfrac{1}{2}EP \tag{3.85}$$

The force per unit of exposed area of dielectric is equal to the energy density in the dielectric. The work done by this force in removing the dielectric is

$$W = \int_0^h F\, dx = \Delta U \tag{3.86}$$

$$U = U_{x=h} - U_{x=0} \tag{3.87}$$

In terms of E_0, the initial field for $x = 0$

$$E_0 = \frac{Q}{K_e \epsilon_0 wh}$$

we find by evaluating either Eq. 3.86 or 3.87

$$W = \Delta U = \tfrac{1}{2}\epsilon_0 E_0{}^2 (K_e - 1) \tag{3.88}$$

If the capacitor had been connected to a battery maintaining a constant potential difference, the work done to remove the dielectric would no longer be that computed above. For the new case, we must include the energy in the battery in our system and equate the work done by the force F in removing the dielectric to the increase in energy of the capacitor plus the increase in energy of the battery.

For the energy of the capacitor we have the expression in Eq. 3.84, but now the electric field E is constant. Calling this constant value $E_0 = V_{ab}/d$, we have for the change in energy due to removing the dielectric

$$\Delta U = U_{x=h} - U_{x=0} = -\tfrac{1}{2}\epsilon_0 E_0{}^2 (K_e - 1)(wdh) \tag{3.89}$$

The energy of the capacitor has decreased because of the removal of the dielectric. It can be shown that the force on the dielectric may always be written

$$F = \tfrac{1}{2}EP(wd) \tag{3.90}$$

regardless of whether a switch connecting the capacitor to a battery is closed or open. If the switch is closed, E is constant and has the value $E_0 = V_{ab}/d$. The work done by the force F is

$$W = F \cdot h = \tfrac{1}{2}\epsilon_0 E_0{}^2 (K_e - 1)(wdh) \tag{3.91}$$

The charge on the capacitor has decreased. The original charge was

$$Q_0 = C_0 V_{ab} = K_e \epsilon_0 \frac{wh}{d} V_{ab}$$

The final charge was

$$Q_f = C_f V_{ab} = \epsilon_0 \frac{wh}{d} V_{ab}$$

The energy supplied to the battery in forcing a charge ΔQ through the battery against its emf is

$$U_{bat} = \Delta Q V_{ab} = (K_e - 1)\epsilon_0 \frac{wh}{d} V_{ab}{}^2$$
$$= (K_e - 1)\epsilon_0 E_0{}^2 \tag{3.92}$$

Combining Eqs. 3.89, 3.91, and 3.92, we find

$$W = \Delta U_{cap} + \Delta U_{bat}$$
$$\tfrac{1}{2}\epsilon_0 E_0{}^2 (K_e - 1)(wdh) = -\tfrac{1}{2}\epsilon_0 E_0{}^2 (K_e - 1)(wdh) + \epsilon_0 E_0{}^2 (K_e - 1)(wdh)$$

SUMMARY

Positive electric charge is composed of certain smallest units called protons. Negative electric charge is composed of smallest units called electrons. The magnitude of these charges on protons and electrons is equal. They are called the electronic charge e,

$$e \simeq 1.6 \times 10^{-19} \text{ coulomb}$$

The mass of the electron is

$$m = 9.1 \times 10^{-31} \text{ kg}$$

The ratio of the mass of the proton to that of the electron is

$$\frac{M_P}{m} \simeq 1837$$

Atoms are made up of positively charged nuclei surrounded by electrons. The positive charge of a nucleus is Ze, and in a neutral atom there will be Z electrons surrounding a nucleus. Z is called the atomic number. Atomic radii are of the order of 10^{-10} meter. Nuclear radii for heavy atoms are of the order of 10^{-14} meter.

An electron volt is the amount of energy which an electron acquires in falling through a potential difference of 1 volt. One electron volt $= 1.6 \times 10^{-19}$ joule. Atomic collisions may be elastic, or such that the kinetic energy of the impinging particles is equal to their kinetic energy as they recede from each other. Inelastic collisions, in which kinetic energy is converted into light, or into ionized atoms and electrons, commonly occur for impact energies of the order of several electron volts.

If an electric field is applied to an ionized gas or liquid the clouds of positive and negative charge drift in opposite directions with a velocity determined by their mobility,

$$v_{dr} = \mu E$$

The current due to a drifting cloud of charge is

$$i = nev_{dr}A$$

where n is the number of charges per unit volume, and A is the cross-sectional area of the conductor.

In a metallic conductor, the current is carried by free or movable electrons and their number is independent of the electric field.

$$i = (ne\mu) \left(\frac{A}{L}\right) V_{ab}$$

This leads to Ohm's law for the current-voltage relationship in a metallic wire,

$$iR = V_{ab}$$

the resistance R of the wire being

$$R = \rho \frac{L}{A} \text{ ohms}$$

$$\rho = \frac{1}{\sigma} = \frac{1}{ne\mu} \text{ ohm-meters}$$

where the resistivity ρ, or its reciprocal, the conductivity σ, is a quantity determined by the structure of the metal of which the wire is made.

The resistivity of metals increases with temperature. Over a considerable range in the vicinity of room temperature the resistance of a conductor at any temperature T may be expressed in terms of its resistance at 20°C by an equation of the form

$$R_T = R_{20}[1 + \alpha(T - 20)]$$

where α is the temperature coefficient of the resistivity.

The polarization P of a dielectric medium is the induced dipole moment per unit volume. At the surface of a dielectric normal to P, the induced charge density, σ_i, is numerically equal to P, and is positive if P is directed toward the surface and negative if P is directed away from the surface. The displacement in a dielectric is defined by the relation

$$D = \epsilon_0 E + P$$

If we write $D = \epsilon E = K_e \epsilon_0 E$, where K_e is called the dielectric coefficient, and if the polarization is proportional to the applied field so that

$$P = kE$$

where k is the electric susceptibility, then

$$\epsilon = \epsilon_0 + k$$

$$K_e = k/\epsilon_0 + 1$$

When an electric field is changing, a displacement current is present in the field. The density of this current J_D at any point is given by the time rate of change of the displacement.

$$J_D = \frac{dD}{dt} \text{ amperes/meter}^2$$

The displacement current in a parallel plate capacitor of area A is $i_D = J_D A$ and is just equal to the conduction current i_c which charges it.

When a capacitor of capacitance C is connected to an alternating potential difference

$$V_{ab} = V_0 \sin 2\pi ft$$

the current through the capacitor is a displacement current,

$$i_c = i_D = \frac{V_0}{X_C} \sin \left(2\pi ft + \frac{\pi}{2}\right) = I_0 \cos 2\pi ft$$

where the reactance is

$$X_C = \frac{V_0}{I_0} = \frac{1}{2\pi fC}$$

and the current leads the voltage by 90°.

The electric field in a parallel plate capacitor whose plates are given a charge Q, or a charge density $\sigma_f = Q/A$, is

$$E = \frac{D}{\epsilon} = \frac{\sigma_f}{\epsilon} = \frac{\sigma_f}{K_e \epsilon_0} \text{ volts/meter}$$

This field is reduced by the presence of the dielectric from the value that would have been produced by the charge density σ_f in a vacuum because of the induced charge density σ_i on the surface of the dielectric. The expression for E might also have been written

$$E = \frac{\sigma_f - \sigma_i}{\epsilon_0}$$

a fact showing that in computing the electric intensity E all charges must be taken into account, whereas in computing the displacement only the free charges are to be taken into account.

In the presence of a dielectric medium occupying all space, Coulomb's law of force between two charges, q and q', becomes

$$F = \frac{1}{4\pi\epsilon} \frac{qq'}{r^2}$$

where ϵ is the permittivity of the medium in which the charges are embedded.

Gauss's law in the presence of dielectric media becomes

$$\int_S D_n \, dA = \Sigma q$$

and by the application of this law and

$$\oint E_t \, ds = 0$$

expressing the fundamental properties of the electrostatic field, it is possible to show that at the boundary between two dielectrics:

$$D_{n\,1} = D_{n\,2}$$

$$E_{t\,1} = E_{t\,2}$$

The energy density in a polarized dielectric is

$$u = \tfrac{1}{2}ED = \tfrac{1}{2}\epsilon_0 E^2 + \tfrac{1}{2}PE$$

PROBLEMS

1. Two parallel plates 1 mm apart are located in an evacuated vessel. The difference in potential between them is 100 volts. (a) An electron is liberated at rest from the cathode. How long will it take the electron to reach the anode? (b) A proton is liberated at rest from the anode. How long will it take the proton to reach the cathode?

2. An electron is situated in an electric field oscillating at a frequency of 60 cycles per second with an amplitude of 100 volts/meter, $E = 100 \sin 377t$ volts/meter. (a) What is the amplitude of the oscillation of the electron, if we assume its average drift to be zero? (b) Answer the above for a proton. (c) Answer a and b if the frequency of the oscillation is 10^9 cycles/sec.

★3. In Millikan's oil drop experiment to determine the charge on an electron, it is desirable to know the mass of the oil drop. This may be determined through observing its velocity of free fall in air. Any object having a density greater than air will be accelerated when released at rest. The downward force of gravity will be opposed by an upward frictional force which is proportional to the velocity. The gravitational force will accelerate the object until it is just balanced by the viscous drag. At this velocity the two opposing forces balance. The work done by gravity is converted into the energy of motion of the air. This final velocity for a sphere of radius r falling in a viscous fluid or gas was shown by Stokes to be

$$v = \frac{2}{9} \frac{r^2 g}{\eta} (\rho - \rho_0)$$

where g is the acceleration due to gravity, η is the coefficient of viscosity of the fluid, and ρ and ρ_0 are the densities of the sphere and the surrounding fluid, respectively. In a particular experiment the plates are 10 mm apart, and a potential difference of 5000 volts can just hold a particular oil drop with a single electronic charge on it against the force of gravity. How long would it take this drop to fall 1 mm when the plates are short-circuited? What is the diameter of the drop? If in the equation for the velocity cgs units are used, lengths must be expressed in centimeters, and η in poises, or gram/cm sec. In the above experiment $\rho = 1$ gram/cc, ρ_0 may be neglected, $g = 980$ cm/sec^2, and $\eta = 1.8 \times 10^{-4}$ poise.

★4. In Millikan's oil drop experiment, the following data were recorded:

Plate separation	1.60 cm
Distance of fall or rise	1.021 cm
Potential difference	5085 volts
Viscosity of air	1.824×10^{-4} poise
Density of oil	0.92 gram/cm^3
Average time of fall	11.88 sec
Successive times of rise	22.37 sec
	34.80 sec
	29.25 sec
	19.70 sec
	42.30 sec

From the expression given above for the terminal velocity of free fall, find an expression for the terminal velocity when any force F is applied. Calculate the successive changes in charge on the oil drop, and obtain an average value of e from these data. (See Problem 3 above.) A reasonable procedure is to compute the total charge on the drop for various rise times, to list these in order, and to look for a smallest difference.

★5. What is the electrostatic potential energy of a uniformly charged hollow sphere? This energy divided by c^2 represents a mass according to Einstein's famous relation $E = mc^2$, where $c = 3 \times 10^8$ meters/sec. What would the radius of an electron be if all of its mass were of electrical origin? Actually not.all of its mass is of this kind, but the contribution due to the energy of the charge is surely significant.

6. A hydrogen atom may be considered as a proton and an electron separated by a distance of 5×10^{-11} meter. (a) What is the Coulomb force between the two particles? (b) How does this force compare with the gravitational attraction? (The circumference of the earth is about 24,000 mi, and its density is about 5.5 grams/cc.)

7. A beam of 50 Mev protons is incident on a thin sheet of gold. The gold nucleus may be assumed to have a radius of 8.7×10^{-15} meter. Neglect the radius of the proton. The atomic number of gold is 79, and its atomic weight is 197. At these energies, the Coulomb repulsive force has little effect, and only the protons which make direct hits on gold nuclei are stopped. What thickness must the gold foil have in order to stop 1% of the incident protons by direct nuclear collisions? The density of gold is 19.3 grams per cubic centimeter. *Hint:* How many nuclei per unit area spread on a plane surface would cover 1% of the area? In what thickness of foil would you find this number per unit area of surface?

8. (a) How much energy does a proton need in order to strike a silver nucleus whose radius is 7.1×10^{-15} meter? Neglect the radius of the proton. The atomic number of silver is 47. (b) How fast would the incident proton be moving?

9. (a) How much energy does an alpha particle need to strike a silver nucleus? See Problem 8 above. The alpha particle is a helium nucleus. Its atomic number is 2 and its atomic weight is 4. Neglect the radius of the alpha particle. (b) How fast would the incident alpha particle be moving?

10. A thorium nucleus having a radius 9.16×10^{-15} meter and an atomic number 90 ejects an alpha particle (charge $+2e$). Neglect the radius of the alpha particle. (a) How much energy, expressed in electron volts, must the alpha particle have if it

is ejected at rest at the surface of the Th nucleus? (b) Could this alpha particle reach either the gold or silver nuclei described in Problems 7 and 8?

11. The average number of ions produced by an α particle in air may be assumed about 10^5 per centimeter. (a) What will then be the range of a 5-Mev alpha particle in air if on the average 15 ev are required to produce an ion? (b) What would you expect the range of such alpha particles to be in your body? What would you expect to be the consequence of exposure to alpha rays? The number of molecules per mole is 6.02×10^{23}. One mole at normal temperature and pressure occupies 22.4 liters. Human tissue may be treated here as though it were water, with a molecular weight of 18 and a density of 1 gram/cc.

12. Assuming that, from a nuclear point of view, air may be treated as though it were made of nitrogen molecules whose nuclear radii are 5×10^{-15} meter and whose atomic number is 7, what fraction of the particles in a beam of alpha particles such as is treated in Problem 11 should make a nuclear collision in 3 cm of path? See hint in Problem 7 and data in Problem 11.

13. In an experiment on the scattering of alpha particles, the number ΔN scattered into a direction making an angle between θ and $\theta + \Delta\theta$ with the direction of incidence are listed below.

θ degrees	$\dfrac{\Delta N}{\Delta \theta}$
156	2.05
123.5	6.3
110	9.0
100.5	12.5
93	15
87.5	20
83	22
78.5	25
75	33
72.25	40

Is this scattering due to Coulomb forces?

★14. In a hypothetical vacuum tube consisting of two plane electrodes a distance d apart, electrons are released from the cathode at a rate such that the current per unit area is j. Compute the number of electrons per unit volume in the region between electrodes when a potential difference V_0 is applied to the tube, neglecting the forces which the electrons exert on each other. Under what conditions, or for what range of values of V, d, and j, would this neglect be justified? *Hint:* Compute the charge per unit area of the plates, and compare this with the charge in a cylinder of unit cross-sectional area between the plates.

15. (a) What fraction of its energy will a 10-volt electron lose in a head-on elastic collision with a mercury atom? Assume the recoil to be along the line of motion of the incident electron, and assume that the mercury atom was initially at rest. (b) If there is an inelastic collision in which the mercury atom absorbs and reemits 5 ev in the form of light, what will be the energy of the recoiling electron? Neglect the momentum associated with the light.

16. Compute the fraction of its energy that an electron would lose in an elastic collision with an argon atom assuming that the recoiling electron moves at an angle θ to its original direction of motion.

17. A long tubular fluorescent lamp such as is commonly used for lighting con-

tains argon, at reduced pressure, and mercury vapor. In operation the mercury atoms are ionized by collisions with fast-moving electrons. The current is carried by the electrons and positive ions. The argon atoms remain inert, being neither excited nor ionized under the conditions prevailing in the lamp. Argon gas is used to help in starting, to retard the recombination of ions and electrons at the walls, and for other reasons involving the useful life of the lamp. The mercury atoms are also excited and give off ultraviolet radiation, which is absorbed in the phosphor with which the inner surface of the lamp is coated. The phosphor, upon absorbing the ultraviolet light, reemits the visible light which we see. (a) Assuming that the mean energy of the electrons in a fluorescent lamp is 1 ev, what is their equivalent temperature? (b) What is their mobility in such a tube containing argon at a pressure of 3 mm of mercury, assuming that the electrons may be treated as point charges and that the mean free path may be computed from collisions between these point charges and argon atoms having a radius 1.5×10^{-10} meter? The number of atoms of a gas per cubic meter at a pressure of 1 mm of mercury is 3.54×10^{22}. (c) What is the mobility of singly charged mercury ions in such a lamp assuming that their mean velocity is that of ordinary gas atoms at the operating temperature of the lamp, 40°C, and that their diameter is equal to that of the argon atoms? (d) Assuming that the ion density and electron density is the same, what fraction of the current through the lamp is carried by the electrons? (e) If the current through the lamp is 400 ma (milliamperes), what is the number of free electrons per unit volume in the tube? The tube diameter is 1.5 in., and the axial electric field is 100 volts/meter. (f) From the fact that the number of electrons per unit volume is equal to the number of positive mercury ions in the tube, and from the vapor pressure of mercury at 40°C, which is approximately 10^{-2} mm of mercury, compute the fraction of the mercury atoms which are in the ionized state.

18. A current of 1 amp passes through a solution of $CuSO_4$ for 20 min. At the end of this time 0.400 gram of copper has been deposited on the cathode. What is the value of the faraday as given by this information?

19. A metal object has a surface area of 0.25 meter². How long would this have to be suspended in an electroplating $CuSO_4$ solution carrying a current of 10 amp in order to deposit a layer 1 mil (10^{-3} in.) thick?

20. The current flowing in a copper wire 1 mm in diameter is 5 amp. (a) How many electrons flow past a given point in the wire in one second? (b) If these current-carrying (free) electrons are at room temperature and are assumed to have thermal energies of $\frac{3}{2}kT$, what is their average velocity? (As will be discussed in Chapter 13, free electrons in metals actually have much larger energies than $\frac{3}{2}kT$ and correspondingly larger velocities.) (c) What is their drift velocity assuming the number per cubic meter to be 0.84×10^{29}? (d) Since their drift velocity is so small, why does a light bulb turn on almost instantaneously when you snap the switch?

21. A conductor consists of an inner core of steel of radius 1.20 cm and an outer sheath of copper whose thickness is 0.30 cm. (a) What is the resistance of the same conductor compared with that of a solid copper conductor of the same cross-sectional area as the copper surrounding the steel core? (b) If 120 amp flows in the composite conductor, what current flows in each metal? The resistivities of copper and steel are to be taken as 1.77×10^{-8} and 11.8×10^{-8} ohm-meter, respectively.

22. A solid copper conductor having a diameter of 0.5 cm is surrounded by an insulating sheath 1 cm thick having a resistivity of 10^{10} ohm-meters. The cable so formed is laid in sea water so that its outer surface is always at ground potential.

(a) What is the resistance from the center conductor to ground per kilometer of cable? (b) If the center conductor is maintained at 200 volts. what is the leakage current per kilometer?

★23. A cable like that described in Problem 22 is used to carry power to an island 100 km from the mainland. The power station maintains the shore end of the cable 1000 volts above ground, and the load on the island has a resistance of 1000 ohms. The return current flows through the ground, which may be considered resistanceless. (a) What fraction of the power delivered to the cable is used in the load? In solving this problem the concept of a resistance of the conductor per unit length R', and a "conductance" to ground G' per unit length may be useful. The voltage drop in a length L will be $iR'L$, and the current to ground will be $VG'L$, where

$$G' = \frac{1}{R_{ins} \text{ per meter}} = \frac{2\pi}{\rho_{ins} \ln R_b/R_a}$$

(b) After some time of operation the resistivity ρ of the insulator is found to have dropped to 10^7 ohm-meters. What now is the ratio of the power delivered to the load to the total power delivered to the cable? It will be seen that an appreciable fraction of the current delivered to the cable leaks to ground through the insulation. We are no longer justified in computing the leakage current as though the inner conductor were at a constant potential. The procedure to be followed to solve this problem accurately is to solve two simultaneous differential equations. Note that the voltage drop V along a length of cable is $iR' \Delta x$, and that the decrease in current along the cable in a length x is $VG' \Delta x$. This leads to the equations for differential elements

$$\frac{dV}{dx} = -R'i$$

$$\frac{di}{dx} = -G'V$$

To solve these equations, differentiate the first with respect to x and substitute the second, thereby eliminating i. This second-order equation has two arbitrary constants. Prove that the solution is

$$V = A_1 e^{-ax} + A_2 e^{+ax}$$

where A_1 and A_2 are the arbitrary constants in question, and a must have a particular value to satisfy the differential equation. Similarly, show that the current must depend on x as follows:

$$i = B_1 e^{-bx} + B_2 e^{+bx}$$

The four arbitrary constants may be found through substituting into the original equations, and noting that, at the power station, where we choose $x = 0$, the voltage has a specified value, and that, at the load, where $x = L$, the ratio of voltage to current is equal to the resistance of the load.

24. A wire whose cross-sectional area is 0.80 sq mm, specific heat 0.30 cal/gram°C density 8.0 grams/cc, and resistivity 5.0×10^{-6} ohm-centimeter is connected to a battery that causes a constant current of 4.0 amp to flow. What is the initial rate of change of temperature of the wire?

25. When a certain tungsten filament light bulb at room temperature (20°C) is first turned on, it draws a current of 10 amp from the 115-volt line. As soon as the filament reaches its operating temperature, it draws only 1 amp. What is its oper-

ating temperature? Consider the temperature coefficient of resistivity to be a constant and equal to 0.0060 per degree centigrade.

26. How constant must the temperature of a coil of wire be maintained near room temperature if its resistance is to be constant within 0.1%? The temperature coefficient of resistivity of the metal is 0.004 per degree centigrade.

27. Estimate the maximum displacement of the nucleus with respect to its cloud of electrons that can be produced in gaseous argon atoms at normal temperature and pressure, in the atoms of the SiO_2 molecule in quartz, and in copper atoms in solid copper when the current density is such as to heat the copper at the rate of 1000°C/sec. The specific heat of copper may be taken as 0.1 cal/gram and the density as 8.5 gram/cm³.

28. The dielectric constant of gaseous helium at −253°C and at a pressure of 1 atmosphere is $K_e = 1.0010$. Helium may be considered a perfect gas even at this low temperature. (a) Find the dipole moment induced in each helium atom in an electric field of 10^5 volts/meter. (b) What is the value of K_e at 20°C and 1 atmosphere?

29. HCl is a gas consisting of polar molecules in which each molecule has a permanent moment, approximately equal to that computed through assuming (1) that the hydrogen atom has lost its electron to the chlorine atom, and (2) that the center of gravity of the + and − charges are 10^{-10} meter apart. Assuming that the dielectric strength of HCl is approximately equal to that of air, 3×10^6 volts/meter, what is the maximum degree of orientation as measured by the ratio of the average induced dipole moment per atom to the permanent moment that can be achieved at the boiling point of the gas, −84°C? What is the dielectric coefficient under these conditions?

30. An electret is made by melting wax between two metal plates having an area of 10 cm² held 1 mm apart with a voltage of 10,000 volts between the plates. At this temperature the wax behaves like a normal dielectric having $K_e = 5$. The wax is then solidified and retains the polarization imparted to it at the higher temperature. At room temperature the polarization is essentially constant. The plates on either side of the dielectric are left in place. (a) What is the field in the wax if the plates have the previously applied voltage between them? (b) What is the field in the dielectric if the free charge is removed? (c) What is the field in the dielectric if the plates are short-circuited? The plates are now connected to each other through a resistor, $R = 10^{12}$ ohms, and a sensitive galvanometer. The temperature is raised slightly, and the polarization is found to decrease at the rate of 5% per minute, producing a constant current i through R. (d) What current will the galvanometer read? (e) What will be the voltage across the resistor?

31. A parallel plate capacitor connected to a battery stores twice as much charge with a given dielectric as it does with air as a dielectric. Find the susceptibility of the dielectric.

32. A parallel plate capacitor of 5 μf has a plate separation of 2 mm. A dielectric with $K_e = 4$ and a thickness of 1 mm is placed between the plates. What is the capacity with the dielectric in?

33. A parallel plate capacitor is made of two sheets of metal foil 1 meter square, separated by a sheet of paper 0.05 mm thick having a permittivity $6\epsilon_0$. (a) Find the capacitance. (b) Find the charge of and potential difference between the plates when the field in the paper is 12×10^6 volts/meter. (c) How high could the stored electrostatic energy lift 1 mg?

34. A parallel plate capacitor having a separation d between plates has a capacitance C. A dielectric having a dielectric coefficient K_e and a thickness $d/2$ is inserted into the capacitor. What is now the capacitance C' of the capacitor?

35. A capacitor is made of two metal sheets having an area of 10^{-2} meter^2 separated by 10^{-4} meter. One-half of the area between the sheets is filled with a dielectric having $K_e = 2$, and the other half with a dielectric having $K_e = 3$. (a) What is the capacitance of the capacitor? (b) What are the values of D and E in each dielectric when 100 volts are applied to the capacitor?

36. A capacitor is made of two metal sheets having an area of 10^{-2} meter^2 separated by two thin sheets of dielectric pressed together. One of these has a thickness 10^{-4} meter and a dielectric coefficient $K_e = 3$, whereas the other has a thickness of 2×10^{-4} meter and a dielectric coefficient $K_e = 4$. (a) What is the capacitance of this capacitor? (b) When 100 volts are put across this capacitor, what are the values of E and D in each dielectric?

37. Two dielectric slabs of coefficients 3 and 5, respectively, are tightly pressed together, and placed in an electric field E. In the first dielectric, E has a value of 1.50 volts/meter and makes an angle of 30° with the boundary between the two dielectrics. Find E in the second dielectric.

38. What is the amplitude of the displacement of the electron cloud in a copper wire 1 mm in diameter carrying a 60-cycle current with an amplitude of 5 amp? See Problem 2 in this connection.

39. A capacitor of 3 μf and one of 9 μf are connected in parallel and then across a 115-volt 60-cycle a-c line. (a) Find the total current in the circuit. (b) Find the current in each capacitor.

40. The two capacitors in Problem 39 are connected in series across the same line. (a) Find the total current in the circuit. (b) Find the voltage across each capacitor.

41. A slab of dielectric that completely fills the space between the plates of a capacitor has a dielectric coefficient $K_e = 2$. The capacitor, whose capacitance is 100 μμf when the dielectric is in place, is connected to the terminals of a 600-volt battery. The dielectric is withdrawn. (a) How much work is done by the force which withdrew the dielectric? (b) What is the change in energy of the capacitor? (c) How much work was done by the battery?

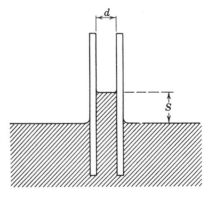

42. A parallel plate capacitor is partly immersed in an insulating liquid as shown below. When the terminals of the capacitor are connected to a 600-volt battery, the level of the liquid rises. (See Fig. 3.26.) Given the following data: $K_e = 10$, $d = 0.2$ mm. By how much does the liquid rise between the plates? Assume the density of the liquid is 1 gram/cc.

Fig. 3.26. Illustration for problem 42.

43. A parallel plate capacitor made of plates having an area A and a distance between plates x, is completely immersed in oil having a dielectric coefficient K_e. The plates are given a charge Q. (a) What is the total energy of the capacitor? (b) What is the change in the energy of the capacitor if the separation between plates is increased by dx? (c) What is the force between the plates?

44. Repeat Problem 43 above, but for the case that the capacitor initially has a solid dielectric, such as a sheet of paper between the plates, and that, when the plates are separated, the added volume is filled with air.

CHAPTER **4**

Applied Electricity

4.1 ELECTRICAL MEASUREMENTS

Two common types of physical measurement are illustrated by the measurement of weight, or mass. The commonest form of weight-measuring device is a spring balance, or other similar apparatus, using levers, in which the force to be measured deflects some observable object such as a pointer, and by means of a calibrated scale the deflection reveals the magnitude of the weight which produced it. This is perhaps the most convenient way of measuring a weight, because of the speed with which the measurement can be made. A more tedious, but potentially more accurate, type of measurement is the direct comparison of the weights, or masses, with standards of weight. This is done by means of a chemical balance in which the calibrated weights in one pan just balance the weight of the unknown. The properties of the balance itself are not involved in the measurement. The balance merely makes an exact comparison possible. Electrical quantities may similarly be measured by means of indicating instruments on meters, which are easy to read, or by comparison with standards. We shall take up electrical meters first.

Although we have already discussed the principles involved in the measurement of volts and amperes, we have not considered in detail how a galvanometer can be used in conjunction with a resistor to measure these electrical quantities directly. We have described the measurement of a potential difference using an electrostatic instrument which draws no current. A galvanometer may also be used as a voltmeter to measure potential difference if it is permissible to draw a small current from the terminals whose potential difference is to be measured. Let us, for example, consider the problem of making a voltmeter capable of measuring the actual terminal voltage of a storage battery whose nominal terminal voltage is 6 volts, using a galvanometer having a sensitivity such that full-scale deflection requires 0.02 amp, or 20 ma.

The battery is assumed to be delivering i amp to an external circuit. The internal resistance of the galvanometer we shall assume to be $r = 25$ ohms. This is the resistance of the coil in the galvanometer. By being connected in series with a suitable resistance R, as shown in

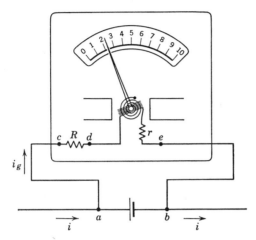

FIG. 4.1.   A galvanometer used as a voltmeter.

Fig. 4.1, the instrument can be made to show a full-scale deflection when the potential difference between the terminals ce of the instrument has some convenient value, for example, just 10 volts. We see that, since Ohm's law must be satisfied,

$$i_g(r + R) = V_{ce} \qquad (4.1)$$

Since the current wanted when $V_{ce} = 10$ volts is 0.02 amp, and $r = 25$ ohms, this leads to

$$0.02(25 + R) = 10$$

$$25 + R = 500$$

$$R = 475 \text{ ohms} \qquad (4.2)$$

A voltmeter of this kind properly calibrated always reads correctly the voltage V_{ce} across its terminals. This is a consequence of Ohm's law. If, however, we wish to insure that the potential difference between two points of a circuit has not been altered by the application of the voltmeter leads to these points, then an additional condition must be satisfied. We must demand that the current drawn by the meter, i_g, be small compared to the line current i. This condition will be satisfied if

R is sufficiently large. Voltmeters are therefore usually high-resistance instruments.

A galvanometer may also be used as an ammeter. For example, a galvanometer requiring 20 ma for full-scale deflection may be used directly as a milliammeter for currents less than this. Used as a voltmeter together with a low resistance, as shown in Fig. 4.2, can also measure larger currents. Effectively, we introduce into the line a resistance R, called a shunt, capable of carrying the current to be measured.

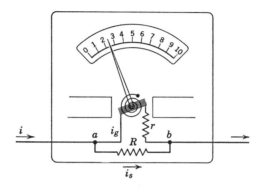

Fɪɢ. 4.2.   A galvanometer used as an ammeter.

A certain voltage will then appear across R, and this can be adjusted to the value required to produce full-scale deflection on the galvanometer. The resistance R "shunts," or bypasses, the galvanometer.

Let us consider the use of the galvanometer described above to measure a large current, say 5 amp, for full-scale deflection. The voltage across its terminals for full-scale deflection must be $i_g r = 0.02 \times 25 = 0.5$ volt. If, then, we pass the 5 amp to be measured through a resistor R such that the voltage drop across the resistor iR is 0.5 volt, then the galvanometer applied to the resistor R will deflect full scale. In the case under consideration $R = 0.5/5 = 0.1$ ohm.

Note that, as in the case of the voltmeter previously discussed, the above statement is true provided the application of the galvanometer to the shunt does not change the voltage across it. If it does, a correction must be made. In order to clarify this point let us consider the circuit shown in Fig. 4.2 in detail. Let the line current be i. This divides inside the instrument at a, one part i_g going through the galvanometer, the other part i_s going through the shunt R. We wish to specify the magnitude of R in such a way that, when the line current i has some prescribed value, then the galvanometer current i_g will be just large enough to produce a full-scale deflection. We have

$$i = i_g + i_s \tag{4.3}$$

and from Ohm's law

$$V_{ab} = i_s R = i_g r \tag{4.4}$$

and therefore that

$$i_s = i_g \frac{r}{R} \tag{4.5}$$

Substituting this result into Eq. 4.3 we have

$$i = i_g + i_g \frac{r}{R} = i_g \left(1 + \frac{r}{R}\right) \tag{4.6}$$

Solving for R, we get

$$\frac{i}{i_g} = 1 + \frac{r}{R}$$

$$\frac{r}{R} = \frac{i}{i_g} - 1$$

$$R = \frac{r}{i/i_g - 1} = r \frac{i_g}{i - i_g} \tag{4.7}$$

For our problem, with $r = 25$ ohms, $i = 5$ amp, $i_g = 0.02$ amp, we have

$$R = 25 \times \frac{0.02}{4.98}$$

$$= 25 \times \frac{0.02}{5(1 - 0.004)} = 25 \times \frac{0.02}{5}(1 + 0.004)$$

$$= 0.1(1 + 0.004) = 0.1004 \text{ ohm} \tag{4.8}$$

Our previous estimate was 0.4% too low, because of our neglect of the fact that, when the galvanometer is connected to the shunt, not all of the line current goes through the shunt and the voltage drop across it is not iR, but $(i - i_g)R$.

Galvanometers of the kind discussed above cannot be used to measure alternating currents because the average value of an alternating current is zero. The rapidly reversing forces on the moving part of a galvanometer will produce no deflection. One way of constructing a-c meters is to make use of the heat generated in a suitably chosen wire. This will produce an expansion which can be made to deflect a pointer. Such instruments are often non-linear, because the heating of a wire is not proportional to the current. According to Joule's law, it is proportional to the square of the current.

Alternating-current meters are calibrated so that the heat produced by an alternating current of I amp through a resistor is equivalent to the heat produced by a direct current of I amp. But the average number of joules per second generated in a resistor in which a current

$$i = I_0 \sin 2\pi ft$$

is flowing is

$$I^2R = \frac{1}{T} \int_0^T i^2R\,dt = \frac{I_0^2R}{T} \int_0^T \sin^2 2\pi ft\,dt = \frac{I_0^2R}{2} \qquad (4.8)$$

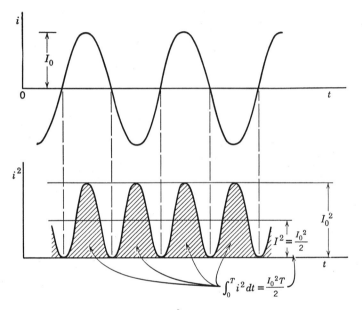

FIG. 4.3. A plot of i and i^2 for an alternating current.

The alternating current and related power dissipation are shown in Fig. 4.3. The alternating current I is the square root of the average value of i^2, or the *root mean square* (rms) current. The rms current I is equal to the amplitude I_0 divided by $\sqrt{2}$.

$$I = I_0/\sqrt{2} \qquad (4.9)$$

Another instrument capable of reading alternating currents is the *dynamometer*. In this instrument the magnetic field is produced by the current to be measured. The torque acting on the movable coil is proportional to the current through it, and to the magnetic field B, which in a d-c meter is produced by a permanent magnet.

$$\tau = C_1 iB$$

But, if the field B is itself proportional to the current i, then

$$B = C_2 i$$

and, combining these equations, we get

$$\tau = C_1 C_2 i^2$$

The torque and also the deflection of the pointer are again proportional to the square of the current through the instrument. A dynamometer deflection is proportional to the square of the current. If the scale is calibrated to read amperes, this reading determines the rms or effective value of the current.

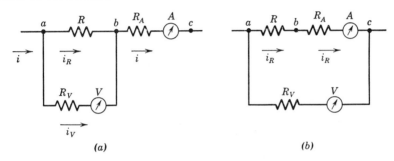

(a)   (b)

Fig. 4.4. Two methods of connecting a voltmeter and an ammeter to measure a resistance.

Electrical meters may be used to measure resistance, since according to Ohm's law resistance is defined in terms of current and voltage. Let us consider a little more in detail just how these quantities might be measured. For the purpose we suppose that we have two meters, an ammeter and a voltmeter.

Let us assume that the voltmeter, ammeter, and resistor are connected as shown in Fig. 4.4a, and that the circuit is connected to a battery at points a and c, so that a current I flows out of the battery into the circuit at a and out of the circuit back into the battery at c. At a the current divides, one part i_R flowing through the resistor, and the other part i_V flowing through the voltmeter. Since no charge accumulates at the dividing point a, we must have

$$i = i_V + i_R \qquad (4.10)$$

At b these two currents recombine to form again the total current i. The terminals a and b are the terminals of the resistor whose resistance is to be measured. The voltmeter connected to these terminals also has a resistance, R_V in the illustration. From Ohm's law we have

$$R = V_{ab}/i_R \qquad (4.11)$$

Although V_{ab} can be read directly from the voltmeter, the current measured by the ammeter is i, rather than the required i_R. This can be computed through noting that V_{ab} may be expressed in terms of the current and resistance of the voltmeter,

$$V_{ab} = i_V R_V \qquad \text{or} \qquad i_V = \frac{V_{ab}}{R_V}$$

We therefore have for the desired quantity i_R

$$i_R = i - \frac{V_{ab}}{R_V}$$

or finally

$$R = \frac{V_{ab}}{i - i_V} = \frac{V_{ab}}{i - V_{ab}/R_V}$$

or

$$\frac{1}{R} = \frac{i}{V_{ab}} - \frac{1}{R_V} \tag{4.12}$$

Notice that if the current through the voltmeter is very small, or, what amounts to the same thing, if the resistance of the voltmeter is very large compared to the unknown R, Eq. 4.12 reduces to the simpler form, Eq. 4.11. Voltmeters are usually high-resistance instruments, so that this condition is usually fulfilled, especially if the unknown resistance is not too large. The connections in Fig. 4.4a are especially favorable for determining the magnitude of low unknown resistances.

Let us now consider the circuit shown in Fig. 4.4b. The current measured by the ammeter is now the current i_R, which we need to know in order to apply Ohm's law, but the voltage is V_{ac} rather than the required voltage V_{ab}. But the voltage drop through the ammeter is

$$V_{bc} = i_R R_A$$

and the unknown resistance may be expressed in the following way:

$$R = \frac{V_{ac} - V_{bc}}{i_R} = \frac{V_{ac}}{i_R} - R_A \tag{4.13}$$

Notice that, if the resistance of the ammeter is sufficiently small, this expression reduces to the simple form $R = V_{ac}/i_R$. Most ammeters are low-resistance instruments, so that this condition is usually satisfied, especially when the unknown resistance is large compared to the resistance of the ammeter. Each of the two connections shown in Fig. 4.4 has its advantages, the first for measuring low resistance and the second for measuring high resistance.

We now come to a consideration of electrical circuits designed for the comparison of electrical quantities. The *potentiometer* performs for the measurement of voltage the same function performed by the chemical balance for the measurement of mass. Once the fundamental standard of mass is fixed, as, for example, the standard kilogram, it is necessary to provide a laboratory with replicas of this standard and convenient fractions thereof which can be used to find the exact equivalent of an unknown. Similarly, once we have established a standard of potential difference, we must find some way of reproducing it in the laboratory, and of dividing it into a number of equal parts. Then, in order to establish the magnitude of an unknown, we must be able to compare it to our standards.

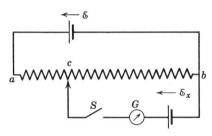

A convenient way to divide a voltage into equal parts is to send a current along a uniform wire. The resistance of any millimeter of its length being just the same

FIG. 4.5.   A potentiometer.

as that of every other millimeter, we have the result that, if the resistance per millimeter is r_m, then the voltage between any two points a distance L mm apart is

$$V = ir_mL$$

Thus if, in the circuit shown in Fig. 4.5, we establish that the potential between two specific points of the resistance wire is V_0, we can specify two other points between which the potential difference will be any desired fraction of V_0. The standard of potential difference is commonly available in the form of very carefully constructed chemical cells which are never used to supply current. The emf of these cells is accurately known, and the points in the circuit of Fig. 4.5 between which the potential difference is just equal to that of the standard cell may be found by placing the standard cell in the place of $\mathcal{E}_x$ in the figure and moving the sliding contact until the galvanometer does not deflect when the switch S is closed. Let this point of balance be c. The potential difference between c and b is now accurately known, and the potential difference between b and any other point on the slidewire may be found by interpolation. In order to establish the magnitude of any unknown emf it must be placed in the position of $\mathcal{E}_x$ in the circuit, and the position of the slidewire at which the galvanometer does not deflect must be found. Actual potentiometers are generally constructed in a somewhat more complicated way to provide ease of manipulation, but the principle underlying their construction and operation is that given above. An important application of potentiometers is in the measurement of temperatures by means of thermocouples, briefly mentioned in Section 1.4, and illustrated in Fig. 1.8. The thermocouple is merely inserted at $\mathcal{E}_x$ of Fig. 4.5, and the potential difference establishes the temperature difference between its two junctions.

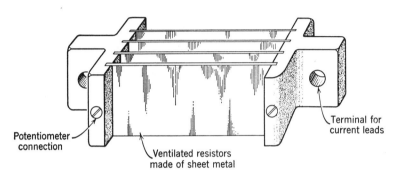

Potentiometer connection

Ventilated resistors made of sheet metal

Terminal for current leads

FIG. 4.6. Schematic drawing of the construction of a shunt for large currents.

Another important application of potentiometers is to the measurement of current. For this, the unknown current is passed through a ventilated resistor, or shunt, whose temperature does not change appreciably with current, and whose resistance is consequently as nearly independent of the current as possible. A typical shunt is shown in Fig. 4.6. The current leads are connected to the large areas at the ends, and the potentiometer leads to small separate binding posts. The potential difference between the potentiometer binding posts is proportional to the current passing through the shunt, and it may be accurately determined with the help of a potentiometer and a standard cell.

In the potentiometer discussed above, designed for comparing voltages, a moving coil instrument, or galvanometer, is used to indicate the existence of a balance. The calibration of the galvanometer is not required. The more sensitive it is, that is, the greater the deflection for a given difference of potential applied to its terminals, the more accurately may two voltages be compared.

Electrical bridges are devices for comparing other electrical elements with each other, such as resistances, inductances, or capacitances. We shall here discuss only the resistance bridge, operated with direct current, and commonly called a *Wheatstone bridge*. An electrical bridge in its simplest form is a device for determining when two elements are equal. In a more generally useful form, it is a device for determining the ratio of the magnitude of two elements.

Consider, for example, two identical wires connected to the terminals of a battery, as in Fig. 4.7a. The currents in the two branches will be the same, and there will also be equal voltage drops along equal lengths of the two wires. A galvanometer "bridged" across the two wires and connecting points equidistant from a will not be deflected. If, now,

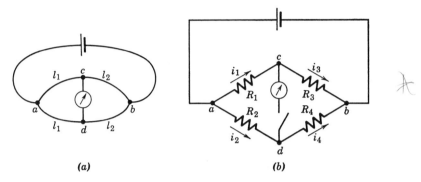

FIG. 4.7. The Wheatstone bridge.

one of the lengths of wire, say ad, is removed and replaced by some other resistor, we may state that if, with the new resistor in place, the galvanometer shows no deflection, then its resistance is the same as that of the wire ac.

This arrangement may be put into a very convenient form for general use in measuring resistances by means of the circuit shown in Fig. 4.7b. At least one of the resistances must be variable and calibrated, say R_4, and two others must have a known ratio, R_1/R_2. For the measurement of an unknown in position 3 of Fig. 4.7b, the bridge must first be balanced. In other words, the variable resistance R_4 must be given such a value that the galvanometer does not deflect when the switch in the galvanometer circuit is closed. Under these conditions the same current flows in R_1 as in R_3. We shall call the magnitude of this current i_1. Similarly the current in R_2 will be the same as in R_4. We shall call this current i_2. It is not necessary that these two currents be equal, as was stipulated in the circuit shown in Fig. 4.7a.

Since, when the bridge is balanced, the galvanometer does not deflect upon the closing of the key, we must conclude that the potential at c is the same as that at d. We therefore have,

$$V_{ac} = V_{ad}$$

or

$$i_1 R_1 = i_2 R_2 \qquad (4.14)$$

By a similar argument we may derive that

$$i_1 R_3 = i_2 R_4 \qquad (4.15)$$

Dividing Eq. 4.14 by 4.15 and multiplying by R_1, we get the unknown resistance in terms of the three known resistances,

$$R_3 = R_4 \frac{R_1}{R_2} \qquad (4.16)$$

The ratio R_1/R_2 is often given some value like unity, or 10, or $1/10$, to simplify computations.

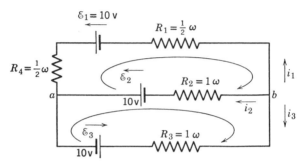

FIG. 4.8.   A d-c network.

4.2   KIRCHHOFF'S RULES

In arbitrarily connected resistors and batteries, the current in any branch of the circuit is determined by the emf's and the resistances. The ideas already developed suffice for the computation of these currents. *Kirchhoff's rules* are a set of principles which help in the systematic solution of circuit problems. They embody previously defined ideas and concepts. We state them below and apply them to the solution of the circuit shown in Fig. 4.8. Such a circuit may also be called a network. In this particular network, there are two branch points, at *a* and at *b*. *Kirchhoff's first rule states that the sum of the currents into any branch point must equal the sum of the currents out of that branch point.*

The first step in obtaining a solution is to assign a symbol and a direction to the current in each branch of the circuit. In many cases the direction of the current cannot be guessed in advance. If any arbitrary direction is chosen, it will be found that the application of Kirchhoff's rules gives a positive numerical value if the assumed direction was

correct and negative if it was not correct.   Let us assume that the
current in each branch of the circuit is, as shown in Fig. 4.8, from b to a.
This is obviously impossible and means that at least one of the currents
will turn out to be negative.   Kirchhoff's first rule applied to point b of
the circuit in Fig. 4.8 leads to the equation

$$i_1 + i_2 + i_3 = 0 \qquad (4.17)$$

The left-hand side of the equation contains all the currents flowing out
of junction b.   The right member of Eq. 4.17, representing all the currents flowing into b, vanishes, as according to Fig. 4.8 there are no such
currents.   The application of the first rule to the other branch point
leads to the same equation.   In general, it will be found that if there
are n branch points, there will be $n - 1$ independent relations between
the various currents.

   Kirchhoff's second rule is a restatement of Eq. 2.27.   *The sum of the*
potential drops around any closed circuit is zero.   A particularly convenient form of this statement when applied to a network of batteries
and resistors follows.   The sum of the emf's around any closed loop is
equal to the iR drops around that loop.   In evaluating these sums, an
iR drop is to be taken positive if the direction of the current is that in
which we are going around the loop, otherwise negative.   The emf's are
to be taken positive if they too are so oriented that the arrow pointing
from the negative to the positive terminal indicates the direction in
which the loop is being traversed.   Otherwise, emf's are to be taken
negative.   We now assign a direction in which we shall traverse each
of the subloops of the circuit to be analyzed.   In Fig. 4.8, this direction
is indicated by the curved arrows and is clockwise.   The resulting equations are

$$
\begin{aligned}
-\mathscr{E}_1 + \mathscr{E}_2 &= -i_1 R_1 + i_2 R_2 - i_1 R_4 \\
-\mathscr{E}_2 - \mathscr{E}_3 &= -i_2 R_2 + i_3 R_3
\end{aligned}
\qquad (4.18)
$$

   The three Eqs. 4.17 and 4.18 just suffice to determine the three currents i_1, i_2, and i_3.   The solution of these equations is greatly simplified,
if, at this point, we substitute numerical values.   The result is

$$
\begin{aligned}
i_1 + i_2 + i_3 &= 0 \\
-i_1 + i_2 &= 0 \\
-i_2 + i_3 &= -20
\end{aligned}
$$

The solution of these equations is

$$
\begin{aligned}
i_1 &= i_2 = 6\tfrac{2}{3} \text{ amp} \\
i_3 &= -13\tfrac{1}{2} \text{ amp}
\end{aligned}
$$

as may readily be verified by substitution. The potential difference V_{ab} computed along any one of the branches is

$$V_{ab} = 3\tfrac{1}{3} \text{ volts}$$

The currents i_1 and i_2 are in the directions shown in Fig. 4.8, but i_3 is actually in a direction opposite to that shown.

If a network contains other circuit elements than batteries and resistors, and if the currents vary with time, the solution proceeds as above. One must expect that, at any time, the sum of the currents into a branch point must equal the sum of the currents leaving that branch point. Further, even if the network includes capacitors, and inductors, which we shall take up in Chapter 6, the sum of the voltage drops around the closed circuit must vanish at every instant. Thus, in principle, these more general conditions may be treated in precisely the same way that we have treated the simple d-c circuit above.

4.3 TIME CONSTANTS

We shall now consider the charging and discharging of a capacitor through a resistor. The circuit to be discussed is shown in Fig. 4.9.

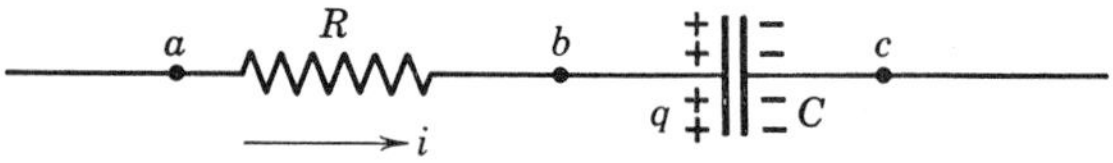

FIG. 4.9.   A capacitor in series with a resistor.

The properties of this series circuit follow from the basic statement that the potential difference between the terminals is equal to the sum of the potential drops across the elements of the circuit.

$$V_{ac} = V_{ab} + V_{bc}$$

But from the definition of resistance we have

$$V_{ab} = iR$$

and from the definition of capacitance we have

$$V_{bc} = q/C$$

The current through the resistor is related to the charge on the capacitor by

$$i = dq/dt$$

so that, combining the last four equations, we get

$$V_{ac} = R\frac{dq}{dt} + \frac{q}{C} \qquad\qquad (4.19)$$

This is a perfectly general equation, applicable whatever the nature of the applied potential difference. We shall here consider only the special case in which V_{ac} is a constant potential difference. In the next section we shall take up the case of a sinusoidally varying voltage. Before proceeding to find solutions of Eq. 4.19 let us consider what it says regarding the flow of energy in the circuit. The rate W at which energy is being fed into the circuit is

$$W = iV_{ac} = i\left(R\frac{dq}{dt} + \frac{q}{C}\right) \tag{4.20}$$

$$= i^2R + qi/C$$

The last term above may be rewritten

$$\frac{qi}{C} = \frac{q(dq/dt)}{C} = \frac{d}{dt}\left(\frac{1}{2}\frac{q^2}{C}\right)$$

so that Eq. 4.20 becomes

$$W = iV_{ac} = i^2R + \frac{d}{dt}\left(\frac{1}{2}\frac{q^2}{C}\right) \tag{4.21}$$

But we have previously found that the electrostatic energy stored in a charged capacitor is just $\left(\frac{1}{2}\frac{q^2}{C}\right)$. We may consequently read Eq. 4.21 as follows: The energy supplied to a circuit containing resistance and capacitance must appear either as heat in the resistor or as stored energy in the capacitor. The rate at which energy is supplied must equal the rate of dissipation of energy to form heat in the resistor, plus the time rate of increase of stored energy in the capacitor. If i is expressed in amperes, R in ohms, q in coulombs, and C in farads, then W is in joules/sec, or watts.

Let us now return to Eq. 4.19 and apply it to the discharging of a capacitor initially having a charge Q_0. The circuit to be discussed is shown in Fig. 4.10. At the time $t = 0$ the switch is closed. We wish to follow the changes that then take place. Before the switch is closed, there is, of course, no current and we have static conditions. V_{ab} must, according to Ohm's law, be zero. V_{ac} must therefore be equal to V_{bc}, which in turn is given by the initial charge on the capacitor and its capacitance. Calling this initial voltage across the capacitor V_0, we have

$$V_0 = Q_0/C \tag{4.22}$$

At the instant of closing the switch, V_{ac} drops to zero and stays zero from that time on, since the switch is assumed resistanceless and therefore can support no potential difference when closed, no matter how large a current it carries. At this instant we therefore must have

$$V_{ac} = 0 = V_{ab} + V_0 \tag{4.23}$$

But this is possible only if a current is flowing through the resistor from b to a. The magnitude of this initial current must further be

$$I_0 = V_0/R = Q_0/RC \tag{4.24}$$

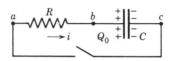

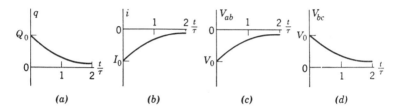

FIG. 4.10.   The discharging of a capacitor through a resistor.

The future course of events is given by Eq. 4.19 with $V_{ac} = 0$, or

$$dq/dt = -q/RC \tag{4.25}$$

The solution of this equation is

$$q = Q_0 e^{-t/RC} \tag{4.26}$$

since this expression satisfies the differential equation, as may be verified by substitution, and also satisfies the initial condition that for $t = 0$, $q = Q_0$. The solution, Eq. 4.26, is plotted in Fig. 4.10a. The charge on the capacitor simply approaches zero exponentially, the rate being determined by the time constant τ,

$$\tau = RC \text{ sec} \qquad \text{✳} \tag{4.27}$$

That ohms multiplied by farads are seconds follows from the fact that ohms are volts per ampere and farads are coulombs per volt, so that

$$(\text{ohms})(\text{farads}) = \frac{\text{volts}}{\text{amperes}} \frac{\text{coulombs}}{\text{volt}} = \text{seconds}$$

The time τ is the time required for the charge on the capacitor to drop to a fraction $1/e$, or $1/(2.72) = 0.37$ of its initial value.

Having found the charge on the capacitor as a function of time, we are in a position to calculate the current through the resistor and the voltage across the two elements. We have

$$i = \frac{dq}{dt} = \frac{d}{dt} Q_0 e^{-t/RC} = -\frac{Q_0}{RC} e^{-t/RC} \tag{4.28}$$

$$= -I_0 e^{-t/RC}$$

The current falls off exponentially with the same time constant as the charge. The minus sign indicates that this is a discharging current. The voltage across the capacitor, V_{bc}, is given by

$$V_{bc} = \frac{q}{C} = \frac{Q_0}{C} e^{-t/RC} \tag{4.29}$$

$$= V_0 e^{-t/RC}$$

The voltage across the resistor V_{ab} is

$$V_{ab} = iR = (-I_0 e^{-t/RC})(R) = -V_0 e^{-t/RC} \tag{4.30}$$

The voltage across the entire circuit

$$V_{ac} = V_{ab} + V_{bc} = 0 \tag{4.31}$$

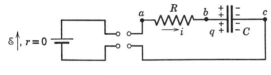

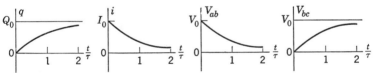

FIG. 4.11. The charging of a capacitor through a resistor.

as it must for a short-circuited circuit. These results are shown in Figs. 4.10b, c, and d.

To complete the discussion we now consider a capacitor being charged through a resistor. We suppose that a capacitor and resistor in series are connected to the terminals of a resistanceless battery whose emf is V_0, at the time $t = 0$. The circuit is shown in Fig. 4.11. We wish to know the subsequent charges, currents, and voltages. The fundamental equation of the circuit we are considering, Eq. 4.19, now has the form

$$V_0 = R \frac{dq}{dt} + \frac{q}{C} \tag{4.32}$$

and its solution is

$$q = V_0 C (1 - e^{-t/RC}) \qquad (4.33)$$

That this is a solution follows from the following argument:

$$\frac{dq}{dt} = \frac{V_0}{R} e^{-t/RC} \qquad (4.34)$$

$$R \frac{dq}{dt} + \frac{q}{C} = V_0 e^{-t/RC} + V_0 - V_0 e^{-t/RC} = V_0$$

Further, the initial condition, that the capacitor is initially uncharged, is satisfied. For $t = 0$, we have

$$q = V_0 C (1 - 1) = 0$$

The charge on the capacitor as a function of time is plotted in Fig. 4.11a. The charge increases with the same time constant $\tau = RC$, previously found, and approaches the final value $Q_0 = V_0 C$. The charging current, given by Eq. 4.34, and the voltages across the two circuit elements are plotted in Figs. 4.11b, c, and d. The sum of the two voltages V_{ab} and V_{bc} is just V_0 at all times.

Examples of the Use of Long and Short Time Constants

As an example, we shall consider the application of an RC circuit, as shown in Fig. 4.12, to the measurement of very high resistances. The switch S is closed, and the battery thereby charges the capacitor. The switch is then

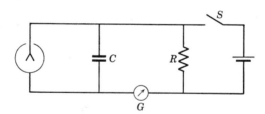

Fig. 4.12.   The use of an RC circuit for measuring high resistances.

opened and the capacitor discharges through the resistor R and the galvanometer. Let us first perform this experiment with $R = 200$ megohms, or 2×10^8 ohms, and $C = 0.1$ μf, or 10^{-7} farads. The time constant $\tau = RC = 2 \times 10^8 \times 10^{-7} = 20$ sec. The initial voltage V_0 will drop by a factor $1/e = 1/2.7$ or about $\frac{1}{3}$ in each 20 sec of elapsed time after S is opened. This drop can be followed through observing the electrostatic voltmeter. If R is unknown, it can be determined from observations of τ and the known value of C. The current in the galvanometer after opening the switch will be

$$i = \frac{V_0}{R} e^{-t/RC}$$

and if the initially applied battery voltage is 200 volts, the initial current is $200/2 \times 10^8 = 10^{-6}$ amp $= 1\,\mu$ amp. The decay of this current may likewise be followed on the galvanometer, provided it has a sufficiently short period. Much larger resistances may be measured within reasonable times if smaller capacitors are used. Thus, for example, if we use 100 $\mu\mu$f, and choose the time constant to be 100 sec, $R = \tau/C = 100/10^{-10} = 10^{12}$ ohms.

To illustrate the use of an RC circuit having a short time constant, we shall discuss the measurement of the speed of a bullet, using the apparatus shown in Fig. 4.13. Before the bullet is fired, the battery voltage V_0 is applied to the capacitor C and is observed on the electrostatic voltmeter. At the instant that the bullet breaks the battery circuit, as shown in Fig. 4.13, the

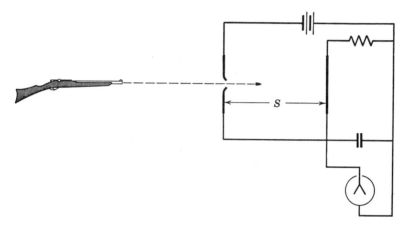

Fig. 4.13.   Measurement of the speed of a bullet using an RC circuit.

battery is disconnected and the capacitor begins to discharge through the resistor R. This discharge continues until the bullet breaks a second conductor, thereby stopping the discharge. The time elapsed $t = S/v$, where v is the speed of the bullet and S is the distance between the two broken conductors. The voltage V registering on the meter at the end of the experiment is

$$V = V_0 e^{-S/vRC}$$

If $S/v = RC$, the voltage will have dropped to about $\frac{1}{3}$ of its initial value. Assuming that the speed of the bullet is about 200 meters/sec, and $S = 2.0$ meters, we have $RC = 10^{-2}$ sec. This could be achieved, for example, by choosing $C = 10^{-7}$ farads and $R = 10^5$ ohms.

4.4   IMPEDANCE

According to Ohm's law, an alternating current in a resistor is proportional to, and therefore necessarily in phase with, the voltage across its terminals. This is not true for a capacitor. The current in a capacitor leads the voltage by 90°, as was shown in the discussion of displacement current in Section 3.6.   For a series circuit such as that shown in Fig. 4.14, in which the same current must necessarily flow through the two elements at every instant, we have the relationship between current and the various voltages involved, shown in the illustration, and described mathematically below.

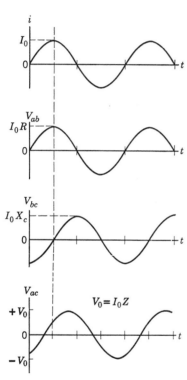

$$i = I_0 \sin 2\pi ft$$

$$V_{ab} = I_0 R \sin 2\pi ft$$

$$V_{bc} = -I_0 X_C \cos 2\pi ft \quad (4.35)$$

The first of these equations specifies the current.   The choice of the sine function is, of course, arbitrary.   If the zero of time had been chosen a quarter of a cycle later, as indicated by the dotted vertical line in Fig. 4.14, the current would have been a cosine function, V_{ab} would also have been a cosine function, and V_{bc} would have been a sine function.   We shall, however, retain the zero such that the current is given by the first of the three Eqs. 4.35. The second follows from Ohm's law. The correctness of the third follows from the property of the capacitor

$$q = V_{bc} \cdot C$$

and the definition of the current in the circuit,

FIG. 4.14.   Current and voltage in a resistor and capacitor connected in series.

$$i = \frac{dq}{dt} = C \frac{d}{dt} \left(-I_0 \frac{1}{2\pi fC} \cos 2\pi ft \right)$$
$$= I_0 \sin 2\pi ft$$

The voltage across the entire circuit may be found by addition,

$$V_{ac} = V_{ab} + V_{bc}$$

This result is also shown in Fig. 4.14 and turns out to be a new periodic function with the same frequency, but with a different amplitude and a different phase.   We have

$$V_{ac} = (I_0 R \sin 2\pi ft - I_0 X_C \cos 2\pi ft) \quad (4.36)$$

which we proceed to show can be written

$$V_{ac} = V_0 \sin (2\pi ft + \phi) \tag{4.37}$$

where V_0 is the amplitude of the applied voltage, and ϕ is the angle by which the voltage leads the current. Using the relation

$$\sin (\alpha + \beta) = \sin \alpha \cos \beta + \cos \alpha \sin \beta$$

we may rewrite the expression, Eq. 4.37, as

$$V_{ac} = V_0 \cos \phi \sin 2\pi ft + V_0 \sin \phi \cos 2\pi ft \tag{4.38}$$

We introduce a new symbol, Z, for the ratio of the voltage amplitude to the current amplitude,

$$Z = \frac{V_0}{I_0} \qquad \blacktriangleright(4.39)\blacktriangleleft$$

where Z is called the *impedance* of the circuit and is measured in ohms. Equation 4.38 becomes identical with 4.36 if

$$V_0 \cos \phi = I_0 Z \cos \phi = I_0 R$$

or

$$\cos \phi = R/Z$$

and

$$V_0 \sin \phi = I_0 Z \sin \phi = -I_0 X_C$$

or

$$\sin \phi = -X_C/Z \qquad \blacktriangleright(4.40)\blacktriangleleft$$

Further, since $\sin^2 \phi + \cos^2 \phi = 1$, we have

$$Z = \sqrt{R^2 + X_C{}^2} \qquad \blacktriangleright(4.41)\blacktriangleleft$$

These last two equations may be used to calculate the phase and amplitude of the voltage in terms of the current, or vice versa. Notice that in the circuit shown in Fig. 4.14 which we are discussing, the angle ϕ defined in Eq. 4.40, by which the voltage leads the current, is negative. In other words, in this circuit, the current leads the voltage. The relationships found mathematically above may be represented geometrically in terms of the vectors shown in Fig. 4.15a, which is called a vector impedance diagram. In order to give a meaning to the sign of ϕ in this diagram, we must agree to draw X_C downward, and to call ϕ negative when Z lies below the horizontal axis, and positive when Z lies above, as we shall later find that it may when other kinds of circuit elements are included. In Fig. 4.15b a similar diagram shows the relation between current and voltage. If we multiply R, X_C, and Z by the amplitude of the current I_0, we will have three vectors describing the voltages across the resistor, across the capacitor, and across the combination. But, in the resistor, the current is in phase with the voltage, and we may therefore draw the current, which is the same in both circuit elements, parallel to $I_0 R_0$. The current leads the voltage by the angle ϕ, as shown.

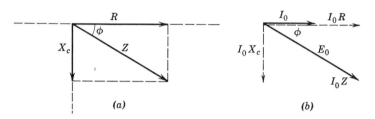

FIG. 4.15.   A vector impedance diagram.

Since no energy is dissipated in a capacitor, but only stored there while the capacitor is charged, we must conclude that all the energy dissipated as heat in the circuit under discussion is so dissipated in the resistor. But this, we have already concluded, is

$$W = I^2 R = \frac{I_0^2 R}{2}$$

If we wish to express the power dissipated in the circuit as a function of the applied voltage and the current, we have, since

$$I = V/Z$$

$$W = I \frac{V}{Z} R = IV \frac{R}{Z} = IV \cos \phi \qquad (4.42)$$

In the above expression, $\cos \phi$ is called the *power factor*.

Calculation of an Impedance

In order to show how these results are to be applied, we proceed to compute the various quantities of interest when we connect the above circuit to a 100-volt, 60-cycle line. We shall assume that the resistance of the resistor is 1000 ohms, and that the capacitance of the capacitor is 1 microfarad. The reactance of the capacitor is

$$X_C = \frac{1}{2\pi f C} = \frac{1}{377 \times 10^{-6}} = 2650 \text{ ohms}$$

The impedance of the circuit is

$$Z = \sqrt{R^2 + X_C^2} = 10^3 \sqrt{1 + (2.65)^2}$$
$$= 2830 \text{ ohms}$$

The rms voltage and the voltage amplitude are

$$V = 100 \text{ volts} \quad \text{and} \quad V_0 = V\sqrt{2} = 141 \text{ volts}$$

The rms or effective current is

$$I = \frac{V}{Z} = \frac{100}{2830} = 0.035 \text{ amp} = 35 \text{ ma}$$

The current amplitude is

$$I_0 = \frac{V_0}{Z} = \frac{141}{2830} = 50 \text{ ma}$$

The angle ϕ is

$$\sin \phi = -\frac{X_c}{Z} = -\frac{2650}{2830}$$
$$\phi = -\sin^{-1}(0.935)$$
$$= -69°$$

The voltage lags behind the current by 69°.
The rate of dissipation of energy is

$$I^2R = IV \cos \phi = 0.035 \times 100 \times 0.358 = 1.25 \text{ watts}$$

An RC Filter Circuit

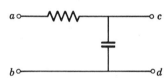

As an example of the application of an RC circuit in an a-c network, we take up one unit of a filter for removing hum or other fluctuations from a d-c line. The circuit to be discussed is shown in Fig. 4.16. For simplicity, we assume that the voltage impressed at the terminals ab has a constant component V_c, and a fluctuating component $V_0 \sin 2\pi ft$. It is desired to compute the reduction of the ripple voltage at the terminals cd. As in this problem no current is being drawn from cd, we will have no direct current flowing, but there will be an alternating current of amplitude

Fig. 4.16. One unit of an RC filter.

$$I_0 = V_0/Z$$

flowing through the RC series circuit between a and b. The impedance will be

$$Z = \sqrt{R^2 + X_c^2}$$

The fluctuating voltage component at cd will be that appearing across the capacitor, or

$$I_0 X_c = \frac{V_0}{Z} X_c = V_0 \frac{X_c}{\sqrt{R^2 + X_c^2}} \tag{4.43}$$

The ripple voltage is reduced by a factor X_c/Z. For this purpose we want to make R large compared to X_c.

4.5 ELECTRONICS

This subject deals with the controlled motion of charged particles, usually electrons, and usually in a vacuum or in a gas at low pressure.

It is a branch of applied physics which is still growing rapidly. We shall here take up a few examples of electronics to illustrate its significance and shall begin by reviewing devices which have perhaps the simplest objective of all, namely, the production of beams of charged particles moving in straight lines in a vacuum. One such is the Van de Graaff generator which has already been described in Chapter 1. Charge is sprayed onto a moving belt, and mechanical forces carry these charges against a retarding electrostatic force to an electrode where they are delivered and collected. The field surrounding this charged electrode produces the desired potential difference.

Modern Van de Graaff generators do not use air as the insulating medium between the points at high or low potential. Other gases having a higher dielectric strength than air are used, and at pressures above atmospheric. When a gas is compressed there are more atoms per unit volume, the distance between collisions along the path of an electron is decreased, and hence the electric field required to give an electron the energy necessary to produce ionization is increased. By the use of gases having a high ionization potential at elevated pressure the size of the apparatus required for some given maximum voltage may be considerably reduced.

An example of a Van de Graaff generator using compressed gas between electrodes is illustrated in Fig. 4.17. A grounded metal cover in the shape of a bell jar contains the insulating gas and forms one electrode. The other is here placed inside the first and, in the illustration, collects positive charge. Negative charge, not shown, is spread over the inside of the cover, and the electric field extends from the positively charged electrode to the case. An insulated and evacuated tube on the right marked "acceleration tube" allows positive ions released at the surface of the positive electrode to be accelerated as they move down the tube toward the grounded target. Here they may be used, for example, to study nuclear reactions between the bombarding particles and the bombarded nuclei.

A quite different principle is used in the cyclotron or linear accelerator for producing high-energy particles. In a cyclotron the path along which the particles move is a spiral, produced by a magnetic field. We shall discuss this in detail in the next chapter. Apart from this, the underlying principle is similar to that used in the linear accelerator, in which the particles move in straight lines. Instead of two electrodes between which the high potential difference exists, as in a Van de Graaff generator, there are many electrodes with smaller differences of potential, and the particles to be accelerated are given small successive impulsive boosts of energy. A section of a linear accelerator is shown in

Fig. 4.18. It may be constructed, for example, of a series of cylindrical sections of metal tubing alternately connected to the terminals of a

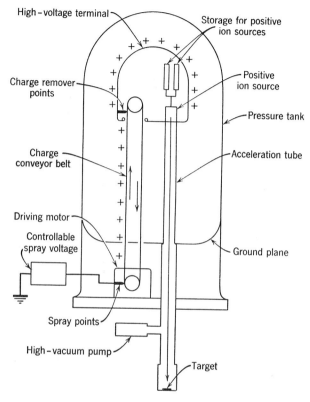

FIG. 4.17. A schematic diagram of a Van de Graaff generator being used to accelerate positive charges.

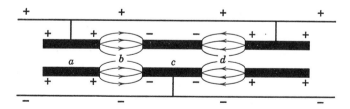

FIG. 4.18. Schematic representation of the electric field inside a linear accelerator.

high-frequency generator. A particle at point *a* within a cavity experiences no force. At *b* some of the lines of force extend to the axis of the system along which a beam is to travel and will act on a charged particle.

This force will accelerate the particle at b if it is positively charged. If, now, while the particle is in the next cavity c, the polarity of the various sections is reversed, upon reaching d it will find the field there of the correct sign to accelerate it further, rather than decelerate it and retard its motion. By periodic reversal of the field, this situation can be repeated over and over again and successive bursts of particles may be sent through the tube.

Although high-energy positively charged nuclear particles, such as protons and alpha particles, are commonly used for nuclear bombardment and the study of nuclear collisions, electrons also are used, sometimes because they produce X rays at the target where they are stopped, and these X rays have many uses, including radiography, or the study of the "invisible" internal structure of opaque objects, and medical therapy. X rays such as are used by dentists and doctors for much of their work do not require the very high-energy electrons in the range of millions of electron volts which can be produced by Van de Graaff generators and linear accelerators. For applications in which some thousands of electron volts suffice, X ray tubes such as that shown in Fig. 4.19, having diameters of a few inches, are used. The required voltages are produced from the city power lines by means of a transformer, to be described in Chapter 6. The electrons are liberated from the heated cathode and produce X rays at the anode, which is generally water-cooled to remove the heat generated by electrons when they are stopped.

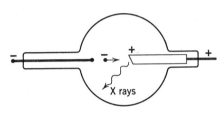

FIG. 4.19.   An X ray tube.

Another, and quite different, instrument involving a beam of charged particles is the cathode ray oscilloscope in which the deflection of a beam of electrons is used to indicate a potential difference. A cross-sectional view of a cathode ray oscilloscope tube is shown in Fig. 4.20. Its outer envelope is an evacuated vessel, usually made of metal and glass. Electrons are liberated at a negatively charged electrode, or cathode, marked C in the illustration, and are accelerated by a positively charged electrode A, nearby. Although some of the electrons hit this electrode and are stopped, some will pass through a hole provided for this purpose, and will proceed down the tube in a narrow pencil or beam. If the deflector plates D are uncharged, no forces will be exerted on the electrons in the beam as they pass down the tube. The instrument is so adjusted that in these circumstances the beam strikes the screen S centrally. This screen is made of fluorescent material covering the inside surface of the glass. It has the special property that it gives off light for a small fraction of a second wherever the electron beam strikes it. If a potential difference is applied to the deflector plates and they become charged, electrostatic forces act on the electrons in the beam, and the position of the spot of light on the screen is changed. If, as a consequence of slowly varying the amount of charge on the deflector plates, the spot moves slowly, the eye can follow the movement directly. The eye cannot see fast movement on the screen in detail unless this movement exactly repeats itself over and over. Under

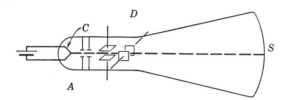

FIG. 4.20. A cathode ray oscilloscope tube.

these conditions the eye does not see the movement itself, but the pattern made on the screen. Thus, if the spot of light moves around in a circle of constant radius slowly, the eye can follow the spot. However, as the speed of the spot is increased, a speed is finally reached at which the eye sees no movement at all, but simply a stationary circle.

The instrument measures the potential difference between the deflector plates at some particular instant of time. Its tremendous importance, however, lies not so much in the fact that it can do so, but that it can do so extremely quickly. The time element in the measurement accounts for the presence of two pairs of electrodes rather than one, which would be sufficient for static measurements. Suppose that we had only one pair of deflector plates, and that we periodically charged them, then discharged them, and then reversed their polarity, with a frequency of say 60 cycles per second. The spot of light on the screen would move to and fro along a straight line with this frequency, which, at the rate of sixty repetitions per second, is too great for the eye to follow, and we should see only a stationary straight line. The length of this line would, to be sure, be determined by the maximum value of the periodically reversing potential, but we could measure nothing else about its variation. Let us suppose that the plates being charged and discharged have horizontal surfaces. The electric force acting on the beam will therefore be vertical, and the straight line observed on the screen will also be vertical. Suppose now that we have a second pair of plates which can produce a horizontal deflection, and that these plates are charged at some slow rate. In addition to the vertical 60-cycle oscillation, we shall have a horizontal movement. The oscillatory

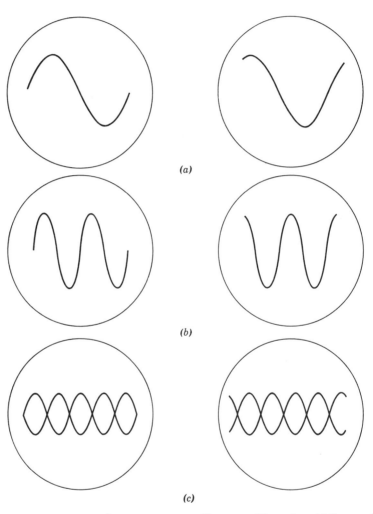

(a)

(b)

(c)

Fɪɢ. 4.21. Patterns to be seen on an oscilloscope with a sinusoidally varying vertical deflection of frequency f, and a linear sweep horizontally with a repetition frequency in (a) of f, in (b) of $f/2$, and in (c) of $2f/5$.

pattern will be spread out over the screen because of the horizontal motion of the spot. Suppose further that, when the spot reaches the edge of the screen, the polarity of the horizontally deflecting plates is suddenly reversed and the horizontal motion repeated. A steady pattern will be formed if the vertical frequency is some simple multiple of the horizontal sweep frequency. A sweep of this kind is called a linear sweep because the horizontal position of the spot is directly proportional to the time, or, in other words, the horizontal position is a linear function of the time. Oscilloscopes are provided with adjustable horizontal sweep frequencies, and with a means of locking them to an arbitrary frequency applied to the vertical deflector plates, so that a stationary pattern may be formed without continual adjustment. Typical patterns to be observed using a linear horizontal sweep and a sinusoidal vertical deflection are shown in Fig. 4.21.

In dealing with sinusoidal oscillations, we are concerned with the amplitude, phase, and frequency which enter into their description. A difference in phase of two currents of the same frequency will produce characteristic patterns when applied to the horizontal and vertical plates of the oscilloscope. Let us assume, for example, that the charge on one set of plates varies so that the horizontal position, say x, of the spot on the screen is given by

$$x = X_0 \sin 2\pi ft$$

and the vertical position, say y, by

$$y = Y_0 \sin (2\pi ft + \phi)$$

Let us further suppose that the amplitudes of these two oscillations are adjusted to equality, so that we may put $X_0 = Y_0 = A$. The patterns observed for $\phi = 0$, $\pi/2$, and $3\pi/4$ will be those shown in Fig. 4.22. An oscilloscope may therefore be used to determine a phase relation between two oscillations.

A form of oscilloscope is the television tube in which the beam scans the entire screen, varying in intensity in just such a way as to produce the desired picture.

The above examples illustrate the use of beams of charged particles. More usually the drift of clouds of charge between electrodes is used as, for example, in the electronic devices called vacuum tubes. The simplest form of vacuum tube is a diode, consisting of a heated cathode and an anode in an evacuated chamber. If no voltage is applied, but the anode and cathode are connected through a galvanometer, a very small current will be found to flow. When electrons leave the cathode, they leave a positive charge behind. They are therefore attracted back to the cathode. There will be a cloud of electrons, forming a negative space charge, just outside of the cathode. A few of the electrons, however, will reach the anode and return to the cathode through

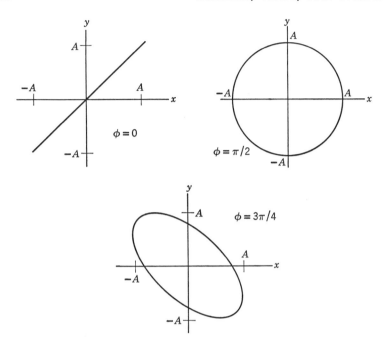

Fɪɢ. 4.22. Patterns observed with phase shifts of 0, 90, and 135°, between the
vertical and horizontal oscillations.

the galvanometer. If, by the introduction of a battery of variable emf
in the galvanometer circuit, the anode is made more and more positive

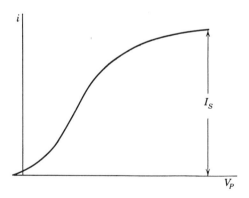

Fɪɢ. 4.23. Current-voltage characteristics of an evacuated diode.

with respect to the cathode, a greater and greater number of electrons
will be attracted to it. When the potential difference is large enough

so that all the electrons evaporated by the cathode reach the anode, the maximum, or saturation current, will be obtained. A further increase in the applied voltage will not produce a further increase in current.

If the applied potential is reversed, the small current which flows at zero voltage is stopped. Such a tube is a rectifier, in that it passes current in one direction only. The current-voltage characteristics of a diode, consisting of a heated cathode and a plate or anode mounted in an evacuated container, are shown schematically in Fig. 4.23. I_s is the saturation current determined by the rate of release of electrons from the heated cathode.

We discuss below a variety of examples of how two-electrode evacuated and gas-filled tubes are used in electrical circuits for special purposes. A description of vacuum tubes with three electrodes, called triodes, will be given in Chapter 7 in connection with the discussion of amplifiers and oscillators.

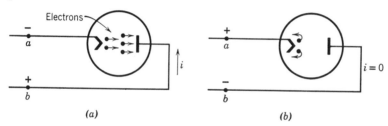

FIG. 4.24. The current in a diode.

A Half-Wave Rectifier

We have seen that a heated electrode in a vacuum tube will boil off electrons, and that if this electrode is made the negatively charged cathode of a circuit

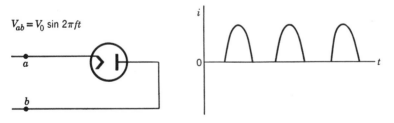

FIG. 4.25. The rectified current passed by a diode.

as shown in Fig. 4.24a, a current will flow. If on the other hand, the heated electrode is made the anode, as in Fig. 4.24b, no current will flow. A diode of this kind may be used as a rectifier. When connected to an alternating potential, it will pass a pulsed current, as shown in Fig. 4.25, and the pulses will be of one sign only.

A Peak Voltmeter

If, now, a capacitor is introduced into the circuit, as shown in Fig. 4.26, it is clear that electrons will be trapped and will accumulate in the section marked c in the diagram. This will go on until the repulsive force exerted on

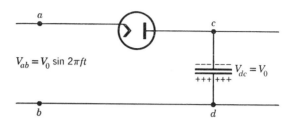

$V_{ab} = V_0 \sin 2\pi ft$

$V_{dc} = V_0$

FIG. 4.26.   An a-c peak voltmeter.

the free electrons in the vacuum tube prevents any further accumulation. This condition will be established when V_{cd}, the potential across the capacitor, is just equal to V_0, the amplitude of the oscillating potential, as is shown by the following argument. We have

$$V_{ab} = V_0 \sin 2\pi ft$$

$$= V_{ac} + V_{cd} = V_{ac} - \frac{Q}{C}$$

and therefore

$$V_{ac} = V_0 \sin 2\pi ft + \frac{Q}{C}$$

But the tube will pass current only when V_{ac} is negative, that is, when electrons are driven away from the heated electrode, and this cannot happen if $Q/C = V_0$, or if $V_{dc} = V_0$. The charge on the capacitor will therefore build up to just this point, and no more.

The diode may also be connected the other way around, as shown in Fig. 4.27. If it is, the upper terminal c will be at a higher potential than the lower one. If instead of an electrostatic voltmeter, which draws no current once it is charged, we use a voltmeter having an internal resistance r, the situation is altered because of the current drawn. If r is sufficiently large, the capacitor will discharge itself only slightly during one cycle, as shown in the graphs in Fig. 4.27. Having been discharged, even slightly, a pulse of current i_d can flow through the diode during the positive peak of the applied voltage, recharging the capacitor to nearly the peak voltage V_0. The capacitor then discharges until the charging is repeated one cycle later.

A Full-Wave Rectifier

A full-wave rectifier can be made using two diodes if the alternating current supplied is provided with a grounded center tap. The circuit to be used is shown in Fig. 4.28. During the positive half-cycle current will flow through tube 1 but not through tube 2 because the voltage is in the wrong direction in this tube. Terminal c becomes positive with respect to ground, and current therefore flows from c to g until the applied voltage drops to zero. During the next half cycle b is positive with respect to ground, and current flows through tube 2, but not through tube 1. The terminal c again becomes positive with

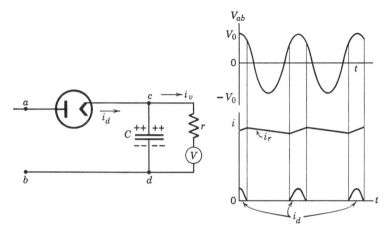

FIG. 4.27. A peak voltmeter under load.

respect to ground, and during this negative half-cycle current flows from b through 2 to c to g. The current through the resistor r has the humped form

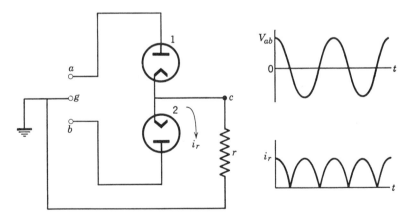

FIG. 4.28. A full-wave rectifier.

shown in the lower graph of Fig. 4.28. This current may be smoothed out by putting a capacitor in parallel with the resistor, as in the circuit shown in Fig. 4.27.

Voltage Regulator

The current voltage characteristic of a gas discharge is not simple. The example of a cold cathode voltage regulator tube is shown in Fig. 4.29. This is an example of characteristics obtainable in a commercially available tube. At currents below 5 ma the characteristics are not specified as they are not made use of. A voltage slightly in excess of 105 volts is required to light the tube. After it is lighted, that is, after a glow begins to appear, the voltage

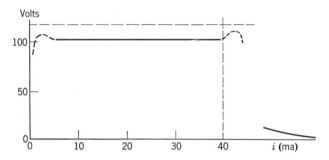

Fig. 4.29. Voltage-current relations in an example of cold cathode voltage regulator.

remains at 105 volts for currents from 5 to 30 ma. In this region the extent of the glowing area around the cathode increases. Between 30 and 40 ma the voltage rises a per cent or so. If now the current is allowed to rise above the maximum in the curve, any slight increase in current will produce a reduction in voltage and, unless the current is limited, it will increase indefinitely until some part of the circuit gives way.

Tubes of this kind are used as voltage regulators between 5 and 30 ma. They must be connected with some device, for instance, a series resistor, which limits the current to 40 ma. A current-limiting device of this kind is often called a ballast.

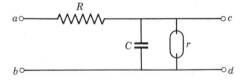

Fig. 4.30. A circuit for producing a saw-tooth voltage.

A Saw-Tooth Generator, or Linear Sweep Generator

In the circuit drawn in Fig. 4.30, there is a gas-filled discharge tube with the following characteristics: At sufficiently low voltages there is no discharge. The tube will pass no current. As the voltage applied to the tube is increased, a voltage which we shall call V_{on} is finally reached, sufficient to start a discharge. The resistance of the tube at this point becomes very small. It can pass large currents with only a small voltage drop across the tube. If the voltage across the tube is now decreased, the tube remains lit and in the conducting state until a voltage which we shall call V_{out} is reached. The latter voltage is much smaller than the voltage required to light the tube.

When a constant potential difference is applied across the terminals a and b, the capacitor begins to charge through the resistor. At first, when there is little charge on the capacitor, and therefore little voltage on it, most of V_{ab} will appear across the resistor. There will be a large charging current which gradually diminishes as the charge on the capacitor, and therefore also V_{cd} increases. Finally, when $V_{cd} = V_{on}$, the tube lights up and, because of its

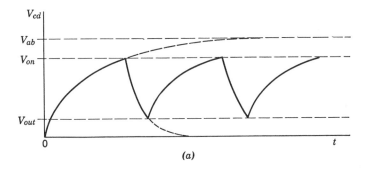

(a)

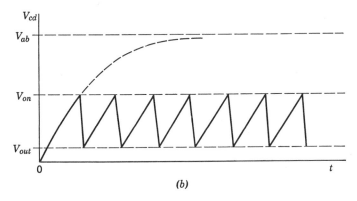

(b)

Fig. 4.31. A plot of V_{cd} in the circuit shown in Fig. 4.30.

low resistance r, very quickly discharges the capacitor until the voltage across it has reached V_{out}, at which point the tube goes out. But, when the voltage across the capacitor has dropped, that across the resistor must have gone up. The charging current from the line is again raised, and the capacitor is again charged. This cyclic process produces a voltage V_{cd} shown in Fig. 4.31. In *a* the constants are so chosen that the exponential form of the charging and discharging process is apparent. When the switch is closed at $t = 0$, the capacitor begins to charge as shown and if the tube were not present would go right on until the voltage V_{cd} across it would be equal to the applied voltage. However, when the voltage V_{on} is reached, it discharges at a faster rate until V_{out} is reached, and the process then repeats itself. In Fig. 4.31*b* the constants are so chosen that the charging and discharging processes are more nearly linear. This saw-tooth form may be used to provide the linear sweep desired on an oscilloscope or television tube.

Photoelectric Tubes

A quite different application of vacuum tubes is in the measurement of light intensities. When light strikes a metal surface electrons may be emitted. This phenomenon is known as the *photoelectric effect*. If the metal surface being illuminated is the cathode of a suitably

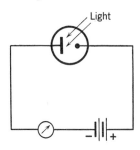

formed vacuum tube, as shown in Fig. 4.32, and an anode at a sufficiently high potential with respect to the cathode is provided, then the current flowing through the tube will be determined by the number of electrons liberated per second and will therefore also be proportional to the light intensity. Such a device is called a *photoelectric cell*.

A very convenient way to amplify the small currents produced by weak light sources is through making use of the fact that an electron making a sufficiently violent impact on a metal can be made, on the average, to knock more than one electron out of the metal. By this means a single photoelectron can be made to produce a cascade, as shown in the *electron multiplier* tube, Fig. 4.33. This can lead to an enormous increase in current in a series of successive impacts.

Fig. 4.32. A photoelectric cell.

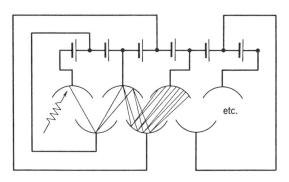

Fig. 4.33. An electron multiplier.

SUMMARY

The deflection of a galvanometer is proportional to the current through it and to the potential difference between its terminals. To measure large currents a known fraction of an unknown current is passed through the instrument, the galvanometer being shunted with a low resistance in parallel. Similarly, to measure high voltages a known fraction of an unknown voltage is applied to the galvanometer terminals, the galvanometer being connected in series with a high resistance. In using an ammeter or voltmeter it must be remembered that the insertion of the instrument into a circuit will modify existing currents and potentials.

A potentiometer is an instrument for comparing voltages. A Wheatstone bridge is an instrument for comparing resistances.

Kirchhoff's rules are useful in analyzing circuits. They state that

(a) The sum of the currents into a junction equals the sum of the currents out of that junction.

(b) The sum of the potential drops around any closed circuit is zero.

The rate of charging or discharging a capacitor through a resistor follows an exponential curve in which the time constant τ is RC sec.

In a series RC circuit in which there is a current

$$i = I_0 \sin 2\pi f t$$

the applied voltage will be

$$V_{ab} = V_0 \sin (2\pi f t + \phi)$$

The angle ϕ specifies the amount by which the voltage leads the current. The impedance of the circuit is defined

$$Z = \frac{V_0}{I_0} = \sqrt{R^2 + X_C^2} = \sqrt{R^2 + \left(\frac{1}{2\pi f C}\right)^2}$$

where X_C is called the reactance of the capacitor. The phase angle ϕ is given by

$$\sin \phi = -X_C/Z$$

The current leads the voltage in an RC series circuit.

Various electronic devices and applications of RC circuits are discussed, including accelerators, oscilloscopes, the measurement of large resistances and of short times, filters for removing ripple from a constant voltage, rectifiers, peak voltmeters for measuring a-c voltages, and saw-tooth generators.

PROBLEMS

1. A uniform wire of total resistance 1200 ohms is connected to power mains which maintain a potential difference of 120 volts across it. A voltmeter connected between one end of the wire and its midpoint reads 50 volts. What is the resistance of the voltmeter?

2. A galvanometer has an internal resistance of 200 ohms, and 12 ma are required to give it a full-scale deflection. What resistance placed in series with it will make it read 200 volts full scale?

3. A 10,000-ohm resistor and a 1000-ohm resistor are connected in series to a 200-volt d-c power source. (a) What is the current drawn? (b) What is the voltage drop across each resistor? What will the voltmeter of Problem 2 read when connected across each of the above resistors?

4. The galvanometer of Problem 2 is to be used as an ammeter reading 100 amp full scale. What shunt resistance is required?

5. A milliammeter having an internal resistance of 10^{-2} ohm and a voltmeter having an internal resistance of 10^3 ohms are to be used in checking the resistance of a 10^3 ohm resistor. A 6-volt storage battery having an internal resistance of 10^{-2} ohm is available for the test. What will the meters read when connected as in Fig. 4.4a and b? Which connection is more convenient?

6. Solve Problem 5 above, except that the resistor to be checked has a resistance of 10^{-2} ohm, and the milliammeter is replaced by a suitable ammeter having a resistance of 10^{-2} ohm.

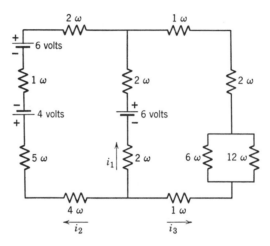

FIG. 4.34.

7. Find the current in each branch of the circuit in Fig. 4.34.

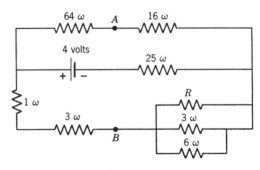

FIG. 4.35.

8. In the circuit in Fig. 4.35, points A and B are at the same potential. Find R.

9. In the circuit in Fig. 4.36, find the potential across and the current through each resistor, as well as the potential across and the charge on each capacitor.

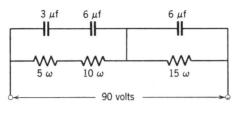

FIG. 4.36.

10. What is the equivalent resistance between the terminals a and b of the circuit in Fig. 4.37?

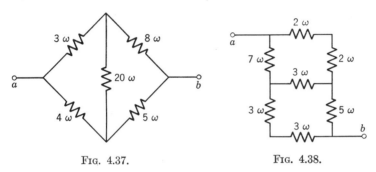

FIG. 4.37.   FIG. 4.38.

11. What is the equivalent resistance between the terminals a and b of the circuit in Fig. 4.38?

12. If in the circuit in Problem 10 the central 20-ohm resistor were a galvanometer having a 20-ohm internal resistance and the 4-ohm resistor were variable, (a) what would have to be its magnitude to balance the bridge? (b) If it were set at a value 10% too high, what would be the galvanometer current if a 6-volt battery were connected to the terminals ab?

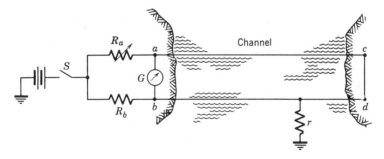

FIG. 4.39.

13. Two identical cables are laid across a channel, as shown in Fig. 4.39. One of them develops a short to ground and an attempt is made to determine the location of this short electrically. A first attempt to measure the resistance from b to ground

directly leads to no useful result because the resistance r to ground is large compared to the resistance of the cable and actually varies with time. A Varley-loop test is then tried. The far terminals c and d are connected together, and the tester is connected to a and b. This effectively sets up a Wheatstone bridge. It is found that the galvanometer does not deflect when the switch S is closed if $R_b = 1.00$ ohms, and the variable resistance R is set at 2.54 ohms. If the cables are 7500 ft long, how far from the terminal b should the cable be raised to effect repairs? Will fluctuations in the resistance r to ground lead to unsteady galvanometer deflections?

★14. A power station delivers direct current at 600 volts to a trolley line 12 mi long. The resistance of the trolley wire plus track return is 0.1 ohm per mile. The motor of a single trolley car on this line puts an equivalent resistance of 4 ohms between trolley wire and track when in operation. (a) What will be the power available to the trolley as a function of distance from the power station?

In order to increase the power available to the trolley at the far end, a storage battery having an emf of 550 volts is connected to the line through an 0.02-ohm resistor. As a function of distance of the trolley car from the power station, find

(b) The power delivered by the station.

(c) The power delivered by the battery.

(d) The power delivered to the trolley car.

15. Capacitors are connected together as shown in Fig. 4.40. (a) With air in all the capacitors, what must be the value of C_x, if the galvanometer G is to show no deflection when the switch is closed? (b) If now a dielectric having a dielectric coefficient K_e is introduced into C_2 so that its new capacitance is K_eC_2, what is the new value of C_x required for no deflection?

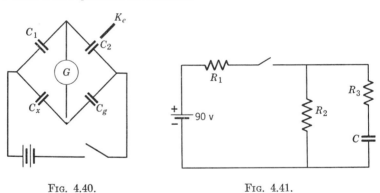

FIG. 4.40.   FIG. 4.41.

16. A 1 μf capacitor in series with a 500-ohm resistor is connected across a 90-volt battery through a switch. Make a rough plot of V_R, V_C, and i vs. time after the switch is closed. How would the curves be affected if the value of R were doubled? If it were halved?

17. A capacitor of 1 μf, charged to 90 volts, is discharged through a 500-ohm resistor. Make rough plots of V_R, V_C, and i vs. time. How would the curves be affected if the value of R were doubled? If it were halved? Compare these curves to those of Problem 16.

18. In the circuit in Fig. 4.41, (a) make a qualitative plot of i_1, i_2, i_3, V_1, V_2, V_3, V_C vs. time after the switch is closed, indicating the magnitude of important quantities. (b) Plot the same quantities after the switch is opened, having previously been closed for a long time.

19. It is desired to measure the resistance of 100-megohm resistor to an accuracy of a few per cent by observing the discharge of a capacitor and by using a stop watch calibrated to 1/10 of a second. Assuming that an accurate voltmeter with a short time constant is available, approximately what value would you choose for the capacitance of the capacitor?

20. A 10-ohm resistor and a 100 μf capacitor are connected in series across a 115-volt 60-cycle a-c line. (a) Find the current through and the voltage across each element. (b) Why isn't the sum of the voltages equal to 115 volts? (c) What is the phase angle?

21. A 30-ohm resistor and a 300 μf capacitor are connected in parallel across a 115-volt 60-cycle a-c line. (a) Find the current through and the voltage across each element. (b) What is the total current drawn? (c) What is the phase angle?

22. A resistance draws 10 amp when connected to a 115-volt 60-cycle a-c line. How big a capacitor must be connected in series with the resistance so that the current will drop to 6 amp? What is the voltage across the capacitor and across the resistor for this connection?

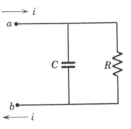

23. In the circuit shown in Fig. 4.42, the current i drawn from the line is $(20 + 1.5 \sin 377t)$ ma. If $C = 0.25$ μf, and $R = 10^3$ ohms, what is the current through the resistor?

Fig. 4.42.

24. (a) In the circuit shown in Fig. 4.27, what are the maximum and minimum values of the voltage V_{cd} if $V_{ab} = 160 \sin 377t$, $C = 0.25$ μf, and $r = 8$ megohms? Neglect any voltage drop through the tube, and neglect the time required to charge the condenser. (b) How much charge is passed by the tube at each pulse? (c) What is the average voltage V_{cd}?

25. Prove that in the circuit shown in Fig. 4.27 the average voltage

$$V_{cd} = V_0 \left(1 - \frac{1}{2Crf} \right)$$

where V_0 is the amplitude of the impressed voltage, and f is its frequency. Neglect any voltage drop through the tube, and neglect the time taken to charge the capacitor.

26. What would be the average voltage V_{cg} across the resistor r in Fig. 4.28, if it had a capacitor C in parallel and the applied frequency were f? (See Problems 24 and 25 above.)

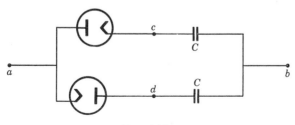

Fig. 4.43.

27. In Fig. 4.43, a 400-cycle voltage having a 200-volt amplitude is put across terminals a and b. Describe the operation of this circuit. (a) What is the voltage V_{cd} when a steady state is reached? (b) What must be the capacitances C if the

voltage fluctuation V_{cd} is to be 5% when a 600-ohm resistor is connected between c and d?

28. (a) Find the radius R of the smallest sphere that can be raised to a potential V if the surrounding gas breaks down when the field reaches a value E_c.

(b) What would be the diameter of a sphere that can maintain a potential of 5 million volts above ground in air, if the dielectric strength of air is 3×10^6 volts/meter?

29. Because of relativistic effects, which we shall study further on, there is a limiting velocity which particles can attain. They can not go faster than the velocity of light. A force acting on them to accelerate them will do work and so increase their energy but will do so by increasing their mass rather than their velocity. Electrons having an energy of a few Mev move with the velocity of light. A linear accelerator is to increase the energy of electrons from 2 Mev to 14 Mev. The voltage between sections has a maximum value of 30 kv. The sections are 5 cm long. What is the approximate length of the instrument? Voltage at what frequency must be applied to the sections? The velocity of light is 3×10^8 meters/sec.

30. A gas discharge tube fires at 75 volts and goes out at 15 volts. Design a circuit to give periodic flashes of the tube at a frequency of 100 per second. Use a 90-volt battery, a resistor, and a capacitor.

31. Sketch the plate current and plate voltage in a diode connected to a 60-cycle emf.

32. Sketch the pattern on an oscilloscope screen if the horizontal linear sweep frequency is twice the vertical frequency of sinusoidal oscillation.

33. A 60-cycle sinusoidal oscillation is connected to the vertical plates of an oscilloscope, and a sinusoidal wave of unknown frequency is connected to the horizontal plates. The resulting pattern is not quite stationary because the two frequencies are not quite equal. It is observed that, in the course of variations of the observed patterns, circular forms appear every 3 sec. What is the difference between the two frequencies?

34. Estimate in any way you can the highest frequencies required in the beam current of a television tube to form pictures with the detail which they have.

35. In a TV tube, if it takes 10^{13} electrons/second striking the screen to produce a visible spot, (a) what current does this beam intensity correspond to? (b) If the electrons have an energy of 10,000 ev, and if the beam is 1 mm in diameter, what is the electron density in the beam? (c) If the tube has nitrogen gas in it at a pressure of 10^{-6} mm of mercury, how does the electron density compare with the gas density?

★36. A bank of twenty-five 2-volt storage batteries having a very large current capacity is available in a laboratory where maximum currents are wanted at various voltages. It is decided to wire the laboratory for 400 amp and to construct a panel with a single fused switch to open the circuit. The batteries are permanently connected in series, with a number of taps leading to terminals on the switchboard. Propose a design which makes it possible to use any desired number of batteries in series, taking the following items into account. The connections on the switchboard are to be made of copper bars 2 in. wide by $\frac{1}{4}$ in. thick bolted down onto flat terminals. It is desired to make and change the connections as simply and quickly as possible, but to design the system in such a way that it is difficult to short out any batteries accidentally.

★37. A photomultiplier tube has eleven terminals and under operating conditions is to have 100 volts between successive pairs of terminals available for accelerating electrons. Under conditions of maximum load, the current between the last multiplying electrode and anode is 0.1 ma. The current amplification is 2×10^6. The illuminated area of the cathode is 1 cm^2. The anode current is 74,000 μa per microwatt of incident illumination.

(a) Design a circuit for connecting this photomultiplier to a 1000-volt supply capable of delivering 1 ma.

(b) If this photomultiplier were used in conjunction with a galvanometer having a sensitivity of 10^{-10} amp/mm deflection on a scale at a distance of 1 meter, would it be more sensitive to light than a dark-adapted eye which we assume to be able to detect a light intensity of about 10^{-16} watt/cm^2? Assume that random fluctuations of the galvanometer current may be neglected.

CHAPTER 5

Magnetic Fields

5.1 MAGNETIC FORCES

A familiar aspect of magnetic phenomena is the strong force which magnets exert on each other. A hammer is violently pulled into the gap of an electromagnet. Small horseshoe magnets repel or attract each other with forces large compared to any other force at a distance with which we are familiar. Perhaps the most important illustration

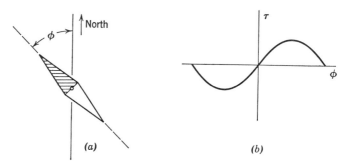

FIG. 5.1. (a) A compass needle. (b) Angular dependence of the torque acting on a compass needle.

of the force between magnets is the torque exerted by the earth on the needle of a magnetic compass. We shall use it to introduce the concept of a magnetic field.

The fact that a compass needle tends always to point north is explained by the fact that the earth itself is a magnet, or has a magnet in its interior, and that the two magnets, earth and needle, exert forces on each other which result in the observed alignment. These forces depend on the "strength" of the two magnets, the distance between them, and their mutual orientation. We shall confine our attention for the moment to some one point on the surface of the earth and to some one compass needle which we shall assume so suspended that we can measure the magnetic torque acting on it and tending to rotate it around its axis. The quantities under discussion are shown in Fig. 5.1a. The torque acting on the needle obeys the following simple law,

$$\tau \propto \sin \phi \tag{5.1}$$

For different compass needles, we should find a similar dependence on angle but a different maximum torque. We might take the amplitude of the torque curve represented by Eq. 5.1 and shown in Fig. 5.1b, as a measure of the magnetic strength of the needle. The quantity charac-

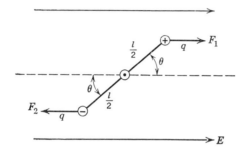

FIG. 5.2.   The origin of the torque on an electric dipole.

terizing the strength of a compass needle is called its magnetic moment. Calling this p_m, we may express the torque acting on the needle by an equation of the form

$$\tau = p_m B \sin \theta \tag{5.2}$$

Here B is a proportionality factor independent of the characteristics of the particular needle used but depending on the place on the earth at which the experiment is carried out. At different points, B has a different value.

The situation appears to be analogous to that of an electric dipole in a uniform electric field E, shown in Fig. 5.2. The force F, acting on the charge $+q$, is qE. Its moment about the axis of the dipole is $qE(l/2) \sin \theta$. The force F_2 acting on the negative charge has the same magnitude and produces a torque around the axis of the dipole in the same sense. The total torque acting on the dipole whose moment p is ql is therefore

$$\tau = pE \sin \theta$$

By analogy with Eq. 5.2, we may consider B to be the magnetic field acting on a magnetic dipole whose moment is p_m. Equation 5.2 may be expressed in vector form,

$$\tau = [\mathbf{p}_m \times \mathbf{B}] \tag{5.3}$$

Although by this means we have established a method of finding the direction of a magnetic field and the relative magnitudes of fields at various points, the absolute magnitude and dimensions of B cannot be specified by Eq. 5.2 or 5.3 until we define the magnitude and dimensions of some standard dipole.

The development of electrostatics was based on the force between electric charges as given by Coulomb's law. This procedure is here inapplicable, and we cannot represent a magnetic dipole as we did an electric dipole in Fig. 5.2 because isolated magnetic charges, or poles, do not exist. We shall see presently how it comes about that, in spite of the fact that there are no free magnetic poles, magnetic dipoles may be generated by electric currents.

Magnetic dipoles might be used as standards to specify magnetic fields. However, compass needles are not suitable for this purpose, because their moments are not reliably constant. At the end of Chapter 7 we shall discuss the magnetic dipole moment of the proton. All protons have very closely, and presumably exactly, the same magnetic moment. This is therefore a most convenient and practically useful magnetic standard. Magnetic fields may be specified in terms of the torque which they exert on the universally available proton. The experimental techniques for doing so, however, have only recently been developed, and our magnetic standards are in fact based on quite different phenomena. We shall therefore leave this question of the magnetic interactions of magnets for a time and take up the interaction of a moving charge with a magnetic field. This is the interaction which is at present regarded as fundamental and in terms of which electrical and magnetic quantities are actually defined.

Although the earth's magnetic field is suitable for demonstrating the torque on a compass needle, it is inconveniently weak for demonstrating the magnetic force on a moving charge. For this purpose an electromagnet is desirable. Just as we found it desirable to study the uniform electric field between the plates of a charged capacitor, so we shall here find it convenient to consider the uniform magnetic field between the flat, parallel pole faces of an electromagnet, shown in Fig. 5.3. Such a magnet may be a permanent magnet, or it may be activated by a current-carrying coil, shown in the figure. The iron in such a magnet is magnetized when the atomic dipoles of which it is made up are aligned. The arrows in the figure symbolize this alignment. The field B which we are to discuss is to be found in the air gap of the instrument.

A magnetic field, like an electric field, may be described in terms of a family of lines in space. These lines represent magnetic fields, or magnetic flux, which is measured in *webers*. They have a very different physical significance from the corresponding lines of electric force. The direction of the magnetic field is along the lines of flux, and its magnitude is given by the number of lines per unit area measured on a surface

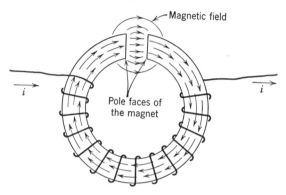

FIG. 5.3.   An electromagnet.

normal to the lines. The units in which the field B is specified in the mks system are webers/meter^2. A unit only 1/10,000 as large, called the *gauss*, is also commonly used.

$$1 \text{ weber per square meter} = 10,000 \text{ gauss}$$

The magnetic field B is called a *field of induction*, and the vector B representing this field is called the *magnetic induction*.

We shall now consider the forces acting on an electric charge q moving with a velocity v through a uniform magnetic field B. An electric charge at rest in a magnetic field experiences no magnetic force. If its motion is in the direction of the field, there still is no magnetic force acting on the charge. If, however, there is a component of the motion at right angles to the field, then a force is exerted in a direction at right angles to both the velocity and the field. If the angle between the direction of motion of a positive charge and the magnetic induction is θ, as shown in Fig. 5.4, the general expression for the magnitude of the electromagnetic force called into play is

$$F = qvB \sin \theta \qquad (5.4)$$

or in vector notation

$$\mathbf{F} = q[\mathbf{v} \times \mathbf{B}] \qquad \blacktriangleright(5.5)\blacktriangleleft$$

The directional relation between these quantities for the special case in which the velocity is at right angles to B, is shown in Fig. 5.5.

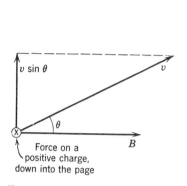

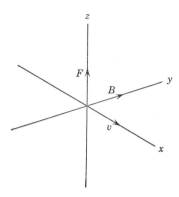

Fɪɢ. 5.4. The force on a charge moving in a magnetic field.

Fɪɢ. 5.5. The directional relation between **v**, **B**, and **F** according to Eq. 5.5.

A Numerical Example

To illustrate this result we compute the force on an electron having an energy of 100 ev, moving in a direction making an angle of 45° with the lines of induction of the electromagnet discussed above. The field will be assumed uniform and equal to 1 weber/meter². A field of this magnitude is large but can readily be produced between the poles of a magnet. The component of the velocity in the direction of the field contributes nothing to the magnetic force acting on the electron. We begin, therefore, by neglecting it and consider only the component $v \sin \theta$ at right angles to the field. We have

$$\tfrac{1}{2}mv^2 = 10^2 \, \text{ev} = 1.6 \times 10^{-17} \, \text{joule}$$

$$v^2 = \frac{2 \times 1.6 \times 10^{-17}}{9.1 \times 10^{-31}}$$

$$v = 6 \times 10^6 \, \text{meter/sec}$$

$$v \sin \theta = 0.707 \times 6 \times 10^6 = 4.1 \times 10^6 \, \text{meters/sec}$$

The magnitude of the electromagnetic force on the electron is then

$$F = evB \sin \theta$$

$$= 1.6 \times 10^{-19} \times 4.1 \times 10^6 \times 1$$

$$= 6.6 \times 10^{-13} \, \text{newton}$$

The significance of a force of this magnitude is perhaps best illustrated through computing its effect on the motion of the electron. A force F at right angles to the direction of motion of a particle results in a circular orbit. We find, for a particle of mass m moving in a circular orbit of radius R with a velocity v, that the centripetal force is

$$F = mv^2/R \qquad (5.6)$$

The way in which charged particles describe circular motion in a magnetic field is shown in Fig. 5.6. Looking in the direction of the field, a positive charge will move counterclockwise. The magnitude of the radius of the orbit in which the electron under discussion moves is

$$R = mv^2/F$$

$$= \frac{9.1 \times 10^{-31} \times (4.1 \times 10^6)^2}{6.6 \times 10^{-13}}$$

$$= 23 \times 10^{-6} \text{ meter} = 0.023 \text{ mm}$$

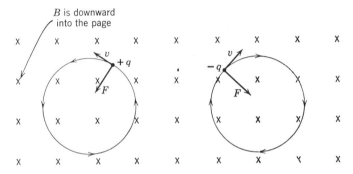

FIG. 5.6.   Circular motion of a positive and of a negative charge q in a magnetic field.

If, now, we include the component of motion in the direction of the field, the magnetic force remains completely unchanged. There is merely added to the circular motion a constant component in the direction of the field. This transforms the circular motion into a spiral. The electron under discussion, and as may readily be inferred, any charged particle moving in a uniform magnetic field, under the influence of magnetic forces only, will move in a spiral. If there is no component of velocity in the direction of the field, the spiral degenerates into a circle. The diameter of this spiral for electrons having energies which may be conveniently imparted with ordinarily available voltage supplies is very small in the strong fields produced by an electromagnet. In weaker fields, such as the earth's field, and for higher velocities, the radius is larger. If, for example, we have a 10-kv electron moving at right angles to the earth's field, which may be of the order of 0.5 gauss, or 0.5×10^{-4} weber/meter^2, the radius of the orbit would be 4.6 meters. A proton with the same velocity would move in an orbit having a radius of almost 10 km.

5.2   EXAMPLES OF FORCES ON PARTICLES

The transverse force which a magnetic field exerts on a moving charged particle has many important applications of which we shall

illustrate a few.   Let us begin by deriving generally applicable expressions for the radius of the circular motion of a charge q having a mass m
moving with a velocity v at right angles to a uniform magnetic field B.
The force acting on such a particle is

$$F = qvB$$

It is always at right angles to the motion.   Therefore, *no work is done*,
and the kinetic energy and velocity of the particle are constant.   As we
have already pointed out, the path of the particle will be circular, the
radius being just such that the radial acceleration v^2/R required for
circular motion is supplied by the magnetic force.   We therefore have

$$F_R = ma_R = m\frac{v^2}{R} = qvB$$

$$R = mv/qB \qquad\qquad (5.7)$$

The ratio of charge to mass of a particle may consequently be determined experimentally in terms of the field, the radius of the orbit, and
the velocity of the particle.

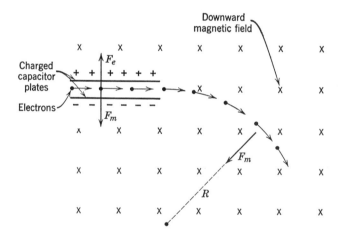

Fig. 5.7.   An electromagnetic velocity selector.

Crossed Electric and Magnetic Fields; The Velocity Selector

Of the three quantities cited above, the velocity is often the most difficult
to be sure of.   One method of determining it utilizes the velocity selector
shown in Fig. 5.7.   The apparatus consists essentially in an electric field
established between two flat charged metallic plates mounted in an evacuated
space in which there is a uniform magnetic field.   The electric field is adjusted
in sign and magnitude to exert on charged particles of the desired velocity

v an electric force just balancing the force exerted on them by the magnetic field. The condition is

$$qE = qvB$$

$$v = E/B \qquad (5.8)$$

These particles (electrons in the illustration) are thus relieved of the deflecting force of the magnetic field and will travel in straight paths. Hence only particles having the desired velocity can get through the straight channel between the plates. Others will move in curved paths, will therefore impinge on one or the other of the flat plates, and will not reach the open space beyond the electric field. The radius of the circular orbits traversed by the particles which get through the apparatus may then be written in the form

$$R = \frac{m}{q}\frac{E}{B^2} \qquad or \qquad m = \frac{RqB^2}{E} \qquad (5.9)$$

Since both electrons and protons are known to have the same charge, experimental determinations of e/m for these particles may be used to show that the mass of the proton is about 1840 times the mass of an electron, at least for velocities small compared to the velocity of light.

Bucherer's Demonstration of the Relativistic Mass of the Electron

An important aspect of Eq. 5.9 is that it may be used to demonstrate a prediction of the theory of relativity. According to this theory, mass should be a function of velocity according to the relation

$$m = \frac{m_0}{\sqrt{1 - \beta^2}} \qquad (5.10)$$

where $\beta = v/c$, the ratio of the velocity of the particle to the velocity of light. The statement of the equivalence of mass and energy

$$E = mc^2 \qquad (5.11)$$

may be used to determine the kinetic energy of a particle. For velocities small compared to the velocity of light, or $\beta \ll 1$, this reduces to the Newtonian form

$$K.E. = mc^2 - m_0c^2 = m_0c^2\left[\frac{1}{\sqrt{1 - \beta^2}} - 1\right]$$

But for $\beta \ll 1$ we have, since $(1 - x)^n = 1 - nx + \cdots$,

$$\frac{1}{\sqrt{1 - \beta^2}} = 1 + \tfrac{1}{2}\beta^2 + \cdots$$

and finally

$$K.E. = m_0c^2[1 + \tfrac{1}{2}\beta^2 + \cdots - 1]$$
$$= \tfrac{1}{2}m_0v^2$$

In an apparatus such as that shown in Fig. 5.7, it is possible to measure both v, as given by Eq. 5.8, and m, as given by Eq. 5.9, and so to test Eq. 5.10. Radioactive substances which emit very fast electrons have long been known to exist. One of the early experiments to check the theory of relativity, and particularly the mass equation, Eq. 5.10, was performed by a German physicist, Bucherer, during the early part of the twentieth century. The results obtained for various groups of electrons are shown in the first two columns of Table 5.1. The velocities of these electrons are expressed as the ratio of

TABLE 5.1   THE RESULTS OF BUCHERER'S DETERMINATION
OF e/m FOR FAST ELECTRONS

$\beta = v/c$	e/m	e/m_0
0.3173	1.661×10^{11}	1.752×10^{11} coulombs/kg
0.3787	1.630	1.761
0.5154	1.590	1.760
0.6870	1.283	1.767

their velocity to that of light. It is clear that e/m is a function of velocity. If we compute e/m_0 from the observed values of e/m using Eq. 5.11, we get the numbers shown in the last column. These are not only consistent among each other but agree with the value of e/m_0 measured in a variety of other ways. The accepted value today is 1.759×10^{11} coulombs/kg.

The Cyclotron

The cyclotron is an apparatus for producing fast charged particles. It makes use of the magnetic force which we are studying in this chapter. Particles may be accelerated by having steady forces applied to them, as in the electric field between the terminals of a Van de Graaff generator, or by having forces applied impulsively for short times, as in the linear accelerator, described in Section 4.5.

The principle of repeated application of force in short pulses was first applied not in linear accelerators, but in a cyclotron, schematically shown in Fig. 5.8. Like the linear accelerator, it accelerates by imparting successive impulses, but the path of the particles is curled up by a magnetic field. The instrument operates as follows. A magnetic field is established between the flat poles of an electromagnet, and two hollow metal half-cylinders, called D's, are placed in this gap. A particle within one D will be acted on by a magnetic force only and will move in a circular orbit around the axis of the magnet. The particle will cross the gap between the two D's, and, if the D's are suitably charged, it will be accelerated. It will then move within the other D in a circular orbit of larger radius, and, when it again emerges into the gap, it may again be accelerated. If the polarity is reversed at the proper intervals, a particle (or a small group of particles) may receive successive accelerating impulses. Its path will be semicircular within the D's, but the radius increases as the particle gains energy. It will therefore move outward in a spiral, as shown in Fig. 5.8.

We can easily establish relationships that determine the main characteristics of cyclotron design. From Eq. 5.6 it follows that the angular velocity ω of a particle moving in a circular orbit due to its interaction with a constant and uniform magnetic field is

$$\omega = v/R = qB/m \qquad (5.12)$$

It follows from this equation that the angular velocity is independent of the radius of the orbit and depends on q/m and the field B only. The kinetic energy of the particle may be written

$$E = \tfrac{1}{2}mv^2 = \frac{R^2q^2B^2}{2m} \qquad (5.13)$$

which shows that in a constant uniform field the energy is proportional to the square of the radius.

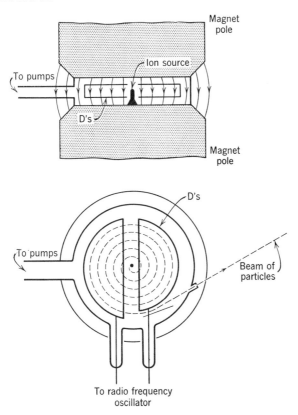

FIG. 5.8.   The accelerating chamber of a cyclotron.

Suppose now that we wish to compute the requirements for a cyclotron in which 10 Mev protons are to be produced, using a field of 18,000 gauss, or 1.8 webers/meter². From Eq. 5.13 we may compute the radius

$$R = (2mE)^{\frac{1}{2}}/qB$$

The mass of the proton is 1.67×10^{-27} kg. Ten Mev is equal to 1.6×10^{-12} joule. The charge of the proton is equal to 1.6×10^{-19} coulomb. The required radius is 0.25 meter, or a diameter of a half meter. This fixes the size of the D's. The magnet must have pole pieces with a somewhat larger diameter to provide the required uniformity of field over the entire D's. A magnet with such pole pieces is a heavy and bulky piece of apparatus, weighing many tons.

Since the electric field applied to the D's must have the same frequency as the protons in their spiral motion, we see from Eq. 5.12 that a *constant* frequency is required, independent of the radius and energy of the particle. In our particular case this frequency may be computed to be 1.73×10^8 radians/sec, or 28 megacycles/sec. The larger the D's and the larger the magnet, the higher the energy that can be achieved—up to a point. The equations used assume that the mass is constant, independent of the velocity of the particle being accelerated. When the velocity of light is approached, this condition is no longer fulfilled. The critical condition, Eq. 5.12, expressing a relationship between the frequency and the field strength, can be fulfilled only if either or both of these quantities vary as the particle gains mass. This is achieved in instruments called synchrotrons, FM cyclotrons, bevatrons, cosmotrons, etc.

5.3 FORCES AND TORQUES ON CONDUCTORS

Since currents in a conductor are charges in motion, we shall have to consider the magnetic forces on these charges as well as on the free charges discussed above. Here we must distinguish two cases. If the magnetic force has a component in the direction of the length of the

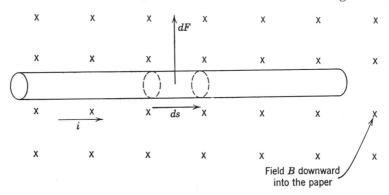

Fig. 5.9.   The mechanical force acting on a wire carrying a current in a magnetic field.

conductor, it will accelerate the charges, produce a current, and be in fact indistinguishable from any electromotive force in the circuit of which the conductor in question is a part. This "induced" emf we shall take up later, in Section 6.1. If, on the other hand, this magnetic force acting on the charges is at right angles to the length of the conductor, as in Fig. 5.9, it will be transmitted to the conductor itself. The electrons are constrained by surface forces and therefore remain within the metal. Consequently, if forces act on the free charges without causing transverse motion (acceleration) through the lattice, the forces must be transmitted by some means to the lattice itself. The situation is further analyzed in the discussion of the Hall effect in Section 6.1.

The magnitude of the force on a conductor carrying a current follows from Eq. 5.2. If there are dN charges of magnitude e in a length ds of a conductor, shown in Fig. 5.9, the force dF acting on this element of length is

$$d\mathbf{F} = e[\mathbf{v} \times \mathbf{B}]\, dN \qquad (5.14)$$

This expression may be put into a more useful form by noting that, if the number of free charges per unit volume in the conductor is n, and its cross-sectional area is A, then

$$dN = nA\, ds$$

In Eq. 3.26 we found that

$$i = nevA$$

and Eq. 5.14 may therefore be rewritten

$$d\mathbf{F} = [i\, ds \times \mathbf{B}] \qquad \blacktriangleright(5.15)\blacktriangleleft$$

If mks units are used consistently, so that i is expressed in amperes, ds in meters, B in webers/meter^2, then dF will be in newtons.

As an illustration of the application of the magnetic force acting on a conductor carrying a current, we shall discuss the basic current-measuring instrument, the galvanometer. In this instrument the magnetic forces act around an axis to produce a torque, which in turn produces an elastic deflection in a pivoted system.

Let us first consider the torque exerted by a uniform magnetic field on a square coil of wire when a current flows through the coil. Such a coil is illustrated in Fig. 5.10. The axis about which the torque is to be measured is indicated by $X\!-\!X$ in the figure.

The magnetic forces on the sides of length b exert no torque about the axis $X\!-\!X$ since these forces are parallel to the axis. The forces on the other two sides are vertically up and down and exert a torque τ given by

$$\tau = Fb \sin\theta$$

If the coil has N turns with a current i in each, then the force F is

$$F = NiaB$$

and the torque is

$$\tau = NiAB \sin\theta \qquad (5.16)$$

Here the area of the coil is designated by $A = (ab)$. We shall not carry through the demonstration, but it is true that Eq. 5.16 is appli-

cable to a coil of any shape and not only to a square coil. Notice that
if we identify NiA in Eq. 5.16 with the magnetic moment p_m in Eq. 5.2,

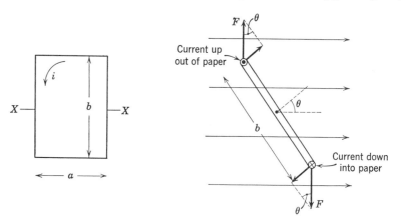

FIG. 5.10. Magnetic torque on a square coil in a magnetic field.

the equations become identical. The magnetic moment of a loop of
wire having N turns of area A, and carrying a current i, is

$$p_m = NiA \qquad (5.17)$$

The direction of the vector p_m is normal to the area A. If viewed in
the direction of p_m, the current is clockwise.

A Numerical Example

These are the forces and torques used to deflect the moving parts of galvanometers and, with a different construction, the rotating parts of electrical
machines. To illustrate their magnitude, let us consider how great a current
would be required to produce a force of 10 lb, or 45 newtons, on a conductor
between the poles of a magnet. Assume the diameter of the poles to be 4 in.,
or 0.1 meter, and a field strength $B = 1$ weber/meter^2.

$$F = Bi$$
$$45 = 1 \times i \times 0.1$$
$$i = 450 \text{ amp}$$

It is clear that to produce large forces, large currents, or many conductors
carrying smaller currents, are required.

5.4 THE FIELDS AROUND CURRENTS

Magnetic fields are produced by moving electric charges. These
charges may be free charges moving in space, or electrons moving in
a coil of wire, or electrons circulating about their nuclei and spinning

about an axis, as in a magnetized piece of iron or permanent magnet. Such moving charges produce magnetic fields in their vicinity.

In this section we shall consider the fields produced by charges moving in a vacuum, or in or near media such as air, copper, water, or a great variety of others which are magnetically almost indistinguishable from a vacuum. We particularly exclude iron, or other ferromagnetic materials, and leave the analysis of effects such materials give rise to for discussion at the end of this chapter.

The procedure involved in arriving at an expression for the magnetic field around a moving charge is typical of many scientific formulations. It is not often that we have so simple a situation as we had in electrostatics, where the fundamental law (Coulomb's law of force) could be arrived at on the basis of direct experimental observation. The field around a moving electron has probably never been plotted out. It could, no doubt, be measured, but only with great difficulty, and probably not with great precision. There are simply more interesting things to be done in the laboratory. Because of the indirect evidence that has been accumulated, we feel certain that we know what the result would be. What has in fact happened is that the magnetic fields around all sorts of shapes of coils of wire carrying currents have been very carefully and exactly measured. Every single observed result is compatible with the assumption that an electric current is a group of electric charges in motion, and that the observed field is the vector sum of the fields of all the charges involved. The magnitude of the magnetic induction at a distance r from a charge q moving with velocity v is

$$B = \frac{\mu_0}{4\pi} \frac{qv}{r^2} \sin \theta \qquad (5.18)$$

The symbols used have the meaning illustrated in Fig. 5.11. In vector notation, Eq. 5.18 may be written

$$\mathbf{B} = \frac{\mu_0}{4\pi} q \frac{[\mathbf{v} \times \mathbf{r}]}{r^3} \qquad \blacktriangleright(5.19)\blacktriangleleft$$

This is the law of Biot and Savart. The constant μ_0 is the *permeability* of the medium (empty space) in which the field is produced. In mks units μ_0 has the dimensions of webers/ampere-meter, and its magnitude is part of the definition of B in Eqs. 5.18 or 5.19. It is

$$\mu_0 = 4\pi \times 10^{-7} \text{ webers/amp-meter} \qquad (5.20)$$

The vector $\mathbf{v}$ is in the direction of motion. The lines of flux are closed circles in planes at right angles to the axis of motion. In any fixed direction, the field intensity falls off inversely as the square of the dis-

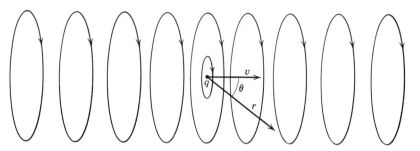

FIG. 5.11.   The magnetic field of a moving charge.

tance.   At a fixed distance from the charge, it is proportional to sin θ.
It vanishes in the direction of motion.   The sense of the field around
the direction of motion is more clearly shown in Fig. 5.12.   It is opposite

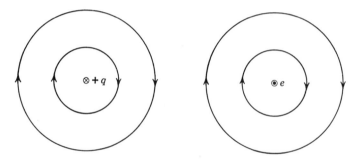

FIG. 5.12.   The magnetic field of moving charges in a plane at right angles to the
direction of motion.   (a) Positive charge moving down into the paper.   (b) A negatively charged electron moving up out of the paper.

for electric charges of opposite sign.   These relationships are such that
a screw with a right-hand thread being driven into the paper in the
direction of motion of a positive charge indicates the sense of circulation
of the lines of flux, as shown in Fig. 5.13.

In order to transform Eq. 5.19 for use in connection with currents in
wires, we must express the current in terms of the charge density in the
conductor.   Let us first set up an expression for the magnetic field due
to the current in an element of length ds of a conductor carrying a
current i, as shown in Fig. 5.14.   If dq represents the number of coulombs
of charge that are moving in this element of length of the conductor,
and if v is their velocity, Eq. 5.18 may be rewritten

$$dB = \frac{u_0}{4\pi} \frac{v \, dq}{r^2} \sin \theta \qquad (5.21)$$

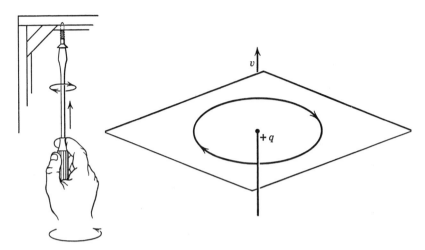

FIG. 5.13. A convenient rule for establishing the direction of a magnetic field around the direction of motion of a positive charge.

If, as in Section 5.3, the number of free charges in unit volume of the conductor is n, and the area of the conductor is A, we have

$$v\, dq = (ven)(\text{volume of length } ds \text{ of the wire})$$
$$= vneA\, ds$$

and since

$$i = neAv$$
$$i\, ds = v\, dq$$

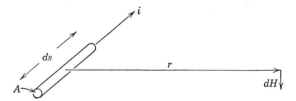

FIG. 5.14. The magnetic field due to an element of length ds of a conductor carrying a current i.

and therefore

$$dB = \frac{\mu_0}{4\pi} \frac{i\, ds}{r^2} \sin \theta \qquad (5.22)$$

In vector notation, Eq. 5.22 may be written

$$\mathbf{dB} = \frac{\mu_0}{4\pi} \frac{[\mathbf{i}\, ds \times \mathbf{r}]}{r^3} \qquad \blacktriangleright(5.23)\blacktriangleleft$$

This is the law of Biot and Savart. The expression Eq. 5.22 is readily integrated for points outside of a straight conductor of finite length. The meaning of the symbols used is shown in Fig. 5.15. We have

$$B = \frac{\mu_0}{4\pi} \frac{i\,ds \sin\theta}{r^2} \tag{5.24}$$

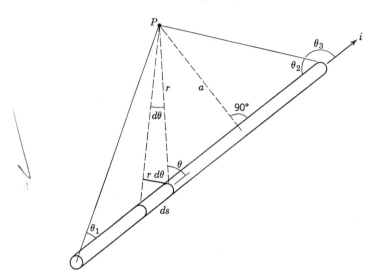

FIG. 5.15.   The symbols used in the computation of the magnetic field around a finite straight conductor.

But, from Fig. 5.15, we see that

$$\frac{r\,d\theta}{ds} = \sin\theta = \frac{a}{r}$$

or that

$$ds/r^2 = d\theta/a \tag{5.25}$$

Eq. 5.24 may therefore be written

$$B = \frac{\mu_0 i}{4\pi a} \int_{\theta_1}^{\theta_3} \sin\theta\,d\theta$$

$$B = \frac{\mu_0 i}{4\pi a} [-\cos\theta]_{\theta_1}^{\theta_3}$$

$$= \frac{\mu_0 i}{4\pi a} [\cos\theta_2 + \cos\theta_1] \tag{5.26}$$

If the wire is very long compared to the distance a, and if the point P

is not too near either end, then the above cosines are each equal to unity, and we may write for the field outside of the wire

$$B = \frac{\mu_0 i}{2\pi a}$$

▶(5.27)◀

We are now in a position to return to the most directly observable aspect of the problem and to specify the forces between current elements, just as, in Chapter 1, we specified the electric force between charges. In Section 5.3 we stated that the force dF due to a current i in an element of length ds of a conductor in a magnetic field B is

$$\mathbf{dF} = [\mathbf{i}\ ds \times \mathbf{B}] \tag{5.28}$$

Let us now consider the field produced by a second element of current $i'\ ds'$. If we are dealing with currents in empty space, we have

$$d\mathbf{B} = \frac{\mu_0}{4\pi} \frac{[\mathbf{i}'\ ds' \times \mathbf{r}]}{r^3} \tag{5.29}$$

Combining Eqs. 5.29 with 5.28, we get

$$d\mathbf{F} = \frac{\mu_0}{4\pi} \frac{1}{r^3}\ \mathbf{i}\ ds \times [\mathbf{i}'\ ds' \times \mathbf{r}] \tag{5.30}$$

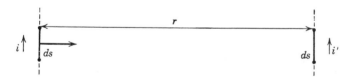

Fig. 5.16.   The force between parallel currents is attractive.

For the special case of two parallel currents flowing in the same direction, as in Fig. 5.16, the expression for the magnitude of the force between the two current elements becomes

$$dF = \frac{\mu_0}{4\pi} \frac{(i\ ds)(i'\ ds')}{r^2} \tag{5.31}$$

Equation 5.31 then may be used for the definition of an ampere. Although this form is not well suited for direct experimental check, it may be used as the basis for calculating the force between rigid circuits of any shape.

In another system of units, called the absolute electromagnetic cgs system, the numerical coefficient in Eq. 5.31 is put equal to unity. The force is expressed in dynes, the distance is given in centimeters, and the unit of current is then called the abampere. It follows from the above that

$$10 \text{ amp} = 1 \text{ abamp} \tag{5.32}$$

The Determination of the Ampere

The expression, Eq. 5.31, for the force between two elements of current is so important that we shall undertake a further discussion in an attempt to indicate the physical significance of the mathematical procedures that have been specified. We shall describe an experiment whose object it is to determine an ampere of current in terms of forces between conductors, using Eq. 5.31.

Since the force between current elements is not measurable, we must first choose circuits of some particular shape. The simplest conditions, and in fact the only ones for which we have carried through the required computations, are realized by two infinitely long straight wires. The field at a normal distance a from a long wire is

$$B = \frac{\mu_0 i}{2\pi a} \tag{5.33}$$

A second wire parallel to the first with a current i flowing in the same direction will be attracted. The force on an element of length ds is

$$dF = i' \, ds \, B = \frac{\mu_0 i i' \, ds}{2\pi a} \tag{5.34}$$

The force on any element of length is the same as on any other, and for a length L we have

$$F = \frac{\mu_0 i i' L}{2\pi a} \tag{5.35}$$

It is not practicable to measure the force on an infinite conductor. The difficulty may be overcome by bending our long straight conductors into coaxial circles having radii very large compared to their separation. It can be shown that under these conditions Eq. 5.35 is approximately applicable, and that correction factors for the error committed may be computed. The length of the conductor becomes $2\pi r$.

Let us then wind a single turn of wire around the edge of each of two circular disks and twist the insulated ends of these wires together. The fields produced by these twisted ends are small because the currents in the two wires will be flowing in opposite directions. We shall neglect their contribution to the forces. One of the circular loops we shall mount rigidly in a horizontal plane, and the other we shall suspend from the arm of a beam balance directly over the fixed loop. If the radius of the circular loops is 10 cm, and if the distance between the loops is 5 mm, the condition that $r \gg a$ will be reasonably well fulfilled. The wire of which the loop is made might have a diameter of about 1 mm. From a handbook we can determine the amount of current which such a wire can carry without overheating. For our experiment, which will not last a long time, and in which the single turn is exposed to the air, 10 amp would be reasonable.

It will be desirable to connect the two coils to be used in the experiment in series, so that the same current flows through each. This plan eliminates one variable in Eq. 5.35, which now becomes

$$F = \mu_0 i^2 \frac{r}{a}$$

or, solved for i,

$$i = \sqrt{\frac{F}{\mu_0} \frac{a}{r}} \text{ amp}$$

If, in conducting the experiment, we should use a current of approximately 10 amp, we should find a force approximately given by

$$F = 4\pi \times 10^{-7} \times 10^2 \times 20 = 2.5 \times 10^{-3} \text{ newtons}$$

or roughly the weight of a quarter of a gram, which is an easily measurable force.

Forces Between Moving Charges

We have described the observable force between circuits in which there are currents in terms of the forces between current elements. The question arises why we do not go even farther into the origin of electric and magnetic forces and describe magnetic phenomena in terms of the forces between moving charges. In other words, if Coulomb's law gives the force between charges at rest, how should we modify it to describe the forces between charges in motion? The answer is that the electric forces between charges in motion are no longer correctly given by Coulomb's law. The electric field around a moving charge is no longer spherically symmetrical. The correct description of the situation is quite complicated. Magnetic forces are called into play, and, in addition, Coulomb's law is modified. However, if we confine our attention to forces between conductors carrying a current, the magnetic forces alone need be considered. No electric field can produce a resultant force at right angles to the current in an uncharged conductor, because the forces on positive and negative charges will cancel. The problem is therefore simplified if we limit ourselves, as we have done, to the forces between conductors and omit consideration of the electric forces between charges in motion. For the range of problems in which we shall interest ourselves, this is not a serious limitation. However, investigators considering such problems as the ionization produced by fast electrons must undertake a more detailed analysis than we have given here.

5.5 PROPERTIES OF CONSTANT MAGNETIC FIELDS

Electric and magnetic fields have various points of similarity, and various points of marked dissimilarity. We saw in Chapter 2 that, although Coulomb's law of force between charged particles sufficed for the description of electrostatic phenomena, an alternative equivalent description in terms of certain integral properties of the electric field was possible. Similarly, although magnetic forces between current elements are specified by Eq. 5.30, we shall find here that a formulation of the properties of the magnetic field quite apart from the interaction of currents in conductors is important.

For the present we shall confine our attention to the fields produced by currents in a vacuum or in air. When we come to consider magnetizable matter in the next section, we shall find that the constant μ_0 must be replaced by a different quantity μ whose magnitude depends on the magnetic properties of the medium surrounding the moving charges. Furthermore, in the electric case we found that the field properties were best described by two vectors, the displacement D and the electric intensity E. Similarly, we shall find that the properties of magnetic fields are best described in terms of two vectors, the magnetic induction B, and the magnetic intensity H. In empty space these fields are related by the equation

$$\mathbf{B} = \mu_0 \mathbf{H} \qquad (5.36)$$

We shall take up the physical significance of the two fields in the next section. From the defining Eq. 5.36 $H = B/\mu_0$ and from Eq. 5.22 we conclude that the dimensions of the magnetic intensity H are amperes/meter.

We shall now summarize the properties of constant magnetic fields and compare them with the properties of constant electric fields. In Section 6.3 we shall indicate certain modifications that must be included when time-dependent fields are considered. We found that, for an electrostatic field, according to Eq. 2.27,

$$\oint E_t \, ds = 0 \qquad (5.37)$$

The integral of the tangential component of the electric field in the direction of ds around any closed path vanishes.

This is not true for magnetic fields. For the case of a circular path of radius r around an infinite straight conductor, we have, using Eq. 5.27,

$$\oint B_t \cdot ds = \oint \frac{\mu_0 i}{2\pi r} \, ds = \mu_0 i$$

The general statement of the law, called *Ampère's circuital law*, illustrated above, is that the integral of the *tangential component of the magnetic field H around a closed path is equal to the current linked through this path*, or mathematically,

$$\oint H_t \, ds = i \qquad \blacktriangleright (5.38) \blacktriangleleft$$

The Meaning of "Linked" Current in Eq. 5.38

For example, let us consider the coaxial cable shown in Fig. 5.17. A current i is flowing down into the paper in the central core. An equal current is flowing up out of the paper along the outer cylinder. We shall first apply Eq. 5.38 to path I which does not surround the cable. This path may be removed to infinity without cutting or crossing the current in the cable at any point. The currents are said not to link the path. The integral for path I is therefore zero.

Path II, on the other hand, links both the current in the core and the current in the outer sheath. These are equal and in opposite directions. Their sum is zero. The total current linked by path II is also zero, and the integral, Eq. 5.38, vanishes for this path.

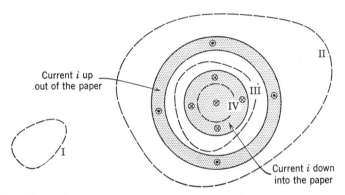

Current i up out of the paper

II

III

IV

I

Current i down into the paper

Fig. 5.17. The application of Ampère's law to the field in a coaxial pair of conductors.

Path III is linked by the current in the central core only, and the integral of the tangential component of H around this path is therefore numerically equal to i. And finally, path IV, which is circular and of radius r, links only a part of the current in the central core and none of the current in the return shell. If the current in the central core, whose radius we shall assume to be r_1, is uniformly distributed, its current density or current per unit area, is $i/\pi r_1^2$. If the area within path IV is πr^2, the current linking path IV is the current density in the central conductor multiplied by the area enclosed by path IV. The contour integral for this case consequently is

$$\oint H_t \, ds = i \, \frac{\pi r^2}{\pi r_1^2} \tag{5.39}$$

A second important property of electric fields is incorporated in Gauss's law, which states that the surface integral of the normal component of the displacement D over any closed surface is just equal to the total free charge within the surface, or from Eq. 2.14.

$$\int_S D_n \, dA = \sum q \tag{5.40}$$

Since there are no free magnetic charges, the corresponding expression to be expected for magnetic fields is

$$\int_S B_n \, dA = 0 \qquad \blacktriangleright(5.41)\blacktriangleleft$$

This equation does, in fact, express an important property of magnetic fields. Lines of magnetic induction, unlike lines of displacement, do not terminate. The electric field consists of lines of force originating on positive charges and terminating on negative charges. The magnetic field B consists of lines of induction which link currents and have no beginning or end.

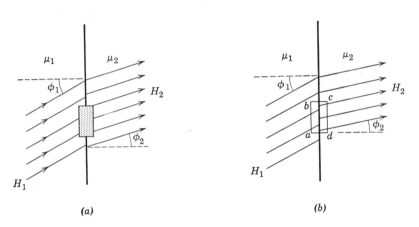

(a)   (b)

Fig. 5.18.   Magnetic boundary conditions.

Magnetic Boundary Conditions

The arguments which we advanced in Section 3.6 for establishing the electrical boundary conditions, Eqs. 3.71 and 3.72,

$$D_{n\,1} = D_{n\,2} \qquad (5.42)$$

$$E_{t\,1} = E_{t\,2} \qquad (5.43)$$

may be repeated without any essential changes for the magnetic case. Figure 5.18 shows the cross section of a boundary between two media. In Fig. 5.18a the dotted rectangle represents the cross section of a pillbox to whose surface we wish to apply the magnetic equivalent of Gauss's law,

$$\int_S B_n \, dA = 0$$

As previously, we make the pillbox very thin, so that the integral over the curved sides contributes a vanishingly small amount to the integral. The remaining terms, due to the flat sides of the pillbox, yield

$$B_{n\,1} = B_{n\,2} \qquad\qquad (5.44)$$

The normal component of the induction is continuous over a boundary.

In Fig. 5.18b the rectangle $abcd$ is a path along which the contour integral

$$\oint H_t \, ds = i$$

is to be taken. If the lengths bc and ad are chosen vanishingly small, the area of the loop may be made as small as desired and the total current passing through the loop approaches zero. The contributions of the sides ab and cd to the integral then yield

$$H_{t\,1} = H_{t\,2} \qquad\qquad (5.45)$$

The use of Eqs. 5.38 and 5.41, specifying important properties of constant magnetic fields, is illustrated below in applications to computations of the fields of coils.

The Fields of Coils

The simplest coil to describe is that formed by placing a closely spaced spirally wound conductor around a cylinder whose length is very great compared to its diameter. Such a solenoid is shown in Fig. 5.19a, and a special

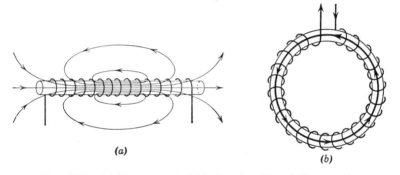

(a)

(b)

FIG. 5.19.   (a) The magnetic field of a solenoid, and (b) a toroid.

form, or toroid, which is particularly suited to the present discussion, is shown in Fig. 5.19b. In the central portion of such a spirally wound cylinder, the magnetic flux is uniformly distributed across its cross section. Near the ends of the coil the flux fringes out, and the field is no longer uniform. By bending the coil into the form of a toroid, as in b, the fringing effect can be avoided. The lines of flux then form closed rings within the toroid.

The field within the ring-shaped toroid can be calculated from the equations specifying the properties of static magnetic fields. From Eq. 5.38 we have, if we integrate along a path going once through the toroid as indicated by the heavy line in the figure,

$$Hl = Ni$$

where N is the total number of turns in the winding, i is the current in the wire, and l is the total length along which the N turns are distributed. If the overall dimensions of the toroid are large compared to the diameter of a turn, then all paths of integration around the toroid have almost the same length. Furthermore, from symmetry we conclude that the field at any one point of the path is the same as that at any other point. The magnetic field in the toroid is therefore approximately uniform and is equal to

$$H = Ni/l \qquad\qquad (5.46)$$

In the case of a very long straight solenoid, as might be expected, the magnetic field in the central portion not too near the ends is the same as that in a toroid

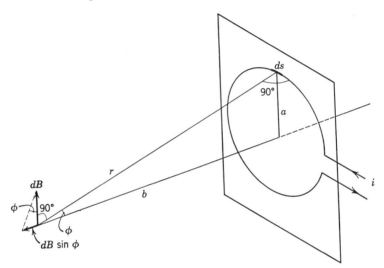

Fig. 5.20.   Magnetic field on the axis of a circular turn.

having the same number of turns per meter. This may be verified through summing the fields due to a lot of individual turns, as we now proceed to show.

The magnetic field due to a current in a conductor may be calculated from Eq. 5.38 if a path can be found along which the field is constant. No such path can be found for the field of a circular coil. We therefore go back to Eq. 5.23 as our starting point. The symbols to be used are defined in Fig. 5.20 for the field dB at an arbitrary point on the axis due to an element of length ds. We then integrate this expression around the complete circular turn. For points off the axis, this turns out to be a very complicated calculation. The field of a single circular turn of wire in fact cannot be described in terms of the functions with which the student is familiar. Rather complicated infinite series are required. For points along the axis of the turn, however, the calculations are quite simple. For reasons of symmetry the resultant field at any point on the axis must be along the axis, and we therefore begin by writing an expression for this component of the field due to an element of length ds of the conductor. It is

$$dB \sin \phi = \frac{\mu_0}{4\pi} \frac{i\,ds}{r^2} \sin \theta \sin \phi$$

or, since $\theta = 90°$,

$$dB \sin \phi = \frac{\mu_0}{4\pi} \frac{ids}{r^2} \sin \phi$$

But the contribution of any one element of length is just the same as that of any other, and we need therefore not perform any formal integration. It is sufficient to replace the element of length ds by the total length of the circular turn, $2\pi a$. The final result may then be put into any of the following forms,

$$B = \mu_0 \frac{ia \sin \phi}{2r^2} = \mu_0 \frac{ia^2}{2r^3} = \mu_0 \frac{ia^2}{2(a^2 + b^2)^{3/2}} \qquad (5.47)$$

At the center of the single turn this reduces to

$$B = \mu_0 i / 2a \qquad (5.48)$$

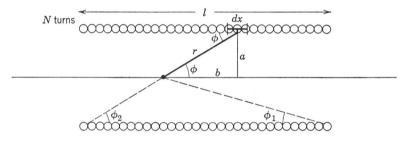

Fig. 5.21. Computation of the field along the axis of a solenoid.

This expression may be used to find the field on the axis of a long solenoid. With the symbols defined in Fig. 5.21 we have, for the field dB due to a length dx, if there are N turns in a length of the solenoid and each carries a current i,

$$dB = \frac{\mu_0}{2} \left(\frac{Ni}{l} \right) dx \frac{a \sin \phi}{r^2} \qquad (5.49)$$

By an argument similar to that used in obtaining Eq. 5.25, we see that

$$dx/r^2 = d\phi/a$$

and upon integrating Eq. 5.49

$$B = \frac{\mu_0 Ni}{2l} (\cos \phi_2 + \cos \phi_1) \qquad (5.50)$$

For the central region of a very long solenoid we may put $\cos \phi_2 = \cos \phi_1 = 1$, and therefore

$$B = \mu_0(Ni/l)$$

or

$$H = Ni/l \qquad (5.51)$$

in agreement with Eq. 5.46.

A further application of Eq. 5.38 is to the field of a long straight wire of radius r_1. From symmetry H_t must be constant around a circle of radius r, and therefore

$$\oint H_t \, ds = H \cdot 2\pi r = i$$

$$H = \frac{i}{2\pi r} \quad \text{for } r > r_1 \tag{5.52}$$

The condition that r must be greater than r_1 is added because it is only then that the current linked by the circle of integration is the total current i. The above equation therefore specifies the magnitude of the field for points outside of the conductor. This result we had previously obtained by applying the law of Biot and Savart. The application of this law to finding the field at points inside of the conductor is much more complicated, whereas it follows directly from Eq. 5.38.

We have already shown that the current linking a circle of radius r in a cylindrical conductor of radius r_1 carrying a current i is $ir^2/r_1{}^2$. We have, from Eq. 5.39,

$$\oint H_t \, ds = i \frac{r^2}{r_1{}^2}$$

But, since $H_t = H$ and has the same value at every point of the circle along which we are to integrate, this reduces to

$$H \cdot 2\pi r = i \frac{r^2}{r_1{}^2}$$

$$H = \frac{ir}{2\pi r_1{}^2} \quad \text{for } r < r_1$$

Within a cylindrical conductor carrying a current, the magnetic field increases directly as the radius. At the surface it has the value $i/2\pi r_1$. Outside the conductor the field decreases and is proportional to $1/r$. If we have a coaxial cable, as in Fig. 5.19, the field between the two conductors is $i/2\pi r$, independent of the radius of either conductor. Outside the outer conductor the field is zero. An extension of the above argument may be used to prove that the field within a hollow cylindrical conductor vanishes.

5.6 MAGNETIZATION

In electrostatic problems we found that the displacement was made up of two parts, one originating in space itself, the second due to the polarization of matter. Similarly we find that in magnetic problems the total magnetic induction B is made up of two parts. One of these originates in empty space. There is always an induction $\mu_0 H$ at any point of space, regardless of whether matter is present or not. If magnetized matter is present there is additional flux due to atomic currents circulating around individual nuclei. In analogy to the electric case, we introduce a vector specifying the magnetic moment per unit volume and consider effects due to magnetization in a particularly simple example. It is the toroidally wound coil, such as is shown in Fig. 5.19b.

A portion of a thin section of the core is shown in Fig. 5.22. The flux produced by the winding itself in the absence of a magnetized core is B_0

$$\mu_0 \frac{Ni}{l} = \mu_0 H \qquad (5.53)$$

where Ni/l are the ampere turns per meter in the coil and H is the magnetic intensity due to the current in the coil. Let us now consider effects due to magnetized matter in the core. We shall suppose that the core of the toroid is made of a material containing n atoms per unit volume each having a magnetic moment $i'A'$, where i' is a fictitious atomic surface current which, flowing around the periphery of an atom of surface area A', would produce a magnetic moment equal to the average actual atomic magnetic moment. We shall call the magnetic moment per unit volume the *intensity of magnetization or magnetic polarization M*, just as we called the electric moment per unit volume, P, the electric polarization. If there are N atoms in a volume V, so that $n = N/V$, we have

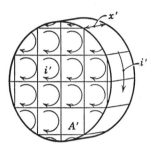

FIG. 5.22. The atomic currents in magnetized matter.

$$M = i'A' \cdot n = i'A'N/V \qquad (5.54)$$

But the volume V may be written as the volume per atom $x'A'$ multiplied by the number of atoms present, N. Equation 5.54 then becomes

$$M = i'A'N/V = i'A'N/Nx'A' = i'/x' \qquad (5.55)$$

The intensity of magnetization M is equal to the fictitious atomic amperes per meter flowing around each atom, or around the surface of the magnetized core. The individual atomic currents may be thought of as canceling each other except at the surface, and we are left with a surface current of i'/x' amp per meter. The total magnetic induction is made up of two parts, one due to the current in the toroidal winding, and one due to the atomic currents.

$$B = \mu_0 \frac{Ni}{l} + \mu_0 \frac{i'}{x'}$$

which may be written in vector form

$$\mathbf{B} = \mu_0 (\mathbf{H} + \mathbf{M}) \qquad \blacktriangleright (5.56) \blacktriangleleft$$

This is a fundamental relation between the three magnetic vectors and is always applicable. The total magnetic induction at any point in space is the sum of two terms, the flux density "carried" by empty space plus that "carried" by magnetized matter.

In many substances the intensity of magnetization is proportional to the applied field, so that

$$M = \chi H \tag{5.57}$$

where χ is called the *magnetic susceptibility*. Combining these equations we have

$$B = \mu_0(1 + \chi)H$$

or

$$B = \mu H \tag{5.58}$$

$$\mu = \mu_0(1 + \chi)$$

where μ is called the *magnetic permeability*.

Most substances are only very feebly magnetic, and sensitive instruments are required to measure their susceptibilities. These feebly magnetic substances are divided into two categories, the *paramagnetic substances*, which are attracted by a magnet, and the *diamagnetic*, which are repelled. A few substances, notably iron, are strongly magnetic. These are called *ferromagnetic*. We shall discuss first paramagnetic substances, whose magnetic properties must be understood before the origin of the strong magnetism of ferromagnetic substances becomes understandable. In the next chapter we shall take up the third category, the diamagnetic substances.

Paramagnetic Susceptibilities

Paramagnetic substances, which are attracted into the strong field in the gap of a magnet, are characterized by the fact that they are composed of atoms which have permanent magnetic dipole moments. If this permanent atomic moment is absent, then the paramagnetism and the attraction are also absent. We have described the magnetic moment of an atom in terms of a current i' circulating around the periphery of an atom of area A'.

$$p_m = i'A'$$

Even though we have not as yet found out how the electrons in atoms are distributed or how they move, we know something of atomic sizes and this suffices for a first estimate of atomic magnetic moments. In order to estimate this, we go back to a simple atomic model that we have already found useful. An outer electron circulating in the field of a single positive charge in a circular orbit must move with such a velocity that the Coulomb force just suffices to keep it in its orbit.

$$\frac{mv^2}{r} = \frac{1}{4\pi\epsilon_0}\frac{e^2}{r^2} \qquad v = e\sqrt{\frac{1}{4\pi\epsilon_0\,mr}} \tag{5.59}$$

But since the current due to an electron moving in an orbit is simply the electronic charge multiplied by the number of times it passes any point in its orbit per second, we have

$$i' = e \frac{v}{2\pi r}$$

The area of the orbit is πr^2, so that the magnetic moment must be

$$p_m = i'A' = e \frac{v}{2\pi r} \cdot \pi r^2$$

$$= \frac{evr}{2}$$

or, using Eq. 5.59,

$$p_m = \frac{e^2}{2} \sqrt{\frac{r}{4\pi\epsilon_0 m}} \tag{5.60}$$

Since atoms have radii of the order of 10^{-10} meter, we can estimate p_m. Substituting into Eq. 5.60 we find

$$p_m \simeq 10^{-23} \text{ amp-meter}^2 \tag{5.61}$$

This is the order of magnitude of the magnetic moment of actual atoms. We may conclude that these permanent moments are due to one or two outer electrons, and that, for reasons that are not as yet clear, most of the electrons in atoms contribute nothing to this moment.

As in estimating electrical polarization, we must get at the statistical aspects of the alignment produced by the field in the presence of thermal disorienting processes. The average magnetic moment per unit volume then is fp_m, where f is the fraction of the atoms which contribute to the magnetization. In the electrical case this fraction f was $p_0E/3kT$, the ratio of the electrical potential energy of the dipole in the field E to a thermal energy factor. Magnetically, we may expect for a dipole in air

$$f = \frac{p_m B}{3kT} = \frac{p_m \mu_0 H}{3kT}$$

For a substance with n dipoles per unit volume

$$M = \frac{\mu_0 p_m^2}{3kT} nH$$

and the magnetic susceptibility M/H is

$$\chi = \frac{\mu_0 p_m^2}{3kT} n \tag{5.62}$$

Substituting the known values of the constants into this equation, and using for n a value appropriate for solids $\simeq 10^{29}$ we get

$$\chi \simeq 7 \times 10^{-6}$$

Magnetic susceptibilities may accordingly be expected to be very small at room temperature. Many substances are found with susceptibilities of this magnitude and, following an inverse temperature law down to very low temperatures, of the order of 1°K. These are the paramagnetic substances. Eq. 5.62 is called Curie's law, after Pierre Curie, who experimentally discovered this form of temperature dependence at the end of the last century.

In paramagnetic substances the permeability differs exceedingly little from that of free space.

$$t\mu = \mu_0(1 + 10^{-3})$$

Such small susceptibilities are usually measured by the forces exerted on specimens by powerful electromagnets. The magnitude of these forces may be estimated from the following considerations.

The energy of a dipole in a magnetic field is $-p_m B \cos \theta$. If it is parallel to the field, $\cos \theta = 1$. If the field is changing in intensity in the x direction, there will be a change of energy as the dipole is moved in this direction, and there will consequently be a magnetic force

$$F_m = -\frac{dU}{dx} = -\frac{d}{dx}(-p_m B)$$

$$= p_m \frac{dB}{dx}$$

For a specimen of volume V having an average dipole moment M per unit volume, the magnetic force when it is placed near a magnet will be

$$F_m = (MV)\frac{dB}{dx} = \chi H V \frac{dB}{dx}$$

or if the specimen is in air

$$F_m = \frac{\mu_0 V \chi}{2}\frac{dH^2}{dx} = \frac{V\chi}{2\mu_0}\frac{dB^2}{dx} \tag{5.63}$$

If a magnet has a field of 2 webers/meter² between its poles and this field falls to roughly zero 0.1 meters away, $dB^2/dx \simeq 4/0.1 = 40$, and the force on 1 cc will be

$$F_m = \frac{10^{-6} \times 10^{-3}}{8\pi \times 10^{-7}} \times 40 \simeq 2 \times 10^{-2} \text{ newtons}$$

or roughly, 2 gm. Such forces require a sensitive balance for precise measurement.

We turn now to strongly magnetic substances, like iron, and many alloys containing iron. The outstanding fact about ferromagnetic substances is that μ/μ_0 typically has values ranging from hundreds to millions, and is not a constant for any one material, but depends on the previous magnetic history of the sample being tested and on the magnitude of the intensity of magnetization. Starting from the point o in Fig. 5.23 in a demagnetized sample, and applying an increasing field, we find that B follows along the dotted curve oc. The initial slope as the magnetization process begins and the curve leaves the origin is called the initial permeability. The initial permeability is usually relatively small. As the magnetization process proceeds, the curve rises at first more steeply and then flattens off. The maximum slope of the *B-H* curve is called the maximum permeability. In very large fields the magnetization *M* approaches its maximum or saturation value M_s, presumably when all the dipoles in the material are aligned, and the permeability again becomes smaller. When the field is de-

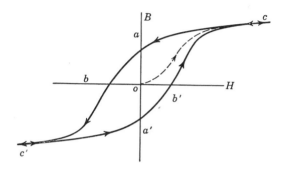

Fig. 5.23.   A hysteresis loop.

creased, the induction *B* does not retrace its previous values but follows along some curve like *ca*. *oa*, called the remanence of the material, measures the degree to which it can remain magnetized without the application of a field. Upon reversing the current in the magnetizing coils, one finds that a certain demagnetizing field *ob* is needed to demagnetize the sample. This is called the coercive force. Upon continuing the cycle, the magnetization curve goes through the points *c'*, *a'*, *b'*, *c*, etc. The closed curve *cabc'a'b'c* is called a *hysteresis loop*. It can be shown that the area of the hysteresis loop is equal to the work done by the electric circuit in producing magnetic changes in the material being cyclically magnetized. For some purposes, for example in permanent magnets, hysteresis loops with large areas are desirable, as in Fig. 5.24. In other applications, for example, magnetic core materials in a-c applications in which electrical energy loss is undesirable, small loops and low hysteresis are desirable.

The large magnetization of ferromagnetic materials as compared to paramagnetic materials is not due to the presence of stronger atomic magnetic dipoles. These are of the order computed in Eq. 5.60 in both ferromagnetic and paramagnetic substances. The difference lies rather in a very strong tendency in ferromagnetic materials for neighboring atomic dipoles to point in the same direction. These orienting forces are of a quantum mechanical origin and were not explained until 1928, when the theory of atomic structure was being developed. These forces produce a local alignment even in the absence of external fields. This is called *spontaneous magnetization*. It is because of this spontaneous magnetization that remanence is possible.

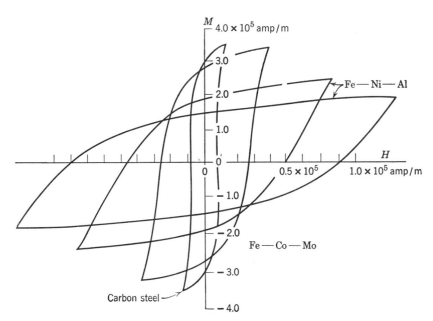

FIG. 5.24.   The magnetic properties of various magnetically hard materials, such as are used for making permanent magnets.

In general, spontaneous magnetization exists in regions, or domains. Within a domain the magnetization is practically complete. Almost all dipoles point in one direction within a domain. The magnetization within different domains points in different directions. When a field is applied, two processes occur. Domains whose magnetization is nearly parallel to the field grow at the expense of domains less favorably oriented. The situation is illustrated in Fig. 5.25. In *a* we have long needle-shaped domains of equal size alternately magnetized to the right and to the left. When a field pointing to the right is applied, the domains magnetized parallel to the field have an energy $-MH$ per unit volume. Those magnetized antiparallel to the field have an energy $+MH$. Those having a lower energy grow at the expense of those having a higher energy. The domain walls move, as shown in Fig. 5.25b. In very pure crystals this movement can go on unhindered. It proceeds reversibly, with very little hysteresis. If, on the other hand, impurities, strains, or other crystallographic imperfections are present, the motion of the domain walls is impeded. It proceeds in jumps, irreversibly. There is a drag exerted on the movement of the domain boundary. There is hysteresis. Work has to be done to move the boundary, and this shows up as heat.

Actual domains can be made visible by the depositing of very fine ferromagnetic colloidal particles from a liquid on a smooth specimen. Wherever domains meet there is a little leakage flux out of the surface, and particles will be attracted to these boundaries. Photographs of domain patterns in iron and cobalt are shown in Fig. 5.26.

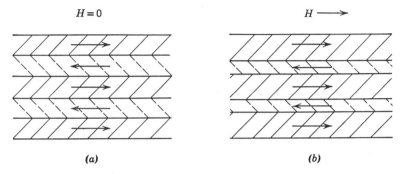

FIG. 5.25. Magnetic domains.

If the magnetization of the domains is not parallel to the field, a second magnetization process occurs. The direction of magnetization is rotated by the field. When the domain growth and rotation processes are complete, the magnetization is saturated. The spontaneous magnetization is everywhere parallel to the applied field.

The spontaneous magnetization is a function of the temperature. As the temperature is increased, the thermal agitation produces more disorientation and the spontaneous magnetization decreases until near a critical temperature called the Curie temperature, after Pierre Curie who discovered it in the course of his magnetic researches, spontaneous magnetization quite abruptly disappears. Above the Curie temperature ferromagnetic materials behave like paramagnetic materials. They are only feebly magnetized by even strong fields. The Curie temperatures of iron, nickel, and cobalt, the most common ferromagnetic materials, are 770, 358, and 1115°C.

5.7 FIELDS INSIDE OF POLARIZED BODIES

There is one point in our discussion of magnetic fields that requires elaboration, namely, the determination of the field H inside of magne-

tized bodies. To recapitulate our specification of magnetic fields, we
begin by considering fields outside magnetized bodies. If all the currents in conductors and all the surface currents due to magnetized

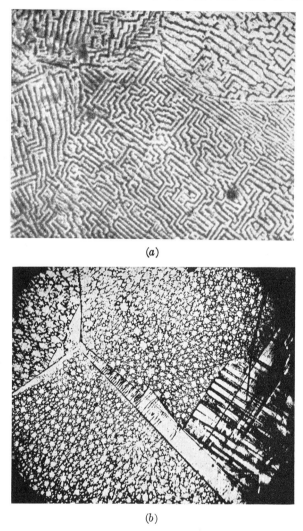

(a)

(b)

Fig. 5.26. Domain patterns (a) in iron and (b) in cobalt.

matter are known, and if we wish to know the field B at some point in
empty space, we must apply the law of Biot and Savart, as expressed
in Eq. 5.23, to all the currents present, both the currents in conductors
and the atomic currents. When B has been found, the value of H

follows from the relation $H = B/\mu_0$. Inside magnetized matter the situation is more complicated. In the case of the toroid we were able to specify the magnetic intensity H. It was

$$H = Ni/l \qquad (5.64)$$

Knowing this and the susceptibility of the core material, we could compute the intensity of magnetization M,

$$M = \chi H \qquad (5.65)$$

and finally compute the induction B

$$B = \mu_0(H + M) \qquad (5.66)$$

It is only for a toroid, however, that Eq. 5.64 may be used, and we must resort to other procedures for other cases. It is not even true in general that H can be computed from the conduction currents alone, as can be seen at once when we consider the external field of a permanent magnet with no conduction current at all.

The problem of computing the fields inside magnetic bodies of arbitrary shape in the presence of arbitrary current distributions is enormously difficult. We shall indicate a procedure for computing B and H from a knowledge of all the currents present, and then show how, in special cases, fields may be computed if only the conduction current and the distribution and susceptibility of magnetizable matter are known.

We have defined B in air, or in a vacuum, in terms of the magnetic force on moving charges, and it is only in air or a vacuum that we can at present specify B. The procedure we shall adopt is to cut infinitesimal cavities of suitable shape into solid bodies, specify B, or $H = B/\mu_0$ in these cavities, and then, with the help of the boundary conditions which we have established, specify B or H in the medium in which the cavities were cut. To illustrate the procedure, we take up the case of the toroid once more and present a method that will be generally applicable to the determination of B and H within a body of any shape.

The basic principle which we adopt is that *in empty space* B, and also $H = B/\mu_0$, may be computed if we take into account all the currents present, both conduction currents in windings, and surface currents on magnetized bodies. We shall first take up the induction B. Let us imagine a very thin disk-shaped cavity with its axis parallel to B, cut into the core material, as in Fig. 5.27a. There will be surface currents at its edge, but, if we let the thickness approach zero, this current approaches zero, and it contributes nothing to the field in the cavity. We therefore find that, in the cavity, the induction is due to the conduction currents in the winding and to the surface currents on the outside surface of the core.

$$B_{cavity} = \mu_0 \left(\frac{Ni}{l} + \frac{i'}{x'} \right) \tag{5.67}$$

The induction is normal to the flat surfaces of the cavity, and we may conclude that, since according to Eq. 5.44 the normal component of B is the same on the two sides of the surface,

$$B_{core} = B_{cavity} \tag{5.68}$$

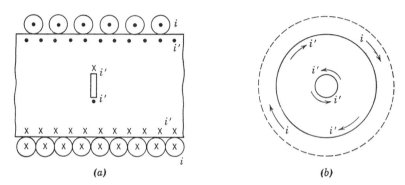

(a)   (b)

FIG. 5.27.   The coil currents and surface currents in a toroid with a core containing a cavity.

To determine H, we cut a long thin cylindrical cavity parallel to the axis of the core. The surface currents on the surface of the cavity will here modify B_{cavity}. In the case under consideration, they will exactly cancel the surface currents on the outer surface of the core. We are left with a field in the cavity

$$B_{cavity} = \mu_0 \frac{Ni}{l} + 0 \tag{5.69}$$

In the case of the long cylindrical cavity, the field is parallel, or tangential, to the surface, and the boundary condition expressed in Eq. 5.45 is applicable. We get

$$H_{core} = H_{cavity} = Ni/l \tag{5.70}$$

in conformity with our previous assumption.

A similar result holds for a long thin rod placed with its axis parallel to a uniform magnetic field. Near its ends the field will be distorted, but near its central portion we can show that $H_{outside} = H_{rod}$. Knowing this, we can compute $M = \chi H_{outside}$, and hence the magnetic induction in the rod,

$$B_{rod} = \mu_0(H_{outside} + \chi H_{outside}) \qquad (5.71)$$
$$= \mu H_{outside}$$

For other shapes the situation is more complex. The calculation is quite simple for a thin plate with its axis parallel to a uniform external field. Here the field will be distorted near the edges of the plate, but near the center we will have a uniform field perpendicular to the surface. Here the normal component of the induction must be continuous. We have

$$B_{outside} = B_{plate} \qquad (5.72)$$

The magnetic intensity within the plate can be determined through cutting a long, thin hole through it or, even more simply, through noting that

$$B_{plate} = \mu H_{plate} \qquad (5.73)$$

Combining Eqs. 5.72 and 5.73, we get

$$H_{outside} = \frac{B_{outside}}{\mu_0} = \frac{B_{core}}{\mu_0} = \frac{\mu}{\mu_0} H_{core}$$

$$H_{core} = \frac{\mu_0}{\mu} H_{outside} = \frac{1}{1 + \chi} H_{outside} \qquad (5.74)$$

$$B_{core} = \mu_0 H_{outside}$$

In this case the field inside the magnetic material is reduced by a factor $1/(1 + \chi)$, which, for high permeabilities, may be considerable. In a long thin rod parallel to the field the induction is μ times the applied field, whereas in a flat plate it is only μ_0 times the applied field because of the reduction of the field within the magnetized material.

The physical reason for the greater difficulty in magnetizing a flat plate as compared to a long needle is to be found in the shape of the field of a dipole. The field is such that another dipole somewhere along the axis of the first will be oriented parallel to the first, whereas a second dipole somewhere in the plane perpendicular to the axis will tend to be oriented antiparallel to the first. Thus in a long thin rod the atoms of one section when magnetized will tend to produce a like magnetization everywhere in the rod, whereas in a plate magnetization at one point will tend to prevent like magnetization at other points.

In objects of intermediate shape between the rod and the plate the reduction of the applied field is less drastic. It can be shown that, for a sphere placed in a uniform field H_0, the field inside the sphere is

$$H_{sphere} = \frac{1}{1 + \chi/3} H_0 \tag{5.75}$$

and similar expressions with different numerical factors are applicable to ellipsoids. These factors are called demagnetizing factors. For ellipsoids magnetized parallel to an axis

$$H_{ellipsoid} = \frac{1}{1 + N\chi} H_0 \tag{5.76}$$

For very elongated ellipsoids, approaching long thin rods in shape, the demagnetizing factor $N = 0$. For spheres $N = \frac{1}{3}$. For greatly flattened ellipsoids, approaching flat plates, $N = 1$.

Note on Electric Fields in Dielectrics

The above discussion may also be applied to electric fields in dielectrics. In the special case of the parallel plate capacitor we have stated that, if σ_f and σ_i are the free and induced charge density on the metal plates and on the dielectric,

$$E = \frac{1}{\epsilon_0} (\sigma_f - \sigma_i)$$

$$P = \sigma_i$$

$$D = \sigma_f$$

and, consequently,

$$\epsilon_0 E = D - P$$

But the result $D = \sigma_f$ is limited to the parallel plate capacitor. In general, the displacement cannot be calculated from a knowledge of the distribution of free charge alone. We must also know the polarization. The general procedure for computing D and E inside a polarized medium may be accomplished by means of cavities. The Coulomb force in empty space, or in a cavity, can be computed from a knowledge of the distribution of all charges, free and induced. Then through choosing rod-shaped and disk-shaped cavities, and using the boundary conditions

$$E_{t\,1} = E_{t\,2}$$

$$D_{n\,1} = D_{n\,2}$$

the fields inside of a dielectric may be computed. The results of the previous discussion may be taken over directly through replacing H by E, and B by D. For ellipsoids we get

$$E_{ellipsoid} = \frac{1}{1 + Nk} E_0 \tag{5.77}$$

where E_0 is a uniform field into which the ellipsoid of susceptibility k is placed. The factor N is zero for long rods, $\frac{1}{3}$ for spheres, and 1 for transversely polarized flat plates.

The Magnetic Circuit

A useful approximate analysis of an electromagnet such as is shown in Fig. 5.3 is the following. If the gap length L_g is very small compared to the diameter of the iron, we may neglect leakage around the edges, and assume that B_g, the induction in the gap, is the same as B_i, the induction in the iron.

$$B_g = B_i \qquad (5.78)$$

From this we may conclude that if the permeability in the iron is μ_i,

$$B_i = \mu_i H_i \qquad H_i = B_i/\mu_i$$

and in the air gap

$$B_g = \mu_0 H_g \qquad H_g = B_g/\mu_0$$

or, since $B_g = B_i = \mu_i H_i$,

$$H_g = \frac{\mu_i}{\mu_0} H_i \qquad (5.79)$$

Now, as we apply Ampère's circuital law, Eq. 5.38, along a path threading all N turns carrying a current i,

$$\oint H \, ds = Ni \qquad (5.80)$$

But, if the length of the iron is L_i, the contribution of this part of the path of integration is $H_i L_i$, and the contribution of the part of the path in the gap is $H_g L_g$. Using Eq. 5.79, we get

$$H_i L_i + H_g L_g = Ni = H_i \left(L_i + \frac{\mu_i}{\mu_0} L_g \right)$$

$$= B_i \left(\frac{L_i}{\mu_i} + \frac{L_g}{\mu_0} \right) \qquad (5.81)$$

Often the permeability μ_i is so large that the first term can be neglected. Since $B_i = B_g$, we have, then

$$B_g = \frac{Ni}{L_g/\mu_0} \qquad (5.82)$$

In this expression, if the total flux in the circuit is Φ, and if the area of the core is A,

$$B_g = \Phi/A$$

$$Ni = \Phi \frac{L_g}{\mu_0 A} \qquad (5.83)$$

It is customary to call the ampere turns Ni a *magnetomotive force*, which drives the flux Φ through the air gap which has a *reluctance* $L_g/\mu_0 A$. If we had not neglected the second term in Eq. 5.81, we should have had for the reluctance of the entire magnetic circuit

$$\frac{L_g}{\mu_0 A} + \frac{L_i}{\mu_i A}$$

or the sum of the reluctance of the gap and the reluctance of the iron. In Eq. 5.83 the reluctance of the iron is neglected.

SUMMARY

A charge q moving with a velocity $\mathbf{v}$ through a magnetic field $\mathbf{B}$ experiences a force $\mathbf{F}$ given by

$$\mathbf{F} = q[\mathbf{v} \times \mathbf{B}]$$

In mks units, $\mathbf{B}$ is measured in webers/meter^2.

The force $d\mathbf{F}$ on a conductor of length ds carrying a current i in a field $\mathbf{B}$ is

$$d\mathbf{F} = [i\, ds \times \mathbf{B}]$$

The torque on a loop of N turns of area A carrying a current of i amperes in a uniform field B is

$$\boldsymbol{\tau} = [\mathbf{p}_m \times \mathbf{B}]$$

where $\mathbf{p}_m$ is the magnetic moment of the current loop,

$$p_m = NiA$$

If the current loop is viewed so that the current flows in a clockwise sense, the direction of $\mathbf{p}_m$ is away from the observer.

Moving charges produce magnetic fields. The magnetic induction $\mathbf{B}$ produced by a charge q moving with a velocity $\mathbf{v}$ at a point specified by a vector $\mathbf{r}$ is

$$\mathbf{B} = \frac{\mu_0}{4\pi} \frac{q[\mathbf{v} \times \mathbf{r}]}{r^3}$$

Since the current in a conductor consists of moving charges, the field $d\mathbf{B}$ due to an element of current $i\, ds$ is similarly given by

$$d\mathbf{B} = \frac{\mu_0}{4\pi} \frac{[i\, ds \times \mathbf{r}]}{r^3}$$

The intensity of magnetization of magnetized matter is defined as the resultant magnetic moment per unit volume $\mathbf{M}$. This is produced by circulating electric charge. The intensity of magnetization $\mathbf{M}$ is expressed in amperes per meter. The susceptibility χ is defined by the relation $\mathbf{M} = \chi\mathbf{H}$. The magnetic induction and intensity of magnetization at any point are related by the equation

$$\mathbf{B} = \mu_0(\mathbf{H} + \mathbf{M})$$

The new vector field H, the magnetic field intensity, in the special case of an infinite solenoid or of a toroid completely filled with a uniform magnetic medium, is

$$H = Ni/l$$

the number of ampere turns per unit length of the current-carrying coil. The permeability is

$$B/H = \mu = \mu_0(1 + \chi)$$

The properties of static magnetic fields are expressed by the integrals

$$\int_S B_n \, dA = 0$$

$$\oint H_t \, ds = i$$

where i is the current linked by the path of integration.
The boundary conditions satisfied by magnetic fields are

$$B_{n\,1} = B_{n\,2}$$
$$H_{t\,1} = H_{t\,2}$$

PROBLEMS

1. A narrow beam of electrons moving in the x-y plane with a velocity v crosses the x axis at an angle θ at a particular instant of time. A magnetic field of strength B_x is parallel to the x axis. (a) What time will elapse before it again crosses the x axis? (b) How far along the x axis will it go in this time?

2. A uniform magnetic field of strength $B_y = 0.005$ webers/square meter lies above and extends down to the x-y plane. A beam of electrons is injected into the region at $x = y = z = 0$ at an angle of 30° with the z axis. The y-z plane contains the path of the beam. If the beam has a velocity of 0.100 that of light, find the point in the x-y plane where the beam leaves the magnetic field.

3. An electron enters a uniform magnetic field perpendicular to the lines of B and performs circular motion with a period of 10^{-8} sec. (a) Calculate the value of B. (b) If the electron enters with a speed acquired by falling from rest through a potential difference of 3000 volts, what is the radius of the circular orbit?

4. Do Problem 3 for a proton which performs circular motion with a period of 10^{-6} sec.

5. A cloud chamber enables one to observe the tracks of charged particles. When a uniform magnetic field exists in the chamber, the tracks are curved. Suppose that tracks of 120 mm radius are observed when the field is 0.100 weber/square meter and that it is known that the particles have the same charge as an electron, and an energy of 3450 ev. What is their mass? What are the particles?

6. Two parallel plates having a potential of 500 volts are 2 mm apart. A beam of electrons of 10,000 ev energy passes between the plates. How strong a magnetic field must be applied in order for the electrons to pass?

7. A very narrow beam of electrons enters a uniform magnetic field perpendicular to its direction of motion. The beam is deviated through a semicircle of average radius 100 mm, and passes out through an exit slit which is 2 mm wide. What are the energies of the electrons which get out through the slit? $B = 50.0$ gauss.

★8. The earth's magnetic field at the equator is about 0.4 gauss. (a) What should the velocity of an electron be if it is to describe a circle around the earth at the equator? (*b*) What is its energy in electron volts? (*c*) Should it travel eastward or westward? $R = 4000$ miles $= 6.44 \times 10^6$ meters.

Note: An attempt to use classical or Newtonian mechanics leads to a velocity greater than that of light. The correct answer may be obtained by using the relativistic expressions

$$E^* = E + m_0 c^2$$

$$R = \frac{m_0 c}{eB} \sqrt{\left(\frac{E^*}{m_0 c^2}\right)^2 - 1}$$

9. A beam of protons passes through a velocity selector whose plates are 2 mm apart and have a potential difference of 1000 volts. The value of the magnetic field is 100 gauss. From the velocity selector, the beam passes into a second magnetic field perpendicular to its direction of motion, having a uniform field strength of 5220 gauss. (*a*) Find the speed of the protons that get through the velocity selector. (*b*) What is the energy of these protons? (*c*) What is the radius of the path the beam follows in the second magnetic field? (*d*) How long does it take a proton to make a complete circle?

★10. Electrons with negligible speed are emitted normally from the negative plate of a parallel plate capacitor. A potential difference V is maintained between the plates, which are a distance d apart, and a magnetic field of strength B is applied perpendicular to the electric field. Show that no electrons reach the top plate if

$$V < \frac{1}{2} \frac{e}{m} d^2 B^2$$

11. A copper bar weighing 100 grams rests horizontally on two rails 20 cm apart, and carries a current of 20 amp from one rail to the other. The coefficient of friction is 0.16. What is the least magnetic field that would cause the bar to slide, and what is its direction?

12. A uniform wire $AD = L'$ of mass m hinged at A rests lightly against a wire CB, as shown in Fig. 5.28. AD can swing in a vertical plane. The distance $AB = L$. A magnetic field is applied normal to the plane ABC. A current i passes along BC and on to A. Neglecting frictional effects, show that for equilibrium

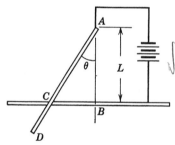

$$\sin \theta \cos^2 \theta = i L^2 B / mgL'$$

Fig. 5.28.

13. A circular loop of wire of area A, carrying a current i, is placed in a uniform magnetic field B so that the field is in the plane of the loop. Show that the torque on the loop is BiA.

14. A small box has a rectangular lid 5×7 cm which weighs 25 grams. The lid is hinged along one of the shorter edges, and has 30 turns of wire wrapped around its edges. The box is placed in a field of 500 gauss lying in the plane of the lid and perpendicular to the hinge. How much current will it take in the wire barely to lift the lid?

15. A cylinder weighing 50 grams is 10 cm long and 2 cm in diameter, and has 5 turns of wire wrapped lengthwise around the middle. The cylinder is placed on a

30° inclined plane with the plane of the loop of wire parallel to the inclined plane. A horizontal field of 250 gauss is applied. What current in the wire is necessary to keep the cylinder from rolling down the plane?

16. A uniform magnetic field of strength B is applied normal to a rigid circular loop of wire of radius a carrying a current i. Find the tension in the loop.

17. An 18,200 ev electron is moving along the x axis in the positive direction. An observer is at $x = 0$, $y = 3$ cm. What is the magnitude and direction of the magnetic field that the observer sees when the charge is at (a) -100 cm? (b) -4 cm? (c) 0? (d) 4 cm? (e) 100 cm?

18. A conductor 1 meter long carrying a current of 1.414 amp is bent into a square. What is the strength of the magnetic field B at the center?

★19. Prove that the magnetic field at the center of a coil having a square cross section, internal radius a_1, external radius a_2, and length $2b$ is

$$H = G \sqrt{\frac{W\lambda}{\rho a_1}}$$

$$G = \sqrt{\frac{2\pi}{5}} \left(\frac{\beta}{\alpha^2 - 1} \right)^{\frac{1}{2}} \ln \frac{\alpha + (\beta^2 + \alpha^2)^{\frac{1}{2}}}{1 + (\beta^2 + 1)^{\frac{1}{2}}}.$$

$\alpha = a_2/a_1$.
$\beta = b/a_1$.
ρ = resistivity of the conductor used.
λ = ratio of the volume of the conductor to the total volume of the coil.
W = power dissipated in the coil.

What is the maximum possible value of G, and for what value of α and β does it occur?

★20. A coil is constructed of slotted circular disks of conducting material having inner and outer radii a_1 and a_2, welded together at the slots to form an edgewise wound spiral. The turns are separated by thin sheets of insulation. In this coil the current density is not uniform but is inversely proportional to the radius. Prove that the field at the center of a coil so constructed will be given by a relation like that in the previous problem, except that

$$G = \frac{\pi^{\frac{1}{2}}}{5} \frac{\ln \left[\alpha \dfrac{\beta + (1 + \beta^2)^{\frac{1}{2}}}{\beta + (\alpha^2 + \beta^2)^{\frac{1}{2}}} \right]}{(\beta \ln \alpha)^{\frac{1}{2}}}$$

What is the maximum value of G, and for what values of α and β does it occur?

21. Find the force per unit length between two long parallel wires 1 meter apart carrying equal but oppositely directed currents of 10 amp each.

22. Two long straight parallel wires carry equal but oppositely directed currents. The wires are separated by a distance $2d$, and each carries a current i. Find an expression for B at any point in the plane containing the wires.

23. Find B due to two long parallel conductors separated by a distance $2d$ and carrying equal currents in opposite directions at any point of a plane normal to and bisecting a line joining the two wires. Where is B a maximum?

24. A long copper bar 2 cm in diameter carries a current of 5000 amp, distributed uniformly throughout its cross section. Find an expression for the field B at points inside and outside the bar.

25. A toroid with a square cross section, height L_1, inside radius r_1, outside radius r_2, is uniformly wound with N turns carrying a current i. The core is made of wood.

(a) What are the values of B at the inside and outside edges of the core? (b) What is the total flux through the windings?

26. A sheet of magnet steel far from other magnets or currents is permanently magnetized with $M = 10^4$ amperes/meter at right angles to the plane of the sheet. What are the values of B and H within the sheet, and just outside the sheet?

27. A small sphere of iron having a susceptibility of 10^3 is placed at the center of a circular coil of 10 turns of wire having a radius of 12 cm, and carrying a current of 400 ma. (a) What are the values of B, H, and M within the sphere? (b) What would be the values of B, H, and M if the iron was in the shape of a long thin needle in the direction of the field of the coil? (c) What would be the values of B, H, and M if the iron were in the shape of a thin disk whose axis is parallel to the field of the coil?

28. The M.I.T. cyclotron magnet has the following specifications. Length of air gap $5\frac{1}{2}$ in. Length of flux path in the iron 18 ft. Diameter of cylindrical section of iron carrying the flux 50 in. The poles are slightly tapered so that the diameter of the poles at the gap is 42 in. The susceptibility of the iron when the flux density is about 1 weber/meter^2 is 5400. The coils on each pole have 1000 turns. What current is needed to produce a field in the gap of 10,000 gauss, or 1 weber/meter^2?

29. What is the force between two parallel dipoles a distance d apart if the dipoles are (a) parallel, and (b) perpendicular, to the line joining them?

30. The pole pieces of a magnet having a cylindrical core of radius r_2 are cut so as to form cones having a common apex and angle ϕ. The points are now cut away to leave flat circular pole faces of radius r_1. (a) If the iron is everywhere magnetized to saturation parallel to the axis, how great is the field on the axis midway between the poles? (b) For what value of ϕ has the field its maximum value?

CHAPTER 6

Induced Electromotive
Force and Inductance

6.1 INDUCED ELECTROMOTIVE FORCE

In Chapter 5 we studied the force acting on free charges in conductors when at right angles to the length of the conductor. The force acting on the charges could not move them through a circuit. The force was transferred to the conductor itself, and the result was a *mechanical*

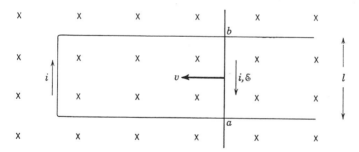

FIG. 6.1. A special case of a circuit in which the flux linkage is changing.

force at right angles to the motion of the charges along the length of the conductor. If, however, the electromagnetic force

$$\mathbf{F} = q[\mathbf{v} \times \mathbf{B}] \tag{6.1}$$

has a component in a direction in which a current can flow, for example, along the length of a wire, it will act to produce a current. It manifests itself as an *induced electromotive force*.

The particular example which we shall use to demonstrate the generation of an induced emf is illustrated in Fig. 6.1. We have here an electric circuit composed of a fixed U-shaped conductor in a magnetic field, the field being at right angles to the plane of the conducting loop. Across the sides of the conductor is a metallic bar, moving with a velocity v in the direction shown. All the charges in this bar experience an electromagnetic force, but it is of consequence only for free, or movable, charges. All the charges fixed in the metal bar are specified to be moving to the left with a velocity v. The free electrons, however, experience an upward force F which is equivalent to a downward electrical field $\mathbf{E}$.

$$\mathbf{E} = \mathbf{F}/q = [\mathbf{v} \times \mathbf{B}] \qquad (6.2)$$

This equivalent or hypothetical electric field can be used to drive a current i around the circuit. The junctions a and b will have the properties of the terminals of a battery. Current will flow out of the positive terminal at a around the circuit to the negative terminal at b. There must be a voltage difference V_{ab} to drive the current through the external circuit, which we shall assume to have a resistance R. The work done by the force F in moving a charge from b to a must be the potential difference V_{ab}. If the resistance of the bar is negligible so that there is no ir drop along it, we have

$$V_{ab} = \mathcal{E} = El = |l[\mathbf{v} \times \mathbf{B}]| \qquad (6.3)$$

The current through the resistance R may now be computed by Ohm's law. The mechanical force which pushes the bar does the work which eventually shows up as heat in the resistor. To see this, we notice that, if a current is produced by the induced emf, a force ilB acts to retard the motion and must be balanced by an equal and opposite mechanical force, namely, the driving force, if the motion is to be maintained. The power supplied by the driving force is Fv or $iB\,(lv)$, which, according to Eq. 6.3, is $i\mathcal{E}$, or just the electrical energy supplied by the induced emf to the circuit.

The result, Eq. 6.3, may be put into a particularly useful form for discussing closed circuits when we notice that moving the crossbar along the fixed U-shaped conductor in Fig. 6.1 changes the flux linkage, or the total number of lines of induction Φ which thread the circuit. Actually any change in flux linkage, whether produced by a change of field strength, or by moving a conductor, produces an electromotive force. In the case illustrated in Fig. 6.1, we have for the rate of increase of the area of the circuit as the bar ab moves to the left

$$dA/dt = -lv$$

and, since the flux linkage Φ is BA, we have

$$\frac{d\Phi}{dt} = B\frac{dA}{dt} = -Blv$$

or, from Eq. 6.3,

$$\mathcal{E} = -d\Phi/dt \qquad (6.4)$$

The electromotive force induced in our single-turn circuit is equal to minus the rate of increase of flux. The minus sign may be taken to mean that the direction of the induced emf is such that the current it produces will diminish that actual rate of change of flux linkage. Thus, in Fig. 6.1, Φ is decreasing, and the induced emf would send a clockwise current around the circuit which would add to the existing flux down into the paper and so retard the overall diminution.

The law expressed in Eq. 6.4 is found to be generally true. If for any reason the flux linking a circuit changes, there is an induced emf proportional to the rate of change of flux linkage. If instead of one turn we have N turns connected in series, then the total induced emf is the sum of the emf induced in the separate turns, or if the coil is in the form of a loop in which the same flux links all the turns

$$\mathcal{E} = -N\frac{d\Phi}{dt} \qquad \blacktriangleright(6.5)\blacktriangleleft$$

This important result is called *Faraday's law of induction.*

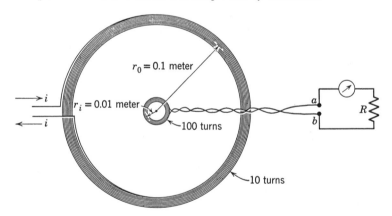

Fig. 6.2.   Two coils arranged to show induced emf.

Inductively Coupled Circuits

As an example of an induced emf in a conductor at rest in a changing field we shall discuss the experiment shown in Fig. 6.2. A 60-cycle alternating current having an amplitude of 10 amp is sent through the large coil. The field at the center of a circular coil of this kind is

$$B = \mu_0\frac{Ni}{2r_0} \qquad (6.6)$$

For the example above, we get

$$B = \frac{4\pi \times 10^{-7} \times 10 \times 10 \sin 377t}{2 \times 10^{-1}}$$

$$= 6.28 \times 10^{-4} \sin 377t \text{ webers/meter}^2$$

The total flux linking the small central coil at any instant is $B \times A = B \times \pi r_i^2$. For the example above, we get

$$\Phi = 6.28 \times 10^{-4} \times \pi \times (10^{-2})^2 \sin 377t \qquad (6.7)$$

$$= 1.96 \times 10^{-7} \sin 377t$$

The induced emf in the inner coil shows up as a voltage.

$$V_{ab} = -N \frac{d\Phi}{dt} = -10^2 \times 377 \times 1.96 \times 10^{-7} \cos 377t$$

$$= -7.4 \times 10^{-3} \cos 377t \text{ volts} \qquad (6.8)$$

Notice that this is the induced emf appearing across the terminals of the coil only if no current is drawn, because only in this case is the total flux linkage given by Eq. 6.7. If there is a current through the inner coil of sufficient magnitude so that the flux which it produces is comparable to the flux produced by the outer coil, then V_{ab} is no longer given by Eq. 6.8. However, for a very large resistance R, the current may be so small that such effects may be neglected. We would then have

$$i = V_{ab}/R$$

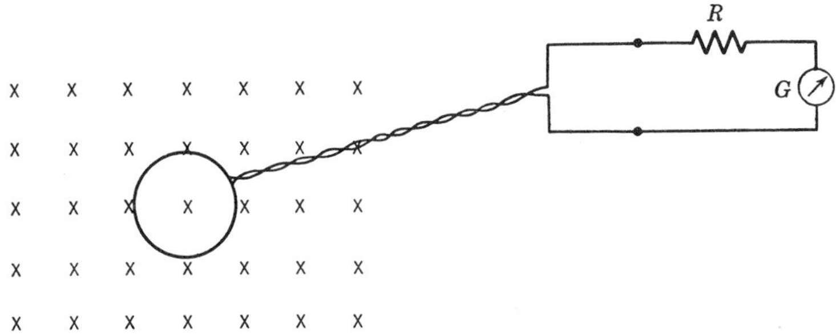

Fig. 6.3.   The ballistic measurement of the strength of a magnetic field.

The Inductive Measurement of Magnetic Fields

As an example of an induced emf in a moving conductor we shall describe the measurement of the strength of a magnetic field by means of the arrangement shown in Fig. 6.3.   A coil of wire having N turns and enclosing an area A is placed in a magnetic field with its axis parallel to the field.   The coil is connected to a ballistic galvanometer.   The resistance of the entire circuit is R. The flux linkage through the coil is now changed, either through removing the coil from the field or through rotating the coil about a diameter.   An emf is induced in the circuit, and a current $i = \mathcal{E}/R$ is generated.   The magnitude of the current depends on the rate of change of flux linkage.   Suppose, now, that the coil is pulled out from the field or turned very abruptly so that the process is completed in a fraction of a second. The current i will flow for only a short time, and a quantity of charge

$$Q = \int i \, dt$$

will be sent through the galvanometer. The resultant deflection will be a measure of Q if the process is completed before the instrument deflects appreciably, as discussed in Section 1.5. The total charge sent through the galvanometer can be computed.

$$i = \frac{\mathscr{E}}{R} = -\frac{N}{R}\frac{d\Phi}{dt}$$

$$Q = \int i \, dt = -\frac{N}{R}\int \frac{d\Phi}{dt}\, dt = -\frac{N}{R}\int d\Phi = -\frac{N}{R}(\Phi_1 - \Phi_0)$$

where Φ_1 and Φ_0 are the flux linkages at the beginning and end of the abrupt change. If the final flux linkage is zero, then

$$Q = -\frac{N}{R}\Phi_1 = -\frac{N}{R}\frac{\Phi_1}{A}A = -\frac{NAB}{R} \tag{6.9}$$

$$B = QR/NA$$

The deflection of the galvanometer is therefore a measure of the initially present field strength.

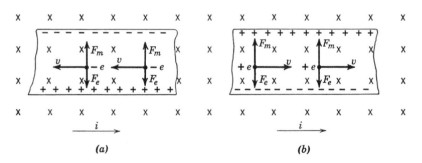

FIG. 6.4. The Hall effect.

The Hall Effect

The magnetic force on charges moving through a magnetic field has one further important application that we shall review here. That is in connection with the Hall effect, discovered in 1879. An electric current in a wire or ribbon consists of moving charges. Under steady conditions, the motion of the charges must be along the length of the conductor. The Hall effect deals with the situation brought about by placing such a conductor with its length at right angles to a magnetic field, as shown in Fig. 6.4a. The current is assumed to be due to the motion of a few negatively charged electrons. In the illustration, the current is to the right and the negative conduction electrons therefore move to the left. The magnetic field, directed into the paper, exerts a magnetic force F_m toward the top of the page on the moving charges. When the current is started, the path of the electrons will be bent upward and negative charge will accumulate on the upper edge of the ribbon until a downward electric force F_e, just balancing the magnetic force F_m, prevents a further accumulation of charge on the edge. The current will then have reached a steady condition and will flow along the length of the conductor. There will, however, be a potential difference between points opposite each other on the two edges of the ribbon. The negatively charged upper edge will be at a lower potential than the positively charged lower edge. This potential difference, which is proportional to the field B, vanishes when $B = 0$, and changes its sign when the direction of B is reversed, constitutes the Hall effect. When, under the conditions shown in Fig. 6.4a, the upper edge is negative, we have what is called a "normal" Hall effect due to the motion of negative charges.

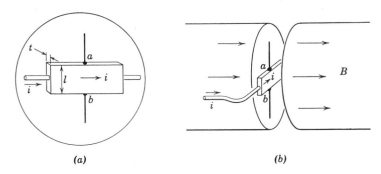

(a)   (b)

FIG. 6.5.   An experimental arrangement for measuring the Hall emf.

In some metals we find, however, that with the same directions of current and field, the upper edge is positively charged, as in Fig. 6.4b. This phenomenon is called the "anomalous" Hall effect and can be explained if we assume that the current is due to the motion of positive, rather than negative charges. If, as in Fig. 6.4b, the current is to the right, and is due to positive charges also moving to the right, the magnetic force due to a field into the paper will be again upward, but the balancing electric force will now be due to an accumulation of positive charges on the upper edge of the ribbon, and the upper edge will be at a higher potential than the lower edge.

The existence of currents apparently due to the motion of positive charges has already been discussed in connection with semiconductors in Section 3.4. We have here an experimental means for distinguishing currents due to a few conduction electrons and currents due to a few holes or vacant places among the conduction or free electrons in a metal.

So much for the qualitative aspects of the experiment. A quantitative discussion, however, adds greatly to our understanding of the significance of the results obtained. To be more definite, we consider that a strip of metal of width l and thickness t is placed between the poles of a magnet, as shown in Fig. 6.5. A current i is passed through the strip, and the difference in potential between two points a and b along a line perpendicular to the current is observed with a potentiometer. When no magnetic field is applied, $V_{ab} = 0$, as the points are on an equipotential. When a field is present, however, a difference in potential proportional to B appears. This is the Hall emf, $\mathcal{E}_{Hall}$. It is simply the emf induced when charges are moved at right angles to the field. Here, instead of moving the entire conductor with a velocity v as in Fig. 6.1, we are moving the electrons only with their drift velocity v_{dr}. The induced emf is given in Eq. 6.3.

$$\mathcal{E}_{Hall} = l v_{dr} B \qquad (6.10)$$

But the drift velocity may be calculated in terms of the current and the number of electrons per unit volume n.

$$i = n e v_{dr} A = n e v_{dr} (l \cdot t) \qquad (6.11)$$

Solving for the drift velocity, we get

$$v_{dr} = \frac{i}{nelt}$$

and substituting into Eq. 6.10,

$$\mathcal{E}_{Hall} = \frac{iB}{net}$$

This may be written

$$\mathcal{E}_{Hall} = C_H \frac{iB}{t} \qquad (6.12)$$

stating that the Hall emf is proportional to the current and the magnetic field, and inversely proportional to the thickness of the sample. These aspects of the experiment are borne out in fact. The Hall coefficient, C_H, which is measured in an experiment, is, according to our analysis,

$$C_H = 1/ne$$

$$n = 1/C_H e \qquad (6.13)$$

From observations of the Hall effect, we can deduce the number of free electrons per unit volume in the metals investigated. Some experimental results are shown in Table 6.1. In the last column the number of atoms per cubic

TABLE 6.1

Substance		C_{Hall}	$n_e = \dfrac{1}{C_{Hall} e}$	n_{atoms}
Cu	Copper	-6×10^{-11}	1.1×10^{29}	0.9×10^{29}
Ag	Silver	-9	0.7	0.6
Au	Gold	-7	0.9	0.6
Li	Lithium	-15	0.4	0.5
Na	Sodium	-25	0.2	0.3
Fe	Iron	$+100$	0.06	0.8
Co	Cobalt	$+25$	0.2	0.9
Ni	Nickel	-60	0.1	0.9
Bi	Bismuth	-500	0.01	0.3

meter as computed from the density and atomic weight are given for comparison with the number of electrons per cubic meter as computed from the Hall effect. The three good conductors, copper, silver, and gold, appear to have slightly more than one free electron per atom. This result seems to be in contradiction to what has been said about conducting processes in metals. To explain it requires a more detailed investigation of the conduction process in these metals, taking into account first of all the fact that the drift velocity is not the same for all electrons. However, even on the basis of our rather oversimplified assumptions, we may conclude that in these metals the number of free electrons is roughly equal to the number of atoms. For lithium and sodium, we have somewhat less than one electron per atom, and for iron, nickel, cobalt, and bismuth, which have higher resistivities, we have markedly fewer electrons than atoms.

Diamagnetism

The same force which produces a momentary current in a loop of wire when the flux is changed, as in Fig. 6.3, must produce some effect on the charges circulating around atoms. An impulsive torque is exerted on the charges. This torque must generate an angular momentum, and this angular momentum of charges in motion must generate a magnetic moment. We have

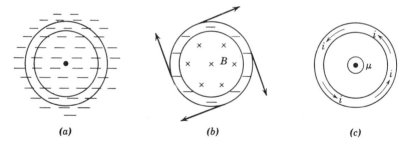

(a)   *(b)*   *(c)*

Fig. 6.6. The origin of diamagnetism.

here an induced magnetization. A magnetic moment is induced in atoms by the application of a field regardless of any permanent magnetic moment which the atom may have. Moreover, the direction of this induced moment is not in the direction of the applied field but in the opposite direction, as is illustrated in Fig. 6.6. In Fig. 6.6a we have the cross section of an atom, consisting of a nucleus surrounded by a cloud of negative charge, which may or may not be in motion. We select a ring of this charge and examine the forces acting on it when a field is applied. From the laws of induction it follows that the force on the negative electrons produces a clockwise torque if the field is down into the paper as in Fig. 6.6b. This will produce a counterclockwise current, as in c, and therefore a magnetic moment up out of the paper, opposite to the applied field. The diamagnetic moment induced in an atom by the application of a field is antiparallel to the field. If no permanent moment is present, the only moment will be the induced moment. The substance is then diamagnetic and is not attracted to, but repelled from, the high field near the poles of an electromagnet. In paramagnetic substances which have a permanent dipole moment, this overshadows the induced diamagnetic effect, which is, however, always present.

We can estimate the magnitude of the induced diamagnetic moment. Increasing the flux linking the ring of radius r in Fig. 6.6 produces an emf around the ring

$$\mathcal{E} = -\frac{d\Phi}{dt} = -\pi r^2 \frac{dB}{dt} \qquad (6.14)$$

This electromotive force is equivalent to a tangential electric field E given by

$$E \cdot 2\pi r = \mathcal{E} \qquad (6.15)$$

The torque T exerted by the field E on the charge Q within the ring is

$$T = E \cdot Q \cdot r = -\frac{\pi r^2}{2\pi r} \frac{dB}{dt} Q \cdot r$$

and the impulse of the torque resulting from the application of the field B is

$$\int T \, dt = \frac{r^2 Q}{2} \int \frac{dB}{dt} \, dt = -\frac{r^2 Q}{2} B \qquad (6.16)$$

The impulse of the torque is equal to the total change in angular momentum, or, if the mass of the charge contained in the ring is M, and this is given an angular velocity ω, we must have

$$Mr^2 \omega = -\frac{r^2 Q}{2} B$$

$$\omega = -\frac{Q}{2M} B$$

But the ratio of charge to mass in the ring must be the same as for the electron or

$$\omega_L = \frac{e}{2m} B \qquad \blacktriangleright (6.17) \blacktriangleleft$$

This angular velocity is written ω_L, as it is called the *Larmor* angular velocity. All the rings of charge around the nucleus rotate with this same frequence. We shall study this in greater detail in connection with the precession of atoms with intrinsic angular momentum in a later chapter.

From Eq. 6.17 we can compute the induced magnetic moment. Since the entire atom precesses with this same angular velocity, we have for any one electron an induced magnetic moment

$$p_1 = iA = \left(-\frac{\omega_L}{2\pi} e\right) \pi \overline{r^2} = -\frac{\omega_L e}{2} \overline{r^2}$$

where $\overline{r^2}$ is the average value of r^2 for the electron in question. For the Z electrons we get a diamagnetic moment ω_L, using Eq. (6.17),

$$p_d = -\frac{Ze^2}{4m} \overline{r^2} \mu_0 H \qquad (6.18)$$

and finally, for the susceptibility of a diamagnetic substance containing n

atoms per unit volume,

$$\chi_d = -\frac{\mu_0 Z e^2}{4m} \overline{r^2} n \tag{6.19}$$

where $\overline{r^2}$ is to be evaluated for all the electrons in the entire atom. Until we know more about the distribution of charge in the atom we cannot evaluate $\overline{r^2}$. For light atoms for which $Z = 1$–10 we may assume that

$$\overline{r^2} \simeq \overline{r^2} \simeq 10^{-20} \text{ meter}^2$$

The induced magnetic moment in a fairly strong field of 1 weber/meter² will then be

$$p_d \simeq -\tfrac{5}{4}\, 1.6 \times 10^{-19} \times 1.76 \times 10^{11} \times 10^{-20} \text{ amp-meter}^2$$
$$- 3.5 \times 10^{-28} \text{ amp-meter}^2 \tag{6.20}$$

which is very much smaller than the permanent moment

$$p_m \simeq 10^{-23} \text{ amp-m}^2$$

found in Section 5.6.

6.2 MAXWELL'S EQUATIONS

We must finally put the equations defining the properties of static electric and magnetic fields into a form applicable to time-dependent as well as constant fields. The complete equations are

(a)
$$\oint E_t \, ds = -\int_S \dot{B}_n \, dA$$

(b)
$$\oint H_t \, ds = \int_S (j_n + \dot{D}_n) \, dA$$

$\blacktriangleright(6.21)\blacktriangleleft$

(c)
$$\int_S D_n \, dA = \sum q$$

(d)
$$\int_S B_n \, dA = 0$$

In these equations the dot above a letter indicates differentiation with respect to time. Thus

$$\dot{B}_n \equiv \frac{dB_n}{dt}$$

Notice first of all that the magnetic and electric equations are no longer separate, as they are for static fields in which $\dot{D} = \dot{B} = 0$. A changing magnetic field implies the existence of an electric field. A changing electric field implies the existence of a magnetic field.

In a and b, the surface S over which the integration on the right side of the equations extends is any surface bounded by the contour around which the line integral on the left side of the equations is to be evaluated.

Here j is the conduction current density, so that $\int_S j_n \, dA$ is the conduction current flowing through the contour, and $\int_S \dot{D}_n \, dA$ is the displacement current flowing through the contour. In Eq. 6.21c and d the surface S is any closed surface, and $\sum q$ is the sum of all the charges within this Gaussian surface.

Equation 6.21a says that the total work done in carrying unit charge once around any closed path is not zero, as it is in the electrostatic case, but is equal to the time rate of change of the normal component of B, integrated over any surface S bounded by the closed path. Equation 6.21a. when applied to a circuit, may be interpreted as defining the new induced emf. The integral

$$\oint E_t \, ds$$

of the tangential component of the electric field around a circuit is the work done on 1 coulomb in going once around the circuit or, in other words, its emf. The time derivative on the right of Eq. 6.21a may be taken outside of the integral sign, so that we have

$$\int_S \dot{B}_n \, dA = \frac{d}{dt} \int_S B_n \, dA$$

Since the integral of the normal component of B over a surface is the total number of lines of flux Φ threading it, we have

$$\oint E_t \, ds = -\frac{d\Phi}{dt} \tag{6.22}$$

or Faraday's law of induction, Eq. 6.5, for a circuit having one turn.

Equation 6.21b is modified in a way similar to Eq. 6.21a. The contour integral of H is equal not to the conduction current only linked by the contour but to this plus the displacement current. A changing electric field in an insulating medium must be regarded as an electric current which produces a magnetic field. The need for such a concept is illustrated by a battery charging a capacitor, as shown below in Fig. 6.7. The contour around which Eq. 6.21b is evaluated is shown as the edge of two different surfaces. Surface S_2 is exclusively in a region where no electric fields, and therefore no displacement currents, exist, but it is pierced by the conductor and the contour may therefore be said to link the current i. Equation 6.21b therefore yields

$$\oint H_t \, ds = i$$

But if an equation like Eq. 6.21b is generally applicable, it must yield the same result regardless of the choice of S. In the form shown, it does. Consider surface S_1. No conduction current pierces this surface, so that we must have

$$\oint H_t \, ds = \int_{S_1} \dot{D}_n \, dA$$

Since the left-hand member is the same for both surfaces, we must show that the right-hand member above is equal to the conduction

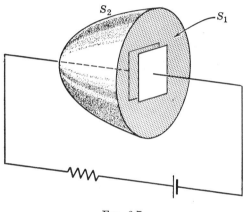

FIG. 6.7.

current i. But we have already shown in Section 3.6 that the displacement current defined by

$$\int_{S_1} \dot{D}_n \, dA$$

as in Fig. 6.7, is equal to the charging current to the capacitor. We now have a new reason for introducing the displacement current. It is needed to account for the magnetic fields in space where D is changing with time. The magnetic field between the plates of the capacitor could not be completely described by conduction currents alone. The displacement current, too, must be taken into account.

Equations 6.21 are called Maxwell's equations in integral form. They describe the properties of electromagnetic fields and form the basis for our understanding of electromagnetic radiation.

6.3 INDUCTANCE

We now apply the ideas involving induced emf's to circuits. Here coils of wire are of especial importance because the magnetic field in the vicinity of N closely spaced conductors carrying a current is N times that of a single wire carrying the same current. Coils are called inductors, or often simply inductances, and paired coils are called mutual inductances. The conventional graphic symbols for inductors are shown in Fig. 6.8. Elements so designated in a diagram are assumed to be resistanceless. The resistance of an inductor is generally shown as a separate resistor. The importance of self-inductance L and mutual inductance M is that, when the currents in coils change,

FIG. 6.8.

emf's are induced, and these of course must be taken into account in considering the properties of the circuits of which they are a part.

The simplest case to consider is that in which the only field to be considered around a circuit element is that produced by the current through the circuit element itself. In this case we may assume that the flux linking the coil is proportional to the current through the coil.

$$\Phi \propto i$$

But since the induced emf is proportional to $-d\Phi/dt$, it must also be proportional to $-di/dt$. We have then

$$\mathcal{E} = -L\frac{di}{dt} \qquad (6.23)$$

The proportionality constant L is called the self-inductance of the coil. In the mks system, the unit of inductance is the henry, which has the dimensions of ohm-seconds. Equation 6.23 may be taken as defining the inductance of a coil. It is an experimental definition. If in a coil to be considered as a pure inductance there is a changing current, there must necessarily appear a voltage difference across the terminals of the coil. Conversely, if an emf is applied to the terminals, there must necessarily be a changing current such that the ratio of the emf to the rate of change of the current is

$$L = -\frac{\mathcal{E}}{di/dt} \qquad \blacktriangleright(6.24)\blacktriangleleft$$

A general statement about the direction of the induced emf is contained in *Lenz's law*. A common statement of this law is: *The direction of an induced emf is such as to oppose the change producing it.* Thus, for

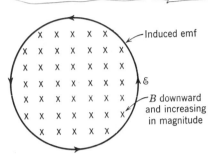

FIG. 6.9. The direction of an induced emf in a changing magnetic field.

example, in the circuit shown in Fig. 6.1, when the motion of the bar was such as to reduce the flux through the loop, the induced emf was in such a direction as to generate a current which would increase the flux linkage. Similarly, when we are dealing with induced diamagnetic currents in atoms, or in a single loop of wire such as is shown in Fig. 6.9, an increasing downward flux produces an emf in such a direction that any current which it produces will be directed upward and so retard the rate of increase of flux which produced the emf.

An alternative, and possibly simpler, rule to follow in determining the direction of an induced emf and the sign of the resulting potential differences involves energy considerations. Just as we found that stored electrical energy was associated with a charged capacitor, so also we

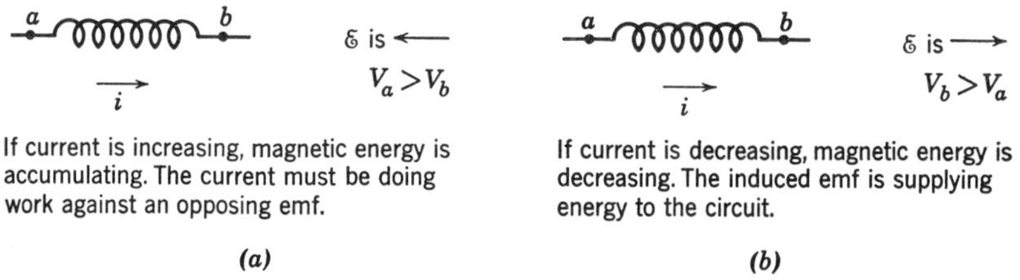

$\overset{a}{\bullet}\!-\!\text{0000000}\!-\!\overset{b}{\bullet}$ $\mathcal{E}$ is $\longleftarrow$

$\overset{\longrightarrow}{i}$ $V_a > V_b$

If current is increasing, magnetic energy is accumulating. The current must be doing work against an opposing emf.

(a)

$\overset{a}{\bullet}\!-\!\text{0000000}\!-\!\overset{b}{\bullet}$ $\mathcal{E}$ is $\longrightarrow$

$\overset{\longrightarrow}{i}$ $V_b > V_a$

If current is decreasing, magnetic energy is decreasing. The induced emf is supplying energy to the circuit.

(b)

FIG. 6.10. Potential difference between terminals of inductors.

shall find that magnetic energy is associated with the fields surrounding coils carrying currents. We shall discuss these energy relations in detail in the next section. Here we require only the knowledge that, as the current in a coil increases, the stored energy also increases. Similarly, as the current decreases, the stored energy also decreases. If a current flows in the direction of the emf, the energy of the source decreases. Conversely, if the current through a source is opposite to its emf, then the energy of the source is increasing. These statements are applied to an inductor in Fig. 6.10. In each case the induced emf is such as to oppose the change of current which produces it. If the current is increasing, the induced emf acts to decrease the current. If the current is decreasing, the induced emf acts to increase the current. Notice also that, as previously discussed for batteries, the terminal from which the emf would send a current into the circuit is at the higher potential.

The experimental definition of self-inductance, Eq. 6.24, which enables us to measure L, may be supplemented by its equivalent which would enable us to calculate the self-inductance of a coil, if we know its shape and the magnetic properties of the core. If the total flux through one turn of a coil when i amp are flowing through it is Φ, and if there are N turns each with the same flux linkage, then we may put

$$N\Phi = \text{constant} \times i$$

If we differentiate with respect to the time, we get

$$N\frac{d\Phi}{dt} = -\mathcal{E} = \text{constant} \cdot \frac{di}{dt}$$

But the constant has already been defined as the self-inductance. We therefore have

$$L = N\Phi/i \qquad (6.25)$$

if the flux Φ links all N turns. If this condition is not fulfilled, a correction must be made. The self-inductance of a coil is then the total flux linkage per unit current.

Mutual inductances may be treated similarly. If we have two coils so arranged that current through the first will produce flux that links the second, then a changing current in the first will produce an emf in the second. The mutual inductance M is now defined so that the emf induced in circuit 2 through varying the current in circuit 1 is

$$\mathcal{E}_2 = -M\frac{di_1}{dt} \qquad (6.26)$$

It turns out that, if we had varied the current in circuit 2, keeping that in circuit 1 constant, we should have found for the emf induced in the first circuit

$$\mathcal{E}_1 = -M\frac{di_2}{dt} \qquad (6.27)$$

We shall prove this reciprocity in the next section. We see, therefore, that the following reciprocal relationship is satisfied

$$M = -\frac{\mathcal{E}_2}{di_1/dt} = -\frac{\mathcal{E}_1}{di_2/dt} \qquad \blacktriangleright(6.28)\blacktriangleleft$$

Mutual inductance, like self-inductance, is measured in henrys. The above equation may be regarded as an experimentally applicable definition of self-inductance, just as Eq. 6.24 is an experimentally applicable definition of self-inductance.

Just as we showed that the self-inductance of a coil could be expressed in terms of flux linkage per unit current, a similar argument may be applied to mutual inductances. If $\Phi_{2\,1}$ is the flux linking N_2 turns of circuit 2 when unit current flows in circuit 1,

$$M = \frac{N_2 \Phi_{2\,1}}{i_1} \tag{6.29}$$

In view of the reciprocity relations, the mutual inductance may equally well be written

$$M = \frac{N_1 \Phi_{1\,2}}{i_2}$$

Example of the Calculation of Self-Inductance

To illustrate the application of these results, we compute the inductance of conductors in two special shapes. In order to compute the self-inductance of a solenoid sufficiently long so that we may neglect end effects, we make use of Eq. 6.25. In the central region, at least, we may put for the total flux in the solenoid

$$\Phi = BA = \mu H A = \mu \frac{Ni}{l} A$$

and since

$$L = N\Phi/i$$

we have

$$L = \mu \frac{N^2 A}{l} \text{ henrys} \tag{6.30}$$

under the assumption that all of the flux links every turn.

Inasmuch as the fields produced by even the simplest coils are so difficult to compute, we may expect the same to be true of their inductance. Almost the only other case that can be expressed in simple terms is that of the coaxial cable. As this is of considerable importance to our later considerations, we shall derive the expression for the inductance per unit length, L', of such a cable. The quantities used in the argument are shown in Fig. 6.11, which is a cross-sectional view of the cable. To avoid discussion of the field inside a solid wire carrying a current, we shall assume the cable to be made up of two thin coaxial cylinders of radius R_1 and R_2, respectively. We shall assume that the currents in the two cylinders are flowing in opposite directions, as they would be if the cylinders are used to carry current from a power source to a load and back again.

The fields in the various parts of the cable may be calculated, as was done in the last chapter, by the application of Eq. 6.21b.

$$\oint H_t \, ds = i + \int_S \dot{D} \, dA$$

Since we are dealing with steady fields, the last term drops out and we have

$$H \cdot 2\pi r = \text{linked current}$$

Both inside the inner cylinder and outside the outer cylinder this expression vanishes, since there is no resultant current linkage. Between the cylinders the field is

$$H = i/2\pi r$$

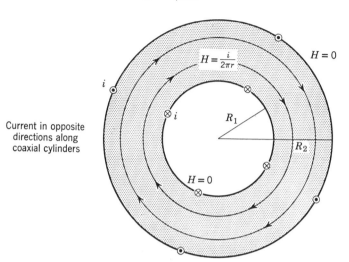

Current in opposite directions along coaxial cylinders

FIG. 6.11. Cross section of a coaxial cable.

The total flux linking the current i in the inner conductor is

$$\Phi = \int_{R_1}^{R_2} l \cdot dr \cdot B = l \int_{R_1}^{R_2} dr \mu_0 \frac{i}{2\pi r} = \frac{\mu_0 l i}{2\pi} \ln \frac{R_2}{R_1}$$

from which the expression for the inductance per unit length follows directly, namely,

$$L' = \frac{\mu_0}{2\pi} \ln \frac{R_2}{R_1} \tag{6.31}$$

For comparison, the expression for the capacitance of coaxial cylinders C' per unit length is

$$\frac{1}{C'} = \frac{1}{2\pi\mu} \ln \frac{R_2}{R_1} \tag{6.32}$$

6.4 MAGNETIC ENERGY

The entire subject of inductive effects is so important and so full of subtleties that we shall discuss it once more from a completely different point of view. Instead of basing the discussion on forces acting on charges moving through a magnetic field, we shall base it on considerations of electromagnetic energy. The two points of view are of course quite equivalent. They lead to the same results.

Perhaps a challenging point of departure is to ask why electrons, which we have considered as particles of charge e and mass m moving down a conductor, have such very different properties from water molecules moving down a pipe. Why, in particular, has the coiling of the conductor into spirals such a profound effect on the observed flow? In a water pipe the force required to put the water into motion is little affected by the shape of the pipe, whether it be laid out in a long straight line or coiled up. The work we have to do to get electrons moving in a wire is very different in the two cases because of the back, or induced, emf, which is much greater when the wire is coiled up than when it is stretched out in a straight line. If we think of these electrons as mass points it is hard to see why this difference exists. It arises, however, from the electromagnetic nature of the electron. We may think of one electron as a particle of charge e and mass m. A collection of such electrons, however, acquires new properties.

We have seen that electrostatic potential energy may be treated as if it were distributed in the electric field with a density

$$u_e = \tfrac{1}{2}ED \qquad (6.33)$$

We now propose to continue the analogy between electric and magnetic fields, and to assume a magnetic energy density in magnetic fields

$$u_m = \tfrac{1}{2}HB \qquad (6.34)$$

This is an assumption whose justification depends on the correctness of its predictions. These predictions, it turns out, are both striking and correct. We shall now take up the essential point in the matter.

Briefly, and in words, before attempting a mathematical description, we begin with the actual origin of magnetic fields, namely, electric charges in motion. The kinetic energy of electrons in motion may be thought of as $\tfrac{1}{2}mv^2$. But, since charges in motion produce magnetic fields, and since we are to associate energy with every point in space where a field exists, we must take into account an expression of the form

$$U_m = \int_{-\infty}^{+\infty} \int_{-\infty}^{+\infty} \int_{-\infty}^{+\infty} \tfrac{1}{2}HB \, dx \, dy \, dz \qquad (6.35)$$

It turns out that these two expressions for the kinetic and magnetic energies of motion are essentially alike for single electrons. It may be that they are two descriptions of one and the same quantity. But for groups of electrons they predict very different results. The form of Eq. 6.35 turns out to be a much more complete description of facts about electric charges. It is to a considerable extent because of certain properties of this description of the motional energy of electrons that the behavior of the electric fluid in wires is so very different from that of water in pipes.

We have all the information we need to evaluate Eq. 6.35, the magnetic energy of an electron due to its motion. We assume for the sake of simplicity that the electron may be treated like a charged sphere of radius R. An element of volume in spherical coordinates may be written

$$dx \, dy \, dz = 2\pi (r \sin \theta) \cdot dr \cdot r \, d\theta \tag{6.36}$$

Substituting this into Eq. 6.35, and integrating over all space outside of the electron, we get, using Eq. 5.18 for the field of a moving charge,

$$U_m = \tfrac{1}{2}\mu_0 \int_R^\infty \int_0^\pi H^2 2\pi r^2 \, dr \sin \theta \, d\theta$$

$$= \frac{1}{2} \frac{\mu_0}{8\pi} e^2 v^2 \int_R^\infty \frac{dr}{r^2} \int_0^\pi \sin^3 \theta \, d\theta$$

$$= \frac{1}{2} \frac{\mu_0}{8\pi} e^2 v^2 \frac{1}{R} \frac{4}{3} = \frac{1}{2} \left[\frac{2}{3} \frac{e^2}{4\pi\epsilon_0 R} (\epsilon_0 \mu_0) \right] v^2 \tag{6.37}$$

This is a most interesting and important result which we must analyze in some detail. Notice first of all that a part of this expression is reminiscent of the *electrostatic* energy of a charged sphere. The electrostatic energy may be found through integrating the energy density $u = \tfrac{1}{2}\epsilon_0 E^2$ over all space, or simply from the expression for the energy of a charged capacitor

$$U_e = \tfrac{1}{2} Q V_{ab} = \frac{1}{2} e \cdot \frac{1}{4\pi\epsilon_0} \frac{e}{R} = \frac{1}{2} \frac{1}{4\pi\epsilon_0} \frac{e^2}{R}$$

Next we must anticipate a result to be discussed in more detail further on when we come to the propagation of electromagnetic waves. We shall find that the velocity of light $c = 1/\sqrt{\epsilon_0 \mu_0}$. For the moment we may confine our attention to the magnitude and dimensions of $\epsilon_0 \mu_0$. We have

$$\epsilon_0 \mu_0 = 8.85 \times 10^{-12} \frac{\text{coulomb}^2}{\text{n-m}^2} \times 12.56 \times 10^{-7} \frac{\text{n-sec}^2}{\text{coulomb}^2}$$

$$= 11 \times 10^{-18} \frac{\text{sec}^2}{\text{meter}^2}$$

or

$$\frac{1}{\sqrt{\epsilon_0 \mu_0}} = 3 \times 10^8 \frac{\text{meter}}{\text{sec}} = c \tag{6.38}$$

We have thus

$$\frac{1}{2} \frac{e^2}{4\pi\epsilon_0 R} \epsilon_0 \mu_0 = \frac{U}{c^2}$$

which, according to the theory of relativity, is equivalent to a mass. This we call the *electromagnetic mass* of the electron. If we had chosen a volume rather than a surface distribution of charge, we should have had a similar expression with a different numerical factor. Thus the factor $\frac{2}{3}$ instead of $\frac{1}{2}$ in Eq. 6.37 might be thought of as having some significant meaning concerning the inner structure of the electron. This subject was pursued at length some decades ago, and the fact that the rest mass of the electron could be identified with the electromagnetic mass if a reasonable value were used for the radius seemed encouraging. If we put

$$m_0 = m_{em} = \frac{1}{2} \frac{e^2}{4\pi\epsilon_0 R} \frac{1}{c^2} \qquad (6.39)$$

$$R = \frac{1}{2} \frac{e^2}{4\pi\epsilon_0} \frac{1}{m_0 c^2}$$

we get, on substituting for the known constants on the right hand side of the equation,

$$R \simeq 1.5 \times 10^{-15} \text{ meter}$$

This is satisfying in that it is much smaller than the atom. It has been shown, however, that the assumption that all the mass of the electron is of electromagnetic origin is not correct. The electron is not so simply constituted as this. There is, however, every justification for saying that the electromagnetic mass contributes an important part of the total.

We see, then, that the magnetic energy of the electron specified in Eq. 6.37 may be written

$$U_m \simeq \tfrac{1}{2} m_0 v^2$$

and the magnetic field contributes an important part of the kinetic energy.

This result may be extended to the range of relativistic effects. If we consider velocities approaching that of light, we find that motion not only produces a magnetic field but also modifies the electric field. The electric field due to a charge in motion is not determined by the position of the charge at the instant of measurement but by its position at a previous time. Coulomb's law of force is therefore to be modified for charges in motion. If the correct expressions for the electric and magnetic fields are taken into account, the total energy of the electron turns out to be the relativistic expression found in Section 5.2

$$\frac{m_0 c^2}{\sqrt{1 - (v/c)^2}}$$

For velocities small compared to the velocity of light, this reduces to the above expressions. It seems most likely that the mass of the electron is largely of electromagnetic origin.

A further and perhaps even more important point about this analysis appears if we consider not one but several electrons. It follows from Eq. 6.39. If we were to squeeze N electrons into the space of a single one, the electromagnetic mass would be proportional not to the number of electrons, but to the square of the number of electrons, because the total charge, which appears as a square, is now Ne. Further, if we do not squeeze them into so small a sphere, the resultant mass, according to Eq. 6.35, will depend on how they were actually arranged. In electric circuits we have to deal with the energy and momentum of many electrons packed closely together in a metal. On the basis of the above remarks we might expect that the kinetic energy and motional inertia due to their magnetic fields are much greater than we should estimate from their individual rest masses alone. This is actually the case. Only when we are concerned with individual electrons in a vacuum is the rest mass m_0 of an electron a significant quantity.

To make these remarks more concrete, let us consider the magnetic field outside a wire as the sum of all the fields due to the individual electrons moving in parallel directions in the wire. Altogether some very large number of electrons will be involved, say n. The total field will then be

$$H = H_1 + H_2 + H_3 \cdots n \text{ terms}$$

The energy density will then be of the form

$$u_m = \frac{\mu_0}{2} H^2 = \frac{\mu_0}{2} [H_1{}^2 + H_2{}^2 + H_3{}^2 + \cdots n \text{ terms } +$$

$$H_1(H_2 + H_3 + H_4 + \cdots n - 1 \text{ terms}) +$$
$$H_2(H_1 + H_3 + H_4 + \cdots n - 1 \text{ terms}) +$$
$$H_3(H_1 + H_2 + H_4 + \cdots n - 1 \text{ terms}) +$$

$$
\begin{array}{ccc}
\cdot & \cdot & \cdot \\
\cdot & \cdot & \cdot \\
\cdot & \cdot & \cdot
\end{array}
$$

There are n such sums of products.

It is clear that the $n(n - 1)$ cross products may far outweigh in importance the n terms due to the individual electrons. The energy density and also the total energy of the system are far greater than the sum of the contributions of individual electrons.

Since we know how to calculate the field of a single electron in motion, we can, in principle at least, calculate the resultant field due to the motion of all the electrons in a conductor carrying a current simply by adding vectorially the fields due to each. By integrating $\frac{1}{2}BH$ over all space we can then evaluate the magnetic energy due to the current flowing in a circuit. Since B and H are each proportional to the generating current, the result for the magnetic energy due to the current in any one circuit will be found proportional to the square of the current flowing in that circuit, or

$$U_m = \frac{1}{2}Li^2 \qquad (6.40)$$

The coefficient L in this equation is characteristic of a particular circuit. It is, as we shall see, the self-inductance of the circuit. Comparing Eqs. 6.40 and 6.35 we have

$$L = \frac{\mu}{i^2} \int H^2 \, dv \qquad (6.41)$$

where the integration is to be extended over all space.

In the above paragraph we have spoken of a single current in a single circuit. For a single endless path around which the current can flow, with no branch points, the definitions are unambiguous. If we have to deal with more than one path in which the currents can be varied independently, the considerations advanced must be modified. We shall consider only the case of two completely separate circuits so placed with respect to each other that their respective fields overlap. At any one point we have for the energy density

$$u_m = \frac{\mu}{2}(H_1 + H_2)^2 = \frac{\mu}{2}(H_1{}^2 + kH_1H_2 + H_2{}^2) \qquad (6.42)$$

where H_1 and H_2 are the fields due to the currents in circuits 1 and 2, respectively. The constant k in the middle term is, according to the rules of vector multiplication, twice the cosine of the angle between H_1 and H_2. The three terms in Eq. 6.42 when integrated, will be proportional to $i_1{}^2$, i_1i_2, and $i_2{}^2$, respectively. The total magnetic energy due to the fields of the two circuits may be written

$$U_m = \frac{1}{2}L_1i_1{}^2 + Mi_1i_2 + \frac{1}{2}L_2i_2{}^2 \qquad (6.43)$$

If the circuits are sufficiently far apart for their fields not to overlap, the total magnetic energy may be computed from the currents in, and the coefficients of self-inductance of, the separate circuits. If, however, their fields overlap, as for instance in the case of two circuits containing windings which, though metallically unconnected, are wound on the same spool so that the magnetic fields overlap, a term containing the product of the two currents will be involved. The coefficient M is the mutual inductance of the two circuits and may be calculated by comparing Eq. 6.42 integrated over all space with Eq. 6.43. We have

$$U_m = \int u_m \, dv = \frac{\mu}{2} \int (H_1{}^2 + kH_1H_2 + H_2{}^2) \, dv$$

$$= \tfrac{1}{2}Li_1{}^2 + Mi_1i_2 + \tfrac{1}{2}Li_2{}^2$$

or

$$M = \frac{\mu k}{2i_1i_2} \int H_1H_2 \, dv \tag{6.44}$$

More useful equivalent means of calculating L and M for particular circuits have been given in the previous section.

Since we can specify the energy of a circuit as a function of its self-inductance and current, we can also specify the rate at which energy must flow into the field when the current is increasing. The rate of transfer of energy to the field in watts must be, according to Eq. 6.40,

$$\frac{dU_m}{dt} = Li \frac{di}{dt} = \left(L \frac{di}{dt}\right) i \tag{6.45}$$

This may be thought of as an induced emf, being charged by the current i. If this source of emf is gaining energy, the charging current must be opposed to the emf, or

$$\mathcal{E} = -L \frac{di}{dt} \tag{6.46}$$

in agreement with our previous considerations.

A similar argument may be applied to coupled circuits. If, in the circuits described by Eq. 6.43, we vary i_1, keeping i_2 constant, emf's will be set up in both circuits, the emf in circuit 1 being determined by its self-inductance, and the emf in the second circuit by the mutual inductance. Differentiating Eq. 6.43 and keeping i_2 constant, we have

$$\frac{dU_m}{dt} = Li_1 \frac{di_1}{dt} + Mi_2 \frac{di_1}{dt}$$

and for the emf induced in circuit 2 by varying the current in circuit 1

$$\mathcal{E}_2 = -M \frac{di_1}{dt} \tag{6.47}$$

in agreement with previous considerations leading to Eq. 6.26. The further result, that

$$\mathscr{E}_1 = -M \frac{di_2}{dt} \tag{6.48}$$

follows at once from Eq. 6.43, for if we vary the current in circuit 2, the induced emf in circuit 1 is that given in Eq. 6.48. The previously stated reciprocity is thereby established.

6.5   TIME CONSTANTS AND REACTANCE

We shall now review some of the properties of inductors in electric circuits. The discussion will be closely parallel to that concerning circuits with capacitance and resistance in Sections 4.2 and 4.3, which should be reviewed. We here take up circuits containing inductance

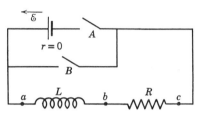

FIG. 6.12. A circuit containing inductance and resistance.

and resistance and leave to the next chapter the phenomena that are found in circuits with both capacitance and inductance.

The circuit to be discussed is shown in Fig. 6.12. We first consider the effect of closing switch A, thereby putting the battery in series with the inductor and resistor. At the instant of closing the switch, there is no current in the circuit, the voltage drop across the resistor is therefore zero, but there is a voltage drop across the inductor given by $L(di/dt)$. This must be equal to the emf of the battery. As soon as the current begins to flow, a voltage begins to appear across the resistor. There is then a smaller drop across the inductor, and the rate of change of current is therefore reduced. Very evidently we may expect a gradual and diminishing increase of current with time. The final equilibrium value of the current will be determined by the resistance R and the emf of the battery. In the end the complete emf of the battery will be across the resistor. There will be no voltage drop across the inductor, because di/dt will be zero. In analogy with previous results, we might expect the current to be given by the following expression,

$$i = I_0(1 - e^{-t/\tau}) \tag{6.49}$$

$$I_0 = \mathscr{E}/R$$

The only unknown in the above expression is the magnitude of the time constant τ appearing in the exponent. We know that it must be some function of L and R. But since the dimensions of L are ohm-seconds (henrys), we might well make a guess that

$$\tau = L/R \text{ sec} \qquad (6.50)$$

It remains now to show that these expectations are in fact correct. To solve the problem mathematically we must set up the circuit equation

$$\mathcal{E} = V_{ac} = V_{ab} + V_{bc} \qquad (6.51)$$

and make use of the properties of the individual circuit elements,

$$V_{ab} = L \frac{di}{dt} \qquad (6.52)$$

$$V_{bc} = iR$$

We wish to find a solution of Eq. 6.51 with the substitutions of Eq. 6.52,

$$\mathcal{E} = L \frac{di}{dt} + iR \qquad (6.53)$$

subject to the condition that, at the instant of closing the switch A, that is, at $t = 0$, $i = 0$. But the proposed solution, Eq. 6.49, satisfies the initial condition and, with the value of Eq. 6.50 for the time constant, also satisfies the differential equation. It is therefore the solution sought.

If now the switch B is closed, so that the voltage drop across the circuit becomes zero, we have

$$0 = V_{ab} + V_{bc}$$

and therefore

$$L \frac{di}{dt} = -iR \qquad (6.54)$$

The solution of this equation satisfying the condition that, at the instant of closing switch B, that is, for $t = 0$, the current through the circuit shall have the value I_0 is

$$i = I_0 e^{-t/\tau} \qquad (6.55)$$

where the time constant has the same value, Eq. 6.50, as in the previous case. The current starts off at its equilibrium value I_0 and decays exponentially to zero.

Let us now consider an alternating potential applied to a pure inductance. We have

$$V_{ab} = V_0 \sin 2\pi f t = L \frac{di}{dt} \qquad (6.56)$$

This equation is satisfied by

$$i = -I_0 \cos 2\pi ft$$

$$I_0 = \frac{V_0}{2\pi fL} = \frac{V_0}{X_L} \qquad (6.57)$$

The correctness of the above may be verified by substitution. The quantity

$$X_L = 2\pi fL \qquad \blacktriangleright(6.58)\blacktriangleleft$$

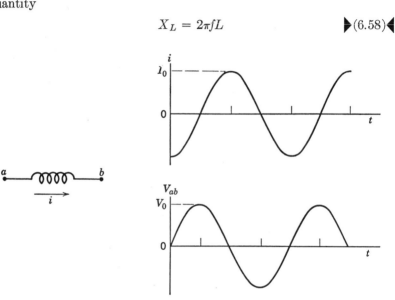

FIG. 6.13.   Voltage and current in an inductor.

is called the *inductive reactance*. Note that it is a function of the frequency, and that it has the dimension of volts per ampere, or ohms. If we divide both sides of Eq. 6.57 by $\sqrt{2}$, we get

$$V = IX_L \qquad (6.59)$$

The rms value of the current flowing through an inductor multiplied by the inductive reactance equals the rms value of the potential difference across the inductor in just the same way that the rms value of the current in a resistor multiplied by its resistance equals the rms value of the potential difference applied to the resistor.   The relationship between current and voltage in an inductor, as given by Eqs. 6.59 and 6.60, is shown in Fig. 6.13.   Notice that in the inductor the voltage reaches a positive maximum a quarter of a cycle before the current, and that consequently the voltage may be said to lead the current by 90°.

This should be contrasted with a capacitor, in which the voltage lags 90° behind the current.

We now consider the vector impedance diagram of a circuit containing inductance and resistance, as in Fig. 6.14. The same current flows through both circuit elements. We shall describe it by

$$i = I_0 \sin 2\pi ft$$

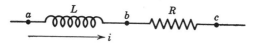

FIG. 6.14. Inductance and resistance in series.

The voltage across the resistor is in phase with the current, and its amplitude is I_0R,

$$V_{bc} = I_0R \sin 2\pi ft$$

The voltage across the inductor is

$$V_{ab} = L\frac{di}{dt} = I_0 2\pi fL \cos 2\pi ft = I_0X_L \cos 2\pi ft$$

Combining these two expressions, we have for the voltage across the two circuit elements in series

$$V_{ac} = I_0R \sin 2\pi ft + I_0X_L \cos 2\pi ft \qquad (6.60)$$

As in the discussion of a capacitance and resistance in series, we must now show that this sum can be put into the form

$$V_{ac} = V_0 \sin (2\pi ft + \phi) \qquad (6.61)$$

Again, using the relation

$$\sin (\alpha + \beta) = \sin \alpha \cos \beta + \cos \alpha \sin \beta$$

We may write the expression of Eq. 6.60

$$V_{ac} = V_0 \cos \phi \sin 2\pi ft + V_0 \sin \phi \cos 2\pi ft \qquad (6.62)$$

If we put

$$V_0 = I_0Z \qquad (6.63)$$

where Z is again the *impedance* of the circuit, Eq. 6.62 becomes identical with Eq. 6.60 if

$$V_0 \cos \phi = I_0Z \cos \phi = I_0R$$

or

$$\cos \phi = R/Z$$

and
$$V_0 \sin \phi = I_0 Z \sin \phi = I_0 X_L$$
or
$$\sin \phi = X_L / Z \qquad \qquad \blacktriangleright(6.64)\blacktriangleleft$$

Also, since $\sin^2 \phi + \cos^2 \phi = 1$,
$$Z = \sqrt{R^2 + X_L{}^2} \qquad \qquad \blacktriangleright(6.65)\blacktriangleleft$$

Notice that in this circuit the phase angle ϕ is positive, whereas in the circuit containing resistance and capacitance it was negative. In the inductive circuit, the voltage leads the current. The vector impedance diagram is shown in Fig. 6.15. According to our previously adopted convention, ϕ is positive when Z lies above R, as drawn.

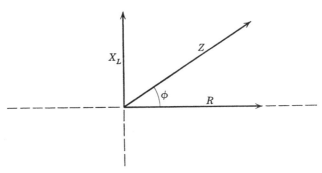

FIG. 6.15. Vector impedance diagram for a circuit containing inductance and resistance.

Notice that, whereas high capacitance and high frequency were associated with a low capacitive reactance, the situation in inductors is quite different. Since $X_L = 2\pi f L$, a high frequency and a high inductance are associated with a high inductive reactance.

Energy is dissipated as heat only in the resistor. We have
$$W = I^2 R$$

and, if this is to be expressed in terms of the current and the voltage applied to the circuit,
$$W = IV \cos \phi \qquad \qquad (6.66)$$

where once again $\cos \phi$ is called the *power factor*.

6.6 SOME APPLICATIONS OF INDUCTIVE FORCES

Motors and Generators

Figure 6.16 is a schematic representation of a rectangular coil having a single turn, in a magnetic field. The coil is mounted on a shaft at right angles to the field. In a the coil is assumed at rest and has a current i supplied by an external source of emf circulating through it. In b, the coil is assumed to be rotating about a diameter perpendicular to the field and its terminals are connected through a resistance R.

In Fig. 6.16a the current flowing around the coil gives rise to a torque

$$\tau_m = iAB \sin \theta \tag{6.67}$$

where A is the area of the coil. The sense of the torque is such as to reduce the angle θ as shown in Fig. 6.16a. This torque can be used to convert electrical

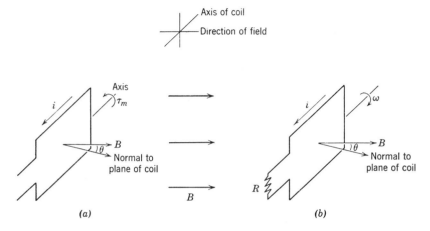

FIG. 6.16.   A coil rotating in a magnetic field.

energy into mechanical energy. The device has the first elements of a simple electric motor. The torque τ_m does mechanical work on a shaft by maintaining a rotation.

In case b the total flux linking the coil is

$$\Phi = BA \cos \theta$$

and, if the coil is rotating with an angular velocity $\omega = d\theta/dt$, the rate of change of flux linkage with the coil and the induced emf is

$$\mathscr{E} = - \, d\Phi/dt = +BA\omega \sin \omega t \tag{6.68}$$

If the terminals of the coil are now connected through a resistor R shown in the illustration a current will flow "in such a direction as to oppose the cause producing it." This cause, under the circumstances shown in the figure, is a decreasing flux linkage. At $\theta = 0$ the linkage is a maximum, and rotation away from this point involves a decrease in flux linkage. The induced emf, and therefore also the current which it induces, will be in such a direction as to increase the flux through the coil, or in the direction shown in the figure. The current through the resistor will be a periodic function of the time. Its frequency will be that of the rotating shaft, or $\omega/2\pi$. This arrangement is an a-c generator, or dynamo. By the introduction of a commutator, the alternating current may be rectified, as shown in Fig. 6.17. In a the terminals of the coil in Fig. 6.16 are connected to brushes which deliver the current to the rings a and b. The resulting voltage is alternating. In part b of the figure the rings are split and connected as shown. Every time the voltage reaches zero, the connections are reversed. The resultant voltage V_{cd} is rectified. For the

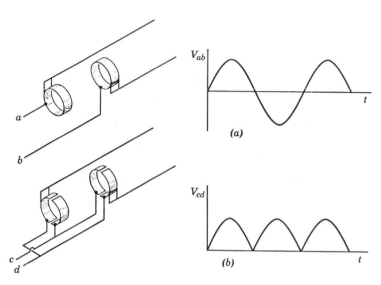

FIG. 6.17. (*a*) Slip rings attached to the terminals of the loop in Fig. 6.16 to produce alternating current. (*b*) A commutator instead of slip rings to produce rectified alternating current.

device to act as a motor, as shown in Fig. 6.16*a*, a commutator must be provided so that the torque due to the current always acts in the same direction. To illustrate the action of motors and generators in more detail we shall take up the geometrically simpler Faraday disk generator. The conclusions reached are quite generally applicable.

Faraday's Disk Generator

As an example of the application of the induced electromotive force in a moving conductor, we consider Faraday's disk generator, illustrated in Fig. 6.18. This consists of a metallic disk rotating about its axis, the axis being parallel to a magnetic field. Sliding contacts at two points of the disk, namely, at the center and at the outer radius R, may be used to conduct currents to an external circuit. Let us first consider the emf induced in a small element of the path between the center and the outer circumference. This is, from Eq. 6.3,

$$d\mathscr{E} = B \, drv = B\omega r \, dr$$

The total emf may be found through integration. It is

$$\mathscr{E} = \int d\mathscr{E} = B\omega \int_0^R r \, dr = \frac{B\omega R^2}{2} \tag{6.69}$$

The emf's produced by such an apparatus are relatively low. For example, a disk 20 cm in diameter rotating at 600 rpm in a field of 1 weber/meter^2 will generate an emf of only about

$$\mathcal{E} = \frac{1 \times 60 \times 10^{-2}}{2} \simeq 0.3 \text{ volt}$$

Although this emf is very low, it should be pointed out that the internal resistance of such a generator may also be very low, so that it is capable of delivering large currents. The power delivered by such a generator is $\mathcal{E}i$.

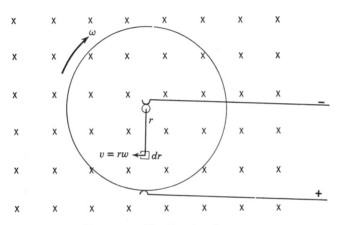

FIG. 6.18.   The Faraday dynamo.

This must be equal to the work done by the forces producing the rotation. If T is the torque applied to the shaft, the power P supplied is

$$P = T\omega \tag{6.70}$$

To prove that this is just $\mathcal{E}i$, we compute the torque dT exerted on an element of current $i\,dr$. This torque is transmitted to the disk by the electrons as a result of collisions with the lattice, or by electrostatic forces, as in the Hall effect.

$$dT = B(i\,dr) \cdot r$$

$$T = \int_0^R dT = iB \int_0^R r\,dr = \frac{iBR^2}{2} = \frac{i\mathcal{E}}{\omega}$$

or, on substituting into Eq. 6.70,

$$P = T\omega = i\mathcal{E} \tag{6.71}$$

In a generator voltage may be produced without doing work if no current is drawn. A current through the moving parts, however, gives rise to new forces, and these must be overcome to supply electrical energy to a circuit connected to a generator.

A generator may be used as a motor if an external source of emf drives a current through the rotating part, or rotor. In Fig. 6.18, if a current flows from the outer rim to the center by any path, a torque $T = iBR^2/2$ will be exerted on the disk. If the motor is not connected to a load, the torque will accelerate the disk. The moving disk will then have induced in it a back emf. The acceleration of the disk will go on until the back emf is equal to the applied emf. There will then be no current and no acceleration. If the motor is made to do work, for example by applying a brake, the speed will be reduced, the back emf will be reduced, and a current will be supplied by the external source of emf. This current will automatically adjust itself so that the work done by the external source of emf, $\mathcal{E}i$, is just equal to the work done by the motor, $T\omega$.

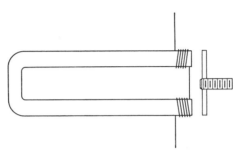

Fig. 6.19.   A microphone.

Microphones

A special kind of generator is a magnetic microphone such as is shown in Fig. 6.19. Its essential parts are a magnet and near its poles a ferromagnetic diaphragm. Sound waves striking this diaphragm alter the distance between poles and diaphragm because of the varying air pressure. When the diaphragm is near the poles, more flux crosses the gap to the microphone than when it is farther away. This fact produces an alternating flux linkage which produces an induced emf, and so a current may be generated having the same periodic structure as the impinging sound wave.

In this instance also, the generator may be used as a motor. If the current from one microphone is sent through another, the pole strengths near the coils will vary periodically and the diaphragm will be set into vibration. This vibration will in turn generate sound waves in the air.

The microphones used in telephones are not made in this way. The change of resistance of carbon granules under pressure is made to vary a current supplied by the line. The energy of the sound wave is thus not transformed into electrical energy, as in the magnetic case, but is merely used to vary the current and power from an independent source.

Transformers

A transformer is a device for changing the voltage at which electric power is delivered. This can be done only with alternating current. The operation of a transformer is illustrated in the following simple case, shown in Fig. 6.20. A primary winding, assumed as resistanceless, in which a current i_p is flowing, is wound on the same iron core as the secondary winding. For the moment we shall assume the secondary circuit open. $R = \infty$ so that $i_s = 0$. The number of turns in the primary and secondary windings is N_p and N_s, respectively. We assume that all the flux goes around the iron core and that there is no leakage. We also assume that no currents are induced in the iron itself. The magnetization is then determined by i_p alone. The induced emf across the terminals of the primary will be, according to Faraday's law,

$$\mathcal{E}_p = -N_p \frac{d\Phi}{dt} \tag{6.72}$$

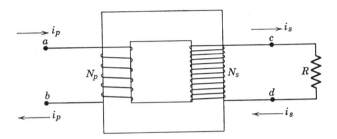

Fig. 6.20. A transformer.

If all the flux linking the primary also links the secondary, there must be an emf across its terminal

$$\mathcal{E}_s = -N_s \frac{d\Phi}{dt} \tag{6.73}$$

or, dividing Eq. 6.72 by Eq. 6.73, we have

$$\mathcal{E}_p/\mathcal{E}_s = N_p/N_s = V_{ab}/V_{cd} \tag{6.74}$$

The voltages across the primary and secondary are directly proportional to the number of turns in the two windings. If there are more turns in the secondary than in the primary, the secondary voltage is higher and the transformer is called a step-up transformer. If the number of turns in the secondary is smaller, the transformer is called a step-down transformer. The current in the primary is given by the applied voltage and the reactance of the primary $X_p = 2\pi f L_p$. If V_0 is the amplitude of the applied voltage i_{p0} the current drawn when the secondary is open-circuited will be

$$i_{p0} = \frac{V_0}{X_p} \sin 2\pi ft = \frac{V_0}{2\pi f L_p} \sin 2\pi ft \tag{6.75}$$

if the voltage is

$$V_{ab} = V_0 \cos 2\pi ft \tag{6.76}$$

The voltage leads the current by 90°. The primary voltage does no work. If, now, we drop the restriction that $i_s = 0$, we can still draw the following conclusions. Since all the flux still links both windings, the primary and secondary induced voltage must be in phase and

$$V_{cd} = \frac{N_s}{N_p} V_{ab}$$

Further, since the secondary is connected to a resistive load, we must have

$$i_s = \frac{V_{cd}}{R} = \frac{N_s}{N_p} \frac{V_{ab}}{R} \tag{6.77}$$

It remains to compute the primary current. This we can determine by noticing that the flux in the core must always be such that

$$V_{ab} = N_p \frac{d\Phi}{dt} \tag{6.78}$$

in order that the law of induction be satisfied. This flux may be written in terms of the current i_{p0} in the primary when the secondary is open. The magnetomotive force acting on the flux in the iron is then $N_p i_{p0}$, and, if R is the reluctance, we must have

$$\Phi = \frac{N_p i_{p0}}{R} \tag{6.79}$$

When the secondary draws a current i_s, the primary current will not be i_{p0} but some new current i_p. The total flux through the iron is now determined by the combined magnetomotive force of primary and secondary currents.

$$\Phi = \frac{N_p i_p - N_s i_s}{R} \tag{6.80}$$

Whether a minus or a plus sign is chosen above depends on what we define as a positive current in the secondary. If we take the current shown as positive, we must use a negative sign in Eq. 6.80 because it opposes the magnetomotive force of the primary. But Eq. 6.79 and Eq. 6.80 must be equal, since, in both cases, they must satisfy Eq. 6.78. We therefore have

$$i_p = i_{p0} + \frac{N_s}{N_p} i_s \tag{6.81}$$

Here the currents are the instantaneous values. If we use Eq. 6.75 for i_{p0} and Eq. 6.77 for i_s, we get

$$i_p = \frac{V_0}{X_p} \sin 2\pi ft + \frac{N_s}{N_p} \frac{V_0}{R} \cos 2\pi ft \tag{6.82}$$

Eddy Currents

We have so far spoken primarily of currents induced by changing magnetic fields along the length of conductors. When metals in bulk are introduced into changing magnetic fields, currents are induced in them in whirls. These currents generate heat and so contribute to energy dissipation. As an example, consider the iron core coil shown in Fig. 6.21. When the current in the coil varies, induced currents are set up around the square core shown in a. By reducing the area available for setting up induced currents, as in b, using a laminated core, the energy loss due to eddy currents is reduced. (See Problem 28 for further discussion of this point.)

Eddy currents in a metal moving in a magnetic field may be used to damp its motion. In the rotating disk shown in Fig. 6.22, the eddy currents set up by the motion of the disk in the locally applied magnetic field dissipate energy and so damp the motion of the disk.

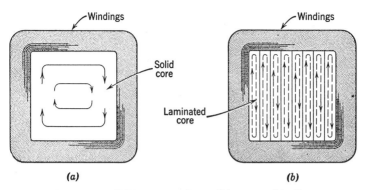

FIG. 6.21.   Eddy currents in a solid core, and in the laminated core of an a-c winding.

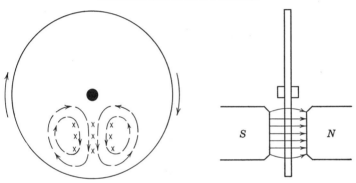

FIG. 6.22.   Eddy current damping of a metal disk.

Choke Coils

An inductance has a high impedance for high frequencies.   Inductances may consequently be used to "choke" high frequency currents.   For example, the circuit shown in Fig. 6.23 will produce full-wave rectification.   The center-tap mutual inductance provides a convenient source of emf for use as previously discussed in connection with Fig. 4.28.   If V_{ab} may be approximated as $V_c + V_0 \sin 2\pi f t$ volts, then the direct current through inductor and resistor will be V_c/R amp, and the full constant component V_c will appear between the terminals c and d.   The a-c impedance will be

$$Z = \sqrt{R^2 + (2\pi f L)^2}$$

The amplitude of the current will therefore be

$$I_0 = \frac{V_0}{Z} \text{ amp}$$

and the a-c voltage amplitude across the terminals cd has been reduced from V_0 to

$$I_0 R = V_0 R/Z$$

If $R = 1000$ ohms, $L = 2$ henrys, $f = 1000$, then $x_L = 2\pi f L = 1.26 \times 10^4$ ohms, $Z = 1.265 \times 10^4$ ohms, and the factor by which the amplitude of the alternating voltage is reduced is 0.079.

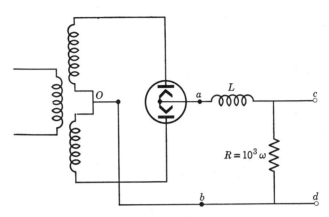

FIG. 6.23.   A full-wave rectifier with choke filter.

SUMMARY

An induced emf will appear in a circuit in which the magnetic flux linkage is changing.   If $\Phi = \displaystyle\int_S B_n \, dA$ is the total flux linking a coil of N turns which bounds the surface S, then the induced emf is

$$\mathcal{E} = -N \frac{d\Phi}{dt}$$

Lenz's law states that the direction of the induced emf is such as to oppose the change producing it.

A magnetic field may be considered to have energy stored in it.   Per unit volume, this is $\frac{1}{2}HB$.   The total magnetic energy of a circuit is

$$U_m = \int \tfrac{1}{2}HB \, dv = \tfrac{1}{2}Li^2$$

where L is the coefficient of self-inductance,

$$L = -\frac{\mathcal{E}}{di/dt} = \frac{N\Phi}{i}$$

If the fields of two circuits overlap, a term Mi_1i_2 must be added to the energy expression, where the mutual inductance M between the two circuits is

$$M = -\frac{\mathcal{E}_2}{di_1/dt} = -\frac{\mathcal{E}_1}{di_2/dt} = \frac{N_2\Phi_{2\,1}}{i_1} = N_1\frac{\Phi_{1\,2}}{i_2}$$

The fundamental properties of time-dependent electric and magnetic fields are expressed by the relations

$$\oint E_t \, ds = -\int_S \dot{B}_n \, dA \qquad \int_S D_n \, dA = \Sigma q$$

$$\oint H_t \, ds = i + \int_S \dot{D}_n \, dA \qquad \int_S B_n \, dA = 0$$

In a pure inductance the amplitudes and rms values of voltage and current are related by the expressions $I = V/X_L$, $I_0 = V_0/X_L$, $X_L = 2\pi f L$.

In an inductor the current lags behind the voltage by 90°. The time constant of an LR circuit is L/R.

PROBLEMS

1. Refer to Fig. 6.1 of the text. If the moving conductor has a resistance of 10 ohms, and if the stationary conductor has no resistance, find the force on the moving conductor necessary to maintain a velocity of 1 meter/sec. $B = 100$ gauss, $l = 5$ cm. Neglect the decrease in field produced by the flow of current in the conductors.

2. A 5-turn rectangular coil 2 × 5 cm is rotated at 5000 rpm in a uniform magnetic field of 250 gauss. What is the induced emf in the coil?

3. A stiff wire conductor 1 meter long is rotated about one end with an angular velocity of 2 radians/sec in a uniform magnetic field of 100 gauss. What is the potential difference developed between the two ends of the wire?

4. Two circular coils, each having a radius of 1 cm, are mounted on a common axis a distance of 1 meter apart. Coil A has 10 turns of wire; coil B has 100 turns of wire. (a) A 2-amp 60-cycle current is passed through coil A. What will be the voltage across the open terminals of B? (b) The 2-amp 60-cycle current is now passed through coil B. What will be the voltage across the open terminals of A?

5. The torque acting on the coil of a galvanometer is proportional to the current through the coil, and also proportional to the deflection

$$\tau = ki = K\theta$$

The current sensitivity of a particular instrument, k/K in radians of steady deflection per ampere, is known from experiment. The period T of the instrument when it swings freely on open circuit is also known from experiment. The constant K is related to the moment of inertia I of the suspension and to the period T. We have

$$\tau = I \frac{d^2\theta}{dt^2} = -K\theta$$

and if $\theta = \theta_0 \sin 2\pi t/T$, then we must have, as can be verified by differentiation,

$$T = 2\pi \sqrt{I/K}$$

This galvanometer, which has a long period and may be used ballistically, is now connected to a coil of N turns having an area A. The total resistance of galvanometer plus coil plus leads is R. Show that, if the coil with its axis parallel to a field B is suddenly withdrawn from the field, the deflection in millimeters of a spot of light reflected from the galvanometer mirror on a scale at a distance of 1 meter is

$$d = \frac{4\pi(k/K)NBA \times 10^{-3}}{RT}$$

6. In an experiment on the Hall effect, both a longitudinal and a transverse electrlic field are present. The equipotentials, which are at right angles to the resultant field, are not parallel to the current. Derive an expression for the angle between the normal to the equipotential surfaces and the current.

★7. Prove that the Hall coefficient may be expressed as the product of the resistivity of the material being used and the mobility of the free charges. Compare the mobility of electrons in a metal with that of electrons in a gas discharge.

★8. Copper wire almost always contains traces of iron. If the wire is heated to a high temperature and suddenly quenched by being dipped into a cold liquid, the iron is retained in solution. It is atomically dispersed. In this state each iron atom retains its permanent magnetic moment which is $p_m \simeq 10^{-23}$ amp-meter^2 Eq. 5.61, and the total effect of the iron atoms is to contribute a paramagnetism such as is discussed in Section 5.6. (a) What percent of iron in solution would decrease the diamagnetic susceptibility of copper $\chi = -1.1 \times 10^{-6}$ by 10%?

If the copper wire is now cold-worked, by further drawing or hammering, the iron is precipitated. If this is in the form of elongated needles in the direction of the wire axis, and if the susceptibility of the wire is measured in a longitudinal field, the magnetization curve would consist of a steeply rising part in low fields, the ferromagnetic iron being saturated before the copper is appreciably magnetized. In larger fields the copper would become diamagnetically magnetized. (b) How much iron would have to be precipitated out of solution to make the resultant magnetization zero in a field of 1 weber/meter^2? Draw a magnetization curve of the specimen for condition b, assuming a negligible amount of iron in solution.

★9. For certain "nuclear magnetic resonance" experiments to be described further on it is necessary to know the magnetic field at an atomic nucleus with great accuracy. Because of diamagnetic effects, the field at the center of a diamagnetic atom is not quite equal to the applied field. Estimate this diamagnetic shielding in an atom of radius R containing a uniformly distributed charge Ze.

10. A parallel plate capacitor having circular plates of radius r and plate separation d is filled with a dielectric having a permittivity ϵ and a resistivity ρ. The terminal voltage is $V_0 \sin 2\pi ft$. Find the integral $\oint H_t \, ds$ around the edge of the dielectric, neglecting edge effects.

11. A coil has an inductance of 0.5 henrys and a resistance of 10 ohms. Find the voltage across its terminals when (a) $i = 10$ amp, $di/dt = 0$; (b) $I = 10$ amp, $di/dt = 2$ amp/sec; (c) $i = 0$, $di/dt = 0$; (d) $i = 0$, $di/dt = 2$ amp/sec; (e) $i = 10$ amp, $di/dt = -2$ amp/sec.

12. Consider two coils with inductances of $L_1 = 3$ henrys, $L_2 = 5$ henrys, $M = 2$ henrys. If $di_1/dt = 1$ amp/sec, $di_2/dt = -2$ amp/sec, find $\mathcal{E}_1$, $\mathcal{E}_2$.

13. Consider the two inductances of Problem 12. When $\mathcal{E}_1 = 5$ volts, $\mathcal{E}_2 = -10$ volts, find di_1/dt and di_2dt.

14. (a) An inductance of 4 henrys and one of 16 henrys are so constructed that all the flux of one links all the turns of the other. Find the mutual inductance between them. (b) The inductances of part a are now arranged so that only half the flux of one links the other. Find M.

15. What is the resultant inductance of two inductances L_1 and L_2 in series and in parallel, assuming the mutual inductance between the two to be zero?

16. Two long parallel wires 0.5 meter apart carry current to and from a source of emf. Midway between the two and in the same plane is a rectangular loop of wire 20 cm $\times$ 2 meters. The long axis is parallel to the outer wires. What is the mutual inductance of the combination?

★17. (a) Two long parallel wires of radius a, separated by a distance d, form a cable. What is the self-inductance of this cable per unit length, neglecting the flux linkage inside the wires themselves?

(b) What is the mutual inductance per unit length of two pairs of conductors such as are described in 17a, with wires in the same plane, the distance between the nearest wires in the two cables being d also?

18. (a) Prove that, for a toroid, the total energy $\frac{1}{2}Li^2$ is equal to the energy density in the magnetic field, $\frac{1}{2}HB$, integrated over the volume of the toroid. Assume the radius of the toroid to be small compared to its length, so that the field in the toroid may be considered uniform.

(b) Prove that this relation is also true per unit length of a coaxial cable.

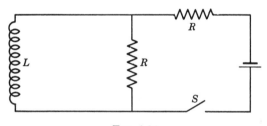

FIG. 6.24.

19. Prove that, when the switch S in the circuit in Fig. 6.24 is opened, the energy stored in the inductor L is converted into heat in the resistor.

20. A 5-henry choke coil and a 25-ohm resistor are connected in series across a battery whose terminal voltage is V through a switch. Make a rough plot of i_L, i_R, V_L, V_R vs. time after the switch is closed. How would the curves be affected if R were halved? If R were doubled?

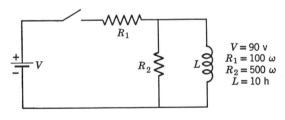

FIG. 6.25.

21. (a) Make a rough plot of i_1, i_2, i_L, V_1, V_2, V_L vs. time after the switch in the circuit illustrated in Fig. 6.25 is closed. (b) Make a rough plot of i_1, i_2, i_L, V_1, V_2, V_L vs. time after the switch is opened, if the switch has previously been closed for a long time.

22. A 500-ohm resistor and a 1-henry choke coil are connected in series across a 115-volt 60-cycle a-c line. Find the current through and the voltage across each element, the phase angle, and the power dissipated in the circuit.

23. A 1-henry choke coil and a 500-ohm resistor are connected in parallel across a 115-volt 60-cycle a-c line. Find the current through and the voltage across each element, the phase angle, and the power dissipated in the circuit.

24. An ideal transformer with no losses in which all the flux through the core links both primary and secondary circuits has 10 times as many turns in the primary as the secondary. It is connected to the 220-volt mains with the secondary open. The primary current under these conditions is negligibly small. (*a*) What is the voltage across the secondary terminals? (*b*) If a 3-ohm resistor is connected to the secondary, what will be the line current and how much power will be delivered by the line?

25. If the line current with the secondary open in Problem 24 were 0.5 amp, what would be the answer to the question asked?

26. A load consuming 3 kw at 150 volts and having a power factor of 0.8 is connected to a generator through a transmission line having a resistance of 5 ohms. What voltage, power, and current have to be supplied by the generator?

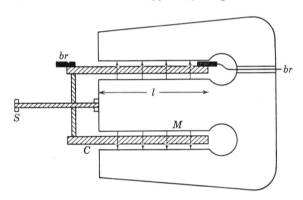

FIG. 6.26.

★27. A homopolar generator similar in principle to the Faraday disk generator is constructed as shown in Fig. 6.26. A copper cylinder C is rotated on a horizontal shaft S. The magnet M provides a radial magnetic field B piercing the copper cylinder over a length l. A voltage Blv is generated between the brushes br which are connected to the terminals of the generator.

(*a*) What voltage could be produced in a large machine in which $B = 1.5$ weber/meter^2, $l = 50$ cm and the radius of C is 25 cm, rotating at 3000 rpm?

(*b*) If the internal resistance of the generator is 0.1 ohm and it delivers 75 amp, what is the torque exerted on the shaft and how much power is being supplied to the load?

★28. The core of a transformer is 4×4 in. in cross section. It is made of laminations of an iron-silicon alloy 0.5 mm thick having a resistivity $\rho = 15 \times 10^{-8}$ ohm-m. Make a plot of the total losses per unit volume in the core for frequencies from 0–100 cycles/sec. Assume the amplitude of the flux oscillations to be 1 weber/meter^2, and a normal hysteresis loss in the iron-silicon alloy of 10^3 watts/meter^3. Estimate the eddy current losses if the core were not laminated.

The following outline indicates how this problem may be solved. If w is the power in watts/meter^3 dissipated by the eddy currents, it can be shown that, from Ohm's law,

$$w = \rho j^2 = \sigma E^2$$

where ρ is the resistivity, σ the conductivity, j the current density, and E the electric field. The induced emf at a distance x from the center of a lamination of width s is

$$\mathscr{E} = A\frac{dB}{dt} = 2xs\frac{dB}{dt}$$

and the electric field E

$$E = (\mathscr{E}/2s) = x\frac{dB}{dt}$$

if x is small compared to s. The average value of w within the sheet is then

$$\bar{w} = \frac{1}{sd}\int_0^{d/2} wS\,dx$$

This gives the average value of w in the stack at any instant as a function dB/dt. To find the time average value we must evaluate

$$\bar{\bar{w}} = \frac{1}{T}\int_0^T \bar{w}\,dt$$

where T is any time long compared to a cycle.

★29. Derive an expression for the eddy current losses per unit volume in a core made of close-packed cylindrical wires of radius R. See Problem 28.

CHAPTER 7

Electromagnetic
Oscillations

7.1 DAMPED SIMPLE HARMONIC MOTION

The oscillation of charged particles is of great importance from many points of view. The oscillations of charges in electrical circuits at low frequencies are used in the transmission of power. At higher frequencies messages are sent over telephone wires. At even higher frequencies radio, television, and radar signals are sent through space, and at still higher frequencies, as we shall see, electromagnetic waves in the form of light and X rays produced by atomic electrons, and γ rays produced by atomic nuclei, are radiated into space and absorbed by matter. The study of these waves constitutes a major part of the remainder of this book.

To introduce the phenomena involved, we return to the fundamental problem, namely, the oscillation of an elastically bound mass. Let us consider a particle of mass M free to move along the X axis but bound to the origin by a force $F = -kx$. The particle, displaced to a point x, experiences a restoring force directed toward the origin and proportional to the displacement x. The equation of motion is, according to Newton's laws,

$$F = -kx = Ma = M\frac{d^2x}{dt^2} \tag{7.1}$$

The solution of this and of the more complex equations to follow is discussed in some detail in Appendix I. For Eq. 7.1 it is

$$x = X_0 \sin (2\pi f_0 t + \alpha) \tag{7.2}$$

where X_0 and α are arbitrary constants, determined by the condition of the system at the time $t = 0$. The frequency of oscillation f_0, however, is not determined by the initial conditions but by the properties of the mechanical system under discussion. By differentiating Eq. 7.2 twice we find

$$\frac{d^2x}{dt^2} = -(2\pi f_0)^2 x$$

and, upon comparing this with Eq. 7.1, we find that our assumed expression Eq. 7.2 is actually a solution of Eq. 7.1 if

$$f_0 = \frac{1}{2\pi}\sqrt{\frac{k}{M}} \tag{7.3}$$

or, in terms of the angular frequency in radians,

$$\omega_0 = 2\pi f_0 = \sqrt{k/M} \tag{7.4}$$

The solution of any equation of the form

$$\frac{d^2x}{dt^2} + \omega_0^2 x = 0 \tag{7.5}$$

where ω_0 is an arbitrary constant will be an oscillatory function of the time with an angular frequency ω_0.

If the system under discussion is damped, for instance by producing heat as the result of frictional forces, the amplitude of the oscillations will gradually decrease, or, if the damping is very pronounced, the oscillations may be entirely suppressed, and the system, after being displaced from its equilibrium position and released, will return to its equilibrium exponentially. Damping forces proportional to the velocity are very common. In this case the equation of motion becomes

$$M\frac{d^2x}{dt^2} = -kx - c\frac{dx}{dt} \tag{7.6}$$

with c a constant determined by the frictional drag. On dividing through by the mass M, the equation will have the form

$$\frac{d^2x}{dt^2} + \frac{1}{T}\frac{dx}{dt} + \omega_0^2 x = 0 \tag{7.7}$$

with T and ω_0 constants determined by the construction of the system discussed. The physical significance of T is that it has the dimensions of a time which is related to the damping, whereas the constant ω_0 specifies the frequency of oscillation of the undamped system. A solution of this equation is a damped oscillation

$$x = X_0 e^{-t/\tau} \sin(\omega_D t + \alpha) \tag{7.8}$$

On substituting this expression into Eq. 7.7 one finds that again the amplitude X_0 and the phase α are arbitrary constants that must be determined by the initial conditions, and that

$$\tau = 2T \tag{7.9}$$

$$\omega_D = \omega_0 \sqrt{1 - \frac{1}{4\omega_0{}^2 T^2}} \tag{7.10}$$

The exponential decay time is just twice the constant T, and the frequency of oscillation of the damped system is related but not equal to that of the undamped system. Only if the damping time T is very long compared to the time of oscillation, or in other words if the system is only slightly damped, is the frequency of oscillation of the damped system ω_D approximately that of the undamped system ω_0.

If the system is greatly damped, so that the time T is small compared to the time of an oscillation, Eq. 7.10 may have no real solution. Specifically, if $(2\omega_0 T)^2 < 1$, ω_D is imaginary and there will be no oscillations. It is shown in the appendix that, in such an overdamped system, the solution consists of two exponentials, having the characteristic times

$$\tau_1 = \frac{1}{2T}[1 + \sqrt{1 - 4\omega_0{}^2 T^2}] \tag{7.11}$$

$$\tau_2 = \frac{1}{2T}[1 - \sqrt{1 - 4\omega_0{}^2 T^2}] \tag{7.12}$$

The most important aspect of the above discussion is that it specifies the conditions under which a mechanical system will oscillate, and that it specifies the natural frequency of oscillation. We turn now to considerations of forced oscillation or the response of the system to a periodic driving force. The facts are that a system having a characteristic undamped natural frequency ω_0 responds markedly to a driving force at this frequency. This marked response is called resonance. Thus when a radio is "tuned" to receive signals from some one broadcasting station, the inherent natural frequency of the receiving circuit is adjusted to that of the electromagnetic waves which are to be received. In this condition, it responds to these incoming oscillations but not to all the many others that are present. The problem at hand is to understand this tuning, or resonance, and to specify the sharpness of the resonance effects. What are the factors that determine the minimum difference in frequency between two signals which are to be received separately?

Before proceeding to a discussion of the reception of signals by electric circuits, we shall complete the discussion in terms of the forced oscillations of a mechanical system. If a mass M is subject not only to a restoring force $-kx$, and a damping force $-c\dfrac{dx}{dt}$, but also to a periodic driving force $F_0 \cos \omega t$, its equation of motion is

$$F = M\frac{d^2x}{dt^2} = -kx - c\frac{dx}{dt} + F_0 \cos \omega t \qquad (7.13)$$

and, after dividing by M and rearranging terms, we have

$$\frac{d^2x}{dt^2} + \frac{1}{T}\frac{dx}{dt} + \omega_0{}^2 x = A_0 \cos \omega t \qquad (7.14)$$

where A_0 is the amplitude of the acceleration. We shall be concerned only in periodic solutions. When the system starts in some arbitrary way to oscillate, the motion will gradually change. But this original motion will gradually tend toward a periodic form having the frequency ω of the applied force,

$$x = X_0 \cos (\omega t - \psi) \qquad (7.15)$$

Under these conditions, the problem is to find the amplitude X_0 of the oscillation and its phase ψ with respect to the driving force. The required solution is

$$X_0 = \frac{A_0}{\sqrt{(\omega/T)^2 + (\omega_0{}^2 - \omega^2)^2}} \qquad (7.16)$$

$$\tan \psi = \frac{\omega/T}{\omega_0{}^2 - \omega^2} \qquad (7.17)$$

These solutions are plotted in Figs. 7.1a and b. Notice that the resonance effects, near $\omega = \omega_0$, are particularly marked when $\omega_0 T \gg 1$. This quantity $\omega_0 T$ is often called the Q of the circuit. A large Q denotes low damping and sharp resonance.

7.2 LRC CIRCUITS

Electric circuits range in complexity from a simple flashlight, for example, to the maze of wires inside many of the little black boxes so common in most modern laboratories, or behind the switchboard of a telephone exchange. Such networks have many branch points at which the current can divide. A very important unit in such a network is the linear string of series-connected elements between branch points. We shall consider here the case of series-connected resistors, inductors, and capacitors, illustrated in Fig. 7.2. In this circuit, the current flowing past any point at some given instant is exactly the same as the

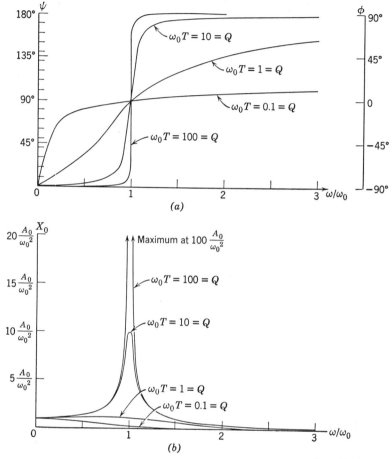

FIG. 7.1. (a) The phase angle, and (b) the amplitude of forced oscillations as a function of ω/ω_0, the ratio of the applied frequency to the natural frequency of the undamped system.

current flowing past any other point at the same instant, whether we are dealing with steady or varying currents. The problem whose solu-

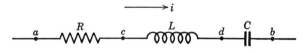

FIG. 7.2. A series-connected LRC circuit.

tion is desired is to find the current, which will in general vary with time, when an arbitrarily varying voltage is applied to the terminals, or, conversely, given an arbitrarily varying current, find the voltage across the terminals. The steps to be taken have already been separately specified. The voltage across the resistor is always equal to the current through it multiplied by its resistance. The voltage across the inductor is always equal to the time rate of change of the current times its inductance. The voltage across the capacitor is always equal to the charge on it divided by its capacitance. The total voltage across the circuit is simply the sum of the voltages across its components. We must relate the current to the time rate of change of the charge on the capacitor, and to the time rate of change of the current in the inductor, and keep the sign of the voltages across the separate units straight. The sum of the voltages across the resistor, inductor, and capacitor will be of the form

$$\text{(Constant)}\, \frac{dq}{dt} + \text{(Constant)}\, \frac{d^2q}{dt^2} + \text{(Constant)}\, q = \text{Applied voltage}$$

$$\downarrow \qquad\qquad\qquad \downarrow \qquad\qquad\qquad \downarrow$$

$$(i) \qquad\qquad\qquad \left(\frac{di}{dt}\right) \qquad\qquad\qquad \int i\, dt \tag{7.18}$$

This is the form of the differential equation which must be solved. Its similarity to Eq. 7.7 is already apparent. We proceed now to the explicit setting up of this equation and its solution. We shall consider first the flow of energy in the circuit shown in Fig. 7.2 when an arbitrary voltage is applied. The rate W at which energy is being supplied to the circuit by the externally impressed potential difference V_{ab} is iV_{ab}, i being the current flowing through each of the three elements in the circuit. The energy supplied to the circuit must show up as heat in the resistor or must be accumulating in the magnetic or electrostatic field associated with the inductor or capacitor. The rate at which energy is being converted into heat in the resistor is

$$i^2 R \text{ watts} \tag{7.19}$$

The energy in the magnetic field surrounding the inductor is $\frac{1}{2}Li^2$, and the rate at which this energy is increasing is

$$\frac{d}{dt}\left(\frac{1}{2}Li^2\right) \tag{7.20}$$

The energy in the electric field around the capacitor is $\dfrac{1}{2}\dfrac{q^2}{C}$, and the rate at which this energy is increasing is

$$\frac{d}{dt}\left(\frac{1}{2}\frac{q^2}{C}\right) \tag{7.21}$$

Combining these three equations we get, for the total rate of transfer of energy to the circuit,

$$W = iV_{ab} = i^2R + \frac{d}{dt}\left(\frac{1}{2}Li^2\right) + \frac{d}{dt}\left(\frac{1}{2}\frac{q^2}{C}\right) \qquad (7.22)$$

$$= i^2R + Li\frac{di}{dt} + \frac{q}{C}\frac{dq}{dt}$$

But, since the rate of accumulation of charge on the capacitor is by definition equal to the current supplying the charge, we have

$$i = dq/dt$$

and finally, after dividing Eq. 7.22 by i,

$$V_{ab} = iR + L\frac{di}{dt} + \frac{q}{c} \qquad (7.23)$$

In this equation, the first term on the right is equal to the potential difference across the resistor and may therefore be written

$$V_{ac} = iR \qquad (7.24)$$

The second term, according to Fig. 7.2, is

$$V_{cd} = L\frac{di}{dt} \qquad (7.25)$$

and the last,

$$V_{db} = q/C \qquad (7.26)$$

Equation 7.23 is therefore equivalent to the statement that the sum of the potential differences across the separate units of the circuit is equal to the total potential difference between the terminals of the circuit,

$$V_{ab} = V_{ac} + V_{cd} + V_{db} \qquad (7.27)$$

It is undesirable to have both the charge and the related current appearing in our fundamental equation. Expressed in terms of the charge on the capacitor Eq. 7.27 has the form

$$V_{ab} = L\frac{d^2q}{dt^2} + R\frac{dq}{dt} + \frac{q}{C} \qquad \blacktriangleright(7.28)\blacktriangleleft$$

or, after differentiation with respect to the time, it becomes an expression involving only the current,

$$\frac{dV_{ab}}{dt} = L\frac{d^2i}{dt^2} + R\frac{di}{dt} + \frac{i}{C} \qquad \blacktriangleright(7.29)\blacktriangleleft$$

These have the form of Eq. 7.14 if we put $T = L/R$ and $\omega_0{}^2 = 1/LC$.

Let us consider the charging of the capacitor in Fig. 7.2 when a fixed voltage V_{ab} is applied to the terminals of the series circuit. Equation 7.28 then has the form

$$\frac{d^2q}{dt^2} + \frac{1}{T}\frac{dq}{dt} + \omega_0{}^2 q = \frac{V_{ab}}{L} \tag{7.30}$$

From Eq. I.8 of appendix I, or Eqs. 7.11 and 7.12 of the preceding discussion, we have, if the process is non-oscillating

$$4\omega_0{}^2 T^2 < 1 \tag{7.31}$$

$$4\omega_0{}^2 T^2 = \frac{4L^2/R^2}{LC} = \frac{4L}{R^2 C} < 1$$

$$q = q_1 e^{-t/\tau_1} + q_2 e^{-t/\tau_2} + \frac{V_{ab}}{L\omega_0{}^2} \tag{7.32}$$

$$1/\tau_1 = \frac{1}{2L/R}[1 + \sqrt{1 - 4L/R^2 C}] \tag{7.33}$$

$$1/\tau_2 = \frac{1}{2L/R}[1 - \sqrt{1 - 4L/R^2 C}]$$

For the sake of simplicity we shall assume not only that $4\omega_0{}^2 T^2 < 1$ but that it is very small compared to 1. It follows, then, that we may expand the expressions 7.33 using the relation

$$(1 + x)^n = 1 + nx + \cdots$$

in which higher powers of x are neglected if $x \ll 1$. This gives for Eq. 7.33, with $n = \frac{1}{2}$, $x = 4L/R^2 C$

$$\frac{1}{\tau_1} \simeq \frac{1}{2L/R}\left[1 + \left(1 - \frac{2L}{R^2 C}\right)\right] \simeq \frac{1}{L/R} \tag{7.34}$$

$$\frac{1}{\tau_2} \simeq \frac{1}{2L/R}\left[1 - \left(1 - \frac{2L}{R^2 C}\right)\right] \simeq \frac{1}{RC}$$

In order to determine the constants q_1 and q_2 we make use of the fact that, for $t = 0$, $q = 0$ and $i = 0$. The first condition is

$$q_1 + q_2 + \frac{V_{ab}}{L\omega_0{}^2} = 0 \tag{7.35}$$

The second condition is found through deriving an expression for the current

$$i = \frac{dq}{dt} = \frac{-q_1}{\tau_1} e^{-t/\tau_1} - \frac{q_2}{\tau_2} e^{-t/\tau_2} \tag{7.36}$$

and at $t = 0$

$$0 = \frac{q_1}{\tau_1} + \frac{q_2}{\tau_2} \tag{7.37}$$

Solving these equations we get

$$\frac{q_1}{q_2} = -\frac{\tau_1}{\tau_2} = -\frac{L}{R^2C}$$

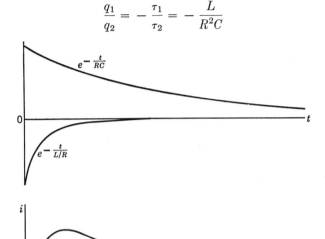

Fig. 7.3.   The charging current to a capacitor through an inductance and a resistance
when a constant voltage is applied.

and, combining this with Eq. 7.35, we get

$$q_1 = \frac{-V_{ab}C}{1 - L/R^2C} \frac{L}{R^2C}$$

$$q_2 = \frac{-V_{ab}C}{1 - L/R^2C}$$

and hence from Eq. 7.32

$$q = CV_{ab} \left[\frac{L/R^2C}{1 - L/R^2C} e^{-t/(L/R)} - \frac{e^{-t/RC}}{1 - L/R^2C} + 1 \right] \tag{7.38}$$

and for the charging current

$$i = \frac{dq}{dt} = \frac{V_{ab}}{R} \frac{1}{1 - L/R^2C} [e^{-t/(L/R)} - e^{-t/RC}] \tag{7.39}$$

The later expression is plotted in Fig. 7.3.

If the condition $4L/R^2C < 1$ is not satisfied, the circuit has a natural frequency of its own and will produce damped oscillations when a constant potential is applied. Let us examine first the extreme case $R = 0$, illustrated in Fig. 7.4. This is the series circuit illustrated in Fig. 7.2 with $R = 0$, and the terminals a and b connected together, so that $V_{ab} = 0$. The equation describing this circuit follows from Eq. 7.28

$$L\frac{d^2q}{dt^2} + \frac{q}{C} = 0$$

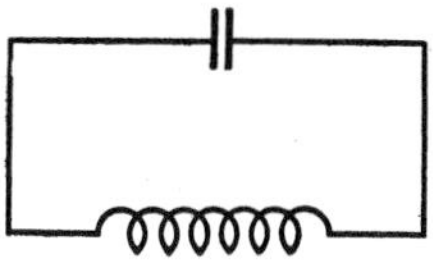

which is analogous to Eq. 7.4. The solution is

$$q = q_0 \sin (\omega_0 t + \alpha)$$

$$\omega_0 = 1/\sqrt{LC}$$

In terms of the frequency f_0 in cycles per second

$$q = q_0 \sin (2\pi f_0 t + \alpha)$$

$$f_0 = \frac{\omega_0}{2\pi} = \frac{1}{2\pi} \frac{1}{\sqrt{LC}} \tag{7.40}$$

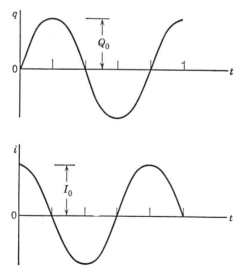

Fig. 7.4. An LC circuit having a natural frequency $f_0 = 1/2\pi \times 1/\sqrt{LC}$.

The current may be found through differentiating the expression for q and will be 90° out of phase, as shown in Fig. 7.5. The current through

Fig. 7.5. The variation of current and charge in the LC circuit shown in Fig. 7.4.

the inductor is a maximum when the charge on the capacitor is zero. The entire energy of the system is therefore at this instant in the magnetic field due to the current. The electrostatic energy of the uncharged capacitor is zero. A quarter of a cycle later, the current in the inductor is zero and the charge on the capacitor has its maximum value. The energy in the magnetic field is now zero. It has all been converted into electrostatic potential energy in the electric field of the capacitor. The energy oscillates to and fro between the two elements of the circuit. The total energy of the isolated system must of course remain constant. The sum of the magnetic and electric energies does not change.

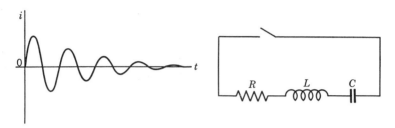

FIG. 7.6. The oscillatory discharge of a capacitor through an inductance and a resistance.

If a resistor is added to the circuit shown in Fig. 7.4, some of the electric and magnetic energy will be converted into heat in the course of every half cycle. If only a small fraction of the energy is lost during every half cycle, the current will still be essentially periodic but with a gradually decreasing amplitude. This is very much like the oscillation of a pendulum in a slightly viscous medium such as air. In a sufficiently viscous medium the pendulum will not oscillate at all. If displaced, it will return to its equilibrium position without oscillation. The same may be said of an electric circuit. If the resistance of the circuit is sufficiently great, the circuit will not oscillate but will exponentially approach the condition of zero charge on the capacitor and zero current on the inductor. The equation for the current is

$$0 = L\frac{d^2i}{dt^2} + R\frac{di}{dt} + \frac{i}{C} \qquad (7.41)$$

Its solution, if $L/R^2C > 1$, is

$$i = I_0 e^{-t/\tau} \sin 2\pi f_D t \qquad (7.42)$$

The circuit and the solution are shown in Fig. 7.6. Referring back to Eqs. 7.9 and 7.10, we find that

$$\frac{1}{\tau} = \frac{1}{2L/R} \qquad \omega_D = 2\pi f_D = \omega_0 \sqrt{1 - \frac{RC}{4L/R}} \qquad (7.43)$$

$$\omega_0 = 1/\sqrt{LC}$$

We now take up forced oscillations in the circuit shown in Fig. 7.7. The applied voltage $V_{ab} = V_0 \cos 2\pi ft$, and Eq. 7.28 becomes

$$V_{ab} = V_0 \cos 2\pi ft = L\frac{d^2q}{dt^2} + R\frac{dq}{dt} + \frac{q}{C} \qquad (7.44)$$

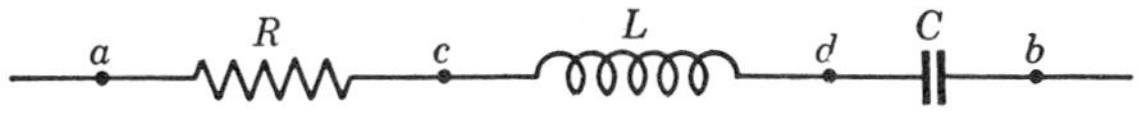

FIG. 7.7.   The series circuit under discussion.

From the solution of the analogous equation 7.14 with $A_0 = V_0/R$, $T = L/R$, $\omega_0{}^2 = 1/LC$, we find, after considerable manipulation, for the solution of Eq. 7.44,

$$q = q_0 \cos (\omega t - \psi)$$

$$i = dq/dt = I_0 \cos (\omega t - \phi)$$

$$I_0 = \frac{V_0}{\sqrt{R^2 + \left(L\omega - \dfrac{1}{C\omega}\right)^2}}$$

$$\sin \phi = -\cos \left(\phi + \frac{\pi}{2}\right) = -\cos \psi$$

$$\sin \phi = \frac{L\omega - \dfrac{1}{C\omega}}{\sqrt{R^2 + \left(L\omega - \dfrac{1}{C\omega}\right)^2}}$$

The expressions $L\omega = 2\pi fL$ and $1/C\omega = \dfrac{1}{2\pi fC}$ will be recognized as the reactance X_L of an inductor, and X_C of a capacitor. We have then, if we call X the reactance of the inductor and capacitor in series,

$$X = X_L - X_C \qquad (7.45)$$

and putting

$$Z = \sqrt{R^2 + X^2} \qquad (7.46)$$

where Z is the impedance of the circuit

$$I_0 = V_0/Z \qquad (7.47)$$

$$\sin \phi = \frac{X}{\sqrt{R^2 + X^2}} = \frac{X}{Z}$$

$$\cos \phi = R/Z \qquad (7.48)$$

These results are illustrated graphically below. The current and voltage are shown in Fig. 7.8 as the projection of rotating vectors. The instantaneous value of the voltage V_{ab} across the series circuit is the projection of the rotating vector V_0 on the horizontal axis,

$$V_{ab} = V_0 \cos \omega t$$

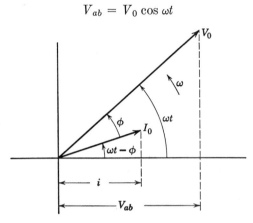

FIG. 7.8.   The current and voltage represented as rotating vectors.

The *voltage leads* the current by an angle ϕ *if* $\phi > 0$. The instantaneous value of the current is the projection of the rotating current vector on the horizontal axis,

$$i = I_0 \cos (\omega t - \phi)$$

If now we draw the current vector horizontally and add to the diagram the three voltage vectors representing the voltage across the resistor $I_0 R$ in phase with the current, the voltage across the inductor having a magnitude $I_0 X_L$ heading the current by 90°, and the voltage across the capacitor $I_0 X_C$ lagging behind the current by 90°, we obtain the situation illustrated in Fig. 7.9. This illustrates how the vector V_0 may be constructed from the current vector and the resistance and reactances of the circuit. This diagram may be simplified through removing the current vector and dividing the other vectors by I_0. The result is the *vector impedance diagram*, shown in Fig. 7.10. The graphical construction of Z and ϕ is of course in agreement with the definitions of Eqs. 7.46 and 7.48.

The time average of the power dissipated in the resistor is

$$W = I_0{}^2 R/2 = I^2 R \qquad (7.49)$$

where I is the rms value of the current,

$$I = I_0/\sqrt{2}$$

This may also be written, since $I_0 R = I_0 Z \cos \phi = V_0 \cos \phi$, or

$$W = I_0 V_0 / 2 \cos \phi = IV \cos \phi \qquad (7.50)$$

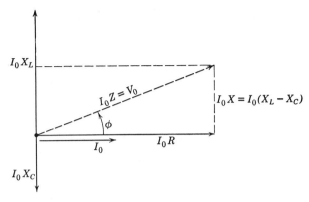

FIG. 7.9. The vector diagram of the current and voltage in a series LRC circuit.

Here again, $\cos \phi$ is the power factor. In order to determine how much power an a-c power supply is delivering to a load it is not sufficient to know the amplitudes or rms values of voltage and current. It is neces-

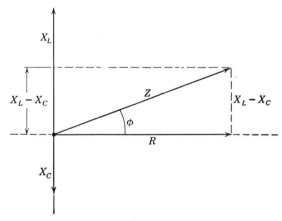

FIG. 7.10. The vector impedance diagram for a series LRC circuit.

sary in addition to know the power factor, or the phase difference between the two. In a purely reactive load with no resistance there is no average power dissipation. In this case energy is delivered to the circuit at some time in each cycle, but it is returned to the source of power a quarter of a cycle later.

The rate at which an alternating voltage having a fixed amplitude delivers power to a series LRC circuit for various frequencies is specified in Eq. 7.51. This is simply related to the mechanical problem discussed in Appendix I. The quantities in the mechanical problem whose solution is given by Eq. I.26 are to be replaced as follows in the electrical problem:

$$F_0 \rightarrow V_0$$
$$M \rightarrow L$$
$$T \rightarrow L/R$$
$$Q = \omega_0 T \rightarrow L\omega_0/R$$
$$\omega_0 = 1/\sqrt{LC}$$

We get then

$$W = \frac{V_0^2}{R} \cdot \frac{1}{1 + 4Q^2 \left(\dfrac{\omega_0 - \omega}{\omega_0}\right)^2} \tag{7.51}$$

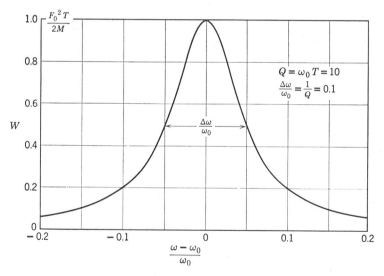

Fig. 7.11.   A power resonance curve for $Q = 10$.

A high Q circuit will show sharp tuning, that is, it will respond strongly to an applied voltage in a frequency range around resonance $\Delta\omega = \omega_0/Q$ as illustrated in Fig. 7.11. In radio circuits, for instance, in which it is desired to tune in on one frequency while excluding others, it is important to have $\Delta\omega$ small and therefore Q large.

A Numerical Example

What are the impedance and power factor of a 1000-ohm resistor, a 1-henry reactor, and a 1 μf capacitor connected in series, at a frequency of 60 cycles/sec, and at what frequency will the impedance have its lowest value?

$$\omega = 2\pi f = 377 \text{ radians/sec}$$

$$X_L = \omega L = 377 \text{ ohms}$$

$$X_C = \frac{1}{2\pi f C} = 2650 \text{ ohms}$$

$$X = X_L - X_C = -2273 \text{ ohms}$$

$$Z = \sqrt{R^2 + X^2} = 2480 \text{ ohms}$$

Power factor $= R/Z = 0.403$

$$\omega_0 = \frac{1}{\sqrt{LC}} = 10^3 \text{ radians/sec} \qquad f_0 = 160 \text{ cycles/sec}$$

At this frequency $X_L = X_C$, $Z = R = 1000$ ohms.

The Impedance of Series and Parallel Circuits

The impedance of a series circuit containing resistance, inductance, and capacitance is

$$Z = \sqrt{R^2 + (X_L - X_C)^2}$$

A series circuit at resonance has a low impedance. It passes a high current.

For a parallel circuit, on the other hand, in which inductance, resistance, and capacitance are each separately connected to the applied voltage V_{ab}, as in Fig. 7.12, the situation is quite different. At any given instant, the voltage across one of the components is the same as that across any other component and is equal to the line voltage.

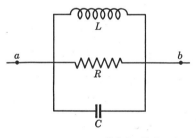

FIG. 7.12. A parallel LRC circuit.

The currents through the three components must be added to give the line current. They must, of course, be added vectorially, as indicated in Fig. 7.13a. If we choose to represent the applied voltage by a horizontal arrow, then we must choose to represent the current through the resistor, I_R, as a horizontal arrow. The current through the capacitor, which leads the voltage by 90°, must be drawn in an upward direction, and the current through the inductor in a downward direction. The magnitudes of these three currents are

$$I_R = V/R$$

$$I_C = V/X_C$$

$$I_L = V/X_L$$

The vector sum of these produces the resultant,

$$I = \sqrt{I_R{}^2 + (I_C - I_L)^2} = \frac{V}{Z}$$

Dividing by V, we have a corresponding relationship illustrated in Fig. 7.13b.

$$\frac{1}{Z} = \sqrt{\frac{1}{R^2} + \left(\frac{1}{X_C} - \frac{1}{X_L}\right)^2} \qquad (7.52)$$

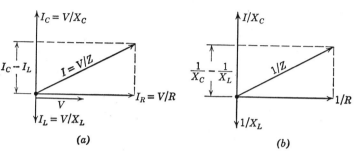

(a)   (b)

FIG. 7.13.   The vector addition of currents in the parallel circuit shown in Fig. 7.12.

At resonance, or when $X_L = X_C$, the impedance of this circuit is large. The current supplied by a voltage source of constant amplitude will be a minimum at resonance. It will be just the current supplied to the resistor. This is not to say that there is no current through the inductance and capacitance, but that they are 180° out of phase from the point of the line. In other words, at resonance the charging current to the capacitor is a local circulating current which flows through the inductor.

7.3   AMPLIFIERS AND OSCILLATORS

This section is intended to show qualitatively how the natural frequency of a circuit can be used to control a generator of a-c power. Although the detailed functioning of such devices is an engineering problem, a review of some of the principles involved may help to make the ideas advanced in the text more familiar and understandable.

The concept underlying this subject involves the *control* of power. The amount of energy supplied to a control mechanism in order to make it function has little or no relation to the amount of power controlled. By turning the valve of a radiator, we can increase or decrease the amount of heat which it supplies. By turning a thermostat dial, we can control the amount of heat which a furnace supplies to a house. By depressing the accelerator pedal in an automobile, we control the amount of energy supplied to the wheels by the motor. By closing a valve in the spillway of a dam, we can control the flow of water. It is clear that the power required to operate the control has little to do with the amount of power controlled.

A three-electrode vacuum tube may be used to control the flow of current in a circuit. In the tube shown in Fig. 7.14 there are three electrodes, the cathode from which electrons are released, the plate toward which they are accelerated, and a grid used to control the flow of electrons from the cathode to the plate.

The cathode generally has to be heated in order to function as an electron emitter, and the battery used to supply the heating current is often called the A battery of the circuit. The voltage between the cathode and plate is called

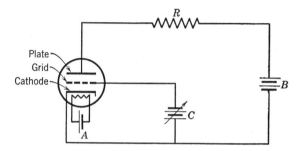

Fig. 7.14. A triode connected so as to control the power supplied to a resistor by a battery.

the plate voltage and is supplied by the B battery, and the grid voltage is supplied by the C battery. If the grid were not present, the tube would be a diode conducting a current depending on the plate voltage as shown in Fig. 4.23. If the grid is present and is given a sufficient negative potential with respect to the cathode, no electrons will pass the grid and the plate current will be stopped. This voltage need not be great if the distance between grid and cathode is small. If now the grid is made more positive, electrons will begin to get through into the region between the grid and the plate where they are swept over to the plate by the B battery. The number of electrons that get through the grid can be controlled by the grid voltage. Very little current is drawn by the grid as it is purposely made very open. The C battery consequently does very little work. It acts as a valve controlling the amount of current in the plate circuit, but the energy to drive this current comes from the B battery. The characteristics of a commercial triode are shown in Fig. 7.15.

The detailed working of a triode as an amplifier may be described as follows. A portion of three curves relating plate current i_p to plate voltage V_p at constant grid voltage V_g is shown in Fig. 7.16.

In addition to the information about the tube characteristics shown by the three solid curves marked $V_{g\,1}$, $V_{g\,2}$, and $V_{g\,3}$, we need to supply one important bit of information regarding the circuit. This is contained in the straight line connecting a point of the i_p axis to a point on the V_p axis. As drawn in Fig. 7.14, the plate voltage and the plate current are related by the equation

$$V_p = \mathscr{E}_B - i_p R \tag{7.53}$$

This is the equation of the straight line in Fig. 7.16 referred to above. When no current is drawn, the plate voltage is the full emf of the B battery. This point is drawn on the V_p axis in Fig. 7.16. As the plate current is increased, the plate voltage decreases linearly in such a fashion that it would cross the

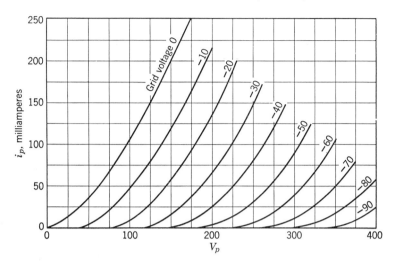

FIG. 7.15.   The characteristics of a triode.

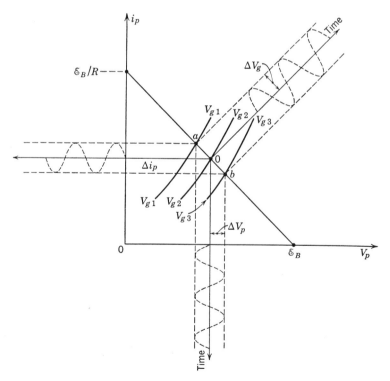

FIG. 7.16.   The voltage amplification of the triode connected as in Fig. 7.17.

i_p axis at $\mathcal{E}_B/R$. This point is also entered, and in this circuit the operation must be represented by motion along this line. Thus, if an alternating signal of amplitude ΔV_g is put on the grid, the plate current will oscillate with an amplitude Δi_p, and the plate voltage will oscillate with an amplitude ΔV_p. These amplitudes are shown in the illustration and may be either estimated graphically or calculated from the tube parameters in the following way. The tube parameters, which may be obtained from the graphically presented characteristics, are defined below:

(a) amplification factor μ:

$$\mu = -\frac{\Delta V_p}{\Delta V_g} \qquad (i_p = \text{const.}) \qquad (7.54)$$

(b) Plate conductance g_p and plate resistance r_p:

$$r_p = 1/g_p = \Delta V_p/\Delta i_p \qquad (V_g = \text{const.}) \qquad (7.55)$$

(c) Transconductance g_m:

$$g_m = \Delta i_p/\Delta V_g \qquad (V_p = \text{const.}) \qquad (7.56)$$

For the tube shown in Fig. 7.15, these quantities have the following values for the linear part of the characteristic.

$$\mu = 4$$

$$r_p = 500 \text{ ohms}$$

$$g_m = 0.008 \text{ reciprocal ohms} \qquad (\text{also called mhos})$$

In general, the relation

$$di_p = \frac{\partial i_p}{\partial V_p} dV_p + \frac{\partial i_p}{\partial V_g} dV_g$$

for

$$\Delta i_p = \frac{\Delta V_p}{r_p} + g_m \Delta V_g \qquad (7.57)$$

must be satisfied. From (7.53) we can derive, since $\mathcal{E}_B$ is constant,

$$-\Delta V_p = R \Delta i_p \qquad (7.58)$$

Combining this with (7.57), we get

$$-\frac{\Delta V_p}{R} = \frac{\Delta V_p}{r_p} + g_m \Delta V_g$$

$$\frac{\Delta V_p}{\Delta V_g} = -\frac{g_m}{\dfrac{1}{R} + \dfrac{1}{r}} = -\frac{r_p R g_m}{R + r_p} \qquad (7.59)$$

This form may be simplified somewhat through noticing that, if we put $\Delta i_p = 0$ in (7.57), we get

$$0 = \frac{\Delta V_p}{r_p} + g_m \Delta V_g$$

$$-\frac{\Delta V_p}{\Delta V_g} = g_m r_p$$

or

$$\mu = g_m r_p \qquad (7.60)$$

Substituting this into (7.59), we get for the voltage amplification in our circuit

$$\frac{\Delta V_p}{\Delta V_g} = -\left(\frac{R}{R + r_p}\right)\mu \qquad (7.61)$$

The use of an amplifier as an oscillator involves what is called *feedback*. The simplest example is perhaps a thermostat connected to the furnace of a house. The furnace supplies heat until the temperature at some desired point reaches a set value. The thermostat then operates a switch which shuts the furnace off. Notice that even here we have an oscillation. After the furnace is off, the house nevertheless continues to get hotter because the radiators are hot. After a certain time, when the radiators have already somewhat cooled off, the house temperature reaches a maximum and begins to cool off. When

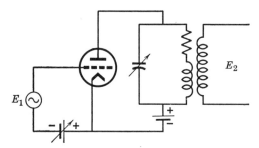

Fig. 7.17. A triode which may be used as an oscillator by connecting the output E_2 to the input E_1 instead of the generator.

the preset temperature is reached, the thermostat turns the furnace on again. After a time, the radiators are again hot, the house after reaching a minimum temperature begins to heat up again, and the cycle is repeated. The thermostat is a simple example of a *servomechanism*.

In order to understand the use of the triode in an oscillator, consider the circuit in Fig. 7.17. An alternating voltage E_1 is connected to the grid and cathode of the triode, and a biasing battery is so adjusted that the fluctuating current of this frequency in the plate circuit will have the desired amplitude. A circuit having a natural frequency of its own is connected in series with a battery in the plate circuit. The inductance in the tunable circuit has a secondary winding whose output we call E_2.

If the tuning of the circuit is varied, it is possible to find a condition such that the phase of E_2 will be the same as that of E_1. This will occur when the natural frequency of the resonant circuit is equal to the driving frequency. Further, by adjusting the biasing voltage on the grid, it is possible to make the amplitude of E_1 equal to that of E_2. But when the circuit is so adjusted that the input power is just equal in amplitude and phase to the output power, we might remove E_1 and connect the output terminals to the input between grid and cathode without interfering with the operation of the circuit. In these circumstances the battery in the plate circuit continually replaces the energy lost in the resistor, and the oscillation becomes self-perpetuating. By varying the parameters of the circuit, it is possible to vary the a-c power output of the oscillator.

7.4 ELECTRIC AND MAGNETIC RESONANCE IN MATTER

We turn now to another important aspect of electromagnetic oscillations, namely, oscillations in atoms, molecules, liquids, and solids. Since these are made up of a variety of parts held together by finite forces, we would expect these constituent parts to be more or less elastically bound and then capable of oscillating around their equilibrium positions. We would expect them to have characteristic natural frequencies of their own, and to exhibit resonance phenomena when subjected to forced oscillations.

Forced oscillations can be produced in matter by oscillating electric or magnetic fields. We have shown that constant fields produce a constant polarization. We now propose to extend these considerations regarding electric and magnetic polarization to include questions of frequency dependence. If there are characteristic natural frequencies for the oscillation of electric charges or magnetic dipoles, we must expect to find frequency-dependent susceptibilities and also heat evolution if the oscillating units are somehow connected with the thermal motions of their surroundings or if their free oscillations are damped.

A few generations ago the oscillations of LC circuits were new and exciting phenomena of great interest to physicists and engineers. Today they are well understood and extensively used. The oscillations of matter are the new and exciting fields for investigation. Although there is no fundamental mystery about them, the details of the phenomena encountered are so varied that there is here still a challenge to the scientific explorer and the engineer. The physicist, the chemist, the biologist, and the engineer are all searching for new insights into how atoms and nuclei are constructed, and how they can be put together to form the known and still unknown molecules, liquids, and solids.

The study of electromagnetic oscillations has been of great help in this effort. We shall review some of the pertinent ideas in the next sections. There is first of all the matter of identifying the oscillating parts. Then there is the determination of the natural frequencies. These are often many, and close together, so that complete analysis of them may be difficult. The measurement of these frequencies tells us about the surroundings of the oscillating parts, particularly about the forces to which they are subjected, and so gives us important insight into the structure of matter. Then there is the important question of the damping constant T in the basic equations of motion with which this chapter begins. The magnitude of the product $T\omega_0$, as we have shown, determines the nature of the resonance phenomena. If $T\omega_0$ is smaller than unity there will be no sharp resonances. If $T\omega_0$ is very large compared to unity, the resonance phenomena will take place only in a very narrow frequency and we must examine the frequency ranges of interest in great detail in order not to miss the resonance phenomena we are looking for. Finally, there is the question of the interpretation of the relaxation time T. A thorough understanding of the surroundings of the oscillating members must enable us to understand not only the observed natural frequencies but also the observed relaxation times, and the latter is often a much more subtle and revealing guide in the study of matter.

Although the detailed analysis of the phenomena sketched above can not be undertaken here, we propose to show how even our simple model of an atom can be used to establish the basis for this most important branch of science and engineering.

7.5 MAGNETIC RESONANCE PHENOMENA

By magnetic oscillations we mean the directional oscillations of magnetic dipoles about some axis. Such oscillation requires the presence of a magnetic field which exerts a torque on

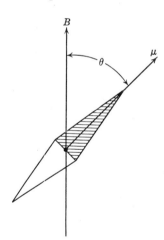

FIG. 7.18. A compass needle in a magnetic field.

the dipole. We shall consider here only the simplest case of the motions of a dipole in a fixed field or a periodically varying field.

We shall consider first an isolated magnetic dipole in space, with a constant and uniform magnetic field acting on it. Since we are to consider angular motion, our discussion must be based on Newton's law of rotation: The rate of change of angular momentum of a body is equal to the torque acting on it. In order to apply this law we must set up a model for our magnetic dipole. Let us first consider the oscillations of a compass needle pivoted at its center, shown in Fig. 7.18.

The torque acting on such a compass needle will be proportional to the angle θ which the needle makes with the field B.

If μ_m is the magnetic moment of the needle,

$$\boldsymbol{\tau}_m = -[\boldsymbol{\mu}_m \times \mathbf{B}] \tag{7.62}$$

or for small displacements,

$$\sin \theta \simeq \theta$$

$$\tau_m = -\mu_m B\theta$$

If the moment of inertia of the compass needle around its pivot is I, the torque is also equal to I times the angular acceleration, or

$$I \frac{d^2\theta}{dt^2} = -\mu_m B\theta \qquad (7.63)$$

The solution of this equation will be an oscillatory motion with angular frequency ω_0,

$$\theta = \Theta \sin \omega_0 t$$

$$\omega_0 = \sqrt{\mu_m B/I} \qquad (7.64)$$

Although this equation gives the natural frequency of oscillation of permanent magnets correctly, as may be verified by experiment, it does not describe the behavior of atomic dipoles. Their oscillations have a frequency proportional to the first power, rather than the square root, of the applied field. We have gone through the above analysis in order to bring out the reason for the difference.

In the above problem we have assumed that the angular momentum of the dipole is $I \, d\theta/dt$, and that in the absence of a magnetic field the angular momentum vanishes. Atomic magnets are not of this kind. The magnetic moment itself is due to circulating charge, and this circulating charge, because of its mass, necessarily has an angular momentum, as shown in Fig. 7.19. The atom is in effect a small gyroscope, and we must consider the motion of this gyroscope in the presence of a field.

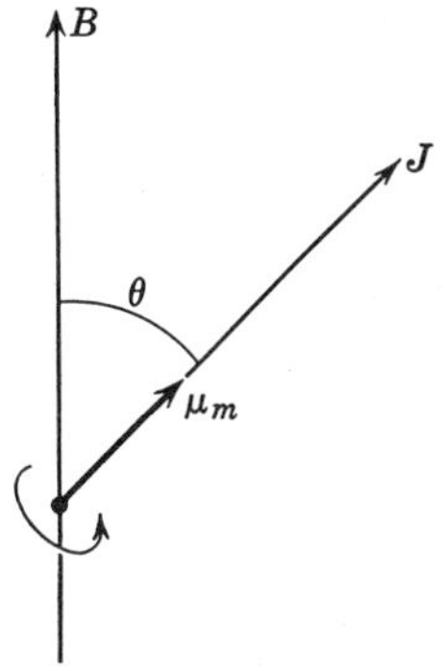

As a model for our atomic gyroscope, we shall take a charge q having a mass m moving in a circular orbit of radius r with a frequency f. The equivalent current, or the number of coulombs passing any point in the orbit in 1 second, is the magnitude of the charge multiplied by the number of times it passes around the orbit per second.

$$i = qf$$

Fig. 7.19. An atomic gyroscopic magnet. The magnetic moment is parallel or antiparallel to the angular momentum, depending on whether the circulating charge is positive or negative.

Since the area is πr^2, we have

$$\mu_m = iA = qf \cdot \pi r^2 = \frac{q}{2} r^2 \omega \qquad (7.65)$$

The angular momentum, J, of the system is

$$J = mr^2\omega \qquad (7.66)$$

or in vector notation

$$\mathbf{J} = mr^2\boldsymbol{\omega} \qquad \boldsymbol{\mu}_m = \gamma\mathbf{J} \qquad (7.67)$$

A permanent magnet is made up of many such small gyroscopes and will therefore also possess an angular momentum about its permanent moment, but this angular momentum is negligible compared to the angular momentum of the oscillating compass needle and may be completely neglected, as in the above discussion of its oscillation.

The ratio of the magnetic moment to the angular momentum of an atomic system is called its *gyromagnetic ratio*,

$$\gamma = \mu_m / J \qquad (7.68)$$

For electrons moving in orbits

$$\gamma = e/2m \qquad (7.69)$$

The gyromagnetic ratio of nuclei and atoms may have a wide range of values which we shall not discuss further at this point. For any particular atomic system γ has a definite value. Notice that Eq. 7.62 may now be rewritten

$$\boldsymbol{\tau} = \gamma[\mathbf{J} \times \mathbf{B}]$$

Now, according to Newton's laws of motion, the torque acting on a system must equal the time rate of change of angular momentum, or

$$\boldsymbol{\tau} = \frac{d\mathbf{J}}{dt} = \gamma[\mathbf{J} \times \mathbf{B}] \qquad (7.70)$$

But this is the equation of motion of a gyroscope which the student has already encountered for the case of a gravitational rather than a magnetic torque. The application of a gravitational torque to a gyroscope produces precession around a vertical axis. The angular velocity of precession Ω is given by the equation

$$\tau = I\omega \sin \theta \Omega$$

for a top whose axis makes an angle θ with the vertical. In our magnetic case, the precessional frequency, called the Larmor frequency, ω_L, is given by

$$\tau = \gamma JB \sin \theta = J \sin \theta \omega_L$$

or

$$\omega_L = \gamma B \qquad (7.71)$$

Note the close relation of this result to that discussed in Section 6.1 in connection with the diamagnetism of atoms. The mathematical proof of the correctness of this result follows from Eq. 7.70. If the field B is parallel to the z axis, we may write for the x, y, and z components of the vectors in Eq. 7.70, using the polar coordinates shown in Fig. 7.20,

$$\frac{dJ_x}{dt} = \frac{d}{dt}\,(J \sin\theta \sin\phi) = \gamma[J_y B_z - 0] = \gamma J \sin\theta \cos\phi\, B_z$$

$$\frac{dJ_y}{dt} = \frac{d}{dt}\,(J \sin\theta \cos\phi) = \gamma[0 - J_x B_z] = -\gamma J \sin\theta \sin\phi\, B_z$$

$$\frac{dJ_z}{dt} = \frac{d}{dt}\,(J \cos\theta) = \gamma(0 - 0) = 0$$

The total angular momentum J of atomic systems is constant. The last of the above equations may therefore be taken to mean that

$$\frac{d}{dt}\cos\theta = 0$$

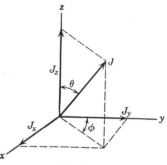

Fig. 7.20.

or that the angle θ is constant. The magnetic field does no work on the electron since the magnetic force is always at right angles to the motion. The magnetic energy $-\mu_m B \cos\theta$ remains constant. The first two of the above equations, after the constant factors $J \sin\theta$ are canceled from both sides, become

$$\frac{d \sin\phi}{dt} = \cos\phi \cdot \frac{d\phi}{dt} = \gamma B_z \cos\phi$$

$$\frac{d \cos\phi}{dt} = -\sin\phi\frac{d\phi}{dt} = -\gamma B_z \sin\phi$$

or simply

$$\frac{d\phi}{dt} = \omega_L = \gamma B_z \qquad (7.72)$$

The system precesses with the Larmor frequency ω_L about the magnetic field.

Having determined the resonance frequency, we must now consider the nature of observable magnetic resonance effects. The analysis of forced rotations is somewhat more involved than the analysis of forced oscillations discussed in the first section of this chapter, but the final results are practically identical. We must have, in addition to the constant field B_z, a field B_0 rotating in the x-y plane. When the angular frequency ω of this rotating field approaches the Larmor frequency ω_L, resonance phenomena take place if the sense of rotation of the field is the same as that of the dipoles being investigated.

A Nuclear Magnetic Resonance Experiment

An example of these resonance effects is illustrated in the following description of an experiment first successfully performed in 1946. Nuclei, like atoms,

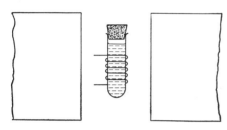

FIG. 7.21. The essential parts of a nuclear magnetic resonance experiment.

spin around an axis and have magnetic moments. The object of the experiment was to observe the Larmor precession of atomic nuclei, particularly protons, in a diamagnetic liquid, solid, or gaseous sample. A test tube a few millimeters in diameter containing the sample to be investigated is placed between the poles of an electromagnet, as in Fig. 7.21. Around the tube is a coil whose axis is at right angles to the magnet field. This coil produces an oscillating field of the desired frequency. This is not a rotating field, such as is required to produce resonance, but it serves the purpose just the same, as may be seen from the following argument. A rotating field, rotating in the x-y plane, may be described as follows: If it is rotating in a clockwise sense, as seen from the positive z axis in Fig. 7.20,

$$B_x = B_0 \cos \omega t$$

$$B_y = -B_0 \sin \omega t \tag{7.73}$$

and, if it is rotating in the counterclockwise direction,

$$B_x = B_0 \cos \omega t$$

$$B_y = B_0 \sin \omega t \tag{7.74}$$

The sum of these two fields is the linearly oscillating field

$$B_x = 2B_0 \cos \omega t$$

$$B_y = 0 \tag{7.75}$$

The linearly oscillating field of the coil in Fig. 7.21 may therefore be thought of as the sum of two rotating fields. Near the resonance frequency, the component rotating in the same sense as the nuclei will produce resonance effects. The other, being effectively far from resonance, will produce no effects.

The experiment proceeds, now, through applying an oscillating voltage to the coil and varying the magnetic field until resonance effects are observed, for example, the selective absorption of energy from the circuit in the vicinity of the natural frequency of the protons. Optical experiments had shown prior to this experiment that the Larmor frequency for protons was approximately given by the expression

$$f_L = \frac{\omega_L}{2\pi} \simeq 4.6 \times 10^7 B \qquad (7.76)$$

Thus, for example, at a field of 7000 gauss, or 0.7 Weber/meter², the Larmor frequency was expected to be in the vicinity of 32 megacycles.

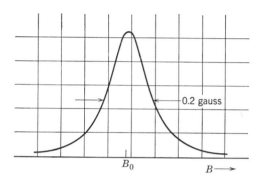

FIG. 7.22. A nuclear magnetic resonance absorption curve for protons in water.

The technique of making these measurements need not concern us here. The effects looked for are very small because of the fact that nuclear magnetic moments are small, being some 2000 times smaller than atomic moments. However, these difficulties have been elegantly overcome in a variety of ways, and energy absorption in the sample as a function of field can be displayed on an oscilloscope or plotted by a recording meter. Such a resonance curve is reproduced in Fig. 7.22. In this curve the magnetic field at resonance is about 7000 gauss and the width of the resonance curve is about 0.2 gauss, so that one might expect that

$$\omega_0 T = \frac{\omega_0}{\Delta\omega} = \frac{B}{\Delta B} = 3.5 \times 10^4$$

Actually this line is spuriously broadened by the observing instrument. The magnetic field is not rigorously uniform and has a slightly different value at various parts of the sample. The nuclei do not all resonate at once, and $\omega_0 T$ in the sample is greater than the value calculated. Resonance curves obtained for a sample of ethyl alcohol in a more homogeneous field are shown in Fig. 7.23b. The protons now have three distinct resonances because the field within the molecule is not uniform. The molecule, shown in Fig. 7.23a, has three groups of protons. The first group, on the left, contains only one proton, and gives rise to the peak on the left in Fig. 7.23b. The next group contains two protons, which are somewhat differently shielded by the surrounding electrons from the single proton in group 1. These two protons give rise to the peak marked 2 in the resonance curve. The third peak is due to group 3 containing three protons. The areas under the three resonance curves are in the ratios 1:2:3, indicating that they are due to 1, 2, and 3 protons respectively. We have here corroboratory evidence that the structure of the alcohol molecule is that shown.

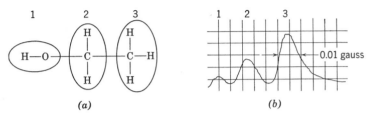

(a)   (b)

FIG. 7.23.   (a) An ethyl alcohol molecule. (b) Proton resonances in ethyl alcohol with moderate resolution.

Recent technical advances have made it possible to go even farther, as shown in Fig. 7.24. The three peaks are found to have a complicated structure which we are not here in a position to understand. It is clear, however, that there is in such resonance curves a wealth of information of importance to the student of molecular structure.

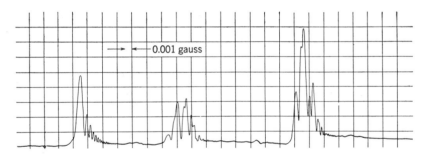

FIG. 7.24.   Nuclear magnetic resonance curve of ethyl alcohol in a more uniform field than was used in Fig. 7.23.

These exceedingly sharp nuclear magnetic resonance curves are possible because of the long magnetic relaxation times of atomic nuclei, leading to large values of $T\omega_0 = B/\Delta B$. Magnetic resonances due to atomic rather than nuclear magnets are also observed. They occur in comparable magnetic fields at frequencies some thousands of times greater and are generally very much broader, essentially because the stronger atomic dipoles disturb each other much more markedly.

The Barnett and Einstein-de Haas Effects

These magnetic resonance effects are due to the fact that atomic and nuclear magnetic moments are associated with angular momentum. The existence of this connection of magnetism and angular momentum, and the first measurements of the gyromagnetic ratio, were made in 1914, long before apparatus for observing resonance effects was available.

An experiment for demonstrating gyromagnetic effects involves an easily magnetizable cylinder suspended longitudinally by a thread. At rest and in a demagnetized state its angular momentum is zero. Imagine that the cylinder is now magnetized by the application of a longitudinal field. This field produces magnetization parallel to itself and therefore exerts no torque on the wire. Since no torque has acted on the cylinder, we conclude from Newton's laws of motion that the angular momentum must still be zero. But, if the material is now magnetized, there must be an electronic angular momentum due to the angular motion of the electrons. These two statements, that the total angular momentum is zero, but that the electronic angular momentum is not zero, are compatible only if the cylinder as a whole has acquired an angular momentum opposite to that of the electrons.

In other words, after magnetization, the cylinder as a whole must be rotating in a direction opposite to that of the electrons. This momentum is in fact present but is very small and difficult to detect. The above effect and its converse, magnetization by rotation, were first observed in 1914–1915 by S. J. Barnett and Einstein and de Haas.

7.6 THE POLARIZATION OF MATTER IN OSCILLATING ELECTRIC FIELDS

The system which we shall describe by way of illustration is an elastically bound charge q of mass M, for example some one atomic nucleus in a solid. Each nucleus must have an equilibrium position to which it will tend to return when displaced. In the presence of a constant electric field in the x direction, the electrical force qE will produce a displacement x satisfying the equation

$$qE = kx$$

The atom will then acquire a dipole moment $p = qx$ under the influence of the external field, and, if the number of atoms per unit volume is n, the polarization P of the solid is

$$P = pn = qxn \qquad (7.77)$$

From the relations

$$D = \epsilon E = \epsilon_0 E + P$$

$$\epsilon = \epsilon_0 + \frac{P}{E}$$

we can now compute the permittivity for oscillating fields as was done in Section 3.6 for constant fields. We have, if $qE = kx$,

$$P = \frac{q^2 n}{k} E$$

$$\epsilon = \epsilon_0 + \frac{q^2 n}{k} \qquad (7.78)$$

However, if the applied field E is not constant but has the form

$$E = E_0 \cos \omega t$$

we may expect the displacement x to be a function not only of the amplitude E_0 but also of the frequency. We should expect, then, that the permittivity also will be a function of the frequency of the applied field.

If the nucleus is elastically bound to its equilibrium position, we expect it to have a characteristic natural frequency determined by its equation of motion, Eq. 7.1,

$$M \frac{d^2 x}{dt^2} = -kx \tag{7.79}$$

the solution of which is

$$x = X_0 \sin \omega_0 t \tag{7.80}$$

$$\omega_0 = \sqrt{k/M}$$

Electrical resonances in solids will be produced at the natural frequencies of oscillation of atomic nuclei and also of the various electrons in the atoms. We take up first the nuclear oscillations. These are closely related to the thermal motions of the atoms. The analysis of the oscillations of nuclei in solids is complicated because of the interaction of the various nuclei with each other. Thus, for example, if we imagined all the nuclei in a solid at rest in their equilibrium positions, and if then we displaced just one slightly, an electric field extending throughout the crystal would be produced by the displaced nucleus and this would in turn slightly displace all the others. Nuclei in solids have complicated interactions and therefore also a complicated vibrational spectrum. We shall simplify the problem by neglecting the interactions and treat the nuclei as independent oscillators all having the same characteristic frequency. Our task now is to compute this frequency.

In our discussion of the polarizability of dielectrics in constant fields, we found for the constant k describing the restoring force exerted on a displaced nucleus in Eq. 3.42

$$F = -kx \qquad k = \frac{1}{4\pi\epsilon_0} \frac{(Ze)^2}{R^3}$$

The characteristic frequency f_n of nuclear oscillations follows immediately, from Eq. 7.80:

$$f_n = \frac{\omega_n}{2\pi} = \frac{1}{2\pi} \sqrt{\frac{k}{M}} = \frac{1}{2\pi} \sqrt{\frac{(Ze)^2}{4\pi\epsilon_0 R^3 M}} \tag{7.81}$$

For most nuclei, the mass number A is about $2Z$, or twice the atomic number. We may therefore put for Z^2/M, approximately $Z^2/AM_P \simeq Z/2M_P$, where M_P is the mass of a proton. If we take $R \simeq 2 \times 10^{-10}$ meter,

$$f_n \simeq 1.5 \times 10^{14} \text{ cycles/sec}$$

This is beyond the range of radio frequencies which can be produced in electrical circuits and even beyond the microwaves which can be generated and transmitted with special equipment to be discussed briefly in the next chapter. From the point of view of electrical circuits, then, we should not expect to find electric resonant frequencies due to nuclear oscillations in the experimentally available range. They occur at frequencies which we shall take up further on in connection with the study of heat and light waves.

It remains now to say something about the characteristic frequencies which we may expect for electrons. The manner in which electrons are bound to atoms, and the frequencies which they can radiate, will be the subject of a later discussion after some of the new aspects of atomic mechanics have been introduced. We here content ourselves with the comment that, if we are concerned with orders of magnitude rather than exact detail, we can arrive at reasonable estimates by computing the frequency of circulation of electrons in circular orbits.

The equation to be satisfied by a charge of mass m moving in the field of a singly charged ion in a circular orbit of radius R and with a velocity v is

$$\frac{mv^2}{R} = \frac{1}{4\pi\epsilon_0} \frac{e^2}{R^2}$$

$$v = \sqrt{\frac{e^2}{4\pi_0 mR}}$$

$$f_e = \frac{v}{2\pi R} = \frac{1}{2\pi} \sqrt{\frac{e^2}{4\pi_0 mR^3}} \tag{7.82}$$

This turns out to be approximately 10 times the nuclear frequency, or

$$f_e \simeq 1.5 \times 10^{15} \text{ cycles/sec}$$

We may further anticipate that, if we are dealing with heavy atoms having not only a large mass number A but also a large atomic number Z, there must be inner electrons circulating in smaller orbits. According to Eq. 7.82 this must mean even higher absorption frequencies. We see that the natural frequencies of atomic electrons lie even farther beyond the experimentally available circuit oscillations than do the nuclear oscillations.

Returning now to the effects to be expected in electrical circuits as a result of the high electrical resonant frequencies predicted above, we consider the forced oscillation of an elastically bound electric charge. Its equation of motion will be

$$M \frac{d^2x}{dt^2} + \text{const.} \frac{dx}{dt} + kx = qE_0 \cos \omega t$$

On dividing this equation by M, we have, using the notation of Section 7.1,

$$\frac{d^2x}{dt^2} + \frac{1}{T} \frac{dx}{dt} + \omega_0{}^2 x = \frac{q}{M} E_0 \cos \omega t \qquad (7.83)$$

In accordance with our previous discussion the displacement of the charge q from its equilibrium position will be given by a periodic function having the same frequency as the applied field.

$$x = X_0 \cos (\omega t + \psi) \qquad (7.84)$$

The behavior of the phase angle ψ and the amplitude X_0 has already been discussed and is plotted in Fig. 7.1. In our present notation $A_0 = qE_0/M$, and the resonance frequency is specified in Eq. 7.80.

It now remains to discuss two important consequences of the above motion induced in the nuclei of a solid by an oscillating field: How much work is done per unit time and unit volume by the field in moving the electric charges, and what then is the rate of heating of the solid? Finally, we must return to the problem of computing the permittivity ϵ of the solid as a function of frequency.

The average power input per atom is given in Eq. I.25 of Appendix I and is plotted in Fig. 7.25a for a sample with n atoms per unit volume. The expression for the average power input is

$$W = \frac{q_2 E_0{}^2 n \omega_0}{2k} \frac{\omega_0 T}{1 + \omega_0{}^2 T^2 \left(\dfrac{\omega_0}{\omega} - \dfrac{\omega}{\omega_0}\right)^2} \qquad (7.85)$$

The permittivity is defined by the relation

$$\epsilon = \epsilon_0 + \frac{P}{E}$$

$$= \epsilon_0 + \frac{qxn}{E} = \epsilon_0 + \frac{q(X_0 \cos \psi) \cos \omega t \cdot n}{E_0 \cos \omega t}$$

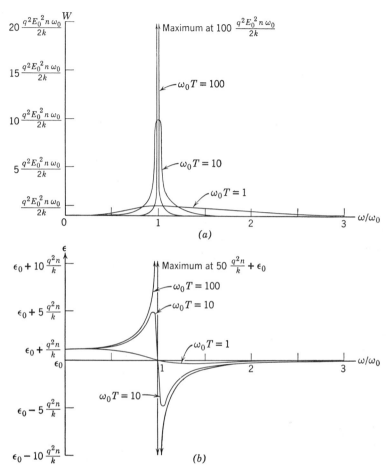

FIG. 7.25. (a) The power loss in watts per unit volume and (b) the permittivity of a solid consisting of n particles per unit volume, each having a charge q and mass M independently bound by a restoring force $-kx$ proportional to a displacement x, and subjected to an applied oscillating field whose amplitude is E_0 and whose frequency is $\omega/2\pi$. The natural frequency of oscillation of these particles is

$$f_0 = \frac{\omega_0}{2\pi} = \frac{1}{2\pi}\sqrt{\frac{k}{M}}$$

$$\epsilon = \epsilon_0 + \frac{qX_0 \, (\cos \psi)}{E_0} \, n = \epsilon_0 + \frac{q^2 M}{k} \frac{\dfrac{\omega_0}{\omega}\left(\dfrac{\omega_0}{\omega} - \dfrac{\omega}{\omega_0}\right)\omega_0{}^2 T^2}{1 + \omega_0{}^2 T^2 \left(\dfrac{\omega_0}{\omega} - \dfrac{\omega}{\omega_0}\right)^2} \quad (7.86)$$

This quantity is plotted in Fig. 7.25b.

At the frequencies which we can produce in electrical circuits we are, as mentioned above, far below resonance. We therefore expect to find an increase of energy dissipation and an increase in the dielectric coefficient with increasing frequency. This expectation is borne out by the facts. However, the real importance of the internal motions of atomic constituents will not be apparent until, in later chapters, we take up the optical properties of atoms and the radiations which they emit.

SUMMARY

Systems capable of free oscillation are characterized by an equation of motion of the form

$$\frac{d^2x}{dt^2} + \frac{1}{T}\frac{dx}{dt} + \omega_0{}^2 x = A$$

where $1/T$ is a damping constant and ω_0 is the natural frequency of the undamped motion. If A is a constant, the motion consists of damped oscillations if $T\omega_0 > \frac{1}{2}$, and of non-oscillatory motion if $T\omega_0 < \frac{1}{2}$. If A is a periodic function of amplitude A_0 and frequency $f = \omega/2\pi$,

$$A = A_0 \cos \omega t$$

the resulting motion will be

$$x = X_0 \cos (\omega t - \psi)$$

$$X_0 = \frac{A_0 T/\omega}{\sqrt{1 + \omega_0{}^2 T^2 \left(\dfrac{\omega_0}{\omega} - \dfrac{\omega}{\omega_0}\right)^2}}$$

$$\tan \psi = \frac{1}{\omega_0 T \left(\dfrac{\omega_0}{\omega} - \dfrac{\omega}{\omega_0}\right)}$$

The quantity $\omega_0 T$, also designated by Q, is important in determining the range of frequencies over which resonance phenomena are important. For values of $\omega_0 T$ large compared to unity, the resonance phenomena are confined to the immediate vicinity of the resonance frequency.

The fundamental equation of an LRC series circuit may be stated in two equivalent ways. First, the energy supplied to the circuit must show up in the electric or magnetic fields of the circuit elements or as heat in the resistor. Second, the potential difference between the terminals must at each instant be equal to the algebraic sum of the potential differences between the circuit elements. The equation may be written in the following form:

$$V_{ab} = L\frac{d^2q}{dt^2} + R\frac{dq}{dt} + \frac{q}{C}$$

If an inductor and capacitor are connected together, they will oscillate, when disturbed, with a characteristic frequency

$$f_0 = \frac{1}{2\pi}\sqrt{\frac{1}{LC}}$$

If a series LRC circuit is driven at a frequency f, the ratio of voltage to current is

$$\frac{V_0}{I_0} = \frac{V}{I} = Z = \sqrt{R^2 + (X_L - X_C)^2}$$

The impedance Z has a minimum value equal to the resistance of the circuit when $f = f_0$, as defined above.

The angle ϕ by which the voltage leads the current is given by

$$\sin\phi = \frac{X_L - X_C}{Z}$$

where

$$X_L = 2\pi fL = \omega L$$
$$X_C = 1/2\pi fC = 1/\omega C$$

The Q of an LRC circuit is

$$Q = L\omega_0/R$$

The width $\Delta\omega$ at half maximum of the power resonance curve is

$$\Delta\omega = \omega_0/Q$$

Matter can be made to show electric and magnetic resonance effects in oscillating fields having suitable frequencies. The simplest magnetic resonance effects are due to the precession of magnetic dipoles in an externally applied field. The precession frequencies of nuclear dipoles in magnetic fields of the order of some thousands of gauss are in the megacycle range, whereas atomic precession frequencies are thousands of times as great. Electric resonances due to the oscillation of elastically bound charges in atoms are beyond the range of frequencies which can be produced in electric circuits.

PROBLEMS

1. A 10-henry choke, a 1 μf capacitor, and a 1000-ohm resistor are connected in series across a 115-volt, 60-cycle, a-c line. Find the current through, and the voltage across, each element; the phase angle; and the power dissipated in the circuit.

2. In Problem 1, if L were variable, what value should it have for maximum current in the circuit? Find the same quantities asked for above, in this case, as well as the Q of the circuit and the half-width of the resonance curve.

3. A 10-henry choke, a 1 μf capacitor, and a 500-ohm resistor are connected together in a series circuit.

(a) Can this circuit oscillate? (b) What are its critical frequencies for spontaneous and forced oscillation? (c) What is its Q? (d) What would be the value of R for critical damping?

4. Make a plot of phase angle vs. frequency for a series LRC circuit connected to an a-c source of variable frequency. Indicate how the curve would be modified for much larger and much smaller values of R.

5. A coil of resistance 2 ohms and inductance 0.1 henry is used in series with a capacitor to show resonance. The only source of emf available is a 115-volt, 60-cycle line.

(a) What is the necessary capacitance? (b) If the capacitor is designed to stand an effective voltage of 500 volts, what additional resistance must be inserted in the circuit to limit the drop to this value?

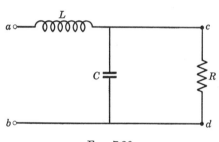

FIG. 7.26.

6. An inductance of 0.1 henry, a 35-ohm resistor, and a 100 μf capacitor are connected in parallel across a 110-volt, 60-cycle/sec line.

(a) How much current will the line supply? (b) What is the power factor?

(7) In Problem 6, for what frequency will the above circuit be at resonance, and what would be the impedance of the circuit at this frequency?

★8. In the circuit in Fig. 7.26, the voltage V_{ab} is given by

$$V_{ab} = A + B \sin 2\pi ft$$

Find the ratio of the alternating to that of the constant component of the voltage V_{cd} across the resistor. The following procedure may be found helpful. Take up first the parallel RC circuit. The total current into it must satisfy $I_p Z_p = V_p$. But the voltage across it is V_{cd}, and the impedance is

$$\frac{1}{Z_p} = \left[\frac{1}{R^2} + \frac{1}{X_C{}^2}\right]^{\frac{1}{2}}$$

and the current will lead the voltage by an angle which must be determined. But the current I_p flows through the inductor. What is the magnitude of the voltage across the inductor? By how much does it lead or lag behind the current I_p, which, incidentally, must also be the line current? The answers to these subquestions may now be put together to provide an answer to the main question.

★9. The filter shown in Fig. 7.26 is connected to the output of a full-wave rectifier, with an additional input capacitor C_1, as shown in Fig. 7.27. If no current were drawn (that is, if the resistance R were infinite) there would be a constant voltage across the capacitor equal to the amplitude of the a-c voltage being rectified. If the resistance R is not infinite, so that a current is drawn, it can be shown that this will consist of a d-c component I_{dc}, and an alternating component whose rms value I_f will be given by

$$I_f = \sqrt{2}\, I_{dc}$$

having the same frequency as the frequency of the voltage being rectified. There will also be harmonics having higher frequencies, but these may be neglected.

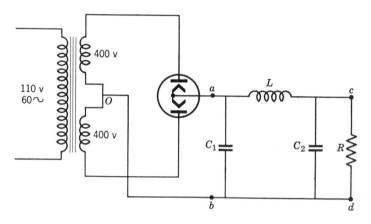

Fig. 7.27.

(a) Show that, if the reactance of the choke coil L (assumed to have zero resistance) is large compared with that of the capacitors, and if R is large compared with the reactance of C_2, then the ratio of the fluctuation component of the output voltage V_{cd} to the constant component will be

$$\frac{V_f}{V_{const}} = \frac{X_{C\,1} X_{C\,2}}{X_L R}$$

This is quite straightforward if we compute V_{ab} by assuming that, if $X_{C\,1}$ is small compared to X_L, essentially all the alternating current at a will flow through C_1, and therefore

$$V_{ab} = \frac{\sqrt{2}\, I_{dc}}{\omega C_1}$$

Similarly, if $X_{C\,2}$ is small compared to X_L, then V_{ab} will appear across the choke coil L. We can then estimate how much current, even though a small fraction of the incoming oscillating component, will pass through L. Finally, knowing this current, we can estimate the voltage across the capacitor C_2, which is the voltage V_{cd}.

(b) If the rectified frequency is 60 cycles/sec, the output rms voltage of the transformer is 400, $C_1 = C_2 = 100\ \mu\text{f}$, $L = 1$ henry, and the filtered output of the rectifier is designed to make 10 ma of direct current available, what will be the amplitude of the ripple voltage across the resistor?

(c) Can you see why, if we were dealing with a half-wave rectifier instead of a full-wave rectifier, the ripple voltage would be 8 times as large?

10. The tube whose characteristics are shown in Fig. 7.18 is operated with a plate voltage of 200 volts and a grid voltage of -20 volts.

(a) Find the plate current i_p, the amplification factor μ, the plate resistance r_P, the transconductance g_m, and the plate conductance g_P.

(b) In the circuit shown in Fig. 7.17 the grid voltage is -30 volts and fluctuates sinusoidally with an amplitude of 0.5 volt. The load resistor R in the plate circuit is 2000 ohms, and $E_B = 300$ volts. What is the resulting amplitude of the plate current and plate voltage oscillations?

11. What would be the precession frequency in a field of 10,000 gauss of an atom whose magnetic moment was due to the circulation of a single electron in a circular orbit of radius 0.5×10^{-10} meter?

12. Magnetic fields are not quite uniform inside atoms and molecules because of the diamagnetic shielding of the outer electrons. For this reason the protons in a complex molecule in an applied field of some definite magnitude, say 1 weber/meter^2, or 10,000 gauss, will not all have exactly the same resonant frequency. A carefully measured resonance curve for the protons in a certain substance shows two resonance frequencies, or two maxima in the absorption curve, one at a frequency 35 cycles per second higher than the other. The two maxima are just clearly resolved. The value of γ for protons is 4300 cycles/gauss. (Notice that this is in cycles, and not radians.) What is the order of magnitude of the relaxation time of the protons in this substance?

13. Make a sketch for power loss and permittivity for forced oscillation of an elastically bound charge as in Fig. 7.25, but for the case of $T\omega_0 = 5$.

14. Plot displacement and force as a function of time for a few cycles for an elastically bound charge (a) if the driving frequency is much less than the natural frequency; (b) if the driving frequency is much greater than the natural frequency; and (c) if the driving frequency equals the natural frequency.

15. Derive an expression for the permittivity as a function of frequency for the case of no damping, or $T = \infty$.

CHAPTER 8

The Poynting Vector and
Electromagnetic Waves

8.1 THE POYNTING VECTOR

Energy can be transmitted through empty space. Broadcasting towers send out radio and television signals which are received at distant points. The sun transmits heat and light through the high vacuum in interplanetary space. We propose now to describe this transmission of energy in detail.

An energy flow through space is best described by means of a vector. The direction of this vector will indicate the direction of movement of the energy. The magnitude of the vector may conveniently be so chosen that it specifies the magnitude of the energy flow, or the number of joules per second which cross unit area measured on a plane perpendicular to the vector.

The vector describing energy flow through space is called the *Poynting vector*, after J. H. Poynting (1852–1914), and is designated by **S**. Its magnitude gives the watts per square meter moving in the direction of **S**. Thus, if **S** is along the x axis of some rectangular coordinate system, the magnitude of **S** would be S_x. The total flow of energy through some area A measured on the y-z plane would be $S_x A$, where A is in square meters.

The transmission of energy through space is an electromagnetic phenomenon and must be related to the electric and magnetic fields which we have already described. Energy, we have seen, may be located in space. Wherever there is an electric field E, we have an energy per unit volume equal to $ED/2$. Wherever there is a magnetic field, we may expect to find additional energy per unit volume equal to $HB/2$. In order to describe the flow of this energy from its sources into space, we must consider some volume element of space in which the total energy is increasing. This energy can be increasing only if energy

305

is flowing inward through the surface. The mathematical derivation of the Poynting vector consists of finding an expression for **S** such that the integral of the normal component of **S** over a closed surface is numerically equal to the time rate of increase of energy in the volume bounded by this closed surface. If A is the surface area of a volume of space containing a total energy U, we must find a vector **S** such that

$$\int_A S_n \, dA = \frac{dU}{dt}$$

The derivation of the Poynting vector is given below. The result is

$$\mathbf{S} = [\mathbf{E} \times \mathbf{H}] \qquad\qquad \blacktriangleright(8.1)\blacktriangleleft$$

Since the electric field in mks units is in volts/meter, and the magnetic field is in amps/meter, the product is (volt · amp)/meter^2, or watts/meter^2. Wherever non-parallel electric and magnetic fields are simultaneously present, there will be a flow of energy at right angles to the plane containing the two. According to the rules of vector multiplication, the magnitude of S is $EH \sin \phi$ where ϕ is the angle between E and H. The direction of S is the direction of advance of a right-handed screw when the sense of rotation is that of a rotation of the electric vector E in the direction of H.

The Derivation of the Poynting Vector

In our previous considerations of the energy associated with electric and magnetic fields, we discussed the two kinds of fields separately. The energy density in the electric field surrounding the charged metallic parts of a capacitor was defined as

$$u_e = ED/2$$

and the energy density in the static magnetic field surrounding a conductor in which there exists a constant current was defined as

$$u_m = HB/2$$

We shall now consider how to describe the movement of energy in space. It is clear that, since we shall be dealing with changing energy densities, we shall be concerned with changing fields and therefore with simultaneously present electric and magnetic fields. For example, when the energy density in the field of a capacitor is changing, the electric field must be changing, there must be a charging current, and this, in turn, will be associated with a magnetic field. Similarly, when a magnetic field is changing, induced emf's must appear and therefore also electric fields. The flow of energy in space must therefore be associated with the simultaneous appearance of electric and magnetic fields, and the description of this flow of energy must somehow be contained in the fundamental equations relating the two fields, namely, the circuital relations of Chapter 6. For a vacuum, which we shall first consider, these may be written

$$\oint H_t \, ds = \int_S \dot{D}_n \, dA$$

and

$$\oint E_t \, ds = -\int_S \dot{B}_n \, dA \tag{8.2}$$

These equations we shall apply to an infinitesimal volume element dv in an attempt to relate the fields at the surface of the volume element to the change in total energy content. The rate of increase of energy within the volume element may be written

$$\frac{\partial U}{\partial t} = \frac{\partial u}{\partial t} \, dv = \frac{\partial}{\partial t} \left(\frac{HB}{2} + \frac{ED}{2} \right) dv \tag{8.3}$$

The next step is to select a particular volume element to study. This will be a cube oriented in a particular way with respect to the fields we are considering. To begin with, we choose the y axis in the direction of the electric

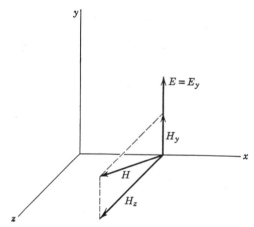

FIG. 8.1. The specification of the coordinate system to be used in describing the Poynting vector.

field. The magnetic field will in general have a component at right angles to the electric field. We shall see that this normal component only is involved in the description of energy flow in space, and that the special case of E parallel to H is of no interest. We now choose the z axis in the direction of the component of H perpendicular to E, and choose the x axis in the usual way so that x, y, z form a right-handed coordinate system, shown in Fig. 8.1. The volume element which we shall use will be a cube whose volume is $dx \, dy \, dz$, shown in Fig. 8.2. The electric field and the z component of the magnetic field are shown. The magnetic field may also have a y component. Expressing our starting point, which is Eq. 8.3, in this coordinate system, we get, since

$$E_x = E_z = 0$$
$$H_x = 0$$

and since

$$HB = \mu_0 H^2 = \mu_0(H_x{}^2 + H_y{}^2 + H_z{}^2) = \mu_0 H_y{}^2 + \mu_0 H_z{}^2$$

$$ED = \epsilon_0 E^2 = \epsilon_0(E_x{}^2 + E_y{}^2 + E_z{}^2) = \epsilon_0 E_y{}^2$$

that

$$\frac{\partial U}{\partial t} = \left(\mu_0 H_y \frac{\partial H_y}{\partial t} + \mu_0 H_z \frac{\partial H_z}{\partial t} + \epsilon_0 E_y \frac{\partial E_y}{\partial t} \right) dx\, dy\, dz$$

$$= (H_y \dot{B}_y + H_z \dot{B}_z + E_y \dot{D}_y)\, dx\, dy\, dz \qquad (8.4)$$

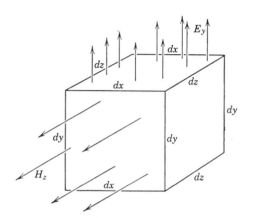

Fɪɢ. 8.2.   The volume element being considered.

Let us now apply the second of Eqs. 8.2 to the various faces of the cube shown in Fig. 8.2.   In order to express B_y in terms of an electric field, we must choose a face of the cube at right angles to B_y, which could be only the upper or lower faces.   One of these is redrawn in Fig. 8.3.   It is clear that the line integral of E around either of these squares must vanish, since E_t, which in this case is either E_x or E_z, vanishes. We conclude that, if E is in the direction of the y axis, then B_y must necessarily be zero, and the first term of Eq. 8.4 is also zero.

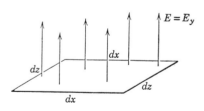

Fɪɢ. 8.3.   The evaluation of

$$\oint E_t\, ds = -\int_S \dot{B}_y\, dA.$$

Before evaluating the second term, notice that since the volume element we are dealing with is assumed to contain no free charges, the total electric flux going in is equal to that going out.   Further, since electric flux enters and leaves only on the lower and upper faces, which have the same area, the flux density must be the same on both faces.   We therefore conclude that in our volume element E_y is independent of y, as shown in Fig. 8.4.

We now take up the second term in Eq. 8.4, and identify B_z with the $\dot{B}_n$ of

Eq. 8.2. The surface area to be considered is one having sides dx and dy, as shown in Fig. 8.5. Along the sides dx, the contour integral has no contribution to make, since the tangential component of E, namely, E_x, is zero. We are left, then, with the contributions of the vertical sides. All along the left-

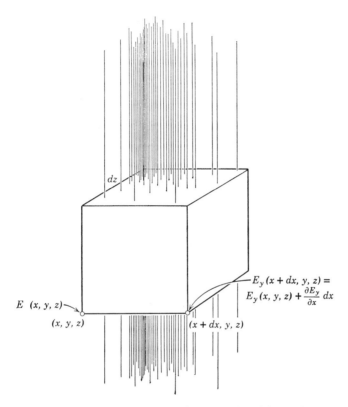

$$E_y(x + dx, y, z) = E_y(x, y, z) + \frac{\partial E_y}{\partial x}\, dx$$

$E(x, y, z)$

(x, y, z)

$(x + dx, y, z)$

FIG. 8.4. E_y is independent of y but varies with x and z.

hand side, the electrical field has the value E_y, and all along the right-hand side it has a different value, $E_y + (\partial E_y/\partial x)\, dx$. The line integral may therefore be written

$$\oint E_t\, ds = \left(E_y + \frac{\partial E_y}{\partial x}\, dx \right) dy - E_y\, dy = \frac{\partial E_y}{\partial x}\, dx\, dy$$

But Eq. 8.2 states that

$$\oint E_t\, ds = -\int_S \dot{B}_n\, dA$$

The right-hand side of this equation applied to the face of the cube for which we have evaluated the contour integral, shown in Fig. 8.5 is simply $-\dot{B}_y\, dx\, dy$.

Equating our results for the contour and surface integrals, we have

$$\dot{B}_z = -\frac{\partial E_y}{\partial x} \tag{8.5}$$

Similarly, in dealing with the third term of Eq. 8.4 we wish to identify $\dot{D}_y$ with $\dot{D}_n$ of the first equation of Eq. 8.2. To do this, we consider a square

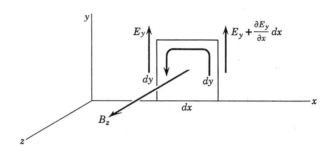

FIG. 8.5.   The evaluation of $\oint E_t \, ds = -\int_S \dot{B}_z \, dA.$

surface of our volume having sides dx and dz at right angles to y, as shown in Fig. 8.6.   It is possible to show that, just as E_y was independent of y, so H_z is independent of z.   The line integral to be evaluated becomes

$$\oint H_t \, ds = H_z \, dz - \left(H_z + \frac{\partial H_z}{\partial x} \, dx \right) dz = -\frac{\partial H_z}{\partial x} \, dx \, dz$$

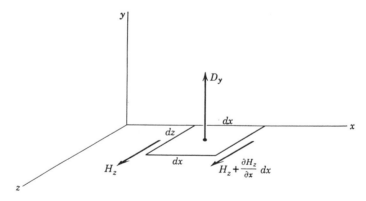

FIG. 8.6.   The evaluation of $\oint H_t \, ds = \int_S \dot{D}_y \, dA.$

Equating this to the integral on the right of Eq. 8.2, which applied to the face of the cube shown in Fig. 8.6 is $D_y \, dx \, dz$, we get

$$-\frac{\partial H_z}{\partial x} = \dot{D}_y$$

Our original expression for the rate of increase of the energy content of the volume element $dx\, dy\, dz$, in Eq. 8.4 can now be expressed in the form

$$\frac{\partial U}{\partial t} = -\left(H_z \frac{\partial E_y}{\partial x} + E_y \frac{\partial H_z}{\partial x}\right) dx\, dy\, dz$$

or

$$\frac{\partial U}{\partial t} = -dy\, dz \left[\frac{\partial}{\partial x} E_y H_z\right] dx \tag{8.6}$$

We now give the quantity $E_y H_z$ a new name. It is the x component of the Poynting vector **S**.

$$S_x \equiv E_y H_z$$

The interpretation of Eq. 8.6 and the general definition of the Poynting vector **S** are facilitated by reference to Fig. 8.7. In accordance with the above,

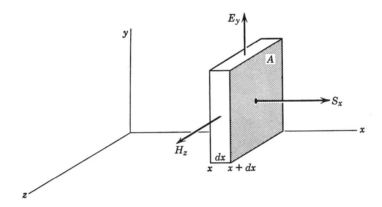

FIG. 8.7.   The Poynting vector.

the energy flow into the volume from the left is AS_x. The energy flow out of the volume is $A\left(S_x + \dfrac{\partial S_x}{\partial x}\, dx\right)$, and the rate of accumulation of energy within the volume, $\partial U/\partial t$, is

$$\frac{\partial U}{\partial t} = AS_x - A\left(S_x + \frac{\partial S_x}{\partial x}\, dx\right)$$

$$= -A \frac{\partial S_x}{\partial x}\, dx$$

But, equating this result with the result of our derivation, as summarized in Eq. 8.6, we have

$$\frac{\partial U}{\partial t} = -dy\, dz \left[\frac{\partial}{\partial x} E_y H_z\right] dx$$

$$= -A \frac{\partial S_x}{\partial x}\, dx$$

or

$$S_x = E_y H_z$$

This result may be generalized for fields in arbitrary directions in any coordinate systems. In vector notation, we may put

$$\mathbf{S} = [\mathbf{E} \times \mathbf{H}] \qquad (8.7)$$

This is the general definition of the Poynting vector.

_____

The energy flow vector $\mathbf{S}$ may be more pictorially described as follows. Suppose we have in some region of space an energy density u_s moving uniformly with a velocity $\mathbf{v}$. The amount of energy crossing unit area normal to the flow in one second is simply $u_s \mathbf{v}$. We may therefore write

$$\mathbf{S} = u_s \mathbf{v}$$

Notice that nothing we have said specifies that u_s must necessarily be the total energy density $u_e + u_m$. It is possible that the vector $\mathbf{S}$ should have its specified magnitude because all the energy in space is moving with a velocity $\mathbf{S}/(u_e + u_m)$. It is also possible, however, that only a part of the electric and magnetic energy in space moves, but with a greater velocity. In some cases, particularly when we are dealing with waves, it can be shown that indeed all the energy in space moves, but this is not a general property to be associated with the Poynting vector. It is only the product $u_s v$ that we can in general specify.

This product, however, suffices for the specification of the momentum per unit volume that we must associate with the moving energy described by the Poynting vector. If mass is energy divided by c^2, then energy per unit volume divided by c^2 must be equivalent to mass per unit volume, or $u_s/c^2 = \rho_s$. But $\rho_s v$ is simply a momentum per unit volume, and we therefore have

$$\frac{\mathbf{S}}{c^2} = \frac{u_s}{c^2} \mathbf{v} = \rho_s \mathbf{v} = \text{momentum per unit volume} \qquad (8.8)$$

With moving energy there must be associated a momentum. The significance of these concepts concerning the movement of energy in space is illustrated in the next section, where they are applied to a series of simple situations with which the student is already familiar.

8.2 THE FLOW OF ENERGY AROUND CIRCUIT ELEMENTS

As a first example, we take up the transmission of energy along a cable from a battery to a load. We shall assume that the resistance of the cable is negligibly small. The difference in voltage between the terminals of the battery will then appear across the terminals of the load, and there will be no voltage drop, and therefore no electric field, along the cable. The cross section of the cable, which we shall take to be composed of two straight wires, is shown in Fig. 8.8. The electric lines of force run from the positively charged cable at a high potential to the negatively charged cable at a lower potential. Since the current flows down the positively charged cable to the load, and in the load from a high to a low potential, we must assume that the current is

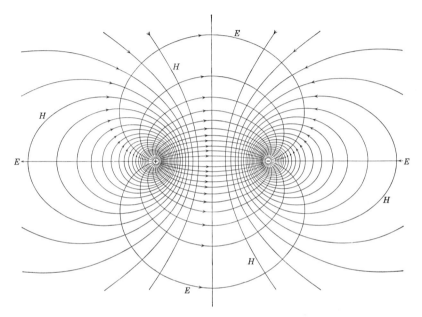

Fig. 8.8.   The electric and magnetic fields around a two-wire cable of negligible resistance carrying power from a battery to a load.

flowing into the paper toward the load along the positively charged cable in Fig. 8.8, and back from the load to the battery along the negatively charged cable. The magnetic lines of flux surround the current into the page toward the load in a clockwise sense, and the current out of the page toward the battery in a counterclockwise sense, as shown. Note that the magnetic and electric fields are everywhere at right angles to each other, and that the Poynting vector, $\mathbf{E} \times \mathbf{H}$, is everywhere in Fig. 8.8 away from the reader into the paper, or from the battery toward the load. The numerical integration of the Poynting vector $\int S\, dA$ over the entire plane would turn out to be numerically equal to the power supplied by the battery to the load. The computation is not difficult, but it is too long to undertake here. Further examples of the flow of energy into a resistor in which heat is being generated, into a capacitor in which electrostatic energy is being accumulated, and into an inductor in which magnetic energy is being accumulated are worked out quantitatively below.

Examples of the Poynting Vector

We shall now describe the flow of energy into a resistor in the form of a straight cylindrical wire of radius r carrying a constant current i. The current flows from a to b because of the presence of a longitudinal electric field of such magnitude that

$$EL = V_{ab} \qquad (8.9)$$

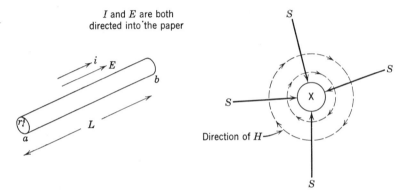

FIG. 8.9.   The flow of energy into a wire carrying a current.

The magnetic field at the surface of the wire is tangential and perpendicular to the length

$$H = i/2\pi r$$

The Poynting vector at the surface of the wire is directed inward, and its magnitude is given by

$$S = EH = \frac{iV_{ab}}{2\pi rL}$$

The rate of flow of energy into the wire is the above multiplied by the surface area A of the wire

$$W = SA = S2\pi rL = iV_{ab} \qquad (8.10)$$

This is just the rate of dissipation of electrical energy in the form of heat within the conductor.

As a further example, let us consider a parallel plate capacitor being charged. Figure 8.10 shows a cylindrical portion of the capacitor sufficiently far from the edges so that fringing fields may be neglected. We have, for the magnetic field H_b at the boundary of the cylindrical surface, from Eq. 8.2

$$\oint H_t \, ds = H_b 2\pi r = \int_S \dot{D}_n \, dA = \dot{D}\pi r^2 \qquad (8.11)$$

The magnitude of the Poynting vector, which is directed radially into the dielectric, is

$$S = EH = \frac{E\dot{D}}{2}r$$

and the rate of flow into the cylindrical volume v under consideration is

$$SA = S2\pi rd = E\dot{D}\pi r^2 d = E\dot{D}v$$

which may be rewritten

$$SA = \frac{d}{dt}\left(\frac{\epsilon E^2}{2}\right)v \qquad (8.12)$$

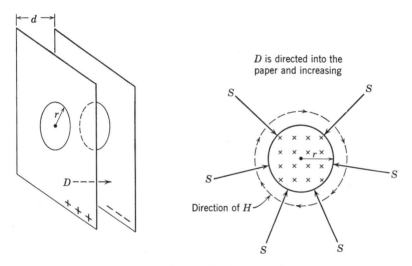

FIG. 8.10.   Energy flow into a capacitor.

In words, this equation says that the flow of energy into the dielectric, as given by the Poynting vector, is just equal to the rate of accumulation of electrostatic energy within the dielectric.

As a simple example involving the storage of magnetic energy, let us consider the central portion of length L of a long uniformly wound solenoid, shown in Fig. 8.11, in which the current is increasing. If the radius of the solenoid is r, the volume v under consideration is $v = \pi r^2 L$ and the total magnetic energy in the section of the solenoid at any time is

$$U_m = \mu_0 \frac{H^2}{2}\pi r^2 L \qquad (8.13)$$

The induced back emf in N turns of the solenoid has the magnitude

$$\mathcal{E} = N\frac{d\phi}{dt} = AN\frac{dB}{dt} = \pi r^2 N\frac{dB}{dt} \qquad (8.14)$$

The induced electric field responsible for this emf is given by

$$E = \mathcal{E}/(N2\pi r) = \frac{1}{2}r\frac{dB}{dt}$$

and the magnitude of the Poynting vector, finally, is

$$S = EH = \left(\frac{1}{2}r\frac{dB}{dt}\right)(H)$$

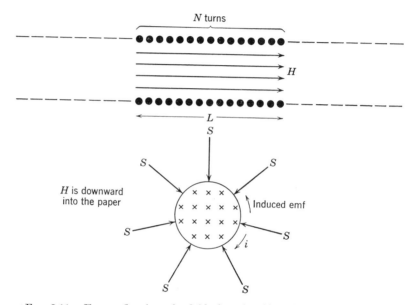

FIG. 8.11. Energy flow into the field of a solenoid as the current increases.

The total inward flow, then is the above quantity multiplied by the surface area of the solenoid, $2\pi rL$, or

$$SA = \pi r^2 L\mu_0 H\frac{dH}{dt}$$

$$= \pi r^2 L\frac{d}{dt}\left(\frac{\mu_0 H^2}{2}\right) \tag{8.15}$$

which is, as was to be expected, the time rate of change of the energy of the solenoid as given in Eq. 8.13.

8.3 TRAVELING WAVES IN CABLES

Let us consider a cable consisting of two wires a fixed distance apart and having some arbitrary very great length. One end of the cable is connected to a source of alternating emf, and this sets up a traveling wave in the cable. We are here avoiding considerations involving a return wave reflected from the far end of the cable. It is for this reason that we assume the cable to be arbitrarily long.

A first point worth examining in detail is the relationship between the voltage at the terminals of the generator and the current supplied to the cable by the generator. When an alternating emf is connected to

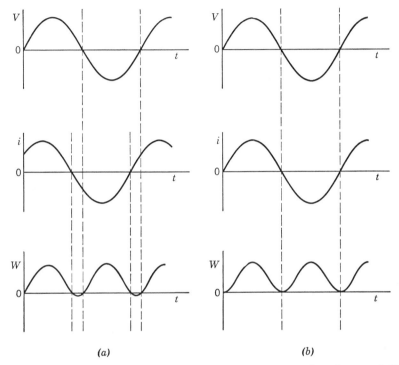

(a)   (b)

Fɪɢ. 8.12.   Energy flow from an a-c power supply (a) into an impedance and (b) into a pure resistance.

a cable, an alternating current flows into the cable. The amplitude and phase of the alternating current supplied by the generator depend on the equivalent impedance of the cable. If the current and voltage are out of phase, as in Fig. 8.12a, electrical energy flows to and fro, sometimes going from the generator into the cable, and sometimes back again. Only when the current is in phase with the voltage, as in Fig. 8.12b, is the flow always in one direction. This is the condition which we must expect in an arbitrarily long cable in which there is no reflected wave carrying energy back into the generator. Only in this case do we have a unidirectional flow of energy from the generator into the cable and along the cable itself.

A wave traveling along a two-wire cable is schematically shown in Fig. 8.13. At the instant shown the terminal a is positive with respect to terminal b. Since the generator is doing work, a current must be flowing out of the positive terminal a and into the negative terminal b. A wave of charge will move down the cable with a velocity which we shall compute. Associated with the moving charge is a current which will have maxima where the charge density is greatest. There will therefore

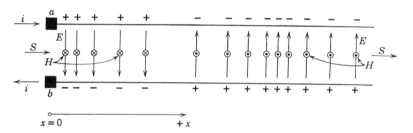

FIG. 8.13.   A traveling wave in a cable.

be a periodic electric field and a periodic magnetic field surrounding the cable. These two fields will be in phase with each other, as will also the voltage and current waves that move along the cable.

We must now take up the mathematical description of a traveling wave. Let us first of all consider the periodic function $y = Y_0 \sin 2\pi x/\lambda$ drawn in the x-y plane of a rectangular coordinate system. This wave has an amplitude Y_0 and is periodic along the x axis. The wave length, or the distance along the x axis in which the function repeats itself, is λ. If we wish to displace this wave a distance x_0 along the positive x axis, we must replace x in the expression for the wave by $x - x_0$. If we wish to describe a wave moving in the positive x direction with a velocity v, we must let $x_0 = vt$. The expression for a traveling wave then becomes

$$y = Y_0 \sin \frac{2\pi}{\lambda} (x - vt)$$

The various waves in the cable may be expressed in a similar form. For example, we might put for the difference in potentials between the conductors of the cable at any point x and at any time t

$$V = V_0 \sin \frac{2\pi}{\lambda} (x - vt)$$

and for the current along the conductors

$$i = I_0 \sin \frac{2\pi}{\lambda} (x - vt)$$

In these expressions we should have to specify the meaning of positive and negative voltages and currents. For example, we might agree to call voltages positive if the upper of the two conductors a in Fig. 8.13 is at a higher potential than the lower. It would then be necessary to specify that positive currents will mean currents away from the generator in the upper conductor. The currents in the two conductors, incidentally, will always be equal but oppositely directed. The electric and magnetic fields around the conductors may be similarly expressed.

A detailed analysis of the propagation of waves in cables is given below. It is shown that the velocity of propagation of waves in two conductor cables is determined only by the properties of the insulator separating the conductors, and not by the shape of the cable. The velocity is the velocity of light and is given in Eq. 8.26

$$v = 1/\sqrt{\epsilon\mu}$$
▶(8.16)◀

For insulators having the electromagnetic properties of free space this is

$$c = \frac{1}{\sqrt{\epsilon_0\mu_0}} = 3 \times 10^8 \text{ meter/sec}$$
▶(8.17)◀

In studying cables we are concerned not only with the velocity of propagation of waves but also with the relationship between currents and voltages. This depends markedly on the frequencies involved. If, for example, we apply a constant potential difference to the two conductors of a short length of cable open-circuited at its end, the only current present would be the leakage current through the insulation. If we apply an alternating potential, this cable will act like a capacitor. There will be a charging current to the conductors and a displacement current through the insulator. This displacement current is proportional to dD/dt, which, in turn, is proportional to the frequency of the applied voltage. It is clear that at high enough frequencies this capacitative effect will be much more important in determining current-voltage characteristics than it is at low frequencies. Similarly, if the cable is terminated in some way that allows current to pass from one of the conductors to the other, for example by a short circuit, and if we apply a constant potential difference to the conductors of the cable, the magnitude of the current which will flow along the cable will be determined by the resistance of the cable. But, if we apply an alternating potential, there will be an additional inductive reactance equal to $2\pi fL$, and this will be more important in determining current-voltage characteristics at high frequencies than at low frequencies. For conducting microwaves, or waves having wavelengths of the order of a meter, or frequencies of the order of hundreds of megacycles per second, the inductance per unit length L' and capacitance per unit length C' are usually more important than the resistance of the conductors or of the insulator. If we neglect these resistive effects, the ratio of the voltage to the current in a traveling wave, called the characteristic impedance Z_0, is given by Eq. 8.28.

$$Z_0 = \sqrt{L'/C'}$$

This ratio not only is a funcion of the electromagnetic properties of the insulating medium but also depends on the shape of the cable.

The Wave Equations for Cables

In discussing waves traveling along a cable we shall assume that the wavelength is very great compared to the transverse dimensions of the cable. As a consequence we may use expressions for capacitance per unit length C' and inductance per unit length L' as previously derived on the assumption that the current i and the charge per unit length q' are essentially uniform. For a coaxial cable having inner and outer radii r_1 and r_2, for example, we have previously found

$$C' = \frac{2\pi\epsilon}{\ln (r_2/r_1)} \qquad (8.18)$$

$$L' = \frac{\mu}{2\pi} \ln \frac{r_2}{r_1} \qquad (8.19)$$

In a traveling wave the current in the conductor is related to the charge per unit length. We have $i = dq/dt$. The current at any point is equal to the number of coulombs per second passing that point. But in a traveling wave moving with a velocity v this number is just equal to $q'v$. The charge pattern moves forward a distance v in one second, and the amount of charge in this length of the pattern is therefore $q'v$. We have then

$$i = dq/dt = q'v \qquad (8.20)$$

for a traveling wave. Note that this equation does not imply that the charges constituting q' actually move with the velocity v, which we shall see is the velocity of light. The current is numerically equal to $q'v$, but it is made up of all the conduction electrons in the metal moving with a very small drift velocity v' in such a way that the current $nev'A$ due to n electrons per unit volume in a conductor of cross-sectional area A will produce the required coulombs per second passing any point.

We must now describe our cable, which we assume to be any form of two-conductor cable, in more detail. In addition to inductance and capacitance distributed along its length, we shall assume that there is a resistance R per unit length of the cable and a leakage through the insulation which we may describe as a conductance G' per unit length such that the leakage current i_l in a length of cable x in which there is a difference of potential V between the conductors will be given by $i_l = G'xV$. For a given voltage the leakage current is proportional to x, and this proportionality factor G' is a characteristic of the cable.

We shall represent a length x of the cable symbolically by the interconnected circuit elements shown in Fig. 8.14. The inductance and resistance are grouped on one side of the cable for convenience in the following discussion. The same results could be arrived at if we considered half the inductance L' and half the resistance R' in each of the two conductors. The voltage difference between the two conductors is V and varies as we go from point to point

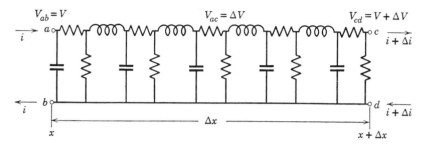

FIG. 8.14.   An equivalent circuit diagram of a cable.

along the cable at any fixed time. If the rate of change of voltage per unit length of cable at some constant time is $(\partial V/\partial x)$, then the change in voltage ΔV in a length Δx of the cable is $(\partial V/\partial x)\,\Delta x$. But there is a voltage drop due to the resistance $iR'\,\Delta x$, and due to the inductance $L'\,\Delta x\,(\partial i/\partial t)$. We have, therefore,

$$\Delta V = \frac{\partial V}{\partial x}\,\Delta x = -iR'\,\Delta x - L'\,\Delta x\,\frac{\partial i}{\partial t}$$

$$\frac{\partial V}{\partial x} = -iR' - L'\frac{\partial i}{\partial t} \tag{8.21}$$

Similarly we can calculate the change in current Δi between x and $x + \Delta x$. If the variation of current with x at any fixed time is $(\partial i/\partial x)$, then the difference in current at x and $x + \Delta x$ is $\Delta i = (\partial i/\partial x)\,\Delta x$. This must be a decrease just equal to the currents flowing from the upper conductor at a higher potential to the lower conductor at a lower potential in the length Δx. This must be the leakage current, $i_l = G'\,\Delta x V$, and the charging current to the capacitors, $\partial(q'\,\Delta x)/\partial t$. But the charge per unit length is given by the capacitance per unit length times the voltage, or $q' = C'V$, and the charging current may be written $\partial C'V\,\Delta x/\partial t = C'\,\Delta x\,\partial V/\partial t$. We therefore find that Δi is a decrease given by

$$\Delta i = \frac{\partial i}{\partial x}\,\Delta x = -G'\,\Delta x V - C'\,\Delta x\,\frac{\partial V}{\partial t}$$

$$\frac{\partial i}{\partial x} = -G'V - C'\frac{\partial V}{\partial t} \tag{8.22}$$

We shall for the moment assume that the resistance and conductance of the cable are zero. The equations specifying the properties of the cable then are

$$\frac{\partial V}{\partial x} = -L'\frac{\partial i}{\partial t}$$

$$\frac{\partial i}{\partial x} = -C'\frac{\partial V}{\partial t} \tag{8.23}$$

It is easy to prove that a solution of these equations is the traveling wave described at the beginning of this section. Substituting the expressions found into Eqs. 8.23 and carrying out the required differentiations, one gets

$$\frac{2\pi}{\lambda} V_0 \cos \frac{2\pi}{\lambda} (x - vt) = L' \frac{2\pi}{\lambda} v I_0 \cos \frac{2\pi}{\lambda} (x - vt)$$

$$\frac{2\pi}{\lambda} I_0 \cos \frac{2\pi}{\lambda} (x - vt) = C' \frac{2\pi}{\lambda} v V_0 \cos \frac{2\pi}{\lambda} (x - vt)$$

or, after canceling the quantities that appear on both sides of the equation,

$$V_0 = L' I_0 v$$

$$I_0 = C' V_0 v \tag{8.24}$$

Multiplying these two expressions by each other, we have

$$I_0 V_0 = L' C' I_0 V_0 v^2$$

or

$$v = 1/\sqrt{L'C'} \tag{8.25}$$

For a coaxial cable, substituting Eqs. 8.18 and 8.19, we find that $L'C' = \epsilon\mu$. This is true not only for a coaxial cable but for any cable. We therefore conclude that the velocity of propagation of waves in any cable depends only on the electromagnetic properties of the insulating medium between the conductors. Furthermore, this is true for any cable that can propagate a wave, even if R' and G' are not zero. We have then, quite generally,

$$v = 1/\sqrt{\epsilon\mu} \tag{8.26}$$

If we divide the two Eqs. 8.24 by each other we obtain

$$\frac{V_0}{I_0} = \frac{L'}{C'} \frac{I_0}{V_0}$$

or

$$V_0/I_0 = \sqrt{L'/C'} \tag{8.27}$$

This specifies the ratio of the amplitudes of the voltage and current in the traveling wave in a cable. This ratio is called the characteristic impedance Z_0 of a cable.

$$Z_0 = \sqrt{L'/C'} \tag{8.28}$$

For a coaxial cable we find

$$Z_0 = \sqrt{\frac{\mu}{\epsilon}} \frac{\ln (r_2/r_1)}{2\pi} \text{ ohms}$$

or, if $\mu = \mu_0$, and $\epsilon = K_e \epsilon_0$, the characteristic impedance is approximately

$$Z_0 = \frac{60}{\sqrt{K_e}} \ln \frac{r_2}{r_1} \text{ ohms} \tag{8.29}$$

A wave traveling down a cable terminated in a resistance equal to its characteristic impedance will be completely absorbed. The energy of the wave will be converted into heat in the resistance. This would not be true for any other termination of the cable. The reflection which then occurs is taken up in the next section.

The usual wave equation which is satisfied by a moving wave of any form, $f(x \pm vt)$, is obtained through differentiating f twice, first with respect to x holding t constant, and then with respect to t holding x constant. The result is

$$\frac{\partial^2 f}{\partial x^2} = \frac{1}{v^2} \frac{\partial^2 f}{\partial t^2} \tag{8.30}$$

In particular, periodic functions of $(2\pi/\lambda)(x - vt)$ satisfy this equation. An equation of this form for V or i is obtained by eliminating one of the two variables in Eqs. 8.23. For example, if we differentiate the first equation with respect to x and the second with respect to t, we get

$$\frac{\partial^2 V}{\partial x^2} = -L' \frac{\partial^2 i}{\partial x \, \partial t}$$

$$\frac{\partial^2 i}{\partial t \, \partial x} = -C' \frac{\partial^2 V}{\partial t^2} \tag{8.31}$$

But since the order of differentiation is immaterial

$$\frac{\partial^2 i}{\partial t \, \partial x} = \frac{\partial^2 i}{\partial x \, \partial t}$$

and on eliminating these from Eq. 8.31 we have

$$\frac{\partial^2 V}{\partial x^2} = L'C' \frac{\partial^2 V}{\partial t^2} \tag{8.32}$$

This is the wave Eq. 8.30 if we identify $L'C'$ with $1/v^2$, as we have already done in Eq. 8.25. By a similar procedure V may be eliminated from Eq. 8.23 yielding

$$\frac{\partial^2 i}{\partial x^2} = L'C' \frac{\partial^2 i}{\partial t^2} \tag{8.33}$$

So far we have assumed that the resistance per unit length R' and conductance per unit length G' of our cable are zero. In fact they never really vanish. A certain amount of heat will be generated in any cable carrying a current, and this will lead to a gradual diminution of amplitude as a wave moves along a cable. This attenuation of the wave, as it is called, is implicit in the complete expression for the relation of current to voltage in Eqs. 8.21 and 8.22.

Not all cables can transmit waves. For example, if we consider a cable in which the terms in Eqs. 8.21 and 8.22 involving R' and G' are large compared to the terms involving L' and C', these equations reduce to

$$\partial V/\partial x = -R'i$$

$$\partial i/\partial x = -G'V$$

Differentiating the first of these equations with respect to x, and combining this result with the second equation, we get

$$\frac{\partial^2 V}{\partial x^2} = -R' \frac{\partial i}{\partial x} = -R'(-G'V) = R'G'V$$

It is easy to verify that, when the constant on the right-hand side of an equation of this form is positive, a solution is

$$V = V_0 e^{-\sqrt{R'G'}x}$$

but periodic functions are not. An alternating potential connected to a cable of this kind will not produce a wavelike disturbance at all but only a disturbance pulsating in phase with the applied voltage and decreasing exponentially in magnitude along the length of the cable.

Cables in general may be called wave guides in the sense that they guide the flow of electromagnetic energy carried by the fields in their vicinity. The term wave guide is often reserved for a cable consisting of a single tubular conductor, having a circular or rectangular cross

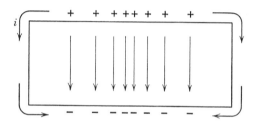

FIG. 8.15. Cross section of a rectangular wave guide showing transverse components of the current.

section. In such a wave guide currents are set up not only along the axis of the guide but also with transverse components, as shown in Fig. 8.15. The Poynting vector will therefore in general be at an angle to the axis of the guide, and the electromagnetic energy may be thought of as bouncing to and fro as it moves down the guide.

8.4 STANDING WAVES; REFLECTION

Standing waves are formed by the superposition of waves traveling in opposite directions. We have seen that a wave traveling to the right, or in the direction of increasing x, may be written

$$V_{right} = V_0 \sin \frac{2\pi}{\lambda} (x - vt)$$

$$i_{right} = I_0 \sin \frac{2\pi}{\lambda} (x - vt) \tag{8.34}$$

The current and voltage must be in phase with each other. The same voltage wave traveling to the left would be

$$V_{left} = V_0 \sin \frac{2\pi}{\lambda} (x + vt) \qquad (8.35)$$

The current wave traveling to the left would be in phase with the corresponding voltage wave, but if we agree to designate positive charges moving to the right in the upper cable of Fig. 8.13, for example, as positive currents, then we must put for our current wave traveling to the left in phase with the voltage

$$i_{left} = -I_0 \sin \frac{2\pi}{\lambda} (x + vt) \qquad (8.36)$$

In adding the above expressions we make use of the trigonometric relations

$$\sin (a - b) + \sin (a + b) = 2 \sin a \cos b$$

$$\sin (a - b) - \sin (a + b) = -2 \cos a \sin b$$

We then have for the voltage and current along the cable when the two waves are present

$$V = 2V_0 \sin \frac{2\pi x}{\lambda} \cos 2\pi ft$$

$$i = -2I_0 \cos \frac{2\pi x}{\lambda} \sin 2\pi ft \qquad (8.37)$$

These standing waves are shown in Fig. 8.16. The time dependence is here such that, for $t = 0$, the voltage is a sine function of x and the current is everywhere zero, as shown by the heavy lines in Figs. 8.16a and b. At this instant there will be a charge distribution along the cable like that schematically shown in Fig. 8.16c. At this instant $t = 0$ the charges are at rest, and the currents are therefore everywhere zero. The charges and currents are varying periodically along the cable with a frequency $f = v/\lambda$. The period of this oscillation is $\tau = 1/f$. Let us examine the condition of the cable a quarter of a cycle later, when $t = \tau/4 = 1/4f$. The voltage is now everywhere zero, because $\cos 2\pi f \cdot 1/4f = \cos \pi/2 = 0$. The current is now a negative cosine function, as shown in Fig. 8.16b. The charge distribution along the cable has disappeared and has been replaced by a current distribution, shown in Fig. 8.16d. Adjacent plus and minus charges move toward each other, producing maxima and minima in the current halfway between the previous charge maxima and minima. Another quarter of a cycle later, or for $t = \tau/2$, the currents have disappeared, and the charge maxima are reversed in sign from those initially on the cable.

The standing wave continues the above cyclic changes.   Energy moves
to and fro along the cable, but there is no net transport in any one

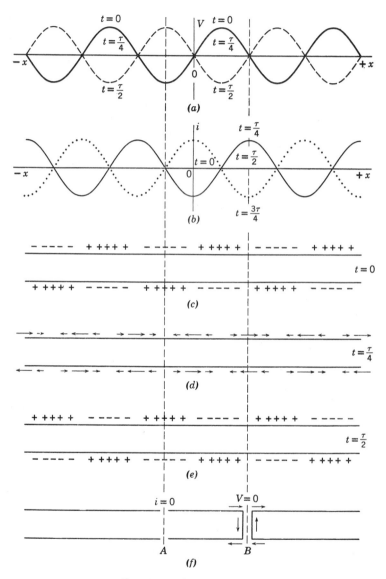

FIG. 8.16.   A standing wave.

direction.   When the currents vanish, as at $t = 0$, the energy is located
in the electric fields produced by the charge distribution of Fig. 8.16c.

A quarter of a cycle later the electric field is everywhere zero, but there are magnetic fields surrounding the currents a quarter of a wavelength from the electric field maxima. The Poynting vectors have periodic maxima between the electric and magnetic maxima, corresponding to a transfer of energy from one of these locations to the other.

The standing waves we have been describing are formed in an arbitrarily long cable in which waves of equal frequency and equal amplitude pass each other in opposite directions. Notice that, at $x = 0$, and at corresponding points along the cable a half wavelength apart, the voltage between the conductors is always zero. Notice also that at other points a half wavelength apart such as A in Fig. 8.16f the current along the wire is zero at all times. If at point A the cable is cut and the ends are held close together the current and charge distribution will not be affected. If the ends of the cable are pulled apart, it is true that the electric fields near the cut will be deformed, but, if the separation between the conductors is small compared to the wavelength, the alteration will not be important. We must think of the wave incident from the left as being reflected at the break, and the sum of the incident and reflected waves may be thought of as responsible for the standing wave pattern. Similarly, the right-hand side of the cable will have a traveling wave incident from the right and a reflected wave moving toward the right. The sum of these two will give rise to the standing waves in this half of the cable.

Similarly, if at B we short-circuit the two conductors and pull the two junctions apart as in Fig. 8.16f, the voltage between the conductors will be zero and the currents which originally flowed longitudinally from one part of the cable to the other now flow across from one conductor to the other.

In Fig. 8.16f, the central section of cable open-circuited at one end and short-circuited at the other has a length $3\lambda/4$. It is easy to generalize this result. A system of standing waves may be maintained in a cable whose length is x and which has one end short-circuited and one end open-circuited provided $x = (\lambda/4) + (n\lambda/2)$, where n is any positive integer or zero. Similarly, a system of standing waves may be maintained in a cable whose length is x and which has either a short circuit at both ends or an open circuit at both ends, provided $x = n\lambda/2$, where n is any positive integer.

These results are precisely equivalent to corresponding results obtained for the natural frequencies of organ pipes. If x is put equal to the length of the organ pipe and $\lambda = v/f$, then the above equations give the natural frequencies.

As a further illustration of these ideas, the cross section of a coaxial cable open at one end and short-circuited at the other and oscillating in its fundamental mode is shown in Fig. 8.17. The curves for the voltage and current as a function of distance along the cable give the amplitude of the voltage or current oscillations at any point.

In addition to complete reflection which occurs at open-circuited or short-circuited terminals, the possibility of partial reflection must be

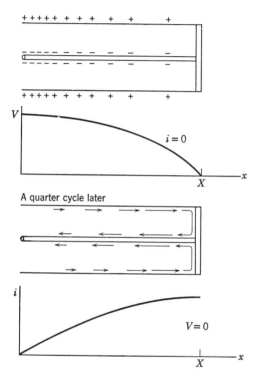

Fig. 8.17. Cross section of a coaxial cable shorted at one end oscillating at the lowest possible frequency.

considered. This may occur at a junction between two cables having different characteristic impedances, or at a terminal at which a part of the incident energy is absorbed. The following discussion of the partial reflection of waves in cables is very similar to that which we shall give in the next chapter concerning the partial reflection of light at the surface of a transparent medium.

The Partial Reflection of Waves at the Junction of Two Cables

We have seen that a wave in a cable will be reflected at an open-circuited or short-circuited terminal. An interesting extension of the ideas leading to this result is to consider what happens when a wave strikes the junction between two cables having differing characteristic impedances. This is an important consideration in circuits involving interconnected cables and other pieces of apparatus.

Let us consider a junction at $x = 0$, in a cable having a characteristic impedance Z_1 for negative values of x, and Z_2 for positive values of x. A wave incident from the left may be partly reflected and partly transmitted. We shall determine the fraction of the incident energy that is reflected.

Let us assume that the amplitudes of the incident voltage and current waves are V_i and I_i and that the amplitudes of the transmitted voltage and current waves are V_t and I_t. These two waves may be written

$$V_i \sin \frac{2\pi}{\lambda} (x - vt) \qquad I_i \sin \frac{2\pi}{\lambda} (x - vt)$$

$$V_t \sin \frac{2\pi}{\lambda} (x - vt) \qquad I_t \sin \frac{2\pi}{\lambda} (x - vt)$$

Similarly for the reflected wave moving to the left, we should have

$$V_r \sin \frac{2\pi}{\lambda} (x + vt) \qquad -I_r \sin \frac{2\pi}{\lambda} (x + vt)$$

The minus sign in the above expression for the reflected current was discussed in connection with Eq. 8.36. We wish to examine conditions at the junction, where $x = 0$. It is necessary that the voltages across the cable just to the left of the junction be equal to that just to the right of the junction, or that

$$V_i \sin \frac{2\pi}{\lambda} (0 - vt) + V_r \sin \frac{2\pi}{\lambda} (0 + vt) = V_t \sin \frac{2\pi}{\lambda} (0 - vt)$$

But since $\sin (-x) = -\sin x$, the above expression may be reduced to

$$-V_i + V_r = -V_t \tag{8.38}$$

Similarly the currents into and out of the junction are equal, or

$$I_i \sin \frac{2\pi}{\lambda} (0 - vt) - I_r \sin \frac{2\pi}{\lambda} (0 + vt) = I_t \sin \frac{2\pi}{\lambda} (0 - vt)$$

or, after simplifying as above,

$$-I_i - I_r = -I_t \tag{8.39}$$

In addition, the voltages and currents in the two cables are related by the characteristic impedances.

$$V_i = I_i Z_1 \qquad V_r = I_r Z_1 \qquad V_t = I_t Z_2$$

Substituting these expressions into Eq. 8.38 and rewriting Eq. 8.39 with plus signs, we have for the conditions to be met

$$-I_i Z_1 + I_r Z_1 = -I_t Z_2$$

$$I_i + I_r = I_t$$

Dividing the first of these equations by Z_2, and adding this to the second, we get

$$I_i \left(1 - \frac{Z_1}{Z_2}\right) + I_r \left(1 + \frac{Z_1}{Z_2}\right) = 0$$

or

$$I_r = \frac{Z_1 - Z_2}{Z_1 + Z_2} I_i \qquad (8.40)$$

In this equation I_r and I_i are amplitudes and must necessarily be positive. Our discussion therefore applies only if $Z_2 < Z_1$. A review of the assumptions we have made shows that the selection of sine rather than cosine functions requires justification. If, for example, we make Z_2 very small compared to Z_1, we have conditions approaching those to be expected at a short-circuited termination. There will be a voltage node at the junction. We must also consider reflections when there are current nodes at the junction. It turns out that if we had written all our traveling waves as cosine functions, as is perfectly permissible, we should have found

$$I_r = \frac{Z_2 - Z_1}{Z_2 + Z_1} I_i \qquad (8.41)$$

which is applicable if $Z_2 > Z_1$. In this case if Z_2 is much greater than Z_1, we approach the condition of reflection at an open-circuited termination, with a current node.

In calculating the reflection coefficient R, or the ratio of the reflected to the incident power, we have, since in both traveling waves current and voltage are in phase,

$$R = \frac{I_r V_r}{I_i V_i} = \frac{I_r{}^2 Z_1}{I_i{}^2 Z_1} = \left(\frac{I_r}{I_i}\right)^2 = \left(\frac{Z_1 - Z_2}{Z_1 + Z_2}\right)^2 \qquad (8.42)$$

8.5 THE RADIATION OF WAVES INTO SPACE

The foregoing arguments require considerable revision to account for the transmission of electromagnetic energy through space without the presence of nearby charges on conductors where the electric lines of force may be terminated. In this section we shall take up two aspects of the problem. First we shall consider qualitatively how energy can detach itself from the moving charges which are responsible for the presence of the electric and magnetic fields in space. Second, we shall want to derive a wave equation describing the propagation of energy through space. Particularly we shall want to show here again that the velocity of propagation is the velocity of light. We must further find some quantity analogous to the characteristic impedance of a cable. In a cable the characteristic impedance is $V/i = Z_0$. In empty space we have to determine the ratio E/H for a propagated wave. Note that the dimensions of this ratio are (volts/meter)/(amps/meter) or volts/ampere, or ohms. We may expect a medium which transmits electromagnetic waves to be physically characterized by two most important quantities, its velocity of transmission and its impedance.

A simple form of radiator is the dipole antenna shown in Fig. 8.18. It consists of two oppositely directed straight wires or bars connected to a high-frequency generator. These bars are given equal and opposite charges, and thus an electric field is created in their vicinity. The sign of the charge on either side of the antenna is periodically reversed. The

Fig. 8.18. A dipole antenna connected to a high-frequency generator.

charging and discharging of the antenna is brought about by currents which produce magnetic fields in the vicinity of the antenna.

We must now follow the charging and discharging process in some detail. The fields around the antenna will be similar to those of a positive and negative charge performing linear oscillations around a common center. These fields are sketched in Fig. 8.19. Part a of this figure shows the initial state of the system in which the two charges are slightly separated and moving apart, the positive charge toward the top of the page and the negative charge toward the bottom. The electric lines of force go from the positive to the negative charge. The magnetic lines of flux will be in the form of circles around the current. The cross section of a few lines of flux around the current is shown to indicate the presence of the magnetic field. The Poynting vector is directed outward. In b the charges have reached their maximum separation and have come to rest. As the charges come to rest, the magnetic field decreases and the Poynting vector near the charges vanishes. When the charges approach each other again, the magnetic field near the charges is reversed and the Poynting vector is directed inward. This sequence of events *near the charges* is shown in b and c. However, at the instant portrayed in b at which the charges are at rest, the magnetic field through all space cannot vanish instantly. It is because of the finite velocity of propagation in space of electromagnetic energy, just as we have already found in cables, that at distant points the magnetic field does not vanish until some later time. As a result these peripheral fields continue to move outward during b and c. Finally, the position of the charges is reversed, as in d, the nearby electric fields are reversed, and the Poynting vector is again directed outward everywhere. However, the electric lines of force, if they had remained unbroken, would have formed a loop and crossed each other, as indicated by the dotted lines. At the crossover point, however, the loop breaks away, and the electric lines of force in the loop close on themselves. This closed loop now moves out and forms the basis of the radiation field. The electric and magnetic fields in the radiation pattern are schematically shown in Fig. 8.20. Note that, in the radiation field, the electric and magnetic fields are in phase with each other and the Poynting vector is everywhere directed outward, describing the radiation of energy away from the dipole. Near the dipole, on the other hand, the electric and magnetic fields have predominantly out of phase components, and most of the energy in the nearby bound fields pulsates to and fro.

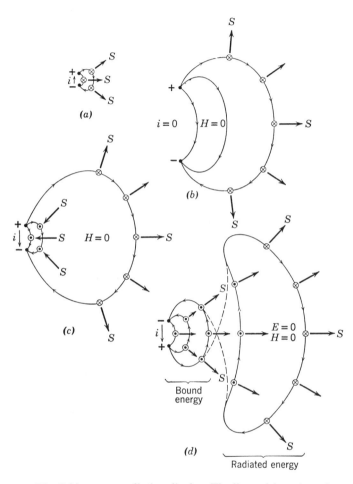

FIG. 8.19.   The fields near a radiating dipole.   The lines of force have been drawn on one side of the dipole only.

This tendency for the energy in the field of an oscillating dipole to move in and out near the dipole can lead us to another conclusion. If we move the charges in Fig. 8.19 infinitely slowly, all the energy in the field when the charges are separated can be regained and none is radiated.   The faster we reverse the polarity of the dipole, the greater will be the tendency to form loops in the field, and consequently also the greater the tendency to radiate rather than reabsorb the energy in the field. For a dipole of this sort in which a total charge Q is oscillated through a distance x, the amplitude of the dipole moment is Qx. If the frequency of oscillation is f, it can be shown that the total radiated energy is proportional to the fourth power of the frequency. This

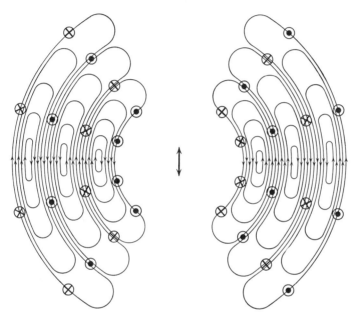

Fig. 8.20. The electric and magnetic fields in the radiation from an oscillating electric dipole.

energy flow is not uniformly distributed but is concentrated around the equatorial plane of the dipole. There is no radiation along the axis of the dipole. The total energy radiated by an oscillating dipole per second, or the radiated watts, W_r, may be shown to be

$$W_r = \frac{\omega^4 (Qx)^2}{12\pi\epsilon_0 c^3} \tag{8.43}$$

where $\omega = 2\pi f$. For such an oscillating charge, the current amplitude will be $I_0 = Q\omega$, and the radiated power in terms of this current amplitude then may be written in the form

$$W_r = \frac{\pi}{3} \sqrt{\frac{\mu_0}{\epsilon_0}} \left(\frac{x}{\lambda}\right)^2 I_0{}^2 \tag{8.44}$$

In arriving at this expression, use was made of the relations $c = \lambda f = 1/\sqrt{\epsilon_0 \mu_0}$. Equation 8.44 may be used to compute the radiation from an antenna such as that shown in Fig. 8.18 provided the wavelength of the radiation is large compared to the length of the wire, or for $x \ll \lambda$. This condition must be satisfied in order that the current in the wire shall have the same value at all points at any one time. If the condition is not satisfied, there will be a wave along the antenna, and this would lead to other results than those given above.

We must now take up the question of the propagation of radiated waves. In the derivation of the Poynting vector we showed that the following expressions might be derived from Maxwell's equations:

$$\mu \frac{\partial H_z}{\partial t} = -\frac{\partial E_y}{\partial x} \tag{8.45}$$

$$-\frac{\partial H_z}{\partial x} = \epsilon \frac{\partial E_y}{\partial t} \tag{8.46}$$

These expressions involve relationships between the electric and magnetic fields. It is clear that electric and magnetic fields that vary with time are not independent, and that certain aspects of the one are necessarily associated with certain aspects of the other.

Upon differentiating Eq. 8.45 with respect to the time, and Eq. 8.46 with respect to x, we get

$$-\frac{\partial^2 E_y}{\partial x\, \partial t} = \mu \frac{\partial^2 H_z}{\partial t^2} \tag{8.47}$$

$$-\frac{\partial^2 H_z}{\partial x^2} = \epsilon \frac{\partial^2 E_y}{\partial x\, \partial t} \tag{8.48}$$

Combining these, we find that

$$\frac{\partial^2 H_z}{\partial x^2} = \epsilon\mu \frac{\partial^2 H_z}{\partial t^2} \tag{8.49}$$

Similarly, by differentiating Eq. 8.45 with respect to x and Eq. 8.46 with respect to the time and combining the resulting expressions, we see that

$$\frac{\partial^2 E_y}{\partial x^2} = \epsilon\mu \frac{\partial^2 E_y}{\partial t^2} \tag{8.50}$$

These are the wave equations for electric and magnetic fields. They imply propagation with the velocity of light,

$$v = \frac{1}{\sqrt{\epsilon\mu}} \qquad\qquad \blacktriangleright(8.51)\blacktriangleleft$$

By far the most important electric and magnetic fields in space that we shall have to deal with are periodic functions of the time. We shall not be so much interested in the general solutions of the wave equation as in the particular solutions of the form

$$E_y = E_{y\,0} \sin \frac{2\pi}{\lambda} (x \pm ct) \qquad (8.52)$$

This may be thought of as a plane wave, or an electric field which at any one time has the same value over planes at right angles to the x axis, and varying sinusoidally along this axis. This field may then be thought of as moving along the x axis without otherwise changing its form. The frequency of the oscillation at any one point is

$$f = v/\lambda$$

A similar discussion could be given for the magnetic field H_z, which would be found to have the form

$$H_z = H_{z\,0} \sin \frac{2\pi}{\lambda} (x \pm vt) \qquad (8.53)$$

The amplitudes of these two fields are however not independent, since Eqs. 8.45 and 8.46 must be satisfied as well as the wave equations. By differentiating the expressions for the fields we find that the conditions to be satisfied imply that

$$-\frac{\partial E_y}{\partial x} = -\frac{2\pi}{\lambda} E_{y\,0} \cos \frac{2\pi}{\lambda} (x \pm vt)$$

$$= \mu \frac{\partial H_z}{\partial t} = \pm\mu \frac{2\pi}{\lambda} v H_{z\,0} \cos \frac{2\pi}{\lambda} (x \pm vt)$$

or that, since $\quad v = 1/\sqrt{\epsilon\mu},$

$$E_y = \pm \frac{\mu}{\sqrt{\epsilon\mu}} H_z$$

$$\sqrt{\epsilon}\, E_y = \pm \sqrt{\mu}\, H_z \qquad \blacktriangleright(8.54)\blacktriangleleft$$

If we remember that E and H are perpendicular to each other, the subscripts y and z may be omitted. We have then for the impedance of free space

$$\frac{E}{H} = \sqrt{\frac{\mu_0}{\epsilon_0}} = \sqrt{\frac{4\pi \times 10^{-7}}{8.85 \times 10^{-12}}} = 377 \text{ ohms} \qquad \text{(approx.)} \quad (8.55)$$

8.6 THE INTERFERENCE OF ELECTROMAGNETIC WAVES

We now propose to investigate the effects obtained when several antennas driven by a common oscillator simultaneously radiate. If the antennas are vertical, they radiate equally in all horizontal directions. The effect of the earth is simply to cut the waves in Fig. 8.19 in half. The earth below the surface is a sufficiently good conductor so that appropriate charges appear where the electric lines of force are terminated. These charges then move out with the wave. For points above the earth, however, the presence of the earth may, to a considerable extent, be neglected.

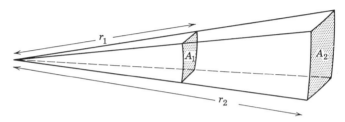

FIG. 8.21. A cone of radiated energy emanating from a point source.

If we consider the radiation field only at points so far removed from the radiating source that the dimensions of the source are negligible, then the radiated energy travels radially outward in straight lines. Let us compute the dependence of the amplitude in such a diverging wave field on the distance from the source. To this end, we focus our attention on a cone of radiation, shown in Fig. 8.21. Since the energy travels radially, all the energy crossing the surface A_1 must also cross the surface A_2. The instantaneous energy flow per unit of area at any point is given by the Poynting vector $\mathbf{S} = \mathbf{E} \times \mathbf{H}$, or, since in a radiated wave H is proportional to and at right angles to E, the Poynting vector is proportional to E^2. The instantaneous value of S is

$$S = EH = \sqrt{\frac{\epsilon}{\mu}} E^2$$

If the amplitude of the electric wave at some point is E_0, it can be shown that the average value of S is

$$S_{av} = \frac{1}{2} \sqrt{\frac{\epsilon}{\mu}} E_0{}^2 \tag{8.56}$$

Since the total energy crossing the areas A_1 and A_2 in Fig. 8.21 per second is the same, we must have

$$S_1 A_1 = S_2 A_2$$

or, since these areas are proportional to the squares of their distances from the source, we have

$$\frac{S_1}{S_2} = \frac{E_0\,_1^2}{E_0\,_2^2} = \frac{A_2}{A_1} = \frac{r_2^2}{r_1^2}$$

The amplitude of the electric field is inversely proportional to the distance from the source,

$$E_0 = C/r$$

where the constant C depends on the total power radiated. For a wave traveling radially out from an antenna with the velocity of light in air c, we have

$$E = \frac{C}{r}\sin\frac{2\pi}{\lambda}\,(r - ct) \qquad (8.57)$$

There will, of course, also be a magnetic wave of the form

$$H = \sqrt{\frac{\epsilon_0}{\mu_0}}\,\frac{C}{r}\sin\frac{2\pi}{\lambda}\,(r - ct) \qquad (8.58)$$

To begin with, let us consider the interference of two beams from vertical antennas a distance d apart, and oscillating in phase with each other, shown in Fig. 8.22. Note that the intensity of the radiation at P

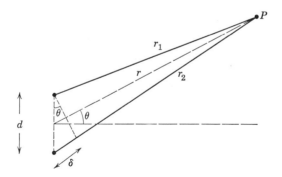

Fig. 8.22. Radiation from two antennas.

depends on the resultant amplitude of the radiations from the two antennas, that this resultant amplitude can range from twice the amplitude of the radiation from either one alone to zero, depending on the phase relation between the two, and that the resultant amplitude depends on the difference in the distances traveled by the two waves from the antennas to P. It is easy to see that, if the two antennas are synchronized, and if the path distances to P are equal, the radiations will be in phase at P. Further, if the difference in path lengths r_1 and r_2 is some integral number of wavelengths, the two waves will likewise be in phase at P. If, on the other hand, the difference in path length is some integral number of wavelengths plus a half wavelength, the radiations will be out of phase and we shall produce what is called *destructive interference*. The waves cancel each other, and no energy will be received at P.

The conditions for constructive or destructive interference are easily established. Let us assume that the point P in Fig. 8.22 is far from the antennas compared to their separation, so that the two paths r_1 and r_2 are almost parallel. The path difference between the two rays is $\delta = d \sin \theta$. For a maximum at P, or for constructive interference, we must have

$$r_2 - r_1 = \delta = d \sin \theta = n\lambda \qquad n = 0, 1, 2, 3 \qquad \blacktriangleright(8.59)\blacktriangleleft$$

and for a minimum at P, or for destructive interference, we must have

$$r_2 - r_1 = \delta = d \sin \theta = (n + \tfrac{1}{2})\lambda \qquad n = 0, 1, 2, 3, \cdots \qquad \blacktriangleright(8.60)\blacktriangleleft$$

The intensity for any angle θ may be computed through writing for the resultant electric field at a point P

$$E_p = E_1 + E_2 = \frac{C}{r_1} \sin \frac{2\pi}{\lambda} (r_1 - ct) + \frac{C}{r_2} \sin \frac{2\pi}{\lambda} (r_2 - ct) \quad (8.61)$$

The same proportionality constant C is used for both beams on the assumption that the two antennas are identical and are driven not only in phase with each other but with the same amplitude. Since we limit our considerations to points far from the antennas compared to their separation, r_1 and r_2 are very nearly equal in length, the beams are traveling in essentially the same directions, the magnetic as well as the electric fields will be colinear, and their amplitudes will be equal. We may then write

$$E_p = \frac{C}{r} \left[\sin \frac{2\pi}{\lambda} (r_1 - ct) + \sin \frac{2\pi}{\lambda} (r_2 - ct) \right] \cdot \quad (8.62)$$

We may not, however, make a similar simplification for the remaining expression involving r_1 and r_2, as will be clear from the following. From Fig. 8.22 we see that we may put

$$r_2 - r_1 = \delta$$

$$r - r_1 = \delta/2$$

$$r_2 - r = \delta/2$$

and consequently Eq. 8.62 may be put into the form

$$E_p = \frac{C}{r}\left[\sin\left\{\frac{2\pi}{\lambda}(r-ct)+\frac{2\pi\delta}{2\lambda}\right\}+\sin\left\{\frac{2\pi}{\lambda}(r-ct)-\frac{2\pi\delta}{2\lambda}\right\}\right]$$

But since

$$\sin(a+b)+\sin(a-b)=2\sin a\cos b$$

we have

$$E_p = \left\{2\,\frac{C}{r}\cos\frac{\pi\delta}{\lambda}\right\}\sin\frac{2\pi}{\lambda}(r-ct)$$

The amplitude of the electric field at the point P is

$$2\,\frac{C}{r}\cos\pi\,\frac{\delta}{\lambda} \tag{8.63}$$

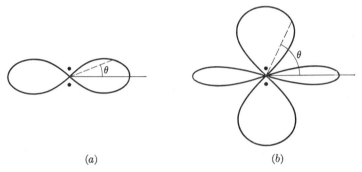

(a)   (b)

FIG. 8.23. Radiation pattern of two vertical antennas in phase with each other, with a separation (a) of a half wavelength, and (b) of a full wavelength.

and the intensity of the radiation, which is given by the Poynting vector, is proportional to the square of Eq. 8.63. If we call I_1 the intensity at P due to either antenna operated alone, we get

$$I = I_1 \cdot 4\cos^2\frac{\pi\delta}{\lambda} \tag{8.64}$$

But from Fig. 8.22 we see that $\delta/d = \sin\theta$, so that the desired expression for the intensity of the beam of the two radiating antennas becomes

$$I = 4I_1\cos^2\left\{\frac{\pi d}{\lambda}\sin\theta\right\} \tag{8.65}$$

As before, we note that maxima are to be expected when $\sin\theta = n\lambda/d$, and that minima are to be expected when $\sin\theta = (n+\frac{1}{2})(\lambda/d)$. The distance r from the antennas determines the magnitude of I_1. The angular dependence is very different for antennas having various separations. Plots of I/I_1 as a function of θ are shown in Fig. 8.23 for separations of the antennas of a half wavelength, and of a full wavelength. The length of the dotted line drawn at an angle θ from the source to the curve is proportional to the intensity I of the radiation in this direction.

The correctness of these predictions concerning the interference of beams, and concerning the velocity of propagation of electromagnetic energy, constitutes a major support of the classical theory of electromagnetic radiation.

8.7 THE ELECTROMAGNETIC SPECTRUM

We have seen that observable facts about electricity, about magnetism, and about their relationship to each other can be put into the form of a wave equation. Important solutions of this equation are sinusoidally varying fields traveling through space with the velocity of light. The frequency, and consequently also the wavelength, are up to this point quite arbitrary. Either might be as large or as small as we wish. We shall now consider the physical limitations on the magnitudes of these quantities.

Low-frequency circuits do not radiate effectively. The wavelength of a 60 cycle/sec oscillation is

$$\lambda = \frac{c}{f} = \frac{3 \times 10^8}{60} = 5000\text{km}$$

The local, or bound field, in which the energy pulsates to and fro, extends at least a quarter of a wavelength from the radiator. Clearly, in order to set up fields of appreciable magnitude at distances of 1000 km, we should require antennas of this order of magnitude and huge driving currents. Radiations of such low frequency would be hard to produce and hard to detect.

Frequencies of the order of a few megacycles per second, or in the radio broadcast band, on the other hand, have wavelengths of the order of 100 meters. These frequencies can readily be radiated and detected. The oscillators used consist of a resonant LC circuit which controls the flow of energy in a vacuum tube circuit. In order to produce high frequencies we must have low inductance and capacitance. In the limit, the lowest achievable inductance and capacitance is that due to the leads inside the vacuum tube connecting its various components to each other. Frequencies of the order of 1000 megacycles with wavelengths under a meter can be generated in this way by the use of circuits with lumped circuit elements. The furthest extension into this high-frequency or microwave region requires other forms of oscillators. Wavelengths of the order of fractions of millimeters have been produced. We shall, however, leave the discussion of radiation from circuits at this point

and take up other aspects of waves having very much shorter wavelengths.
These shorter wavelengths are characteristic of radiations from atomic
systems. The negatively charged electrons in atoms and the positively
charged protons in nuclei can emit electromagnetic radiations. The
various bands of frequency and wavelength have distinctive properties
and names. They are summarized in Fig. 8.24. The scale in this figure

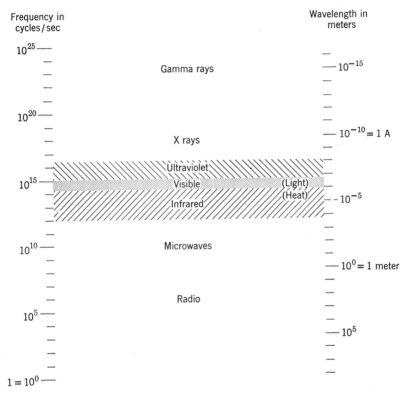

FIG. 8.24.   The electromagnetic spectrum.

is logarithmic. Notice the enormous range of orders of magnitude of
the wavelengths and frequencies of the various radiations. Notice
also that visible light, which we shall next discuss, has wavelengths of
the order of thousands of atomic diameters. Wavelengths of light are
customarily measured in angstrom units, or A.U., or simply A, or in
millimicrons.

$$1 \; A \; = \; 10^{-8} \; cm \; = \; 10^{-10} \; meter$$
$$1 \; \text{millimicron} \; (1 \; m\mu) \; = \; 10^{-3} \cdot 10^{-6} \; meter \; = \; 10^{-9} \; meter$$

One angstrom unit is of the order of atomic dimensions. Visible light has wavelengths from roughly 4000 to 7000 A, or 400 to 700 mμ.

In later chapters in which we discuss the properties of these various radiations, we shall take up the reasons for considering them to be electromagnetic. Our discussion of light will be broken into two parts. The first deals with electromagnetic fields and the propagation of waves. Such effects are well accounted for by the electromagnetic theory which we have developed. The second part deals with absorption and emission and in general with the interaction between electromagnetic radiation and atomic particles. For a description of these phenomena we shall have to advance entirely new ideas about matter and electromagnetic energy.

SUMMARY

The energy density in the electromagnetic field is

$$\frac{ED}{2} + \frac{HB}{2} \text{ joules/meter}^3$$

The movement of electromagnetic energy in the field is given by the Poynting vector

$$\mathbf{S} = [\mathbf{E} \times \mathbf{H}] \text{ watts/meter}^2$$

A particularly important application of the movement of energy is that associated with wave motion. In a traveling wave, energy moves continuously in the direction of propagation of the wave and with the velocity of light. In a standing wave, which may be produced by reflection, energy may be thought of as oscillating to and fro, from regions of intense electric fields to regions of intense magnetic fields. A wave reflected from the open end of a cable will have its direction of propagation reversed by the reversal of its magnetic field, whereas reflection from the short-circuited end of a cable will involve the reversal of the electric field. The velocity of propagation of electromagnetic energy in a cable in which the dielectric has a permittivity ϵ and a permeability μ is

$$V = \frac{1}{\sqrt{\epsilon\mu}}$$

The velocity of propagation of electromagnetic energy in free space is equal to the velocity of light

$$c = \frac{1}{\sqrt{\epsilon_0\mu_0}} \simeq 3 \times 10^8 \text{ meters/sec}$$

Two or more electromagnetic waves are said to interfere or to give rise to an interference pattern. Each wave may be thought of as moving in space as though no other waves were present. The energy in space must be computed from the field formed by addition of the fields of all the waves present. At certain points the various waves may produce fields that cancel each other at all times. At these points we have destructive interference. At other points the Poynting vector may be greater than the sum of the Poynting vectors of the individual waves taken separately. This is called constructive interference.

The condition for destructive interference for radiation from two point sources oscillating in phase with each other at the same frequency is that the fields should be colinear and have the same amplitudes at the point in question, and that the distances from this point to the two radiators should differ by an odd number of half wavelengths.

Electromagnetic waves radiated by electrical circuits have wavelengths ranging roughly from millimeters to kilometers. Electromagnetic radiations with shorter wavelengths are emitted by atoms and nuclei. Visible light, which we shall study next, has short wavelengths ranging from approximately 4 to 7×10^{-5} cm, or from 4000 to 7000 A, where 1 A is 10^{-8} cm.

PROBLEMS

1. A cubical box 1 cm on a side is located in uniform electric and magnetic fields. If the edges of the cube are parallel to the x, y, and z axes of a rectangular coordinate system, and the fields have the components

$$H_x = \frac{H}{\sqrt{2}} \qquad H_y = \frac{H}{\sqrt{2}} \qquad H_z = 0$$

$$E_x = 0 \qquad E_y = 0 \qquad E_z = E$$

compute the flow of energy into or out of the cube through each face and the net rate of accumulation of energy within the cube.

2. A copper wire, having a resistivity $\rho = 1.7 \times 10^{-8}$ ohmmeters, 4 mm in diameter, carries a current of 10 amp. What is the heat dissipation per meter of wire? What are the magnitudes of E and H at the surface of the wire? What are the magnitudes of E and H at a point 1 mm from the axis of the wire? What is the magnitude and direction of the Poynting vector S at the above points? How much power per meter is dissipated in the central cylindrical section of the wire with a radius of 1 mm? How much power per meter length of the wire is supplied to the whole wire, and to the central core?

★3. A coaxial cable carries direct current from a battery to a resistor. The resistance of the cable is negligible, so that there is no voltage drop along either conductor of the cable. Show that the power transmitted along the cable as computed from the Poynting vector in the dielectric between the conductors is equal to the power delivered by the battery to the resistor.

In order to carry out the required proof, it is useful to break the above problem into several parts. The Poynting vector depends on E and H. It is therefore necessary to determine the magnitude and direction of E and H at any radial distance r from the axis of the cable. Since the fields are functions of only one variable, r, it is possible to write an expression for the total rate of energy flow through a ring-shaped area of radial width dr. With this done, it is possible to integrate dS from the inner conductor to the outer conductor. This integral is the total energy flow along the cable. It is equal to the power delivered from the battery to the resistor.

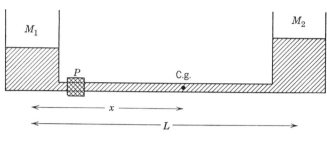

FIG. 8.25.

★4. (a) Two tanks of water having masses M_1 and M_2 are connected by a straight pipe having a cross-sectional area A and a length L. The center of gravity of the system is a distance x from M_1, as shown in Fig. 8.25. A pump P delivers water, flowing with a velocity v, from the first tank to the second at a rate

$$\frac{dM_2}{dt} = -\frac{dM_1}{dt}$$

The total momentum of the moving water in the pipe is $\rho A L v$. This must be equal to the momentum of the entire system, or

$$(M_1 + M_2)\frac{dx}{dt}$$

Prove that the momentum

$$\rho A L v = (M_1 + M_2)\frac{dx}{dt} = L\frac{dM_2}{dt}$$

(b) A long cable having negligible resistance delivers power from a battery to a resistor. Prove that the momentum in the electromagnetic field is just equal to that which could be deduced from the velocity of the center of mass of the system.

★5. A coaxial cable of length x, open at both ends, is suspended with its axis parallel to a uniform constant magnetic field B. The inner and outer conductors are given equal and opposite charges so that the difference of potential between the two is V_{ab}. For simplicity, we may assume that the separation d between the coaxial charged surfaces is small compared to the radius of either one. What are the magnitude and direction of S?

Compute the angular momentum of this circulating energy.

The inner and outer surfaces of the cable are now connected through a small length of wire having a resistance R.

What is the force on the small piece of wire of length d when a current i is flowing through it? What is the torque acting on the cable and wire? What is the total angular impulse imparted to the mechanical system as a result of the discharge? What is the change in angular momentum of the field?

6. A capacitor is connected in series with a switch and an inductor. A right-handed coordinate system having its origin halfway between the conductors and its y axis parallel to the conductors is set up as in Fig. 8.26. The capacitor is charged with the upper plate positive, the switch is closed at the time $t = 0$, and an electrical oscillation is set up. The oscillating electric and magnetic fields at the origin of the coordinate system are parallel to the x and z axes respectively and have amplitudes E_0 and H_0. Plot E_x, S_y, and H_z at the origin for the first few cycles of the oscillation. What is the amplitude of S_y in terms of H_0 and E_0?

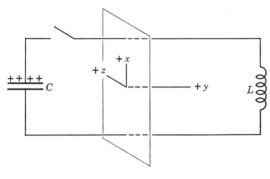

Fig. 8.26.

7. The Poynting vector for a traveling wave may be written in the form

$$\mathbf{S} = \mathbf{E} \times \mathbf{H} = (\tfrac{1}{2}\epsilon E^2 + \tfrac{1}{2}\mu H^2)\mathbf{v}$$

for an electromagnetic wave. Show that at points midway between the two wires of the cable shown in Fig. 8.13 E and H are perpendicular to each other, and that the ratio of their magnitudes is

$$E/H = 1/\epsilon v$$

and that, on combining the above expressions, one gets $v = 1/\sqrt{\epsilon\mu}$. Could this argument be applied to any point in the vicinity of any cable?

8. Plot a traveling wave in a cable for four instants a quarter of a period apart.

9. Plot a standing wave in a cable for four instants a quarter of a period apart.

10. Compute the three lowest resonant frequencies of a coaxial cable 3 meters long, assuming that the properties of the insulation are given by ϵ_0 and μ_0, (a) when both ends of the cable are open, and (b) when one end is short-circuited.

11. Compute the amplitude of the current and voltage waves in a coaxial cable having an outer conductor whose radius is three times the radius of the inner conductor when it is delivering 100 watts to a resistance equal to the characteristic impedance of the cable. The insulation of the cable has a dielectric coefficient $K_e = 2.25$.

12. A coaxial cable is connected at one end to a 600 cycle/second oscillator having an amplitude of 100 volts. The insulation in the cable has a dielectric coefficient $K_e = 2.2$. The cable is terminated with its characteristic impedance, which is 55 ohms.

(a) What is the amplitude of the current wave? Is it in phase with the voltage?

(b) What are the frequency and wavelength of the traveling wave in the cable?

(c) Plot the current and the instantaneous power dissipation in the load as functions of time for a few cycles. What is the average power delivered to the resistor?

13. A cable such as that shown in Fig. 8.13 carries a single pulse, in which the upper conductor is positively charged, toward a termination on the right. Draw this pulse and the fields surrounding it before and after reflection, first from an open end, and then from a short-circuited end. Note that in the first case i and H are reversed on reflection but V and E are left unchanged, whereas in the second case i and H are left unchanged but V and E are reversed. Note also that the Poynting vector is reversed in both cases by the reflection.

14. (a) What are the wavelengths of electromagnetic waves in empty space having frequencies of 10, 30, 300 megacycles/sec? (b) What are the frequencies of electromagnetic waves having wavelengths of 100 meters, 10 cm, 3 mm?

15. A plane electromagnetic wave, moving in the x direction, has a frequency of 150 megacycles per second. If its amplitude is such that the Poynting vector at the plane $x = 0$ has a mean value of 10^{-12} watt/meter^2 what is the amplitude of the electric oscillations at the point $x = 100$ meters?

16. A radio station broadcasts 4 kw at a frequency of 1.5 megacycles from an antenna 40 meters long. What is the amplitude of the antenna current?

17. Assuming that the electric dipole whose total radiation is described by Eq. 8.43 consists of an electronic charge, $Q = 1.6 \times 10^{-19}$ coulomb, oscillating with an amplitude of atomic dimensions, $x = 10^{-10}$ meter, how long would it take to radiate 1 ev of energy, (a) if it radiated visible light with a wavelength 5×10^{-7} meter, or (b) in the far infrared with a wavelength of 10^{-4} meter?

18. Two antennas radiating in phase with each other are 100 meters apart. In what directions would the radiated intensities have a minimum if the frequencies of oscillation were (a) 1.5 megacycles/sec; (b) 6 megacycles/sec; (c) 12 megacycles/sec?

19. A broadcasting station using vertical antennas is to be set up south of a town which it is to serve. Two antennas separated by a quarter of a wavelength are to be used and are to be operated not in phase but with a phase difference of a quarter of a cycle. How should the masts be oriented with respect to the town, and which antenna should lead in phase?

20. Two vertical radio antennas situated on a north-south line and 150 meters apart oscillate at a frequency of 6 megacycles per second in phase with each other. At what angles from the north-south axis will the radiated signal be a minimum?

21. Two vertical radio antennas situated on a north-south line and 100 meters apart oscillate at a frequency of 4 megacycles per second in phase with each other. At what angles from the north-south axis will the radiated signal be maximum?

★22. Three vertical radio broadcasting antennas operating in phase with each other are placed in a straight line, the distance between adjacent antennas being three wavelengths. What are the directions for maxima and minima in the interference patterns at large distances?

★23. Three vertical radio broadcasting antennas operating in phase with each other are located at the corners of an equilateral triangle. The distance between antennas is two wavelengths. Discuss the interference pattern at large distances.

CHAPTER 9

Optics: Reflection and Refraction

9.1 THE PROPAGATION OF LIGHT IN ISOTROPIC MEDIA

Light is an electromagnetic wave having a wavelength large compared to atoms. It can therefore be reflected and refracted at surfaces, and it is not greatly influenced by structural features of atomic dimensions. For this reason light cannot directly reveal much about the size and shape of atoms and molecules.

Light is an electromagnetic wave having dimensions small compared to objects which we customarily handle with our fingers or see with our eyes. It therefore can reveal the degree of detail with which we are familiar.

Being an electromagnetic wave with electric and magnetic fields perpendicular to the direction of propagation, light can be polarized, that is, it can be made to show symmetry properties depending on the orientation of the above fields.

Light is an electromagnetic wave propagated with a velocity $1/\sqrt{\epsilon\mu}$. The permittivity is a function of frequency because of electronic resonance phenomena, and the velocity of light in transparent solids and liquids is therefore dependent on frequency.

These are the facts about light which we shall spell out further in this section.

One aspect of the physical situation to be described is illustrated in Fig. 9.1. In a we are dealing with a wave striking an aperture whose size is comparable to the wavelength, as, for example, in the case of an ocean wave striking an opening in a breakwater. The wave inside spreads out fanwise, and, as it spreads out, its amplitude decreases. When it has traveled many wavelengths, its amplitude is small compared to that of the original incident plane wave.

347

In *b* it is assumed that the wavelength is small compared to the size of the aperture. Instead of shaded bands to indicate the crests and

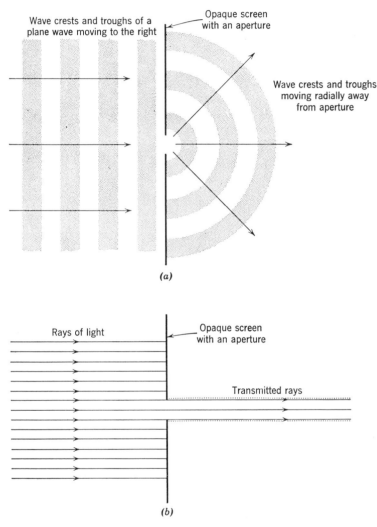

(a)

(b)

Fig. 9.1. The propagation of a wave through an aperture, (a) when the wavelength is comparable to the size of the aperture, and (b) when the wavelength is small compared to the size of the aperture.

troughs of the wave, parallel lines are drawn in the direction of propagation. These are *rays* of light. The aperture now defines a beam. It is true that the edges of this beam are not perfectly sharply defined, as is indicated by the dotted line at the edge of the beam. We shall return to this point later on. For many purposes, however, this slight fuzziness at the edge of a beam may be neglected, and we shall begin by considering optical problems in which the edges of shadows may be considered sharp. This is called geometrical optics, as opposed to wave optics which concerns itself with the interference and diffraction of waves and which we shall take up in the next chapter.

If we can accept the wave nature of light as reconcilable with everyday experience because of the smallness of the waves, we must still reconcile ourselves to the notion that it is a transverse electrical oscillation. A variety of simple experiments can prove to us that light can be polarized, or that in certain circumstances there can be asymmetrical aspects of a light beam which electromagnetic theory explains in terms of the orientation of the electric vector in the light wave. An electrical light wave may be plane polarized, or circularly polarized, or elliptically polarized, or it may be unpolarized. A plane-polarized wave is one in which the magnitude of the electric vector changes periodically but not its orientation. A circularly or elliptically polarized wave is one in which the end of the electric vector at any point moves in a circle or an ellipse. We shall confine ourselves here to a discussion of plane-polarized light. Unpolarized light is light made up of many superposed waves in which the polarization varies in a random fashion, being on the average symmetrical about the direction of propagation.

Polarization may be produced by scattering from very small particles. Surfaces which are large compared to a wavelength will reflect light. However, when the surface dimensions to be considered become small compared to a wavelength, new considerations are required. Qualitatively, we may think of the electric vector in the incident light wave as inducing an oscillating electric dipole moment. This oscillating dipole moment, in turn, radiates energy as does an antenna. No energy is radiated along the axis of the dipole. The radiation emitted at right angles to the axis of the dipole will have its electric vector parallel to the axis of the dipole. Thus, if we shine plane-polarized light onto a cloudy liquid, no scattered light will be emitted in the direction of the electric vector of the incident light. If we illuminate the cloudy liquid with a beam of unpolarized light, we shall find the scattered light plane polarized, as shown in Fig. 9.2.

A most convenient way of producing or detecting plane-polarized light is to pass it through a sheet of material called *Polaroid.* These sheets transmit only light polarized in a particular plane. They are made up of small crystals or large molecules all oriented in the same way. The crystals or molecules have the property of absorbing all the light polarized in one plane, and therefore of transmitting only light polarized at right angles to this plane. If the light scattered from the cloudy liquid in Fig. 9.2 toward the observer is viewed through a sheet of Polaroid, there will be one orientation of the sheet at which a maximum amount of light is transmitted, whereas if the Polaroid is rotated through 90° none of the scattered light will be transmitted.

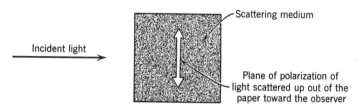

FIG. 9.2. Polarization by scattering.

At this stage of our considerations, however, the most convincing evidence that light is actually an electromagnetic wave is that its velocity of propagation is that predicted by Maxwell's electromagnetic equations. This velocity of propagation of electromagnetic waves in a vacuum is, as we have seen,

$$c = \frac{1}{\sqrt{\epsilon_0 \mu_0}}$$

It is possible to evaluate this quantity by means of purely electrical and magnetic measurements. For example, we start with the definition $\mu_0 = 4\pi \times 10^{-7}$ henry/meter exactly. Using this and the expression for the force between conductors carrying a current, we can establish the magnitude of currents in terms of standard weights. Then, by letting known currents flow for known times, we can establish known charges. Then, in terms of known charges and Coulomb's law, we can establish the magnitude of ϵ_0. With such data the velocity of light turns out to be

$$c = \frac{1}{\sqrt{\epsilon_0 \mu_0}} = 2.9979 \pm 0.0001 \times 10^8 \text{ meter/sec} \qquad (9.1)$$

The velocity of radio waves and of visible light may be determined experimentally. The results are continually being improved. A recent estimate is

$$c = 2.9978 \pm 0.0001 \times 10^8 \text{ meter/sec} \qquad (9.2)$$

in excellent agreement with the theoretical value. The history of these measurements of the velocity of light is a fascinating chapter of physics, starting with Galileo's attempt to observe the time elapsed for a flash from a lantern to travel to a distant mountain peak and back. Considering the fact that light travels at the rate of 186,000 mi in 1 sec, a distance almost eight times around the world, it is small wonder that Galileo's attempt failed. The first successful attempts involved astronomical distances, so that the times to be measured were of the order of several seconds. Our ability now to measure time in fractions of microseconds has made it possible to use convenient terrestrial distances for our determinations.

Although the velocity of light in air is, within a few parts in 10,000, the same as the velocity in a vacuum, considerable differences arise when we come to transparent solids or liquids. These changes should, according to electromagnetic theory, be given by the permittivity and permeability of the medium through which the light is traveling. The permeability of most transparent media is, closely enough for our purposes, equal to that of a vacuum. The permittivity, however, may vary considerably. Writing $\epsilon = K_e \epsilon_0$, we get

$$v = \frac{1}{\sqrt{K_e}} \frac{1}{\sqrt{\epsilon_0 \mu_0}} = \frac{c}{\sqrt{K_e}}$$

The square root of the dielectric coefficient K_e we call the *index of refraction*. We shall designate it by the symbol n. The velocity of light in any transparent medium may now be expressed in terms of the index of refraction of the medium, and the universal constant c as follows

$$v = c/n \qquad (9.3)$$

The discussion in Section 7.6 indicated that the characteristic natural frequencies of electrons in solids make the permittivity a function of frequency, and, therefore, since

$$n = \sqrt{K_e} = \sqrt{\epsilon/\epsilon_0} \qquad (9.4)$$

in non-magnetic media, we must expect the index of refraction, and also the velocity of propagation, to be a function of frequency. The measured index of refraction for various transparent solids as a function of frequency is shown in Fig. 9.3. This dependence of the index of refraction on frequency is called *dispersion*. There are here indications of a characteristic absorption frequency in the ultraviolet, much less marked for LiF than for the other substances shown. In fact, LiF does transmit ultraviolet radiation, whereas the other substances shown absorb quite strongly. The range of frequencies shown is below the absorption frequency, and from Fig. 7.25b we should expect the permittivity, and therefore also the index of refraction, to increase as the resonance frequency is approached. This is borne out in Fig. 9.3. The index of refrac-

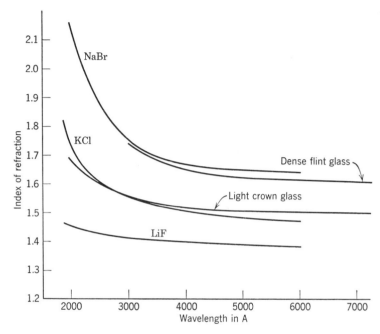

Fig. 9.3. The index of refraction of various substances in the ultraviolet and visible portion of the spectrum.

tion increases as we go from the visible toward the shorter ultraviolet wavelengths. The index of refraction of a few substances for yellow light is given below.

TABLE 9.1 THE INDEX OF REFRACTION OF VARIOUS SUBSTANCES FOR YELLOW LIGHT HAVING A WAVELENGTH OF 5890 A*

Glass	1.46–1.96
Quartz	1.544
Ethyl alcohol	1.361
Water	1.333

* 1 A $= 10^{-10}$ meter.

The wavelength of a ray of light in different media is directly proportional to the velocity of propagation of the ray, or inversely proportional to the index of refraction. The student should convince himself that the frequency of a propagated wave is the same at all points of its path, regardless of the medium in which it is observed. To do this, it may be helpful to notice that peaks and troughs of a traveling wave do not accumulate anywhere along its path. Consider, then, two points along this path. In some long time T the number of peaks that pass one of these points must be the same as the number of peaks that pass

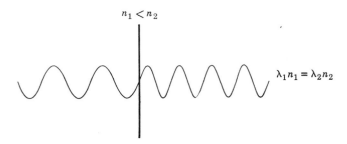

$n_1 < n_2$

$\lambda_1 n_1 = \lambda_2 n_2$

FIG. 9.4. A wave of constant frequency traveling with greater velocity in the medium on the left than in the medium on the right.

the other. This is equivalent to saying that the number of cycles per second, or the frequency at the two points, must be the same. From this result, the wavelengths in the two media may be computed. We have for media 1 and 2, having indices of refraction n_1 and n_2, shown in Fig. 9.4,

$$f_1 = f_2$$

$$\lambda_1 f_1 = v_1 = c/n_1$$

$$\lambda_2 f_2 = v_2 = c/n_2$$

and, after dividing,

$$\frac{\lambda_1}{\lambda_2} = \frac{n_2}{n_1} \quad \text{or } \lambda_1 n_1 = \lambda_2 n_2 \tag{9.5}$$

We have discussed the propagation of light in isotropic media only. The velocity of propagation is then independent of the direction in which the light travels and independent of the degree or kind of polarization. These results are no longer true when light travels in anisotropic crystals. The complex phenomena encountered can be explained by the fact that the polarizability of crystals is different in different directions, and that therefore the effective index of refractions for a plane-polarized wave will depend on the orientation of the electric vector in the crystal. The reason for the complications is thus apparent. We shall not pursue the study of crystals at this point but shall take the matter up again in Chapter 11 in connection with their atomic structure.

9.2 HUYGENS' PRINCIPLE; REFLECTION AND REFRACTION

The propagation of light is described by a differential equation, a wave equation, in which the only constant that appears is the velocity of propagation. In this form the wave equations for various kinds of disturbances, elastic, acoustic, or electromagnetic, are quite similar, and we must expect certain aspects of propagation, reflection, and refraction to depend only on the velocity of propagation. These are the properties that can be derived from *Huygens' principle*, which we shall take up here. We leave to the next section the discussion of the characteristically electromagnetic aspects of reflection and refraction.

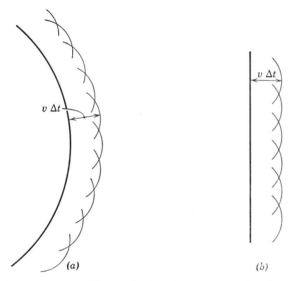

FIG. 9.5.   The application of Huygens' principle to a spherical and to a plane wave propagated in free space.

The rigorous formulation of Huygens' principle is beyond the scope of this discussion. Qualitatively, it says that any point on a wave front, such as shown in Fig. 9.5, may be thought of as a radiating source emitting a secondary wave, often also called a Huygens wavelet. The oscillation at some other point at later times may be computed, through adding the effects of all the secondary waves from all points of the wave front. For spherical and plane waves in a homogeneous medium the propagation of the wave front in a time Δt may be computed through drawing all the secondary waves. Their envelope on the forward side of the old wave front is the new wave front whose position was to be computed. The non-appearance of a back wave becomes understandable only if the calculations are carried through rigorously rather than qualitatively, as above.

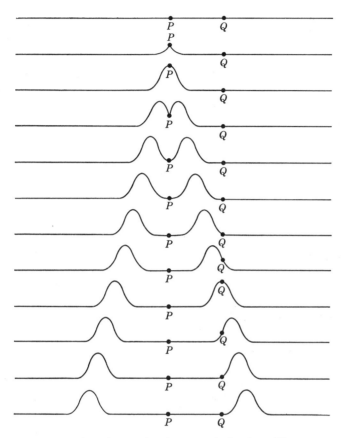

Fɪɢ. 9.6.   The generation of two pulses in a stretched string. The curves represent the condition of the string after successive time intervals, starting at the top.

Huygens' Principle Applied to a Pulse Traveling along a Stretched String

In order to show qualitatively that no back wave is to be expected from the secondary Huygens' wavelets, we shall consider two pulses generated in a stretched string by the movement of the point P in Fig. 9.6. For the moment we disregard point Q. It is simply another point in the string. As P is moved up and then back again to its original position, the string is distorted as shown, and two pulses are formed, one traveling to the right, and one to the left. As the pulse passes point Q, Q undergoes the same motion that P did some time earlier and the string to the right of P is deformed in the same way. It is clear that we may think of the motion of Q as generating a pulse which moves off to the right. However, it is also clear that we would not expect the motion of Q to generate a pulse going to the left, since the deformation of the string on the left of Q is clearly not that required to produce a pulse, and, in fact, no pulse arises in this direction. If we think of the motion of Q as generating the propagated wave, then we must think of the incoming wave as just canceling the secondary back wave.

————

The laws of reflection and refraction of light may be derived from Huygens' principle. We shall consider the plane surface shown in Fig. 9.7, with an incident plane wave. The indices of refraction on the two sides of the surface are n_1 and n_2, respectively, so that the velocities of propagation in the two media are

$$v_1 = c/n_1$$

$$v_2 = c/n_2$$

We shall here concern ourselves only with the direction of propagation of the reflected and refracted waves.

In Fig. 9.7a is a representation of a wave front OA at some arbitrary time $t = 0$. The direction of propagation is normal to the wave front. The angle of incidence, i, is defined as the angle between the direction of the incoming rays and the normal to the surface. The position of the wave front at later times Δt, $2\,\Delta t$, $3\,\Delta t$, $4\,\Delta t$ is shown by dotted lines. At these various times the incoming wave front intersects the reflecting surface at points B, C, D, and E. Let us now consider the Huygens wavelets that originated at the points A, B, C, D, and E at the times $t = 0$, Δt, $2\,\Delta t$, $3\,\Delta t$, and $4\,\Delta t$. These wavelets at the time $t = 4\,\Delta t$ are shown in Fig. 9.7b. The wavelet originating at A has been growing for a time $4\,\Delta t$ and therefore has a radius $4v_1\,\Delta t$. The wavelets originating at B, C, D, and E have been growing for times 3, 2, 1, and 0 times Δt and therefore have radii $3v_1\,\Delta t$, $2v_1\,\Delta t$, $v_1\,\Delta t$, and 0. The wave front of all these wavelets is shown as OE in Fig. 9.7b.

If the angle of reflection r' is defined as the angle between the reflected ray and the normal to the surface, we have

$$\sin r' = \frac{4v_1\,\Delta t}{AE}$$

But from Fig. 9.7a we have

$$\sin i = \frac{4v_1\,\Delta t}{AE}$$

and therefore

$$i = r' \qquad\qquad \blacktriangleright(9.6)\blacktriangleleft$$

which is the law of reflection.

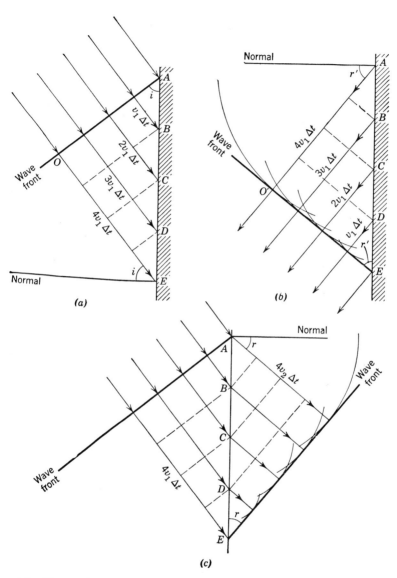

FIG. 9.7.   Huygens' principle applied to reflection and refraction at a plane surface

In deducing the law of refraction we must consider the Huygens' wavelets on the right side of the surface, or, in medium 2, shown in Fig. 9.7c. Calling the angle of refraction, r, that between the refracted ray and the normal to the surface, we have

$$\sin r = \frac{4v_2 \, \Delta t}{AE}$$

or, combining this with the above expression for the angle of incidence,

$$\frac{\sin i}{\sin r} = \frac{v_1}{v_2} = \frac{n_2}{n_1}$$

The relationship between the angles of incidence and refraction and the indices of refraction of the two media involved is called Snell's law.

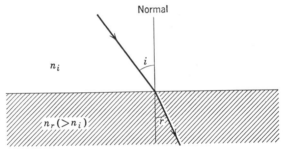

Normal

n_i

i

$n_r(>n_i)$

r

FIG. 9.8.   An illustration of refraction at a plane surface.

If n_i is the index of refraction of the medium in which the incident ray is propagated, and if n_r is the index of refraction of the medium in which the transmitted ray is propagated, Snell's law, illustrated in Fig. 9.8, states that

$$n_i \sin i = n_r \sin r \qquad \blacktriangleright(9.7)\blacktriangleleft$$

Note that a ray is bent toward the normal in going from one medium into another having a greater index of refraction, as in going from air into water or glass.

Since the index of refraction is in general a function of frequency, or wavelength, different colors will be deviated by different amounts in going from one medium to another. This effect may be used to separate the frequencies of colors which constitute any given ray, as in the case of the prism illustrated in Fig. 9.9.

A special case of importance occurs when n_r, the index of refraction of the medium in which the refracted ray is propagated, is less than n_i, the index of the medium in which the incident ray is propagated.

Snell's law may be put in the form

$$\sin i = \frac{n_r}{n_i} \sin r$$

where according to our assumption the ratio n_r/n_i is less than unity. Now, obviously, since sin r cannot possibly be greater than unity,

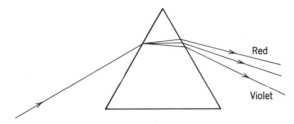

FIG. 9.9. The separation of rays of different wavelength in traversing a prism.

sin i cannot possibly be greater than n_r/n_i. This limiting value of the angle of incidence is called the critical angle, i_c. For greater angles of incidence, there is no way of satisfying Snell's law. There is conse-

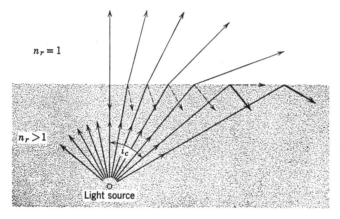

FIG. 9.10. The paths of light rays from an underwater light source.

quently no refracted ray, only a reflected ray. For angles of incidence greater than the critical angle, *all* the light must be reflected, since none is transmitted. Reflection in these circumstances is called "total reflection." The conditions are illustrated in Fig. 9.10.

9.3 REFLECTING POWER

In the discussion of the preceding paragraph we made use of none of the electromagnetic aspects of light except its velocity. We must now reconsider the phenomena that takes place when a light ray strikes a boundary between two transparent dielectric media, particularly phenomena affecting the electric and magnetic fields involved. We should expect to obtain not only the laws of reflection and refraction which we derived from Huygens' principle but also an interpretation of the frac-

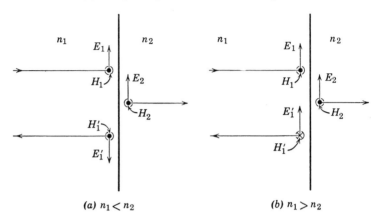

(a) $n_1 < n_2$ (b) $n_1 > n_2$

FIG. 9.11. Reflection and refraction at a surface.

tion of the incident light which is reflected and the fraction refracted at an interface.

We shall begin with the simplest optical problem involving a surface, namely, normal incidence of a plane wave at a plane interface between two transparent dielectrics. We may expect that the incident wave will give rise to two other waves, one transmitted and one refracted, so that we shall have three in all to deal with. We shall need, for our discussion, the relationship in Eq. 8.54 between the electric and magnetic fields in a plane wave

$$\sqrt{\epsilon}\, E = \sqrt{\mu}\, H \qquad \text{or} \quad H = n \sqrt{\frac{\epsilon_0}{\mu_0}}\, E \qquad (9.8)$$

and the boundary conditions to be satisfied at the interface (Eqs. 3.73, 3.74, and 5.44 and 5.45).

$$D_{n\,1} = D_{n\,2} \qquad B_{n\,1} = B_{n\,2} \qquad (9.9)$$

$$E_{t\,1} = E_{t\,2} \qquad H_{t\,1} = H_{t\,2}$$

We shall apply Eqs. 9.8 and 9.9 to a normally incident wave using the notation and the geometrical relationships shown in Fig. 9.11, in which for the sake of clarity the three rays in question are shown slightly displaced with respect to each other. The vectors shown are instantaneous values at the boundary and may be thought of as varying with time as the waves move toward and away from the surface. The problem at hand is to attempt to satisfy the boundary conditions (Eq. 9.9) and the relationship (Eq. 9.8) by the superposition of the three waves which we expect to find.

At the boundary, either the electric or the magnetic vector in the reflected ray must be reversed in order to reverse the direction of propagation, as specified by the Poynting vector. We shall assume for the moment that we are dealing with case a of Fig. 9.11, and that the electric vector is reversed whereas the magnetic vector is unchanged. The electromagnetic boundary conditions are particularly simple for the case of normally incident radiation, since we have only tangential vectors to consider. The normal components of B and D vanish, since they are in the direction of propagation of the wave, and the tangential components of E and H must have the same values on either side of the boundary. Designating the absolute magnitude of the electric and magnetic vectors at the boundary in the incident ray by E_1 and H_1, in the reflected ray by E'_1 and H'_1, and in the transmitted ray by E_2 and H_2, we have to satisfy the boundary conditions by putting

$$E_1 - E'_1 = E_2 \qquad (9.10)$$

$$H_1 + H'_1 = H_2 \qquad (9.11)$$

But from Eq. (9.8) we see that

$$H_1 = n_1 \sqrt{\frac{\epsilon_0}{\mu_0}} E_1 \qquad H'_1 = n_1 \sqrt{\frac{\epsilon_0}{\mu_0}} E'_1 \qquad H_2 = n_2 \sqrt{\frac{\epsilon_0}{\mu_0}} E_2 \quad (9.12)$$

Substituting these results into Eq. 9.11, we get

$$E_1 + E'_1 = \frac{n_2}{n_1} E_2 \qquad (9.13)$$

and finally on combining this result with Eq. 9.10

$$E'_1 = \left(\frac{n_2 - n_1}{n_2 + n_1}\right) E_1 \qquad (9.14)$$

which specifies the magnitude of the electric vector in the reflected ray in terms of the magnitude of the electric vector in the incident ray. For the transmitted ray the corresponding result is

$$E_2 = \left(\frac{2n_1}{n_2 + n_1}\right) E_1 \qquad (9.15)$$

Notice that, if n_2 is greater than n_1, according to Eq. 9.14, E'_1 is positive, as is to be expected for the magnitude of a vector if its orientation was properly chosen originally. We therefore conclude that a plane-polarized ray is reflected with a reversal of the electric vector at a boundary at which the reflecting medium has the greater index of refraction, as, for example, in the case of light in air being reflected at a glass or water surface. If, however, n_1 is greater than n_2, as would be the case for a ray traveling under water and being reflected at an air surface, the reflection takes place with a reversal of the magnetic rather than the electric vector. These points, though apparently of little significance at this stage, will be shown to be essential to an understanding of the optical properties of thin films which we shall discuss in Chapter 10.

The reflecting power of a surface for normal incidence is given by the ratio of the intensities, or of the Poynting vectors, describing the reflected and incident rays. Using the above results we have, for the reflecting power R,

$$R = \frac{S'_1}{S_1} = \left(\frac{E'_1}{E_1}\right)^2 = \left(\frac{n_2 - n_1}{n_2 + n_1}\right)^2 \tag{9.16}$$

Reflection at a metallic surface is more complicated because of the presence of conduction currents and the consequent dissipation of energy in the metal. The transmission of light in metals is closely related to the transmission of waves in cables with resistance (described at the end of Section 8.3).

If we had considered light incident at an arbitrary angle of incidence i, we should have had to specify the orientation of the E vector in the incident ray and we should have had to assume arbitrary angles r' and r for the directions of the reflected and refracted rays. The solution of the problem would have proceeded as above, with the finding that for any orientation of the electric vector

$$i = r'$$

$$n_i \sin i = n_r \sin r$$

as in the discussion of Section 9.2, and the additional information that, if the electric vector in the incident ray is parallel to the reflecting surface, then the electric vector in the reflected and refracted rays will also be parallel to the reflecting surface, and the ratio of the intensities of the reflected and incident rays, or the reflecting power R, is

$$R = \frac{\sin^2 (i - r)}{\sin^2 (i + r)} \tag{9.17}$$

This function is plotted in Fig. 9.12. If, on the other hand, the electric vector in the incident ray is in the plane of incidence, i.e., the plane containing the incident ray and the normal to the surface, then the electric vector in the reflected and refracted rays will also be in this plane, and the reflecting power is

$$R = \frac{\tan^2 (i - r)}{\tan^2 (i + r)} \qquad (9.18)$$

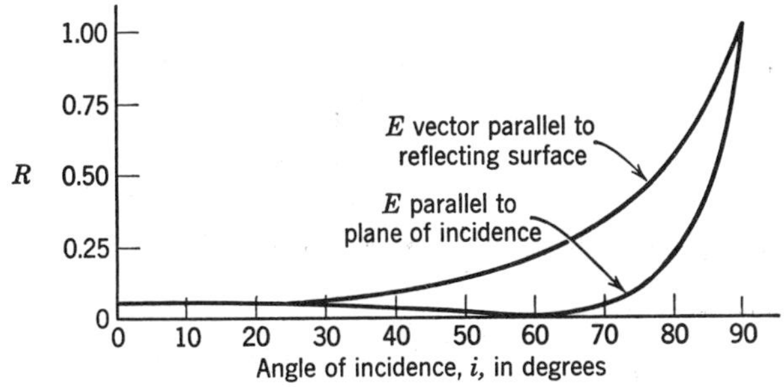

Fig. 9.12. The reflecting power of a surface for oblique incidence.

This discussion indicates how to use the expressions for the reflecting power of a surface for light incident at oblique angles. If the incident light is unpolarized, we may resolve it into two plane-polarized components. Each of these will be partly reflected and partly transmitted. But, from Fig. 9.12, we see that in general different fractions of these two rays will be reflected. In general, the reflected light and the transmitted light will be partly polarized. The reflected light will have its electric vector predominantly parallel to the plane of the reflecting surface. At one particular angle of incidence, the reflected light will be completely polarized. This is called *Brewster's angle* or simply the *polarizing angle*. In Fig. 9.12 it is in the vicinity of 60°. This situation arises when the denominator of Eq. 9.18 becomes infinite, or when $i + r = 90°$. We can express the polarizing angle in terms of the indices of refraction concerned by the following argument. We have from Snell's law

$$n_i \sin i = n_r \sin r$$

If the angle of incidence is the polarizing angle i_p, we also have

$$i_p + r = \pi/2$$

and consequently

$$n_i \sin i_p = n_r \sin \left(\frac{\pi}{2} - i_p \right) = n_r \cos i_p$$

or

$$\tan i_p = \frac{n_r}{n_i} \qquad \blacktriangleright (9.19) \blacktriangleleft$$

When light of any polarization is incident on a surface at the polarizing angle specified by Eq. 9.19, none of the component with the electric vector parallel to the plane of incidence is reflected. In other words, the electric vector in the reflected light can only be parallel to the plane of the reflecting surface. Reflection at the polarizing angle can be used to produce plane-polarized light.

9.4 THE FORMATION OF IMAGES

We see objects because rays from points on the object enter the eye. We here wish to emphasize the fact that not only one ray but a small bundle of diverging rays from every point on the object enters the eye. It is this divergent bundle that gives us the sensation of seeing the point

FIG. 9.13.   Rays of light from two points on an object which are required for seeing these points.

of origin of the bundle of rays. Such a bundle of rays entering an eye from two points on an object is shown in Fig. 9.13. In the process of seeing, the entire path of the light rays is not important. The eye takes into account only the nature of the rays as they enter the eye itself. Whether the rays actually come from the object, as shown in the figure, or whether they come out of some kind of optical instrument in these particular directions, is immaterial. The eye will see the same thing.

Two ways in which optical instruments can make us see an object at a place where, in fact, it is not, are shown in Fig. 9.14. In the first the optical instrument, a lens, takes rays diverging from a point and makes them converge at some other point in their path. Beyond this point they again diverge, and an eye intercepting this diverging bundle will see the object at the point of divergence. This point of divergence is called an image of the object. It is called a real image, that is, one through which the rays actually pass, to distinguish it from the image in case *b* of Fig. 9.14. Here the optical instrument used is a mirror, though in fact it need not be. Similar effects can be produced with lenses. The rays entering the eye appear to diverge from a point behind the mirror, though in fact the mirror is opaque. The image at this point is called a virtual image, that is, one through which the rays do not actually pass.

The rest of this chapter deals with study of the formation of images. In this section we take up plane surfaces and begin with images formed by reflection. The symbols to be used are shown in Fig. 9.15. From the

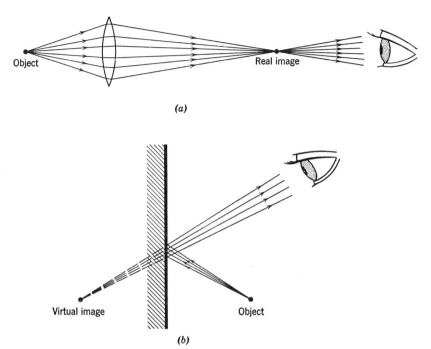

(a)

(b)

Fig. 9.14. Real and virtual images.

law of reflection and the geometry of Fig. 9.15, in which the ray OV strikes the mirror normally and is therefore reflected on itself, we find that the following angles are equal:

$$i = r' = \alpha = \beta$$

and that consequently

$$\tan \alpha = \tan \beta$$

Therefore

$$PV/OV = PV/IV$$

and finally

$$OV = IV \tag{9.20}$$

The two rays shown appear to diverge from a point as far behind the mirror as the object is from the front surface. However, since the actual magnitude of the angle of incidence does not appear in Eq. 9.20, we conclude that not only the two rays shown but all reflected rays diverge from this image. The image formed by a plane mirror is a perfect image, independent of the kind of light used, the indices of refraction of the two media forming the plane-reflecting surface, or the angle at which the image is viewed.

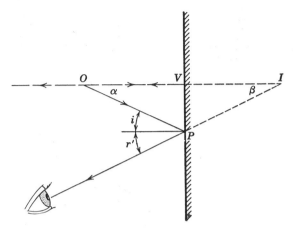

FIG. 9.15. An image formed by reflection.

The concept of the formation of images according to the law expressed in Eq. 9.20 greatly simplifies the solution of problems involving multiple reflections. An example of the solution of such a problem is shown in Fig. 9.16. The images formed by single reflections in mirrors one and two are marked I_1 and I_2, respectively. The image formed by rays reflected at both surfaces is marked $I_{1\ 2}$.

The images formed by refracted rays at a plane surface are not perfect, as we shall see. The symbols to be used in the discussion are shown in Fig. 9.17. As in the case of reflection, we begin by considering the normal ray and one other having an angle of incidence i. Snell's law may be put into the form

$$\frac{\sin i}{\sin r} = \frac{n'}{n} \tag{9.21}$$

From the figure, we have

$$i = \alpha \qquad r = \beta \tag{9.22}$$

$$\frac{IV}{OV} = \frac{VP/OV}{VP/IV} = \frac{\tan \alpha}{\tan \beta} = \frac{\sin \alpha}{\sin \beta} \frac{\cos \beta}{\cos \alpha} \tag{9.23}$$

On substituting Eqs. 9.21 and 9.22 into Eq. 9.23 we get

$$IV = OV \times \frac{n'}{n} \frac{\cos r}{\cos i} \tag{9.24}$$

From Eq. 9.24 it is clear that the point of intersection I of the normal ray and the refracted ray extended back is not the same for all rays, and that therefore the image formed will be imperfect. One imperfection results

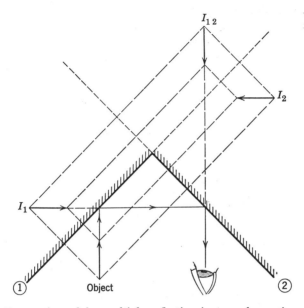

FIG. 9.16. Images formed by multiple reflection in two plane mirrors at right angles to each other.

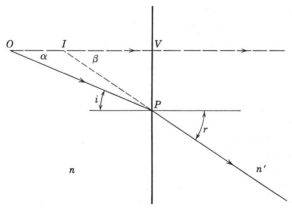

FIG. 9.17. An image formed by refraction.

from the fact that the indices of refraction are functions of wavelength, and that therefore the different colors present in the light from the object will form images at slightly different points. A second imperfection lies in the fact that, even for rays of one color, the refracted rays do not all appear to come from a single point but from a general area. If our eye made use of all the rays emitted by the object over a wide range of angles, we should, in consequence of the above, see a very blurred image. However, here, as in many other optical problems, the smallness of the bundle of rays which the eye uses is responsible for our seeing sharp images. For example, if we view the object under discussion normally

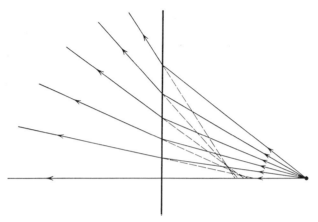

Fig. 9.18.   Refraction of rays at a plane surface.

to the refracting surface, all the rays entering the eye will make a very small angle with the vertical. Both cos i and cos r under these circumstances are very nearly equal to unity, and the image seen will be at a distance below the surface, according to Eq. 9.24,

$$IV = OV \frac{n'}{n} \qquad (9.25)$$

The paths of rays making a wide range of angles with the vertical are shown in Fig. 9.18. It will be seen that, although these rays cross in a large area, any small bundle of rays appears to come from a point, and that the position of this point is different for different bundles.

Images can also be formed by reflection or refraction at spherical surfaces. We shall derive some expressions that are useful in connection with optical problems. The following arbitrary rules and conventions are adopted. These are not universally used, and the student may find other formulas in other books, simply because the conventions regarding the use of symbols are different.

1. Draw all figures with the light incident on the reflecting or refracting surface from the left.

2. Consider object distances s positive when the object lies on the left of the vertex of the reflecting or refracting surface (see the point marked V in Fig. 9.19).

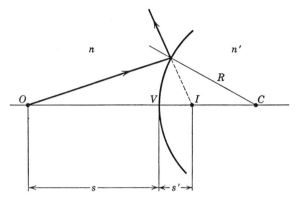

FIG. 9.19. Symbols used in discussing rays passing through a spherical surface.

3. Consider image distances s positive when the image lies on the right of the vertex.

4. Consider radii of curvature positive when the center of curvature lies on the right of the vertex.

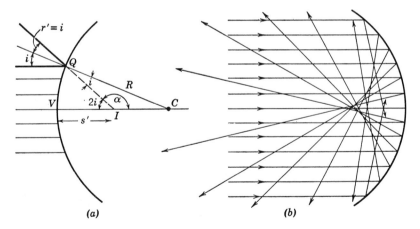

(a)   (b)

FIG. 9.20. Reflection of parallel rays at a spherical surface.

5. Consider angles positive when the slope of the ray with respect to the axis (or chosen radius of curvature) is positive.

6. Consider transverse dimensions positive when measured upward from the axis.

We begin by examining a bundle of parallel rays reflected at a spherical surface and consider a single ray striking the surface at the point Q, as shown in Fig. 9.20a. From the law of sines, which says that the ratio of the lengths of two sides of a triangle is equal to the ratio of the sines of their opposite angles, we have for the triangle ICQ.

$$\frac{IC}{QC} = \frac{R - s'}{R} = \frac{\sin i}{\sin \alpha} = \frac{\sin i}{\sin (\pi - 2i)} = \frac{\sin i}{\sin 2i} = \frac{1}{2 \cos i}$$

or that

$$s' = R\left(1 - \frac{1}{2 \cos i}\right) \tag{9.26}$$

This shows that the various rays in the parallel bundle will not appear to diverge from a single point. The image will therefore have imperfections similar to those found for the case of refraction at a plane surface. This kind of imperfection, called *spherical aberration*, is shown in greater detail in Fig. 9.20b. For sufficiently small mirrors, rays parallel to the axis will make only very small angles of incidence, cos i may be taken equal to unity, and we then have

$$s' = R/2$$

A spherical mirror whose diameter is small compared to its radius of curvature will focus rays from a distant point object. The image distance will be half the radius. Such spherical mirrors are limited in their effectiveness in gathering light to form an image because of their limited size. Astronomical instruments make use of paraboloidal rather than spherical mirrors because, for very remote objects, spherical aberration may be avoided even if large diameters, and rays making a considerable angle with the axis, are used. However, this useful property is lost at small object distances, which we shall now take up.

The more general case of the focusing of rays by a spherical mirror is illustrated in Fig. 9.21. From the triangle ICQ we have, since

$$\alpha + \beta + i = \pi$$

$$\alpha = i - \phi$$

$$\beta = \pi - 2i + \phi$$

$$\frac{IC}{QC} = \frac{R - s'}{R} = \frac{\sin i}{\sin \beta} = \frac{\sin i}{\sin (\pi - 2i + \phi)} = \frac{\sin i}{\sin (2i - \phi)} \tag{9.27}$$

Similarly, from triangle OQC, we have

$$\frac{OC}{QC} = \frac{s + R}{R} = \frac{\sin (\pi - i)}{\sin \phi} = \frac{\sin i}{\sin \phi} \tag{9.28}$$

If we limit ourselves to rays making only very small angles with the axis, or paraxial rays (and it is only such rays which will form a point image of a point object), we may put the sines of all the angles above equal to the angles themselves.   Under these conditions Eqs. 9.27 and 9.28 above may be combined to give an expression for the image distance s' in terms of s and R only,

$$\frac{1}{s} - \frac{1}{s'} = -\frac{2}{R} \qquad (9.29)$$

This is the equation which formulates the optical properties of spherical mirrors quantitatively for paraxial rays.   It is valid for concave mirrors

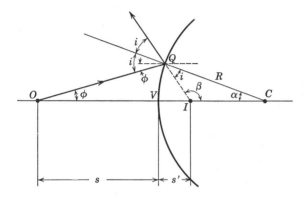

Fɪɢ. 9.21.   Focusing of paraxial rays by a spherical mirror.

(for which R must be written as a negative quantity) as well as for the convex mirrors discussed above.   The point halfway between the center and the vertex of such a mirror is called its *focal point,* and the distance from the vertex to this point is called the *focal length* f of the mirror. The focal length of concave mirrors is customarily given as positive and that of convex mirrors as negative.   We therefore have in terms of our conventions

$$f = -\frac{R}{2} \qquad (9.30)$$

Images formed by reflection at spherical surfaces may be constructed graphically.   For this purpose it is necessary to use an extended object. In Fig. 9.22, which illustrates the process, the object is an arrow of height y and the image is an arrow of height y'.   For the purposes of the construction it is desirable in general to locate not only the object and the reflecting surface but also the center C and the focal point F.

In Fig. 9.22*a* two rays have been drawn from the tip of the object, one parallel to the axis, which is reflected as though it came from the focal point, and one to the vertex, which is reflected so that the angles *i*

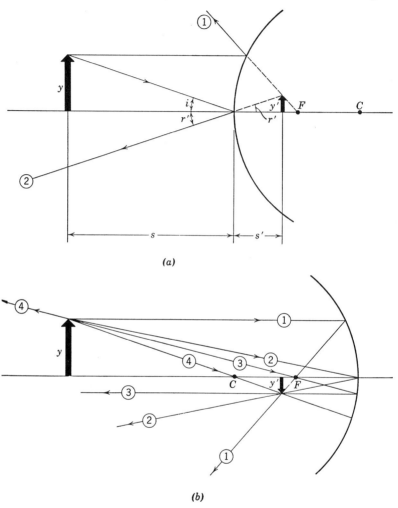

(a)

(b)

FIG. 9.22. Geometrical construction of the image formed by a spherical mirror.

and r' are equal.   The apparent point of intersection of these two rays is sufficient to locate the image.   It is apparent from the geometry of the figure that the magnification, or the ratio of the image height to the height of the object, is given by

$$m = y'/y = s'/s \qquad (9.31)$$

which can be numerically computed from Eq. 9.29. Two other rays
could be drawn in Fig. 9.22a, one in the direction of the center of the
mirror, which would be reflected back on itself since it is incident
normally to the surface, and one in the direction of the focal point F.
The latter would leave the mirror parallel to the axis. The truth of this
statement can easily be verified mathematically but is self-evident if
we notice that rays are reversible. In any optical apparatus a ray, on
being reversed in direction, will retrace its incoming path.

All four rays are drawn in Fig. 9.22b, which shows the formation of
an image by reflection in a concave spherical mirror.

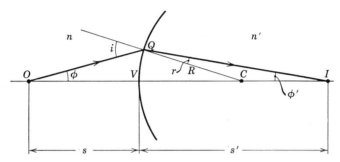

FIG. 9.23.   Refraction of paraxial rays at a single spherical surface.

Images may be formed by rays refracted at spherical surfaces as well
as by reflected rays. Here again we shall see that a widely divergent
bundle of rays diverging from a point will not be focused at a point.
As a result, lenses, unless specially corrected, also give rise to spherical
aberration. We shall discuss only the case of small lenses and paraxial
rays. In this limiting case spherical aberration is avoided, as we shall
see in the following discussion. Refracting surfaces will focus light of
different color at different points because the index of refraction is a
function of wavelength. This defect may be avoided by the use of
compound lenses, involving different kinds of glass with different dispersion. In the.following discussion we shall neglect these difficulties
and treat only the formation of images by paraxial rays of a single
wavelength.

Before taking up lenses with two surfaces, we shall discuss the refraction of paraxial rays at a single spherical interface between two media
of indices n and n', as shown in Fig. 9.23.

We have, from the law of sines, applied to triangle OQC,

$$\frac{s + R}{R} = \frac{\sin (\pi - i)}{\sin \phi} = \frac{\sin i}{\sin \phi} \tag{9.32}$$

and from triangle IQC

$$\frac{s' - R}{R} = \frac{\sin r}{\sin \phi'} \qquad (9.33)$$

Dividing Eq. 9.32 and Eq. 9.33 and using Snell's law in the form

$$\frac{n'}{n} = \frac{\sin i}{\sin r}$$

we get

$$\frac{s + R}{s' - R} = \frac{\sin i \sin \phi'}{\sin r \sin \phi} = \frac{n' \sin \phi'}{n \sin \phi} \qquad (9.34)$$

But for paraxial rays we may put

$$\frac{\sin \phi'}{\sin \phi} = \frac{\tan \phi'}{\tan \phi} = \frac{QV/s'}{QV/s} = \frac{s}{s'}$$

which, substituted into Eq. 9.34, becomes

$$\frac{s + R}{s' - R} = \frac{n'}{n} \frac{s}{s'} \qquad (9.35)$$

This is one form of the lens equation for paraxial rays. It can be re-written in the following more usual equivalent form:

$$\frac{n}{s} + \frac{n'}{s'} = \frac{n' - n}{R} \qquad (9.36)$$

Thick Lenses

This is the fundamental equation of geometrical optics. By way of illustration we shall apply it to the problem illustrated in Fig. 9.24a. An object is placed 6 cm in front of a thick lens having an index of refraction 1.333, or 4/3. Both lens surfaces are convex and have radii of curvature 1 cm and 5 cm, as shown. The thickness of the lens is 5 cm. Where is the image formed by this lens?

Let us first consider the left-hand surface only. We are concerned with the change in direction of these rays at the first surface and may, for the purposes of the discussion, assume that the glass on the right of the surface is of indefinite extent, as shown in Fig. 9.24b. Applying Eq. 9.36 to this case we have

$$\frac{1}{6} + \frac{4}{3s'} = \frac{1}{3}$$

$$s' = 8 \text{ cm}$$

When the rays strike the second surface, the refraction does not depend on the location of the first surface. We may therefore consider the second surface

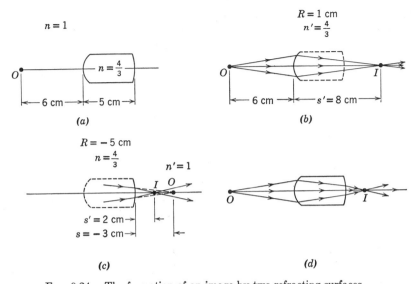

(a) (b)

(c) (d)

FIG. 9.24.   The formation of an image by two refracting surfaces.

only, as shown in Fig. 9.24c. Applying Eq. 9.36 to this case, we have

$$\frac{4}{3(-3)} + \frac{1}{s'} = -\frac{1}{3(-5)}$$

$$s' = 45/23 \simeq 2 \text{ cm}$$

The path of the rays through the entire lens is shown in Fig. 9.24d.

To compute the magnification produced at a single refracting surface we examine the situation illustrated in Fig. 9.25. As in the discussion

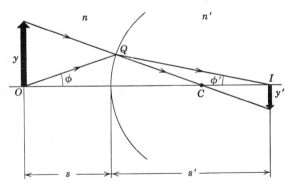

FIG. 9.25.   The magnification produced at a single refracting surface.

of Fig. 9.23, we assume that the rays from an object at O are focused at I, but with the added feature that the height of the object at O is y.

We now draw the ray from the tip of the object through the center of curvature of the refracting surface. This ray will be undeviated, since it strikes the surface at the point Q normally. We now draw the ray OQI. Because of the similarity of the two right triangles shown, we conclude that

$$\frac{-y'}{y} = \frac{CI}{CO} = \frac{s' - R}{s + R} \qquad (9.37)$$

But by use of Eq. 9.35 this may be rewritten as follows:

$$-y'/y = ns'/n's$$

for paraxial rays. We have, finally, for the magnification m

$$m = \frac{y'}{y} = -\frac{ns'}{n's} \qquad (9.38)$$

A negative magnification means an inverted image.

Thin lenses may be treated in the manner used for the two refracting surfaces above, with the added simplification that the image distance of the first surface is the negative of the object distance for the second. Calling this distance D, we have for the two surfaces of a thin lens of index n in air

$$\frac{1}{s} + \frac{n}{D} = \frac{n - 1}{R_1}$$

$$-\frac{n}{D} + \frac{1}{s'} = \frac{1 - n}{R_2}$$

which, when solved simultaneously, gives the thin lens equation

$$\frac{1}{s} + \frac{1}{s'} = (n - 1)\left(\frac{1}{R_1} - \frac{1}{R_2}\right) = \frac{1}{f} \qquad (9.39)$$

The reciprocal of the right side of this equation is called the focal length of the lens and can be computed from the radii of curvature of the two surfaces and the index of refraction of the lens. The first focal point is defined by the object distance required to produce an image at infinity. For converging or positive lenses this first focal point is on the left of the lens, as shown in Fig. 9.26, and the focal length is positive. The second focal point is defined by the image distance for an object at infinity. For a positive lens the second focal point is on the right. The focal points are in the opposite order for a negative lens.

Images produced by thin lenses may be constructed geometrically by means of a procedure very similar to that described for mirrors. A graphical construction for a positive and a negative lens is shown in Fig. 9.27.

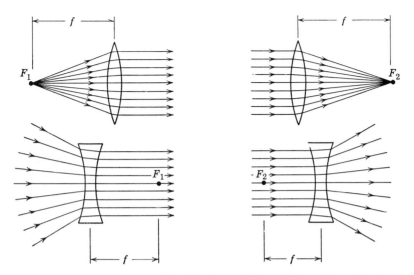

FIG. 9.26.   The first and second focal points of thin positive and negative lenses.

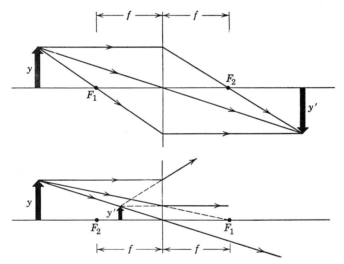

FIG. 9.27.   Geometrical construction of images formed by thin lenses.

9.5   THE EYE: COLOR, MAGNIFICATION

The most important parts of the eye, in so far as the process of forming an image is concerned, are shown in Fig. 9.28.   Light enters the eye through a tough transparent skin C, called the cornea.   Immediately behind the cornea is a chamber containing a watery liquid called the aqueous humor of the eye.   At the rear of this chamber is an opaque membrane with a circular opening of variable size.   The membrane is called the iris, and the opening P in the iris is called the pupil. The size of the pupil is varied in order to control the amount of light entering the eye. When looking at an object in a faint light, the pupil of the eye is large as compared to its size when looking at a brightly lighted scene. Behind the iris is the crystalline lens L held in place by the ciliary muscle. When this muscle is relaxed in a normal eye very distant objects are focused on the retina R. As the muscle is tensed, the focal length of the

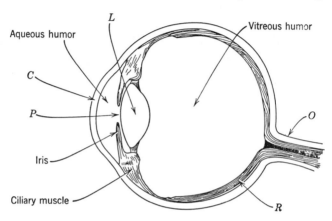

FIG. 9.28. The eye.

optical system is decreased and nearer objects are brought into focus on the retina. This process is called accommodation, and the limits of accommodation are called the near point and the far point of the eye. In a normal eye, the far point is at infinity and the near point is about 15 cm from the eye. The distance of most distinct vision is about 25 cm. The retina is composed of the ends of a great many nerve fibers which enter the eye through the optic nerve O. The eyeball itself is filled with a transparent viscous liquid known as the vitreous humor.

As shown in the previous chapter, a refracting prism may be used to analyze or separate the wavelengths or frequencies present in any given bundle of light rays. Our eyes interpret these different frequencies as different colors. The order of the colors as seen by the eye in order of increasing wavelengths is

Red
Orange
Yellow
Green
Blue
Indigo
Violet

It must be borne in mind, however, that color on the one hand and wavelength or frequency on the other are two different things. There is not even a unique correspondence between the two. Although we can say that a given frequency has a particular color, we cannot reverse the statement and say that a given color has a given frequency. There are many combinations of light of different frequency ranges that have the

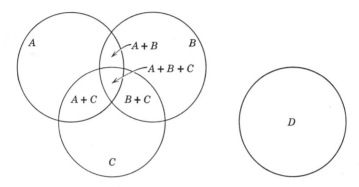

Fig. 9.29. Color mixing and matching.

same color. The eye, unlike the ear, is not an analytical instrument A trained ear can hear separately the individual frequencies that go into the combination called a chord. A sound having a single frequency cannot be duplicated by a combination of sounds having many different frequencies.

The eye responds to frequencies in an entirely different way, described in Fig. 9.29. Suppose that we have three projection lanterns making overlapping spots of light on a screen, and that each spot is of an arbitrary color A, B, or C. The overlapping regions will in general all be of a different color, which can be varied through changing the intensity of the light source in each of the lanterns. Further, if the three colors A, B, and C are red, green, and blue, the so-called primary colors, a particularly wide range of colors can be matched in the overlapping zone through changing only the relative intensities of the components. Even though all colors D cannot be matched, they can at least be specified in the sense that, if $A + B + C$ cannot be made to match D, then at least $D + A$ can be made to match $B + C$ or $D + A + B$ can be made to match C.

An object being examined with the eye seems large when the retinal image is large or, what amounts to the same thing, when the angle subtended by the object at the eye is large. The sun appears no larger than a coin held a foot or so from the eye since the angle subtended by the two, and therefore also the linear dimensions of the retinal image, are comparable. The situation is illustrated in Fig. 9.30a. An object y subtends an angle θ_0 at the eye, where

$$y/s_0 = \tan \theta_0 \qquad (9.40)$$

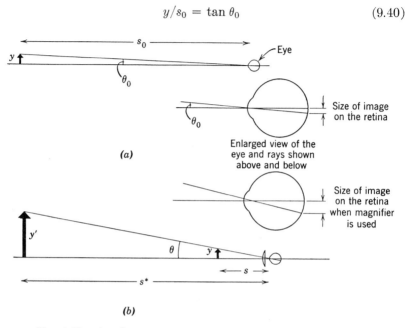

FIG. 9.30. Angular magnification produced by a magnifying glass.

s_0 being the distance of most distinct vision. Through placing a positive lens near the eye and moving the object up closer to the eye, say a distance s from the lens, as shown in Fig. 9.30b, a virtual image may be formed at s^*, where

$$\frac{1}{s} + \frac{1}{s^*} = \frac{1}{f}$$

f being the focal length of the lens. The angle now subtended by both the object and the virtual image formed by the lens is θ, where

$$y/s = y^*/s^* = \tan \theta$$

The angular magnification produced by the magnifier we shall designate by M. Since for small angles we may replace the tangent by the angle itself, we have

$$M = \frac{\theta}{\theta_0} = \frac{\tan \theta}{\tan \theta_0} = \frac{s_0}{s} \qquad (9.41)$$

There is a range of useful magnifications depending on just where the image is located. If we place the image at the distance of most distinct vision, we can find the corresponding object distance by solving the lens equation

$$\frac{1}{s} + \frac{1}{s'} = \frac{1}{f}$$

with

$$s' = -s_0$$

This gives

$$M = \frac{s_0}{s} = \frac{s_0}{f} + 1 \tag{9.42}$$

At the other extreme, if we place the image at infinity, we have

$$\frac{1}{s} + \frac{1}{\infty} = \frac{1}{f}$$

$$M = s_0/f \tag{9.43}$$

The practical limit to the magnifying power of a lens is in the vicinity of

$$M = 20\times$$

9.6 SIMPLE OPTICAL INSTRUMENTS

The simple magnifier discussed above, or equivalent lens systems called oculars or eyepieces, are ideal for aiding the eye in the examination of detail that is otherwise almost, but not quite, visible at the distance of most distinct vision. For the examination of very distant objects, or exceedingly small objects, other means must be employed. The means actually used in the microscope and in the telescope are quite similar. A real image of convenient size is first formed, usually by means of a positive lens, and this real image is then examined with an eyepiece. We shall consider first the main features of the compound microscope.

The successive images formed by the two lenses or lens systems of a compound microscope are shown in Fig. 9.31. The magnification m_0 produced by the objective is given by

$$m_0 = -s'/s$$

which, by use of the lens equation, may be rewritten

$$m_0 = -\frac{s'}{f_0} + 1 \sim -\frac{s'}{f_0} \tag{9.44}$$

Since the purpose of the instrument is to enlarge, it is desirable to choose s' large and the focal length of the objective, f_0, small. Although it is in principle possible to make s' very large by making very long microscopes, this is not done in practice, because, as we shall see in the next chapter, the limit of useful magnification is set by the wavelength

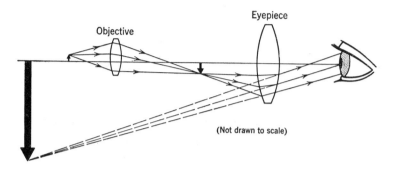

FIG. 9.31. The compound microscope.

of the light used. This limit can be reached in an instrument of convenient size, and as a result s' in Eq. 9.44 is generally taken to be 18 cm. The magnification of an objective having a focal length of 2 mm is therefore 180/2, or 90. When the image formed by the objective is viewed through an eyepiece, it is magnified again and the total magnifying power of the compound microscope becomes

$$M = m_0 M_e = (-s'/f_0)(s_0/f_e)$$

$$= -\frac{18}{f_0} \times \frac{25}{f_e} \tag{9.45}$$

where f_0 and f_e must be expressed in cm. The magnification of a microscope with an objective having a focal length of 2 mm and an eyepiece having a focal length of 2.5 cm would be 900×.

In a telescope the distant object being examined may be considered to be at infinity. The image is therefore formed at the second focal point of the objective, as shown in Fig. 9.32. The magnifying power of a telescope is defined as the ratio of the angle subtended by two points on the object being examined, for example, two stars, and the angle subtended by corresponding points on the image which the eye sees. In Fig. 9.32a we see the path of rays from a star on the axis of the telescope. In Fig. 9.32b we see the paths of rays from another star which, with the unaided eye, would be separated from the first by an angle θ. These rays on leaving the telescope make an angle θ' with the axis, and

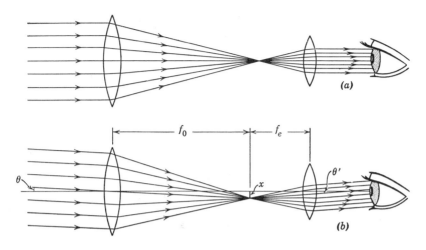

Fig. 9.32. The telescope.

the magnifying power of the telescope is therefore

$$m = -\frac{\theta'}{\theta} = -\frac{x/f_e}{x/f_0} = -\frac{f_0}{f_e} \qquad (9.46)$$

In a telescope an objective with a long focal length is desired. Telescopes therefore tend to be large. In addition, in order to see very faint objects, as much light as possible must be gathered and focused in the image. This means that the diameter of the lens should be large. An additional reason for large telescope objectives is discussed in Chapter 10.

A camera is in many ways similar to an eye. A positive lens is used to form a reduced real image on a photosensitive surface. An adjustment must be made to focus on objects at different distances. In the eye the focal length of the lens is changed. In a camera different lenses may be used, or the distance from the lens to the film may be varied, as shown in Fig. 9.33. An iris diaphragm is used primarily to control the amount of light entering the instrument, but also to control the depth of focus, as illustrated in Fig. 9.34 which shows rays coming from objects at different distances. Both cannot be exactly in focus at the same time. The illustration shows the camera adjusted so that the nearer of the two objects is actually in focus. The size of blurred large image of a distance point in a is much greater than in b where the size of opening at the lens is much smaller. In the latter case, however, the amount of light entering the camera is reduced, and relatively longer exposure times will be required.

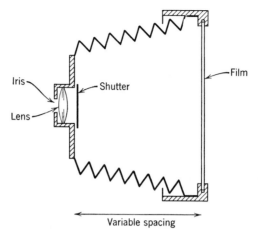

Iris

Shutter

Lens

Film

Variable spacing

Fig. 9.33. A camera.

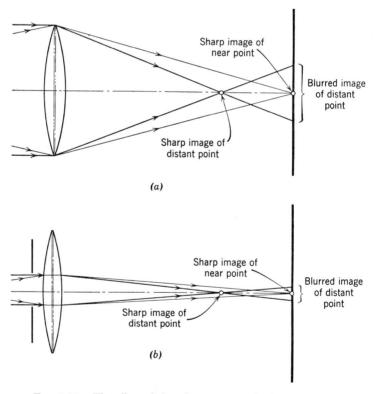

Sharp image of
near point

Blurred image
of distant
point

Sharp image of
distant point

(a)

Sharp image of
near point

Blurred image
of distant
point

Sharp image of
distant point

(b)

Fig. 9.34. The effect of size of aperture on the depth of focus.

One aspect of a projection lantern is very much like a camera, namely, the formation of a real image of an object by means of a positive lens. The lantern is perhaps more like a camera run backward, since a large distant image of a nearby object is formed, as shown in Fig. 9.35a. In order to produce a large bright image, special means of illuminating

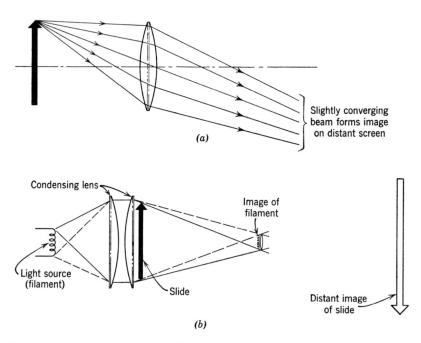

(a)

Slightly converging
beam forms image
on distant screen

Condensing lens

Image of
filament

Light source
(filament)

Slide

Distant image
of slide

(b)

FIG. 9.35.   A projection lantern: (a) shows the formation of the image only, whereas (b) shows also the effective concentration of light in the image.

the object are required.   Since the object is usually a transparent slide, a bright light is placed behind it.   Since the light from a small source such as an incandescent filament diverges, only a small fraction of it, so placed, would reach the projection lens and, therefore, also, only little of the light striking the slide.

SUMMARY

Light travels in a vacuum with the same velocity as the electromagnetic radiations emitted by circuits.

$$c = \frac{1}{\sqrt{\epsilon_0\mu_0}} \sim 3 \times 10^8 \text{ meter/sec}$$

In transparent material bodies light travels with a lesser velocity

$$v = c/n$$

where n is called the index of refraction of the transmitting medium. The index of refraction is a function of frequency, or wavelength. In general, the velocity of light is $1/\sqrt{\epsilon\mu}$ in a medium whose permittivity and permeability are ϵ and μ at the frequency in question, or, since for transparent media $\mu = \mu_0$, we may put

$$v = \frac{1}{\sqrt{\epsilon\mu}} = \frac{1}{\sqrt{K_e}} \frac{1}{\sqrt{\epsilon_0\mu_0}} = \frac{c}{\sqrt{K_e}} = \frac{c}{n}$$

The laws of reflection and refraction, namely, that the angle of incidence equals the angle of reflection, and that $n_i \sin i = n_r \sin r$, may be derived from Huygens' principle and the relation between the velocity of propagation and the index of refraction.

The fraction of the incident light intensity which is reflected at a surface depends on the angle of incidence and the state of polarization of the incident light, and on the indices of refraction of the two media on either side of the reflecting surface. The complete laws of reflection and refraction may be derived through applying the previously derived electromagnetic boundary conditions. In anisotropic media, whose polarizability is different in different directions, the index of refraction depends on the direction of propagation and on the state of polarization of the transmitted light.

For many purposes the reflection and refraction of electromagnetic waves from surfaces whose linear dimensions are large compared to a wavelength may be described in terms of rays. Rays are particularly useful in describing the formation of images. If the rays of a bundle which diverges from some point on an object are so deflected that they diverge or appear to diverge from some other point in space as well, then that other point is called an image point.

The location of an image formed by a reflecting or refracting surface may be computed from the laws of reflection and refraction. Only paraxial rays, or rays nearly parallel to the axis, are focused into an image in most optical systems. Simple conventions and formulas are given for computing the size and location of images formed by mirrors and lenses. These involve particularly the conception of focal points, or points at which parallel rays are focused, or from which diverging rays are rendered parallel.

Important optical instruments are the magnifying glass, which makes small objects appear large. (it is important to understand how such magnifiers function), and the microscope and telescope. These instruments consist of two lenses or lens systems. There is first an objective which forms an enlarged or apparently enlarged real image, and then an eyepiece, or magnifier, for viewing this image in detail.

PROBLEMS

1. (*a*) In air, sodium yellow light has a wavelength of 5893 A. What is its frequency? (*b*) In crown glass, sodium yellow light travels at a speed of 1.975×10^8 meters/second. What is the index of refraction of crown glass for sodium yellow light? (*c*) What is the wavelength of sodium yellow light in crown glass? What is its frequency? How does this compare with its frequency in air?

2. (*a*) What is the critical angle for light passing from water ($n = 1.33$) to air? (*b*) What is the critical angle for light passing from diamond ($n = 2.4$) to water?

3. A galvanometer makes use of a beam of light reflected from a plane mirror. When the mirror turns through an angle of 10°, through what angle does the reflected beam of light turn?

4. A ray of light strikes a 0.005-meter-thick piece of window glass ($n = 1.5$) at an angle of 45°. In the glass, what angle does the beam make with the normal? When the beam leaves the window what angle does it make? How far sideways has the beam been displaced?

5. Light passes from water ($n = 1.33$) to glass ($n = 1.6$). In the glass it makes an angle of 45° with the normal. What angle with the normal does it make in the water?

6. Can you think of any evidence to show whether the electric field in a beam of visible light passing through a transparent medium produces primarily nuclear displacement, or acts primarily on individual electrons? *Hint*: Try comparing Fig. 7.25(*b*) with Fig. 9.3 in some detail.

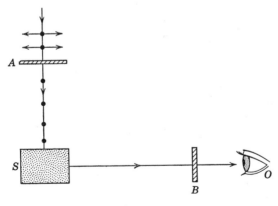

FIG. 9.36.

7. Unpolarized light passes through a Polaroid *A* with its axis so oriented that, in the transmitted light, the electric vector is normal to the plane of the paper, as in Fig. 9.36. This light falls on a soap solution *S* where it is scattered and viewed by an observer at *O* through a second Polaroid *B*. (*a*) Will the light intensity seen by the

observer vary as the Polaroid B is rotated? (b) The Polaroid A is rotated through 90°. Does the light intensity now vary as B is rotated?

★8. (a) Unpolarized light penetrates two Polaroids whose transmitting axes make an angle θ with each other. How does the intensity of the transmitted light depend on the angle θ?

(b) The Polaroids are now crossed so that no light passes through the combination. A third Polaroid is introduced between the two crossed Polaroids. Its axis makes an angle ψ with that of the first. What fraction of the incident unpolarized light is transmitted by the first two Polaroids, and by all three?

9. Prove that for normally incident light at the plane interface between two dielectrics the intensity of the incident beam is just equal to the sum of the intensities of the reflected and transmitted beams.

★10. An air core coaxial cable is connected to another having the same dimensions but having a dielectric between conductors. Show that the condition that V and i shall have the same values on both sides of the junction is equivalent to the condition that the tangential components of E and H shall be the same on both sides of the junction. What fraction of the incident power is reflected?

11. (a) What is the value of Brewster's angle of light incident from air on the surface of water ($n = 1.33$)? (b) What is the value of Brewster's angle for light incident from water to air?

12. A beam of unpolarized light is incident at Brewster's angle at the surface of a dielectric whose index of refraction is 1.5. What fraction of the incident intensity is reflected?

13. A man 6 ft tall has a mirror just large enough so that he can see himself entirely in it. How tall is the mirror?

14. The south wall of a large dark room is a mirror. A man is seated facing south in this room on a platform capable of being moved east and west. The perpendicular distance from the man to the mirror is 10 ft. Near the center of the room, and 15 ft from the mirror, are two small lights, a red one and a blue one. The red one is to the east and the blue one is to the west. Considering that the man sees the lights in the direction in which rays from the lights reach him, show in a diagram where the man sees the lights. How far away will they appear? Which will be on the man's left?

15. In the above room, the east, as well as the south, wall is covered with a mirror. The movable platform is reoriented so that the man looks southeast into the corner where the two plane mirrors meet, and the platform is capable of movement at right angles to this direction. The lights are rearranged so that when he is opposite the corner they are just behind him, with the blue to his left, and the red to his right. Be prepared to discuss what the man will see.

★16. A horizontal beam of light is normally incident on the glass side of a tank containing a solution in which the concentration varies from top to bottom. The index of refraction is greater at the bottom than at the top. (a) Draw some Huygens' wavelets at the incident surface, and be prepared to discuss the path of the light in the solutions. (b) Explain the wet appearance of dry streets on a hot day.

★17. A 6-ft man stands on the edge of a circular swimming pool 12 ft in diameter, and everywhere 6 ft deep. (a) In what direction must he look to see the opposite bottom corner of the pool when it is filled with water? (b) Where is the image which the man is looking at? Graphical solutions are probably easiest for a and b. (c) If he looks straight down, what will be the apparent depth of the pool?

18. Given a concave mirror whose radius of curvature is 10 cm, find the magnification and the image distance for the following object distances: 20, 10, 8, 5, 2, and 0 cm. Verify your calculations by geometrical construction.

19. A glass cube 1 cm on a side having an index of refraction $n = 1.5$ has a speck at its center. What regions of the cube surface must be covered to prevent the speck from being seen in any direction?

20. A narrow pencil of parallel light rays is normally incident on a solid glass sphere of index of refraction n and radius R. Where are the rays brought to a focus?

21. The radii of a thin double convex lens are 20 cm and 8 cm. The lens forms the image of an object 40 cm to the left of the lens at a position 48 cm to the right of the lens. What is the focal length of the lens? What is the index of refraction of the lens material? An object is placed 16 cm from the lens. Find the position of the image, and check by graphical construction.

22. A thin convex lens of focal length 15 cm and refractive index 1.53 is immersed in water of index 1.33. Where is the image of an object placed 100 cm from the lens, the whole system being in water?

23. A person with normal vision has a range of accommodation from 35 cm to infinity. Over what range would he be able to see objects distinctly when wearing spectacles of focal length -4.0 meter?

24. What is the magnifying power of a glass ball 2.0 cm in diameter if the glass has an index of refraction of 1.5?

25. A compound microscope comes equipped with objectives of focal lengths 2.0 mm and 6.0 mm and with oculars of magnifying power $4\times$ and $16\times$. Find the magnifying powers obtainable. What are the focal lengths of the oculars?

26. A telescope focused so that the final image is at infinity is sighted at the sun. How far and in what direction must the eyepiece be moved to project a sharp image of the sun on a screen 2 meters back of the eyepiece? The focal length of the eyepiece is 5.0 cm.

27. How might a concave mirror be used in the construction of an astronomical telescope? What would be some advantages of such an instrument?

28. It is desired to project a lattern slide 3 in. by 4 in. so as to make an image 3 ft by 4 ft on a screen. The projection lens has a focal length of 12 in. What should be the distance of the lens from the screen? From the slide to the lens?

29. Two cameras having lenses with focal lengths of 2 in. and 10 in. respectively are used to photograph the same distant scene. How do the sizes of the images on the two films compare? If equal shutter speeds are used, how should the apertures compare for equal exposure of the films?

30. A certain camera having a lens of focal length 15 cm has extensible bellows, which permits the lens to be moved to a maximum distance of 25 cm from the film. What is the least distance that an object may be situated from the lens so as to form a sharp image on the film? What is the size of the image with respect to the object?

CHAPTER 10

Optics: Interference
and Diffraction

10.1 THE INTERFERENCE OF LIGHT RAYS; GRATINGS

In Section 8.6 we have already discussed the interaction of several beams of electromagnetic radiation and have shown how to calculate the interference patterns that are produced. In so far as the transmission of energy through space is concerned, the difference between a radio wave and a light wave is merely one of scale. In the light wave the wavelengths are shorter and the frequencies are higher. Although the phenomena are fundamentally identical, the experimental conditions under which they can be observed are different, primarily because we have far less control over the sources of radiation. Whereas the source of the interfering radio waves which we have considered is a few antennas all driven by the same continuously oscillating circuit, light sources are composed of many atoms radiating independently and intermittently. No light source emits an arbitrarily long perfectly sinusoidal wave as does a radio antenna. Light sources emit a series of independent wave trains that have no phase relationship to each other, and that also differ more or less, depending on the particular circumstances, in frequency, amplitude, and state of polarization. The interaction of such an assembly of pulses will obviously involve other considerations than the interaction of the steady wave trains produced by circuits.

However, the basic ideas of electromagnetic theory are valid if properly applied. The situation may be summarized by saying that two electromagnetic waves can cancel each other at a point of space, or can produce complete destructive interference if they have (a) the same frequency, (b) the same amplitude, (c) the same state of polarization, and finally if (d) they are and remain 180° out of phase with each other.

Young's famous experiment, performed in about the year 1800, demonstrated the interference of light rays. Its essentials are illustrated in Fig. 10.1. A monochromatic light source, for instance, the yellow flame of a gas burner in which there is a little sodium chloride, or the radiation from an electric light bulb containing a continuous distribution of wavelengths, is used to illuminate a single slit S_1. Let us consider

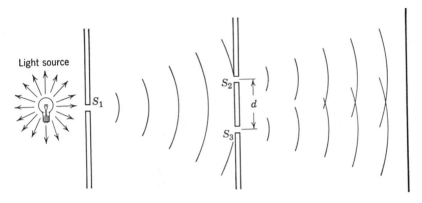

FIG. 10.1. Young's experiment.

first the monochromatic case, or any one wavelength in the continuum. Huygens' wavelets may be thought of as originating from this slit. It functions as a very small light source. Beyond this slit S_1 are two further slits S_2 and S_3, from which two sets of Huygens' wavelets emerge. These wavelets are related in phase since they are stimulated by the same original wavelet from S_1. Beyond these is an opaque screen on which a series of light and dark bands parallel to the slits appear. The position of the bright maxima may be computed from the condition that the difference in path length of the two rays to the point in question must be some integral number of wavelengths. Using the quantities designated in Fig. 10.2, we see that the required condition for an interference maximum at a point P far from the slits is that

$$r_2 - r_1 = d \sin \alpha = n\lambda \qquad (10.1)$$

But for small angles

$$\sin \alpha \simeq x/R \qquad (10.2)$$

and by combining Eqs. 10.1 and 10.2 we can compute the position of the maxima. The conditions for a maximum contain the wavelength, and therefore different wavelengths will have maxima in different places. If white light containing all wavelengths were used, there would be a colored band on either side of the central white maximum.

The reason for the single slit screening the light source may similarly
be understood in view of the following argument. It is clear that Eq.
10.1 is the condition for an interference maximum only if the light passing

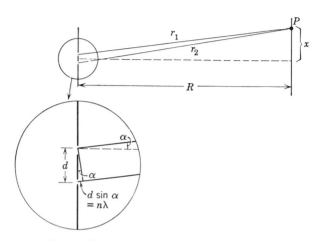

FIG. 10.2.   The conditions to be satisfied for an interference maximum.

through the two slits has the same phase in each.   This condition is
satisfied only if the rays to the two slits have traveled the same distance,
as is the case in Fig. 10.1, if S_1 is sufficiently small.   If we replace the
first slit by an extended source, rays from different parts of the source
will travel varying distances to the two slits and will therefore produce
interference maxima at different points of the screen.   These displaced
patterns will tend to cancel each other and will give rise to a general
illumination, but not to the bright and dark bands which are produced
by the arrangements shown.   In order for an interference pattern to be
visible, the light source must be small enough so that the Huygens wavelets originating from the various parts of the source all have the same
phase difference at the slits S_2 and S_3.

The arrangement shown has the practical disadvantage that only
very little light can get through the three slits, and the resulting interference pattern is therefore very dim, and hard to see.   A brighter pattern can be made by use of a mirror, as shown in Fig. 10.3.   The small
source at P sends out rays toward the screen S.   A mirror M intercepts
some of these, and they are reflected as if they came from the image
at P'.   The overlapping rays will produce an interference pattern just
as though they came from two separate sources between which a fixed
phase relation is maintained.

The distribution of intensity on the screen S due to the interference of rays from two slits is given by the same expression derived in Section 8.6. If the intensity at the screen due to light from one slit alone is I_1, the intensity of the combined beams, in the symbols of Fig. 10.2, is

$$I = 4I_1 \cos^2 \left\{ \frac{\pi d}{\lambda} \sin \alpha \right\} \qquad (10.3)$$

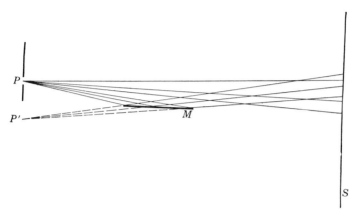

Fig. 10.3. An alternative device for showing interference patterns between rays from a source P and its image P'.

If the distance to the screen is large enough so that $\sin \alpha \simeq \tan \alpha = x/R$, the above reduces to

$$I = 4I_1 \cos^2 \left\{ \pi \frac{d}{\lambda} \frac{x}{R} \right\} \qquad (10.4)$$

As above, we see that the intensity will have its maximum value, $4I_1$, when $dx/\lambda R$ has an integral value, or zero. The intensity vanishes when $dx/\lambda R$ is an integer plus a half. The intensity distribution on the screen is shown in Fig. 10.4a.

The interference patterns obtained with more than two sources are more complicated, but in the optical region of wavelengths are very important. We shall consider the case where the number N of interfering apertures becomes very large. Light transmitted or reflected from such a series of parallel slits, called a *grating*, shows not the broad interference maxima of Fig. 10.4a but the sharp maxima of Fig. 10.4b. These sharp intense images of the slit are called spectral lines. At the zero order there is a maximum for all wavelengths. The first, second, and higher order maxima will come for values of x depending on the wavelength involved. Thus, if light containing two or more different wavelengths is incident on a grating, there will be two or more different maxima at each order of interference except the zero order, where the maxima coincide.

To understand the origin of the sharp lines produced by a grating, consider the rays from N equally spaced apertures a distance d apart,

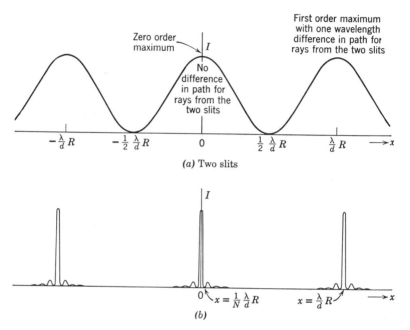

(a) Two slits

(b)

Fig. 10.4. (a) The interference pattern due to two slits. (b) The interference pattern due to N equally spaced slits.

shown in Fig. 10.5. In the forward direction all the rays to a sufficiently distant point P will have the same length, and we may expect a zero order maximum as for two slits. The first minimum as we consider rays making a small angle α with the forward direction will come not when the difference in path length of *adjacent* rays is $\lambda/2$ but at a much smaller angle. Divide the grating into two halves, the lower and upper halves shown in the illustration having the same number of slits. When the path difference δ between the ray from the first slit and the central slit marked $N/2$ is one-half wavelength, these two rays will cancel each other. Similarly, for this same direction the second ray and that marked $N/2 + 1$ will cancel each other. Similarly, we can see that all the rays will cancel in pairs. The first minimum will therefore occur when

$$\delta = \frac{Nd}{2} \sin \alpha = \lambda/2 \qquad (10.5)$$

$$\sin \alpha = \lambda/Nd \qquad (10.6)$$

$$x \simeq R \sin \alpha = \frac{1}{N} \frac{\lambda}{d} R \qquad (10.7)$$

There will be subsidiary maxima on each side of the central maxima, having smaller intensities. Thus, if we divide the grating into three zones, the rays from the first two will cancel when $\delta = Nd/3 \sin \alpha = \lambda/2$ or for $\sin \alpha \, 3\lambda/Nd$. But this leaves the rays from the lower third of

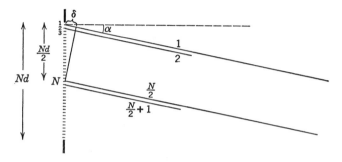

FIG. 10.5. Light transmitted by a grating.

the grating uncanceled, and these rays are responsible for the adjacent maximum. The pattern for a grating having 35 lines illuminated with a single wavelength is shown in Fig. 10.4b. The vertical scale is greatly reduced. The height of the intensity maxima is really very much greater than in Fig. 10.4a, since the total area under the curve in both cases is simply the total energy coming through all the slits. There are not only more slits, but the energy flow is crowded into a narrower band of wavelengths.

10.2 THIN FILMS; INTERFEROMETERS

We now take up a somewhat more complicated case of interference, namely, that due to the interaction of rays successively reflected by the surfaces of a thin film, as shown in Fig. 10.6. The complication arises from the fact that we must take into account not only the phases of the successively reflected rays but also their intensities. The result obtained is that there are maxima and minima whose positions depend on the direction of the incident light, and on the thickness of the film. We shall confine ourselves to a simple case which illustrates the points involved. In the first place, we shall consider monochromatic light normally incident, or nearly so, as shown in Fig. 10.7. The angle of incidence is exaggerated in order not to confuse the figure by having the incident and reflected rays almost overlapping. It further turns out that the computation of the conditions for a maximum or a minimum in the reflected light taking into account all the internal reflections

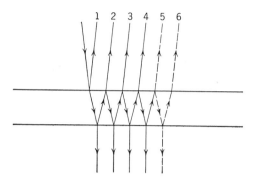

Fig. 10.6.   Successive reflections in a thin film.

produces the same result as that obtained by using only the rays marked 1 and 2 in Fig. 10.6. We shall consequently limit ourselves to these two reflected rays. We shall consider the case of a thin film having an index greater than that of the medium on either side, as, for example, in

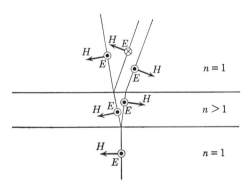

Fig. 10.7.   Reflection of light from a thin film.

the case of a soap film in air. In Section 9.3 we gave the phase relationships for a ray reflected at a single surface. This is here applied to the successively reflected parts of the incident ray for the case that the film thickness is small compared to the wavelength, so that all parts of the ray shown are in phase except for the reversals at the boundaries. In other words, the time taken for the wave to traverse the film is assumed to be very small compared to a period. It should be noticed that the electric vector of the incident ray is reversed at the first reflection and that the magnetic vector is unchanged. The transmitted ray remains in phase with the incident ray. At the lower surface the magnetic vector is reversed in the reflected ray and the electric vector remains unaltered. The net result is that both vectors in the two reflected rays are 180° out of phase and tend to cancel each other. There will therefore be a minimum intensity in the reflected light. In the limit as the film thickness diminishes, the reflection vanishes, and all the light is transmitted.

In considering thicker films, it should be noticed that, if the time required for the ray to traverse the film is an integral number of periods, the conditions outlined above are essentially unaltered. One of the reflected rays will be out of phase with the other, and there will be a minimum in the reflected intensity. Quantitatively, if T is the time required for a ray moving with a velocity $v = c/n$ to traverse a film of thickness t twice, once in each direction, we have

$$T = 2t/v = 2nt/c \qquad (10.8)$$

But if this time T is to be an integral number, say k, of periods τ, we have, since the period is the inverse of the frequency,

$$T = k\tau = k/f = k\lambda/c \qquad (10.9)$$

Combining Eqs. 10.8 and 10.9 and solving for the thickness, we have

$$t = \frac{k\lambda}{2n} \qquad (10.10)$$

as the condition for a minimum in the reflected intensity.

Maxima in the reflected intensity are obtained when the thickness of the film is halfway between the values given above, or when

$$t = \frac{(k + \frac{1}{2})}{2n} \lambda \qquad (10.11)$$

The phase changes produced by the two reflections are then just canceled by the difference in path length of the two rays.

A particularly important application of the interference patterns produced by thin films is in the inspection of optical surfaces. We shall here review the formation of interference fringes between a plane and a spherical convex glass surface, illustrated in Fig. 10.8. The light and dark rings formed in the air film between the lens and the plate are called Newton's rings. The index of refraction of the air film being investigated is 1, and the thickness of the film required for a minimum in the reflected light is therefore, according to Eq. 10.10,

$$t = k\lambda/2$$

But from the geometry of Fig. 10.8 we have

$$t = R(1 - \cos\theta) = 2R\sin^2\theta/2$$

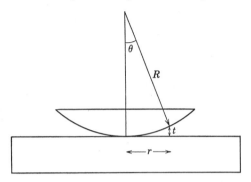

FIG. 10.8. Definition of symbols used in describing Newton's rings.

For small angles θ we may set

$$\sin^2\frac{\theta}{2} = \left(\frac{\theta}{2}\right)^2$$

and

$$\theta = r/R$$

and consequently as the condition to be satisfied by the radius of a dark ring

$$t = \frac{k\lambda}{2} = 2R\left(\frac{r}{2R}\right)^2 = \frac{r^2}{2R}$$

or

$$r = \sqrt{kR\lambda} \qquad\qquad (10.12)$$

For a bright ring the radius is

$$r = \sqrt{(k + \tfrac{1}{2})R\lambda} \qquad\qquad (10.13)$$

If the surfaces are not accurately spherical or flat, Newton's rings will not be accurately round. The shape of these interference fringes can be used to detect imperfections in optical surfaces.

Many devices for forming interference fringes are in use in optical laboratories. One of the best known is the Michelson interferometer illustrated in Fig. 10.9. It can be used to measure distances directly in terms of the wavelength of light. Light from a source S is made parallel by a lens L and falls on a glass plate A inclined at 45° to the direction of the incident beam. The front surface of this plate has a coating of metal of just the thickness required to transmit about half of the incident light and to reflect the remaining half. These two beams are reflected by the mirrors M_1 and M_2 back to A, where a part of the combined beams are transmitted to an observer at O. A second glass plate

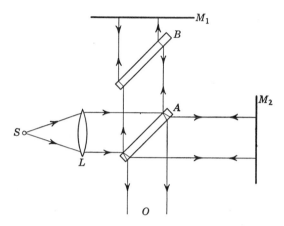

FIG. 10.9. The Michelson interferometer.

B having the same thickness as A is introduced so that both beams may traverse the same total thickness of glass. This is important, if light of many different wavelengths is used, because of the dispersion of the glass. If the path length of the two beams is the same, they will recombine in phase and the beam transmitted to O will have a maximum intensity. If now one mirror is displaced by a quarter wavelength, so that one beam travels a half wavelength farther than the other, the two beams will recombine destructively and there will be a minimum in the intensity transmitted to O. As one of the mirrors is moved in the direction of its normal, alternate maxima and minima in the light transmitted to O will be observed. By counting these maxima, the displacement of the mirror can be expressed in wavelengths of light. This is of great importance not only in providing us with an absolute standard of length but also in making precise length measurements of many kinds, for instance, in establishing the uniformity of a threaded rod.

10.3 DIFFRACTION; FRESNEL ZONES

In the previous sections we have discussed the interference patterns produced by the interaction of individual point sources or rays of light. This involved the summation of the effects due to a number, usually a small number, of individual waves. The word interference is generally used to describe the interaction of such a group of rays each of which has a single constant phase relationship to the others. When the distribution of phases in an interacting group of rays becomes continuous, one

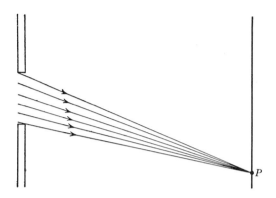

FIG. 10.10.   Fresnel diffraction.

speaks of diffraction rather than interference. Thus, for example, if we wish to estimate the light intensity at a point P on a screen which is receiving light through an aperture, as shown in Fig. 10.10, we must

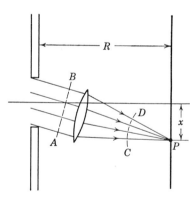

FIG. 10.11.   Fraunhofer diffraction.

construct Huygens' wavelets originating from all points of the aperture and add their contributions to the field at P. But, as may be seen from the figure, the path length, and therefore also the phase of the wavelets, varies from point to point, and we may expect variations in intensity from point to point on the screen. If the screen is near enough to the aperture so that the rays converge, as in Fig. 10.10, one speaks of a *Fresnel diffraction pattern.* If, on the other hand, the distance from the aperture to the screen is very large compared to the size of the aperture so that the rays combining to produce the illumination at point P on the screen are essentially parallel, the resulting pattern is called a *Fraunhofer diffraction pattern.* A Fraunhofer pattern may be produced on a screen at relatively small distances by use of a lens, as in Fig. 10.11.

It may seem at first glance that the lens will alter the relative phases of the various rays that pass through it and so alter the diffraction pattern. A detailed analysis, however, shows that any difference in phase between two points on a wave front approaching a lens is preserved for corresponding points on the wave front after traversing the lens. Thus, for example, if all points on the plane wave front AB in Fig. 10.11 are in phase, all points of the curved wave front CD will also be in phase and will reach point P in phase. This is a general characteristic of image formation by lenses which the interested student can prove using the analysis of the last chapter and the dependence of wavelength on index of refraction $\lambda_1 n_1 = \lambda_2 n_2$.

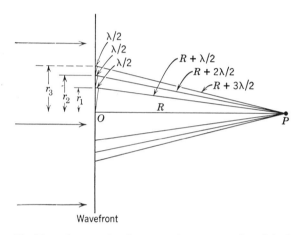

FIG. 10.12. The Fresnel zones of a plane wave for computation of the intensity at P.

The diffraction pattern due to a slit consists of a series of light and dark lines, whereas that due to a circular aperture consists of concentric rings. We shall take up in detail, first, the Fresnel diffraction due to a circular aperture, using approximations that help us avoid certain mathematical complications.

Let us consider the cumulative effect at P in Fig. 10.12 of all the Huygens wavelets originating on the plane wave front which is moving in the direction of the arrows from left to right. Let the distance from P to the wave front be R, and let the normal to the wave front from P intersect it at O. Now construct concentric circles on the wave front about O having radii $r_1, r_2, r_3, \cdots, r_n$ such that the distances from P to these circles are $R + \dfrac{\lambda}{2}, R + \dfrac{2\lambda}{2}, R + \dfrac{3\lambda}{2}, \cdots, R + \dfrac{n\lambda}{2}$, respectively. The equations for the radii r_n are

$$r_n{}^2 + R^2 = \left(R + \frac{n\lambda}{2}\right)^2$$

$$= R^2 + n\lambda R + \left(\frac{n\lambda}{2}\right)^2$$

If we neglect the last term in comparison to the first two, which we may do if $\lambda \ll R$, and solve for r_n, we get

$$r_n = \sqrt{n\lambda R} \qquad (10.14)$$

We now wish to compute the resultant amplitude A at P due to the wavelets arising in the zones of the wave fronts described by the above concentric circles. Note that, since the path difference from any two points of the central zone to P is less than $\lambda/2$, the resultant phase difference of any two wavelets will be less than 180°. We may therefore give them all the same sign and put for the resultant amplitude at P due to the first or central zone some positive number a_1. The resultant amplitude at P due to all the wavelets originating in the second zone will now necessarily be negative. The various wavelets originating in this zone will have distances to cover to P differing by less than $\lambda/2$, and will therefore differ in phase by less than 180°. The average path length, however, is $\lambda/2$ greater from zone 2 than it was from zone 1, and we conclude therefore that a_2 must be negative. The contributions due to wavelets from the successive zones will therefore be of opposite sign, and we may write

$$A = a_1 - a_2 + a_3 - a_4 + \cdots \qquad (10.15)$$

The magnitude of the various terms in this expression will vary because of three factors. First, the areas of the zones change slightly in going from one to the next. Second, the angle between the direction of propagation of the wave front and the direction to P changes from one zone to the next. Third, the distance to P changes. The net effect of all these factors is that the magnitude of the contributions from the successive zones gradually decreases as we go from smaller to larger radii. The change is smooth and gradual, so that the contribution of any one zone is very nearly equal to the average of the two contributions on either side.

$$a_n = \frac{a_{n+1} + a_{n-1}}{2} \qquad (10.16)$$

Using this theorem, and rewriting Eq. 10.15 in the form

$$A = \frac{a_1}{2} + \frac{a_1}{2} - a_2 + \frac{a_3}{2} + \frac{a_3}{2} - a_4 + \frac{a_5}{2} + \frac{a_5}{2} \cdots$$

we see that the total contribution due to n zones may be written approximately

$$A = \frac{a_1}{2} \pm \frac{a_n}{2} \tag{10.17}$$

where the positive sign is to be used if n is odd, and the negative sign if n is even. If we are considering a large plane wave, so that there are very many zones, a_n may be neglected compared to a_1, and we have

$$A = a_1/2 \tag{10.18}$$

This result may at first seem strange. It says that the net effect at P due to all the wavelets from an infinite plane wave is only half of the contribution to be expected from the first zone alone. In other words,

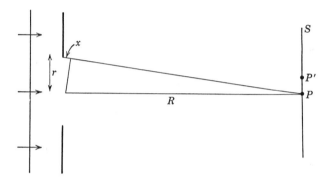

Fig. 10.13. A plane wave, circular aperture of radius r, and screen S.

if we placed a screen at the position of the plane wave front of Fig. 10.12 with an aperture that left only the first zone uncovered, then the amplitude at P would be twice that produced by the unobstructed wave. This is true. The energy of the undisturbed wave is uniformly propagated in the forward direction. If we place a screen with an aperture in the path of the wave, the energy in the wave is non-uniformly radiated through the aperture. To see this we now consider the pattern of light intensity to be expected behind a circular hole in a screen normally illuminated by a plane wave.

In Fig. 10.13 the screen S is to be considered movable; so that the distance R from screen to aperture is variable. A plane wave is incident on the circular aperture of radius r. We consider first the light intensity at the central point P. The difference in path length to P for rays from the center of the aperture and from the edge of the aperture is x, and the following relation must be satisfied:

$$r^2 + R^2 = (R + x)^2$$
$$= R^2 + 2xR + x^2$$

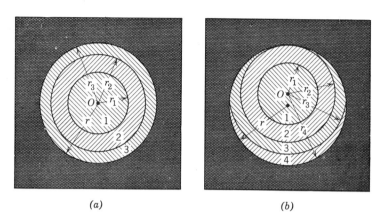

(a)   (b)

FIG. 10.14.   The Fresnel zones in the circular aperture of Fig. 10.13 (a) for the point
P on the screen S, and (b) for the point P'.

and, if $x \ll R$,

$$x = r^2/2R \qquad\qquad (10.19)$$

Now x may be written as some number n of wavelengths where n need
not be integral., We have

$$n = r^2/2R\lambda \qquad\qquad (10.20)$$

and we see that, as R increases, the number of wavelengths of path
difference decreases, and therefore that the number of Fresnel zones exposed changes.   In Fig. 10.14a the distance R is such that $x = 3\lambda/2$,
and three zones are exposed.   At greater distances R fewer zones are
exposed.   It may then happen that the intensity at P goes through successive maxima and minima as the distance R is varied.

We now focus our attention on point P', off the axis in Fig. 10.13, for
some one fixed distance R.   The Fresnel zones at the aperture are
shown in Fig. 10.14b.   They are not all completely exposed, and, in
calculating the amplitude at A, the changing exposed areas of the zones
must be taken into account.   When this is done, it is found that the
light intensity at P' goes through successive maxima as the distance
from the axially located point P is increased.   Photographs of Fresnel
diffraction patterns for holes of various sizes are shown in Fig. 10.15.

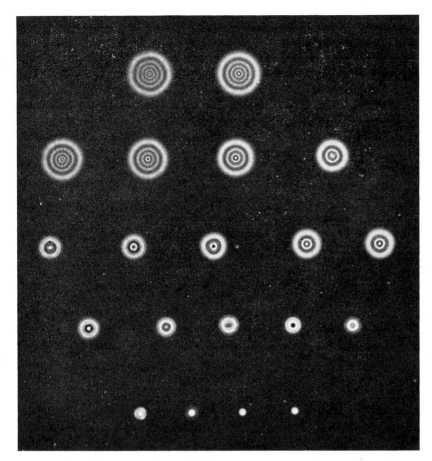

FIG. 10.15. Fresnel diffraction patterns for holes of various sizes. Taken from
Francis W. Sears, *Optics*, Addison-Wesley, Cambridge, Mass, 1945.

The smaller holes produce the larger diffraction pattern shown on the
upper left. Note that as the size of hole is varied the central spot may
be either light or dark. Similar patterns might be obtained through
using a hole of constant size and varying the distance from hole to screen.

Fresnel diffraction patterns due to apertures of different shapes are
more complex, but they show the same tendency to redistribute the
energy transmitted in some non-uniform fashion. Another form of
aperture of particular importance is the slit. We shall discuss this in
some detail, but only for the case of Fraunhofer diffraction, which has
a special importance in describing the performance of optical instruments and lenses.

10.4 FRAUNHOFER DIFFRACTION DUE TO A SLIT

We now take up the Fraunhofer diffraction pattern of a single slit. Plane waves of monochromatic light are assumed incident on a slit from the left, normally, so that the electric vectors at all points across the slit at any one instance are in phase with each other. The symbols to be used are shown in Fig. 10.16. The argument runs parallel to that

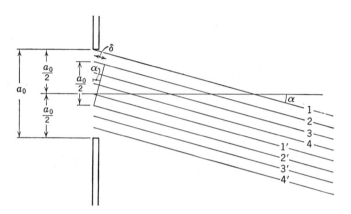

FIG. 10.16. Fraunhofer diffraction due to a single slit.

previously used for the discussion of the interference pattern due to a grating. Instead of considering light from a finite number of small slits, we must add the contributions of an infinite number of infinitesimal sections. We proceed, as before, to determine the directions in which the radiated intensity is zero. For this purpose it is convenient to group the rays in pairs as 1 and $1'$, 2 and $2'$, etc., in the illustration. Rays 2 and $2'$, for example, will cancel each other if their path difference δ is a half wavelength, or if

$$\sin \alpha = \frac{\delta}{a_0/2} = \frac{\lambda/2}{a_0/2} = \frac{\lambda}{a_0} \qquad (10.21)$$

But the condition that any other pair of rays, such as 1 and $1'$ or 3 and $3'$, cancel is that given above. We conclude that, if Eq. 10.21 is satisfied, the sum of the fields due to all the rays at point P in Fig. 10.17, for instance, will be zero if

$$\sin \alpha = \lambda/a_0$$

Similarly, if we divided the rays into any even number of groups, with a separation at the slit of $a_0/4$, $a_0/6$, etc., we should find destructive interference in pairs for directions given by

$$\sin \alpha = \frac{\lambda/2}{a_0/4} = \frac{2\lambda}{a_0} \qquad (10.22)$$

$$\sin \alpha = \frac{\lambda/2}{a_0/6} = \frac{3\lambda}{a_0} \qquad \text{etc.}$$

or intensity minima on the screen in Fig. 10.17 at the positions

$$x = R \tan \alpha$$

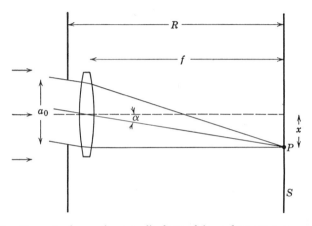

FIG. 10.17. One set of rays from a slit focused by a lens on a screen S. $R = f$ if the lens is at the aperture, here drawn a small distance away for clarity.

For sufficiently small angles, we may replace the tangent by the sine, and the above condition becomes

$$x = \frac{R\lambda}{a_0}, \frac{2R\lambda}{a_0}, 3\frac{R\lambda}{a_0}, \qquad \text{etc.} \qquad (10.23)$$

Between these minima are intensity maxima, of which the central one is by far the most important. The actual distribution of light intensity in the Fraunhofer diffraction pattern due to a slit is derived at the end of this section. It is

$$\frac{I}{I_0} = \left(\frac{\sin z}{z}\right)^2 \qquad z = \pi a_0 \frac{\sin \alpha}{\lambda} \qquad (10.24)$$

where I_0 is the intensity maximum at the center of the central bright band. The correctness of Eq. 10.24 should be verified by calculation. The intensity distribution is plotted in Fig. 10.18. The reason for the smallness of the secondary maxima may be qualitatively understood through dividing the slit into an odd, rather than an even, number of bands and noting that the effects of these cancel in pairs, leaving one

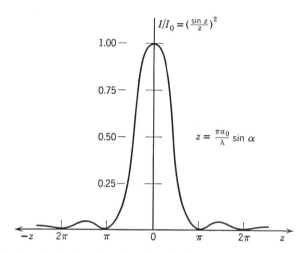

FIG. 10.18. Graph of the intensity distribution of the Fraunhofer diffraction pattern due to a slit.

band over. The higher order maxima are then due to wavelets originating from a smaller area at greater angles to the incoming wave front and are therefore relatively weak.

Derivation of Eq. 10.24 for Diffraction from a Slit

In the slit shown in Fig. 10.19, we are considering light diffracted at an angle α. The slit width is a_0, and we chose the origin of coordinates at the center of the slit. The Huygens wavelets originating in a part of the slit of width dx will be proportional to dx. Let us choose the phase so that our measurements are with respect to the wave originating at $x = 0$. We would have for this wave

$$k\, dx \sin 2\pi f t$$

and for a wave originating at a distance x from the origin, as in Fig. 10.19,

$$k\, dx \sin\left(2\pi f t - 2\pi \frac{\delta}{\lambda}\right)$$

or, since $\delta = x \sin \alpha$,

$$k\, dx \sin\left(2\pi f t - 2\pi \frac{x \sin \alpha}{\lambda}\right)$$

The result of all the wavelets will be

$$\int_{-a_0/2}^{a_0/2} k \sin\left(2\pi f t - 2\pi \frac{x \sin \alpha}{\lambda}\right) dx$$

If we put

$$z = \pi a_0 \frac{\sin \alpha}{\lambda} \tag{10.25}$$

the above integral becomes

$$\int_{-a_0/2}^{a_0/2} k \sin\left(2\pi ft - 2\frac{z}{a_0} x\right) dx = \left[\frac{ka_0}{2z} \cos\left(2\pi ft - 2\frac{z}{a_0} x\right)\right]_{-a_0/2}^{a_0/2}$$

$$= ka_0 \frac{\sin z}{z} \sin 2\pi ft \tag{10.26}$$

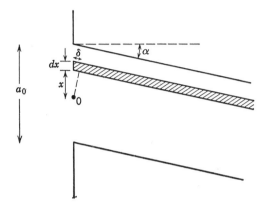

Fig. 10.19. Symbols used in deriving Eq. 10.24.

The intensity is proportional to the square of the amplitude. We therefore get for the ratio of the intensity of the wave diffracted through an angle α to the undiffracted wave at $\alpha = 0$

$$\frac{I}{I_0} = \left(\frac{\sin z}{z}\right)^2$$

which is Eq. 10.24.

The Diffraction of Light by the Slits of a Grating

In discussing Young's experiment on the interference of rays from two point sources, we computed the angular positions in which intensity maxima might be expected but we did not specify how bright these maxima would be. In the discussion of the diffraction pattern due to a single slit we have the clue required to resolve this point. We shall here again consider a normally illuminated transmission grating, The intensity radiated in any direction from a slit is given by Eq. 10.24. The amplitude of the oscillation in any given interference maximum is necessarily limited by the amplitude of the radiation in this direction from each of the individual slits. The spectra that can be obtained by shining light on various numbers of parallel slits, or lines ruled on a mirror, with various ratios of slit widths to slit spacings, and with various angles of incidence for the incoming light, can readily be computed. Such instruments are called diffraction gratings and are used in spectroscopic investigations to analyze the various frequencies present in a beam of light. They serve the same purpose as a prism spectroscope, but, as will be shown in Section 10.5, they have a higher resolving power, that is, they can distinguish

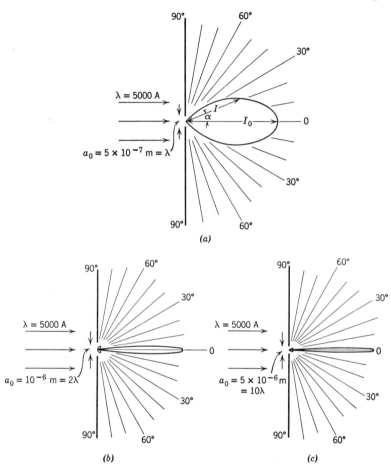

FIG. 10.20. (a) Diffraction pattern produced by a slit whose width is 1 wavelength. $a_0 = \lambda$. (b) Diffraction pattern produced by a slit whose width is 2 wavelengths. $a_0 = 2\lambda$. (c) Diffraction pattern produced by a slit whose width is 10 wavelengths. $a_0 = 10\lambda$.

smaller differences in wavelength. The principles involved in the functioning of a grating are illustrated below.

To begin with, let us consider the diffracted light from a single slit more in detail and quantitatively in terms of particular wavelengths and slit widths. The point with which the student should familiarize himself is that wide slits transmit light primarily in the direction of the incident light, whereas narrow slits spread the light out in a fan-shaped pattern. We have gone through the mathematics, and in this repetition of the results it is important not merely to check that the formulas have been properly applied but rather to understand why the physical conditions being discussed lead to the particular results predicted by the formulas.

Recapitulating, we have for the intensity of the *diffracted* beam produced by light of wavelength λ incident normally on a slit of width a_0, and diffracted through an angle α,

$$\frac{I}{I_0} = \left(\frac{\sin z}{z}\right)^2 \qquad z = \pi a_0 \frac{\sin \alpha}{\lambda}$$

For green light of wavelength 5000 A, incident normally on a slit whose width is 1, 2, and 10 times the wavelength, we have the diffraction pattern plotted

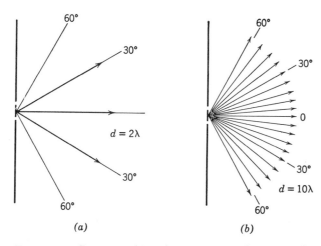

(a)   (b)

Fig. 10.21.   Direction of interference maxima due to two slits.

in Figs. 10.20a, b, and c. The length of the vector from the slit to the contour plotted represents the intensity of the diffracted light in the direction of the vector on an arbitrary scale in which the intensity in the forward direction is I_0. Qualitatively we may describe these figures by saying that a sufficiently narrow slit will diffract, or radiate light, in all directions, but that, as the slit gets wider, light rays from the various parts of the slit interfere with each other and the dark regions in the shadow of the sides of a wide slit are dark because of interference effects.

Similarly, if we consider the *interference* pattern due to two very narrow slits whose separation is 2 and 10 wavelengths, or for green light having a wavelength of 5000 A with a separation of 10^{-6} and 5×10^{-6} meter, respectively, we get interference maxima in the directions shown in Figs. 10.21a and b, computed from Eq. 10.1 with the numerical results given in Table 10.1.

The effects due to *two finite slits* may now be estimated by combining the above results. For example, let us consider two slits having a width $a_0 = 2\lambda$, or $a_0 = 10^{-6}$ meter, and separated by 5 times this distance, or $d = 5 \times 10^{-6}$ meter $= 10\lambda$. The location of the interference maxima is given in the right-

TABLE 10.1　TABLE OF VALUES OF α SATISFYING
SIN $\alpha = n\lambda/d$　　($\lambda = 5000$ A)
(The values of α given determine the positions of interference maxima)

n	$d = 10^{-6}$ meter $= 2\lambda$	$d = 5 \times 10^{-6}$ meter $= 10\lambda$
1	30°	5.7°
2	90	11.5
3		17.4
4		23.6
5		30.0
6		36.9
7		44.5
8		53.1
9		64.1
10		90.0

hand column of Table 10.1. The intensity of the diffraction pattern for $a_0 = 2\lambda$ is shown in Fig. 10.20b. The first minimum occurs when

$$z = \frac{\pi a_0}{\lambda} \sin \alpha = 2\pi \sin \alpha = \pi \quad \text{or for } \alpha = 30°$$

We may therefore expect the amplitude of the successive maxima to decrease, and for the maximum at $\alpha = 30°$ to be absent. The intensity distribution plotted as a function of z is shown in Fig. 10.22a. The fifth order maximuim, in which there is a difference in path length of rays from the two slits amounting to 5 wavelengths, is, as shown, suppressed.

The effect of having not two but many equally spaced slits as previously discussed is to sharpen the lines produced in the diffraction pattern, with the result shown in Fig. 10.22b. The ability of a grating to separate lines in the diffraction pattern due to almost equal wavelengths is discussed at the end of the next section.

10.5　RESOLVING POWER

In the preceding chapter we discussed the formation of images from the point of view of geometrical optics. We showed that a bundle of rays originating from some point on an object could be made to converge again in such a way as to form an image. The analysis involved the assumption of the rectilinear propagation of light rays in homogeneous media and of the laws of reflection and refraction applicable at the boundary between two media. The assumption of rays and sharp shadows was only an approximation to the truth. Light is an electromagnetic wave. Light waves can interfere with each other under proper circumstances, just as we have seen that radio waves do. They can travel around corners, as sound waves or water waves do. These wave aspects of light also play a part in the formation of images.

To see how this comes about we must examine images in detail. How faithfully can we expect the object being examined to be reproduced? A pattern of waves can hardly be expected to reveal detail much smaller than the wavelength of the waves being used. Light, whose wavelength

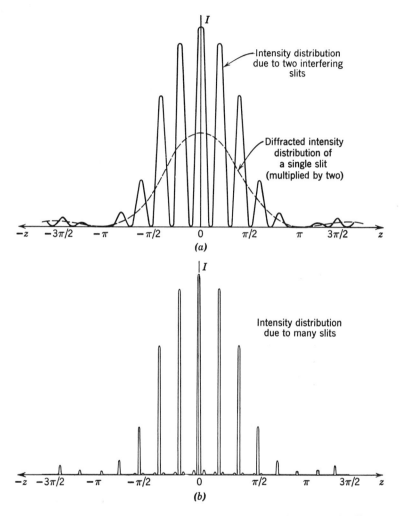

FIG. 10.22. (a) The diffraction pattern due to two finite slits. (b) The diffraction pattern due to a grating (many slits) having the same separation and width as in a.

is thousands of times larger than an atom, can hardly be expected to show up atomic structure. We should not expect to form an image of a pebble on a beach by observing reflected ocean waves.

Actually the amount of detail to be found in an image depends on two characteristic lengths, one associated with the light and the other associated with the lens. Experimentally, we should find, if with some lens we produced an image of an object of variable size, that the size of the image was proportional to the size of the object down to some lower limit. If the size of the object is decreased beyond this limit, the image size remains constant. The size of the image of small, or "point," sources depends on the wavelength of the light being used and on the diameter of the lens. A large lens can produce a smaller image of a point source than can a small lens. A large lens produces a more perfect image than a small one because the "spots" on the image representing "points" on the object are smaller. When we examine an object in great detail, for example, if with a microscope we examine a living cell, or if with binoculars we examine a distant ship, or if with a telescope we examine the moon, a convenient description of the amount of detail we can see is in terms of the linear or angular separation between points that can be seen separately, or "resolved" from each other. This is the general significance of the resolving power of a lens, which we shall describe in detail further on.

The examination of illuminated or radiating objects so as to discover as much as possible about their structure is one important area for the application of the wave theory of light; another is the analysis of the light itself, particularly with regard to the wavelengths present. A spectroscope is an instrument for analyzing light. Light enters the instrument through a narrow slit, and, by means of lenses or mirrors, an image of this slit is formed. The size of this image again has a lower limit. By making the slit narrower we can make the image narrower only up to a point. The size of the smallest possible image is again determined by the wavelength of the light and by the size of the lenses and mirrors used in forming the image.

In a spectroscope it is desirable to form small images of the slit because the instrument is so constructed that the location of the image depends on the wavelength of the light used. Thus, if the light coming into the slit contains a wavelength in the red and another in the green, two separate images will be formed in different places, one red and one green. If we seek a limit, if we want to distinguish between wavelengths that are almost, but not quite, equal, we must find out what determines that smallest difference between two wavelengths that can be observed. This is an exceedingly important question in connection with atomic structure. Here again, it is important to determine the limit to which we can go and to understand what limits the spectroscopic resolving power of the instruments we must use.

In Fig. 10.20 we showed the diffraction patterns of slits of various sizes. Their common feature was the formation of a central bright image with faint auxiliary images on either side. The narrower the slit, the greater the angle through which the light is diffracted. A similar discussion might be given for circular holes. They would also produce Fraunhofer diffraction patterns at distant points consisting of a central bright spot surrounded by relatively very faint rings. By insertion of a

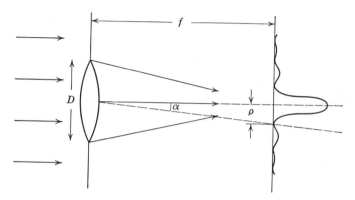

FIG. 10.23. The diffraction pattern produced by a lens using light from a distant point source.

lens behind the circular aperture, the distant Fraunhofer diffraction pattern may be focused at the focal plane of the lens. The symbols to be used in discussing this pattern are shown in Fig. 10.23. The angular deviation of rays at the edge of the central bright spot is given by a relationship very like that in Eq. 10.21 derived for a slit. The angular size (half breadth) of the central circular spot is given by

$$\sin \alpha = 1.22 \frac{\lambda}{D} \qquad (10.27)$$

where D is the diameter of the opening, or, if the lens is not stopped down by a diaphragm, D is simply the diameter of the lens. The radius of the central spot is designated by ρ, and the plot along the screen represents the intensity distribution of the diffracted light.

Instead of speaking of the Fraunhofer diffraction pattern due to the circular aperture, we may, with equal propriety, speak of the diffraction pattern due to the lens. It now becomes clear that, because of the wave nature of light, a lens cannot produce an arbitrarily sharp image. In a sharp image, of a distant star for instance, we wish to make ρ as small as possible with a lens of given focal length. But since

$$\rho/f = \tan \alpha \simeq \sin \alpha$$

we may write

$$\rho = 1.22\lambda \frac{f}{D} \qquad (10.28)$$

It is clear that, in order to make the image small, the lens must have a large diameter. This is what might have been inferred qualitatively from Fig. 10.20. The larger the opening, the smaller the angular spread of the pattern.

The limit of resolution of a lens is reached when the images of two points are a distance ρ apart, such that the central bright spot of one falls on the first dark ring of the second. In angular measure this limit of resolution, or resolving power, is given in Eq. 10.27. This is the smallest angular separation of two stars, for instance, that can be separated in the image formed by a perfect lens or one with no spherical or chromatic aberration.

Spectroscopic Resolving Power

A spectroscope is an instrument used to analyze the wavelengths present in a light beam, and its resolving power is a measure of its ability to distinguish between two almost equal wavelengths. Thus, if $\Delta\lambda$ is the smallest distinguishable difference between wavelengths λ, and $\lambda + \Delta\lambda$, then the resolving power is defined as $\lambda/\Delta\lambda$. (See frontispiece.)

The essential part of a spectroscope is a prism or grating which deflects rays having different wavelengths by different amounts. In Figs. 10.24a and b this aspect of a spectroscope is illustrated. Parallel rays of any one wavelength are deviated through an angle θ and emerge as a parallel bundle of width W. The deviation is a function of wavelength. If this dependence is known or, in other words, if we know $d\theta/d\lambda$, then we can compute the difference in angle $\Delta\theta$ between emerging rays having wavelengths λ and $\lambda + \Delta\lambda$. The relation is

$$\Delta\theta = \frac{d\theta}{d\lambda}\Delta\lambda \qquad (10.29)$$

For a prism having an index of refraction n_p, we may expect $d\theta/d\lambda$ to be proportional to $dn_p/d\lambda$. The proportionality constant will depend on the apex angle, A, of the prism. It can be shown that for any isosceles prism traversed by a beam parallel to its base

$$n_p \sin\frac{A}{2} = \sin\left(\frac{A+\theta}{2}\right)$$

For small angles this relation takes the particularly simple form

$$n_p \frac{A}{2} = \frac{A}{2} + \frac{\theta}{2}$$

$$\theta = (n_p - 1)A$$

$$\frac{d\theta}{d\lambda} = A\frac{dn_p}{d\lambda} \qquad \text{(prism)} \qquad (10.30)$$

For a grating having many rulings a distance d apart, the dependence of the angular position of a maximum in the interference pattern is the same as for two slits, given in Eq. 10.1,

$$\sin \theta = \frac{n\lambda}{d} \qquad (10.31)$$

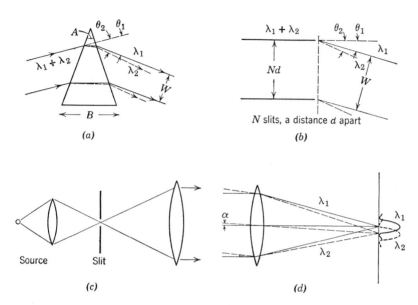

Fig. 10.24. The deflection and focusing of rays in a spectroscope.

where n refers to the order of the interference maximum, or the number of wavelengths in the difference in the path length from adjacent slits to the image (see Fig. 10.2). For the grating we have

$$\cos \theta \, d\theta = \frac{n}{d} \, d\lambda$$

$$\frac{d\theta}{d\lambda} = \frac{n}{d \cos \theta} \qquad \text{(grating)} \qquad (10.32)$$

Although these considerations of the deviations produced by gratings and prism are important, they do not yet tell the whole story concerning spectroscopic resolving power. We have still to consider our ability to separate bundles of parallel rays traveling at a small angle to each other. The parallel rays coming into the spectroscope are produced as shown in Fig. 10.24c. The image of a light source is focused on a slit. This brightly illuminated slit is at the focal point of a collimating lens which transmits a parallel beam incident on the prism or grating. The beam emerging from the prism or grating is now refocused by a second lens, and each wavelength present produces an image of the slit, as shown in Fig. 10.24d. The diffraction pattern at the focal point of the lens is determined by the width W of the incident beam.

The minimum angle $\Delta\theta$ between two beams forming resolvable images must be, according to the convention we have adopted, at least equal to the half angle subtended by the central image. According to Eq. 10.21 this must satisfy the relation

$$\sin\alpha = \lambda/W \qquad (10.33)$$

Here W plays the same role as a_0 in Eq. 10.21. We are interested in high resolving power, so that α is small, and we can put $\alpha = \sin\alpha$. Then, if $\Delta\theta$ must at least equal α to produce resolvable images, we find, from Eq. 10.29 that $\Delta\lambda$ must satisfy the following conditions,

$$\Delta\lambda = \frac{d\lambda}{d\theta}\,\Delta\theta$$

$$= \frac{d\lambda}{d\theta}\,\alpha$$

$$= \frac{d\lambda}{d\theta}\,\frac{\lambda}{W}$$

or the resolving power is given by

$$\frac{\lambda}{\Delta\lambda} = W\,\frac{d\theta}{d\lambda} \qquad (10.34)$$

For a prism having a small apex angle, the resolving power, using Eq. 10.30 is found to be

$$\frac{\lambda}{\Delta\lambda} = (WA)\,\frac{dn_p}{d\lambda} \qquad (10.35)$$

In order to estimate this magnitude, we must calculate the coefficient $dn_p/d\lambda$ For heavy flint glass, we have approximately

$$n_p = 1.65 \quad \text{for} \quad = 4000 \text{ A} = 4 \times 10^{-7} \text{ meter}$$
$$= 1.62 \quad \text{for} \quad = 6000 \text{ A} = 6 \times 10^{-7} \text{ meter}$$

which leads to

$$\frac{dn_p}{d\lambda} = \frac{1.65 - 1.62}{(6-4) \times 10^{-7}} = \frac{0.03}{2 \times 10^{-7}} = 1.5 \times 10^5 \text{ meter}^{-1}$$

In applying Eq. 10.35 we must use the same units of length in expressing W and λ. Since we have used meters in specifying wavelength, we must use meters in specifying W. For a large prism we might have $W = 0.1$ meter and $A = \frac{1}{2}$ radian. The resolving power, with the approximations used, would be

$$\frac{\lambda}{\Delta\lambda} = 0.1 \times \tfrac{1}{2} \times 1.5 \times 10^5 = 7500 \qquad \text{(prism)} \qquad (10.36)$$

A glass prism of this kind could easily resolve the two yellow spectral lines, called the D, lines of sodium. Their wavelengths are approximately 5890 and 5896 A, respectively, and the difference in wavelength is 6 A. According to Eq. 10.36, the smallest resolvable difference in wavelength using the above prism would be

$$\Delta\lambda = \frac{\lambda}{7500} = \frac{5890 \text{ A}}{7500} \simeq 0.8 \text{ A}$$

which is much less than the actual 6 A.

To estimate the resolving power of a grating, we get from Eqs. 10.32 and 10.34

$$\frac{\lambda}{\Delta\lambda} = W \frac{n}{d \cos\theta} \qquad (10.37)$$

But from Fig. 10.24 we see that

$$\frac{W}{Nd} = \cos\theta$$

and Eq. 10.37 therefore reduces to

$$\frac{\lambda}{\Delta\lambda} = nN \qquad \text{(grating)} \qquad (10.38)$$

where n is the order of the spectrum used, and N is the total number of lines on the grating. A grating 3 in. long ruled so that there are 10,000 lines per inch will contain 30,000 lines. In the third order spectrum its resolving power will be 90,000 or over 10 times that of the prism discussed above.

Gratings are usually ruled on a metallic mirror and are used as reflecting instruments. Instead of placing a lens in the reflected beam to focus the light, one may make the ruled mirror itself concave so as to produce a focused reflected beam. Such gratings are called concave gratings.

SUMMARY

Because light consists of electromagnetic waves, optical interference patterns may be produced in the same way that the interference patterns due to radio waves are produced. Since the interference pattern between waves coming from two or more points depends on the phase relationship between the waves generated, light independently radiated from different points will not show interference.

If we have to consider the radiations not from a few point sources but from all points on a finite portion of a wave front, then the interaction of the various Huygens wavelets produces diffraction patterns. Fresnel diffraction patterns are formed by converging rays. The summation of the effects of such converging rays from an extended source is simplified by dividing the area of the extended source into "Fresnel zones." The Huygens wavelets originating from adjacent zones are 180° out of phase at the point in question where the rays converge. A Fraunhofer diffraction pattern is formed by parallel rays at distant points or by means of a lens. The Fraunhofer diffraction pattern of a normally illuminated slit whose width is a_0 is given by

$$I = I_0 \left(\frac{\sin z}{z} \right)^2$$

$$z = \frac{\pi a_0}{\lambda} \sin \alpha$$

α is the angle between the direction in which the intensity I is measured and the normal to the slit. In a transmission grating consisting of many equally spaced slits, the amount of light radiated from each slit in any given direction is determined by the size of the slit. This diffracted light from various slits then produces an interference pattern. The distance between slits determines the direction in which interference maxima occur. The actual magnitude of these maxima is determined by the amount of light diffracted into these directions by each slit. The total number of slits determines the sharpness of the intensity maxima.

Circular openings produce characteristic diffraction patterns which determine the amount of detail that a lens can reproduce. If D is the diameter of a lens, f its focal length, and ρ the radius of the image in the focal plane of a distant object, then

$$\rho = 1.22\lambda \frac{f}{D}$$

or, if α is the angle subtended by ρ at the lens, then the smallest possible angular separation between points to be resolved in an object is

$$\sin \alpha = 1.22 \frac{\lambda}{D}$$

PROBLEMS

1. In Young's double-slit experiment, suppose that the two slits are separated by 10^{-4} meter, the distance to the screen is 1 meter, and the wavelength of light is 5461 A. Find the distances from the central maximum to the first five bright maxima. Do the same for a slit separation of 10^{-5} meter.

2. In the above problem, how many bright maxima are there in principle for each of the two slit separations?

3. In the same experiment, suppose that the single slit is placed 0.10 meter from the two slits, which are 0.001 meter apart and 1 meter from the screen. How wide, approximately, can the single slit be before there is no interference pattern on the screen? How wide can it be if the two slits are separated by 0.001 meter?

4. Light from a narrow slit passes through two parallel slits 3×10^{-4} meter apart. The interference bands on a screen 2 meters away are 4.47×10^{-3} meter apart. What is the wavelength of the light? What is the order of the spectrum? Consider that visible light extends from 4 to 7×10^{-7} meter in wavelength.

5. Light from a point source is incident normally on a screen containing two

small holes 35.0×10^{-7} meter apart. The incident light contains the two wavelengths, 5.0×10^{-7} meter and 7.0×10^{-7} meter. In what directions will the interference pattern produced by the two holes transmit none of the incident light?

6. Light coming from a point source S and having a wavelength 5.8×10^{-7} meter strikes two holes in a screen a distance 29.0×10^{-7} meter apart, as shown in

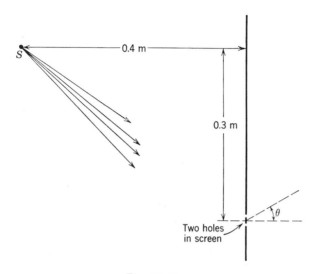

FIG. 10.25.

Fig. 10.25. (a) What is the difference in phase between the incident light rays at the two slits? (b) In what directions, or for what values of θ, will the interference pattern at distant points have intensity maxima?

7. Light composed of two wavelengths 6000 A and 5000 A falls at normal incidence on a thin piece of glass which has an index of refraction $n = 1.6$. What thickness must the glass be in order to produce maximum reflection for one of these wavelengths and maximum transmission for the other? Which is reflected?

8. A camera lens is coated so that there will be no reflection of green light 5460 A. How thick must the coating be if the index is 1.80? Assume n_g (a) greater than, (b) less than, 1.80.

9. In a set of Newton's rings formed as in Fig. 10.8 the radius of the 50th ring is 10^{-2} meter. Find the radius of the spherical glass surface. The wavelength of light used is 5893 A. What would be the pattern formed if white light instead of monochromatic light were used?

10. A planoconvex lens made of glass having an index of refraction $n = 1.5$ and having a radius of curvature $R = 0.1$ meter, is placed on a flat piece of glass having an index of refraction $n = 1.8$, as shown in Fig. 10.8. $\lambda_{air} = 6 \times 10^{-7}$ meter, $R = 0.1$ meter. (a) Is the central spot of the system of Newton's rings formed bright or dark as seen in reflected light? (b) Find the radius of the third dark ring if the wavelength of the light used is 6×10^{-7} meter in air. (c) If the air film between the lens and the glass plate is replaced by a liquid having an index of refraction $n = 2$, what would be the radius of the third dark ring?

11. An air wedge is formed between glass plates having an index of refraction $n = 1.5$ and is normally illuminated with light having a wavelength 5×10^{-7} meter in air, as shown in Fig. 10.26. (a) As seen by reflected light, will the tip (point) of the wedge look light or dark? (b) What is the spacing between adjacent bright bands? (c) What is the effect of replacing the upper plate by one having an index $n = 2$ and filling the air prism with a liquid having an index of 1.8?

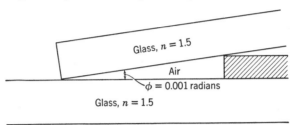

Glass, $n = 1.5$

Air

$\phi = 0.001$ radians

Glass, $n = 1.5$

FIG. 10.26.

12. (a) Monochromatic light of wavelength 600 mμ originates at a distant point source and passes through a circular opening onto a screen 1 meter away. Find the diameter of the circular opening if it exposes n Fresnel zones. (b) This same light passes through a circular opening 2 mm in diameter. Find the distances of the screen from the opening that are larger than 0.5 meter for which there will be a central bright spot. (Give numerical answers.)

13. In an experiment designed to show Fraunhofer diffraction from a single slit, parallel light strikes a slit 1 wavelength wide normally. A screen is placed 1 meter away, and a lens of 1 meter focal length is placed right at the slit. Find the positions of the first five maxima on the screen. Do the same for a slit 10 wavelengths wide. In principle, how many diffraction maxima are there?

14. (a) Using a diffraction grating with 8000 grooves per inch and light of wavelength 5500 A incident normally, at what angles do maxima occur? (b) If the third order maximum for red light 6500 A coincides with the fourth order maximum for violet light, what is the wavelength of the violet light?

15. The angular deviation of a third order spectrum line produced by a transmission grating 2 cm wide with 110 lines per millimeter normally illuminated is 11° 11'. What is the wavelength of the light? If another line can barely be resolved, in this order, from the one just mentioned, what is the difference between the wavelengths?

16. Parallel light falls normally on a plane reflection grating with 1000 lines per millimeter. In what direction is the first order spectrum of sodium light reflected from the grating? ($\lambda = 5890$ A.) What is the answer if the angle of incidence is 30°?

17. An idealized grating with alternate perfectly clear and perfectly opaque spaces gives a spectrum in which all the even orders are missing. What is the ratio of the widths of the clear and opaque spaces?

★18. Discuss the intensity distribution of monochromatic light transmitted by an idealized grating consisting of alternate clear and opaque strips.

★19. According to Eq. 10.22, the intensity minima of the diffraction pattern of a slit,

$$I = I_0 \left(\frac{\sin z}{z}\right)^2$$

occur for $z = \pi, 2\pi, 3\pi, \cdots$. The intensity maxima will occur approximately halfway between these minima, or for $z = \dfrac{3\pi}{2}, \dfrac{5\pi}{2}, \dfrac{7\pi}{2}, \cdots$, and the corresponding values of I/I_0 will be $(2/3\pi)^2, (2/5\pi)^2, (2/7\pi)^2, \cdots$. Compute the exact location of the subsidiary maxima, and compare the correct intensities with the above approximate values.

20. If yellow light is observed at an angle of 36° with a grating ruled with 5000 grooves per cm, what is the wavelength of the light?

21. The limits of the visible spectrum are nearly 4000 to 7000 A. (a) Find the angular breadth of the first order visible spectrum formed by a plane grating with 12,000 lines per inch. (b) Does the violet of the third order visible spectrum overlap the red in the second order spectrum? If so, by how much (approximately)?

22. Light containing two wavelengths of 5000 and 5200 A is normally incident on a plane diffraction grating having a grating spacing of 10^{-5} meter. If a 2-meter lens is used to focus the spectrum on a screen, find the distance between these two lines (in millimeters) on the screen: (a) For the first order spectrum. (b) For the third order spectrum.

23. Which of the following statements are true and which false?

(a) Light from a distant point source falls normally on a small circular opening in a screen. Beyond the hole a second screen is placed at a distance x, and a diffraction pattern appears on it. The central spot of the diffraction pattern is always bright, regardless of the distance x.

(b) A lens of focal length f is placed behind the above circular opening, and the second screen is placed at the focal point of the lens. The central spot of the diffraction pattern is bright.

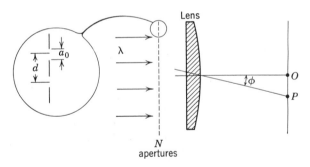

Fig. 10.27.

The following statements refer to Fig. 10.27.

(c) If the incident light is unpolarized, no interference maxima or minima are formed.

(d) There will always be an intensity minimum at P if $\sin \phi = \lambda/d$.

(e) The third order spectrum will be found at P if $\sin \phi = 3\lambda/d$.

(f) The first minimum next to the central image at 0 is at P if $\sin \phi = \lambda/Nd$.

24. Which of the following statements are true, and which false?

(a) Light from a distant point source falls normally on a small circular opening in a screen. Beyond the hole, a second screen is placed at a distance x and a diffraction pattern appears on it. The central spot of the diffraction pattern may be bright or dark, depending on the distance x.

(b) A lens of focal length f is placed behind the above circular opening, and the second screen is placed at the focal point of the lens. The central spot of the diffraction pattern is bright.

The following statements refer to Fig. 10.27. The light incident on the grating is from a ditstant point source.

(c) If the incident light is circularly polarized no interference maxima or minima are formed.

(d) There will always be an intensity minimum at P if $\sin \phi = \lambda/a_0$.

(e) The third order spectrum will be found at P if $\sin \phi = 3\lambda/a_0$.

(f) The first minimum next to the central image at 0 is at P if $\sin \phi = \lambda/Nd$.

25. Two narrow slits 0.14 mm apart are illuminated by a flame giving sodium light ($\lambda = 5890$ A). What must be the diameter of a lens 6 meters away to resolve the images of the two slits?

26. In Problem 25, at what distance will the same lens resolve the images of the slits if they are illuminated with light of wavelength 4.86×10^{-7} meter?

27. What is the limit of resolution, for $\lambda = 5.60 \times 10^{-7}$ meter, of the large refracting telescope in the Yerkes observatory (diameter of objective 1.02 meter)?

28. (a) Find the angular separation in seconds of arc of the closest double star which can be resolved by the 100-in. Mt. Wilson telescope, assuming a wavelength of 6000 A. (b) Suppose such a binary star is found at a distance of 100 light-years from the earth. What is the distance between the two stars in this binary star?

29. (a) A battleship displays two small red lights whose radiated wavelength is 6500 A at a vertical separation of 5 ft. These lights are observed by another vessel 20 mi away through binoculars with objective lenses 50 mm in diameter. What is the separation between the centers of the diffraction disks in terms of the radius o each disk? Sketch the appearance of these two lights as viewed through the binoculars. (b) Would an observer be able to resolve these two lights with his unaided eye?

30. What is the smallest separation of objects on the planet Mars that can be seen with a telescope having an objective 0.3 meter in diameter? The radius of the earth's orbit about the sun is 150×10^6 km, and that of Mars' orbit is 225×10^6 km. Consider a wavelength of 5×10^{-7} meter.

31. An observer at an airport is watching the approach of a plane carrying two lights 10 meters apart. At about what distance can he see the two lights separately, assuming perfect vision, a pupillary diameter of 2 mm, and a wavelength of the light of 5×10^{-7} meter?

32. Compute the approximate radius of the central diffraction disk formed on the retina of the eye by a distant point object, assuming a pupillary diameter of 2.0 mm. The distance from the cornea to the retina is about 1 in., and the index of refraction of the vitreous humor, the medium in which the image is formed, is 1.33. Assume $\lambda = 5500$ A.

33. Two pinholes, 1 mm apart, are made in a screen and placed in front of a bright source of light. They are viewed through a telescope with its objective stopped down to a diameter of 1 cm. How far from the telescope may the screen be for the pinholes still to appear as separate sources for a wavelength of 5000 A?

34. A range finder, Fig. 10.28, is an instrument used for estimating the distance between an observer and some remote object. It consists of two lenses, each of which can, with the help of the mirror system shown, produce an image at P. When the object being viewed is sufficiently far away (a star, for example) the incoming rays

are parallel and the angle ϕ is zero. If now an object at some nearer point P_0 is examined, the rays to the two lenses make an angle ϕ with each other and the mirror M_2 must be rotated through some small angle θ in order to superimpose the two

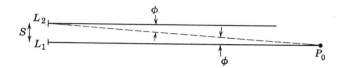

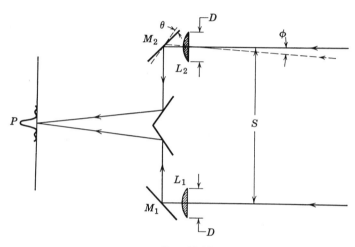

Fig. 10.28.

images at P. Compute the uncertainty δx in the determination of the distance x to the object, due to the size of the diffraction disks produced by distant point sources at P.

If the distance S between the lenses is 10 meters, and if the lens diameters are 10 cm, what is the uncertainty, due to the size of the diffraction pattern, in the measurement of the distance to an object approximately 10 km away? Assume $\lambda = 5 \times 10^{-7}$ meter.

CHAPTER 11

The Experimental Basis
of Atomic Physics

11.1 WAVES AND PARTICLES

On a macroscopic scale waves and particles are very different things.
A particle, such as a baseball, for instance, is an object to which we
ascribe an independent existence. A wave, on the other hand, is not an
object in this sense but an attribute of a medium. An ocean wave may
or may not be present on the surface of the ocean.

On a submicroscopic scale, we have spoken of particles and waves as
though they were comparably distinguishable. Although no one has
seen an electron, we have referred to it as a particle. Although no one
has detected the pulsation of a light wave, we have confidently spoken
of it as a wave. We now come to a series of experiments on which
atomic physics is based, experiments which have completely changed
our conception of creation. It is not an assembly of particles and waves
like the dust and noise around us. It is much more mysterious. Atomic
particles also have the aspect of waves. Electromagnetic waves also
have the aspect of particles. Both satisfy all the criteria which we can
set up for the recognition of particles or for the recognition of waves.
Let us briefly review what we mean by these statements.

Electrons, for example, were introduced at the beginning of this book
as small particles carrying a charge e and having a mass m. The "particle" aspect of the electron was indicated by several lines of evidence.
Millikan's oil drop experiment indicated that the charge on an object
always was some integral multiple of e. Also, the rest mass of all
electrons was found to be exactly the same. No such thing as a fraction
of an electron has ever been detected. Further, although an electron
moving through space cannot be continuously and precisely observed,
as we can observe a baseball, for instance, yet departure times, arrival
times, and approximate trajectories may be observed. All these observa-

tions are to be expected of particles having momentum and kinetic energy analogous to the momentum and kinetic energy of macroscopic objects.

On the basis of this evidence it is tempting to conclude that the electron *is* a particle, just as a baseball is a particle. In fact, however, to describe an object which we cannot observe by means of terms having to do with the direct evidence of our senses has little meaning. Our senses tell us that a baseball is round, hard, white, and cold. We can observe it continuously. It moves according to Newton's laws of motion. The electron, on the other hand, we cannot observe at all in this sense. What really happens is that we move physical objects in some directly observable way (for instance, we may close a switch), and then certain other observable changes take place in nature (for instance, the pointer on an instrument moves to a new position). By means of arguments involving an electron of charge e and mass m we are able to predict ahead of time the consequences of our actions, for example, how far the pointer will move when we close the switch. If the idea of an electron of charge e and mass m enables us to predict many events correctly and leads to no incorrect conclusions, we may say that we believe, that we have faith, that a particle which we call an electron exists. But what we really mean is that the assumption of a particle of mass m and charge e obeying Coulomb's and Newton's laws leads to correct conclusions about nature *in certain circumstances*. We must find out by experiment what the limits of validity of this model are. One limit, we shall see, is reached when we consider the propagation of electrons through crystals. They do not behave like particles. They behave like waves. We conclude that the electron is neither a particle nor a wave. An electron is the sum of its properties. We know more and more about electrons as the range of predictable phenomena is increased. We must not be surprised if, as we press farther into hitherto unobserved areas in nature, the modes of existence and the laws describing them change from those with which we were first familiar.

We now come to a similarly unfamiliar and new aspect in the description of electromagnetic phenomena. We began this course with the description of electric and magnetic fields, and out of these developed the idea of electromagnetic radiation in the form of waves which could carry energy through space, and which we showed could be diffracted by gratings. We now shall introduce evidence that the energy carried by these radiations must also be considered lumped into units, usually called *quanta*, or sometimes *photons*, having mass, momentum, and energy. In this chapter we shall review the evidence for the existence of these quanta. It is fully as convincing as the evidence for the particle aspect of "particles," such as electrons.

11.2 WAVES IN CRYSTALS

A most important early landmark in the development of atomic physics was the recognition of the existence of waves having an appreciably shorter wavelength than that of light. The measurement of wavelengths is best accomplished by diffraction from a grating. The grating formula

$$\sin \theta = n\lambda/d$$

for the interference maxima shows that for appreciable angular separation λ should be comparable to d, and that for wavelengths much shorter than that of light gratings with much closer rulings than those of optical gratings would be required. Such gratings are hard to make but are found to exist in nature. At the beginning of this century von Laue discovered that crystals could serve as gratings to produce diffraction patterns, and that X rays were electromagnetic waves with short wavelengths that could be diffracted by crystals. We now take up a review of these facts.

In gases atoms are arranged more or less at random and are far apart. In liquids the atoms are held close together by attractive forces, but thermal agitation is still sufficient to permit rapid diffusion of atoms among each other. This fairly violent random thermal motion prevents the formation of any marked regular arrangements of the atoms in a liquid. At sufficiently low temperatures the arrangement of the atoms is not determined by the thermal agitation, but by the interatomic forces. The nature of these forces is such that some one particular form of clustering of the atoms in a crystalline array has a lower potential energy than other arrangements. As the disturbing influence of thermal agitation decreases, the atoms of a substance will tend to arrange themselves in this particular way. Although atoms may still occasionally change places and diffuse through the body of the crystal, particularly near surfaces, or if holes, impurities, or other crystallographic imperfections are present, the main form of thermal motion is vibration around some equilibrium position in the regular pattern established by the interatomic forces.

We have seen that a regular arrangement of scratches on a surface, in other words, a diffraction grating, interacts in a very striking manner with waves having wavelengths comparable to the spacing between scratches. The three-dimensional periodicities in the structure of crystals may likewise be expected to produce characteristic effects in the interaction with waves. Moreover, since the periodicities in crystals are of the order of atomic dimensions, or 10^{-10} meter, we may expect to find the most interesting effects for shorter wavelengths than are encountered in the range of visible light, which are around 10^{-6} to 10^{-7} meter. The investigation of such waves has been so important to physics, and it is so important that the student be convinced of the reliability of this method of studying wave motion, that we shall take up the description of crystals in some detail.

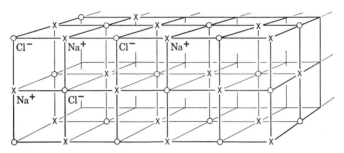

FIG. 11.1. The arrangement of sodium and chlorine ions in a rock salt crystal.

Crystals are regular arrangements of atoms. There are, in the main, three categories. The first is called an ionic crystal, of which a simple example is rock salt, or NaCl, shown in Fig. 11.1. The sodium chloride molecule, when dissolved in water, breaks up into a positively charged sodium ion and a negatively charged chlorine ion. In the molecule, the two particles retain their charged character, the work required to pull them apart being very nearly that computed on the assumption that the attractive forces are electrostatic. In the crystal the particles are also ions. They are arranged at the corners of an imaginary pile of cubes. The atoms are of course large enough so that they fill in most of the volume of the crystal. We show here only the nuclear positions. Along any line of cube edges positive and negative charges alternate. Each positive ion has six nearest negatively charged neighbors one cube edge away. The NaCl molecule loses its identity in such a crystal. Large single crystals of rock salt are readily obtainable, and the distances between atoms may be accurately deduced from the molecular weights of the constituents and the density of the crystal.

A crystal is commonly described in terms of a unit cell, which is the smallest block of the crystal which is repeated over and over unchanged along the three axes of the crystal. For NaCl, if the distance between adjacent Na^+ and Cl^- ions is d, the unit cell is a cube having an edge length $2d$, since this is the shortest distance between like particles along an edge. The smaller cell, having an edge d, is not exactly repeated in an adjacent cell, in which the Cl^- and Na^+ ions are interchanged.

The second class of crystal is the molecular crystal. Such a crystal is shown in Fig. 11.2. Molecules have a structure of their own which in

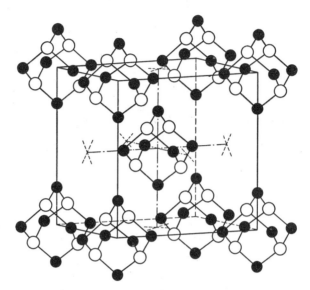

Fig. 11.2. A molecular crystal, hexamethylenetetramine, $C_6H_{12}N_4$. The unit of structure and the molecular configuration.

some cases is preserved when they form crystals. Some molecular crystals may contain more than one kind of molecule, for example, potassium cobaltinitrite

$$6KNO_2 \cdot 2Co(NO_2)_3 \cdot 3H_2O$$

The third type is typified by the pure metals. We shall consider in particular those which crystallize in the so-called "face-centered cubic" form shown in Fig. 11.3. The simple cubic form consists of an arrangement like the NaCl crystal shown in Fig. 11.1, but with all the atoms of a single kind only. A unit cube of such a lattice is shown in Fig. 11.3a. The length of each side is a. A face-centered lattice is arrived at through placing atoms not only at the corners but at the centers of the faces of the cube, as shown in Fig. 11.3b. Each atom has twelve nearest neighbors, the distance between them being $a/\sqrt{2}$. Many metals crystallize in this form, for example, copper, silver, and gold.

The aspect of crystallographic arrangements of atoms which we particularly wish to emphasize is the formation of plane layers of atoms. Understanding of the interaction of waves and crystals can be built up through considering the effects due to individual atoms, but the mathematical complications are considerable. By far the simplest statement of the results is given in terms of the crystallographic planes which charac-

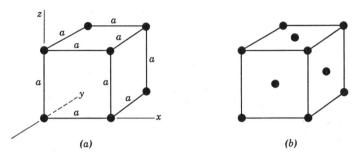

(a)   (b)

Fig. 11.3.   Unit cell of a simple cubic and a face-centered cubic lattice.

terize a lattice. We might consider that the simplest interaction between waves and obstacles is reflection at a plane surface. This should therefore be a fruitful starting point in considering waves in crystals.

Miller Indices

The conventional manner of designating a crystallographic plane is in terms of the "Miller indices" (hkl). Let us consider three axes x, y, z parallel to our unit cube and shown in Fig. 11.3a. Any plane may be defined by its intercepts p, q, and r on these axes. If atoms are arranged in uniformly spaced parallel planes, one of these planes will go through the atom at the origin. The intercepts of the next plane through our unit cube are the reciprocal of the Miller indices. Thus, for example, the (111) planes of our face-centered lattice are shown in Fig. 11.4a. The cube edge is here taken as unit length. The ar-

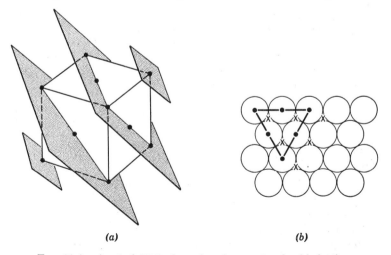

(a)   (b)

Fig. 11.4.   A set of (111) planes in a face-centered cubic lattice.

rangement of atoms in this plane is shown in Fig. 11.4b. Here the black dots represent atomic positions, and the circles around them represent approximate atomic sizes. This is the closest packing possible for spherical objects arranged in a plane. This close packing extends to the arrangement of layers with respect to each other. In the layer above the one shown, the atoms would be located at the points indicated by crosses or in the depressions between spheres arranged in a triangle. The face-centered cubic lattice is characterized by close packing.

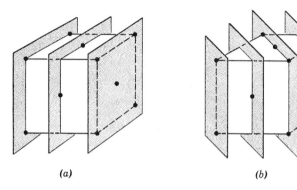

(a)   (b)

Fig. 11.5.   The (200) and (220) planes of a cubic face-centered lattice.

Two other crystallographic sets of planes are shown in Fig. 11.5. They are the (200) and (220) planes, respectively. In Fig. 11.5a the intercept on the x axis of the plane next to the one that passes through the origin is $\frac{1}{2}$. The planes are parallel to both the y and the z axes. The intercepts on these axes may be thought of as infinitely far away. The reciprocals of these numbers are 2, 0, and 0, which are the Miller indices. Two other sets of planes are equivalent to the (200) set. They are the (020) and (002) planes. The (220) planes shown in Fig. 11.5b are parallel to a face diagonal and are crystallographically equivalent to the (202) and (022) planes.

An atom in the patn of a wave with which it interacts, such as an electromagnetic wave, for example, will be periodically polarized and will emit spherical wavelets. The atoms in a crystal through which a wave is passing will each emit spherical wavelets, and the diffraction effects may be computed through adding these wavelets together. This we have already done for an incident plane wave on a single plane surface. The Huygens wavelets reinforce each other to produce a new reflected wave whose direction of propagation is given by the law of reflection. The angle of incidence equals the angle of reflection. This reflected ray will contain all the wavelengths present in the incident light. It is true that if the reflecting surface contains periodicities, as in a grating, then additional diffracted rays will appear, but in these diffracted rays at any particular angle θ^* only a certain particular wavelength λ^* will appear. We shall neglect these special rays and consider only the more intense rays that are specularly reflected from a single surface, with the angle of incidence equal to the angle of reflection, regardless of wavelength.

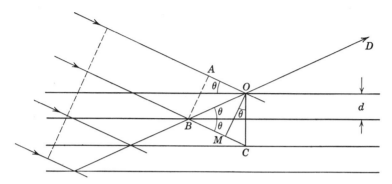

FIG. 11.6.   The reflection of waves by parallel planes.

If parallel rays fall on a crystallographic surface, the atoms in this surface will radiate secondary wavelets and these secondary wavelets will form a specularly reflected ray just as did the Huygens wavelets. Let us now consider the effect of adding successive parallel atomic planes, separated by a distance d as shown in Fig. 11.6. We shall assume that the planes are at least partly transparent, and that the velocity of propagation of the wave between planes is the same as the velocity of the incident wave. We seek the condition that the components of the reflected ray OD, due to reflection at successive planes, shall add and therefore produce a maximum intensity.

Let the dotted line AB be a wave front, perpendicular to the incoming rays. The condition that the rays reflected at B and O interfere constructively, or that their amplitudes add, is that the path difference be an integral number of wavelengths.

$$BO - AO = n\lambda \qquad (11.1)$$

where n is an integer. From the construction of the figure we see that

$$BO = BC$$
$$AO = BM$$

and therefore that

$$BO - AO = BC - BM = MC = n\lambda$$

The distance MC can be expressed in terms of the spacing of the planes d, and the angle θ which the incident rays make with the crystallographic planes.

$$\sin \theta = MC/2d$$

Note that θ here is the complement of the angle of incidence which is used in optics to specify the direction of an incoming ray. Equation 11.1 may be rewritten

$$2d \sin \theta = n\lambda \qquad \blacktriangleright(11.2)\blacktriangleleft$$

which is called Bragg's law. It says that in general rays of arbitrary wavelength incident at an arbitrary angle will not be reflected. Only if the relation in Eq. 11.2 is satisfied will reflection take place. Note that,

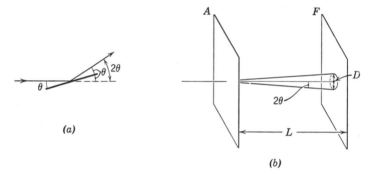

FIG. 11.7.   The origin of Debye-Scherrer rings or powder patterns.

if $\lambda > 2d$, it is impossible to satisfy Bragg's law, or that waves will be diffracted from crystals only if their wavelengths are less than twice the distance between planes. Note also that Eq. 11.2 provides a means for producing monochromatic waves, or waves of a single wavelength. If we have a source of short waves of arbitrary spectral distribution, we may selectively reflect those of a particular wavelength from a crystal at the Bragg angle specified by Eq. 11.2.

A most important practical modification of the above considerations involves the application of the Bragg law to a polycrystalline sample or to a powder in which individual crystal grains are randomly oriented. Let us assume that a ray is incident on such a powder, and that the wavelength λ is such that the Bragg relation is satisfied for some given value of n at the angle θ. The reflected ray will be deviated through an angle 2θ, shown in Fig. 11.7a. All the crystals so oriented that their planes make an angle θ with the incoming ray will reflect. It is clear that these reflected rays will form a cone whose half-angle is 2θ, as shown in

Fig. 11.7*b*, and that the intersection of this cone with a plane perpendicular to the undeviated ray, at a distance L from the sample at A, will produce a circle of diameter D, with

$$\tan 2\theta = \frac{D/2}{L} \tag{11.3}$$

We now come to the applications of these ideas to diffraction of X rays. As we have pointed out in Chapter 3, a gas-filled discharge tube in which a current is maintained can give off light as a consequence of collisions between high-speed electrons and gas atoms. Differences of potential of only a few volts are required for the production of light. If now the tube is exhausted, electrons are supplied at a heated cathode, and the potential difference between electrodes is increased to tens of kilovolts, invisible X rays are produced at the anode. These rays are very penetrating and produce marked ionization in any matter which they traverse. Although these X rays have many medical and therapeutic qualities, they can be very harmful and destructive if improperly used because of the ionization and consequent chemical changes which they produce in living tissue.

The wavelengths of X rays may be established through demonstrating the validity of the Bragg law, Eq. 11.2, for diffraction from a crystal with known lattice spacing. This can be done, for example, with a rock-salt crystal. X rays produced at the electrode of a tube analyzed in this way show first of all a continuous spectrum whose range depends primarily on the voltage applied to the tube in a manner that we shall discuss further on. On top of this continuous distribution certain wavelengths may appear with particular intensity. The wavelengths found in this line spectrum depend primarily on the material used as the target for the electrons. Radiations having wavelengths of the order of an angstrom unit, 10^{-10} meter, or less, are readily produced.

Monochromatic X rays may be used in an arrangement such as is shown in Fig. 11.8*a* to produce ring-shaped patterns, called Debye-Scherrer rings. The rays are scattered from a polycrystalline sample at A placed at the center of a strip of film bent into a circle around the scatterer. The conical shape of the scattered rays leaves the traces on the film shown in Fig. 11.8*b*, which is the pattern produced by scattering from copper. The observed pattern is indeed that which would be expected on the basis of the Bragg law.

By way of illustrating the range of effects that can be accounted for, we reproduce Figs. 11.9 and 11.10. The apparatus used in obtaining Fig. 11.9*b* is shown in *a*. The small spots on the film are due to backward reflections of the incident beam from various crystallographic planes.

These are known as Laue spots. They are due to the reflection of particular wavelengths that satisfy the Bragg law. The faint lines are due to additional radiation originating within the crystal as a result of the absorption of the incident radiation and to the reemission of fluores-

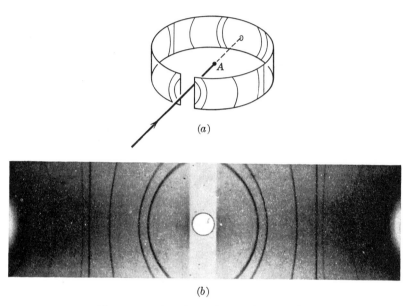

(a)

(b)

Fig. 11.8.   A Debye-Scherrer photograph.

cent rays. These fluorescent rays are strongly divergent, rather than parallel, and give rise to the curved Kossel lines, as they are called, shown in Fig. 11.9b. A photograph obtained with a strongly divergent incident beam of X rays is shown in Fig. 11.10. All these results are accounted for in detail by the application of the basic ideas advanced above.

11.3   ELECTRON AND NEUTRON DIFFRACTION

We now come to the evidence for the remarkable fact that beams of electrons are diffracted by crystals as though they were waves having a wavelength

$$\lambda = h/mv \qquad \blacktriangleright(11.4)\blacktriangleleft$$

where h is a new physical constant, called Planck's constant, and mv is the momentum of the particle being diffracted. Planck's constant will appear over and over in the description of atomic phenomena. Its approximate value is

$$h = 6.62 \times 10^{-34} \text{ joule-sec}$$

To obtain the significance of Eq. 11.4 we compute the magnitude of the wavelength of an electron which has an energy of 100 ev or which

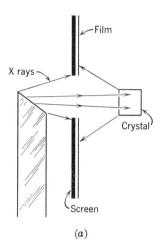

(a)

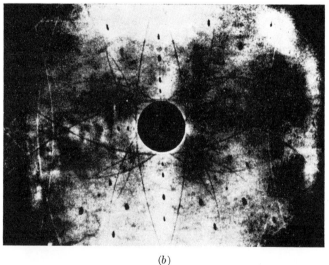

(b)

FIG. 11.9. Kossel lines from a copper crystal (Bormann).

has fallen through a potential difference of 100 volts. The velocity of such an electron, since $\frac{1}{2}mv^2 = eV$, is

$$\left(2\,\frac{e}{m}\,V\right)^{\frac{1}{2}} = (2 \times 1.76 \times 10^{11} \times 10^2)^{\frac{1}{2}} = 5.93 \times 10^6 \text{ meter/sec}$$

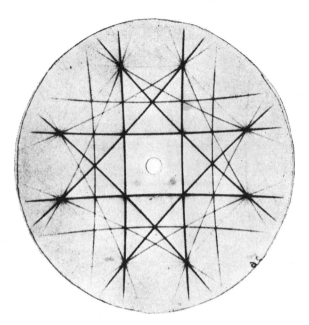

Fig. 11.10.   A wide-angle X ray diagram from rock salt (Seemann).

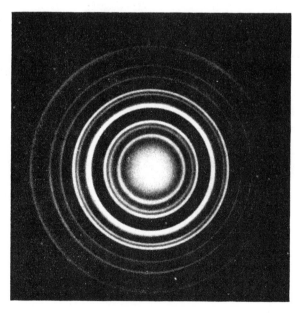

Fig. 11.11.   Electron diffraction pattern obtained by transmission through polycrystalline SnO_2.

The wavelength is

$$\lambda = \frac{6.62 \times 10^{-34}}{9.1 \times 10^{-31} \times 5.93 \times 10^6} = 1.23 \times 10^{-10} \text{ meter}$$

$$= 1.23 \times 10^{-8} \text{ cm} = 1.23 \text{ A}$$

This is just in the range of interatomic spacing in crystals and therefore the right order of magnitude to produce diffraction effects.

Instead of being diffusely scattered by collisions with individual particles, electrons are "reflected" from crystallographic planes, much as X rays are. A ring pattern formed by shooting a beam of electrons through a polycrystalline sample of SnO_2 is shown in Fig. 11.11. This is qualitatively similar to a Debye-Scherrer diagram with the rings quite close together as might be expected for short wavelengths.

The Experimental Evidence for $\lambda = h/mv$

Let us review the evidence for Eq. 11.4 quantitatively and in detail. For this purpose a series of experiments by G. P. Thompson and A. Reid in 1927–1928 is most instructive. A beam of electrons accelerated with a known voltage is fired through various thin foils onto a photographic plate. The diameters of the rings obtained, like those in Fig. 11.11, are then measured and compared with theoretical predictions.

As a first step, let us compare the theoretical expression of Eq. 11.4 for the wavelength with the experimental result. From Eq. 11.3 we have for the diameter of any ring for small θ

$$D = 2L \tan 2\theta = 4L\theta$$

and from the Bragg law

$$\theta \simeq \sin \theta = n\lambda/2d$$

$$D = 2\frac{L}{d} n\lambda \tag{11.5}$$

But, if the electrons are accelerated by falling through a potential difference V, their kinetic energy E is

$$E = \tfrac{1}{2}mv^2 = eV$$

and their momentum therefore is

$$mv = \sqrt{2m(\tfrac{1}{2}mv^2)} = \sqrt{2mE} = \sqrt{2meV} \tag{11.6}$$

If relativistic mass changes are taken into account the above result must be modified. The correct expression is

$$mv = \sqrt{2meV}\left(1 + \frac{eV}{2m_0c^2}\right)^{\frac{1}{2}} \tag{11.7}$$

In the following the last factor in no instance amounts to more than 3%, but in other experiments in which energies of over 1 Mev were used, the agreement between theory and experiment is equally satisfactory. Substituting Eqs.

11.4 and 11.7 into Eq. 11.5 we have

$$D = 2\frac{L}{d}\, n\, \frac{h}{\sqrt{2meV}\left(1 + \dfrac{eV}{2m_0c^2}\right)^{\frac{1}{2}}}$$

or

$$D\sqrt{V}\left(1 + \frac{eV}{2m_0c^2}\right)^{\frac{1}{2}} = \text{constant} \tag{11.8}$$

The extent to which this expression is satisfied is shown in Table 11.1. The variation of the diameter of a diffraction ring produced by aluminum and also gold with the accelerating voltage used in forming the electron beam, as well as the constancy of the left side of Eq. 11.8, are illustrated.

TABLE 11.1

	V	D	$D\sqrt{V}\left(1 + \dfrac{eV}{2m_0c^2}\right)^{\frac{1}{2}}$
Aluminum	17,500	3.1	415
	30,500	2.45	434
	31,800	2.32	418
	40,000	2.12	430
	44,000	2.08	445
	48,600	1.90	430
	48,600	1.98	446
	56,500	1.83	446
	56,500	1.80	438
Gold	24,600	2.50	398
	31,800	2.15	390
	39,400	2.00	404
	45,600	1.86	405
	54,300	1.63	438
	61,200	1.61	410

Equally good results were obtained for all the metals investigated, including platinum, silver, copper, lead, iron, nickel, tin, and also for several compounds. We may conclude that the variation of the patterns with applied voltage is that required by Eq. 11.4.

We next inquire whether all the rings can be accounted for correctly by the known lattice structure of the diffracting substance. For this purpose a set of results on gold are to be examined in detail. We must find a convenient way of describing the various values of the spacing between planes, d, in the face-centered cubic lattice in which gold crystallizes.

If a plane has the intercepts p, q, and r on the axes of a rectangular coordinate system, the normal distance from the origin to this plane is

$$[p^{-2} + q^{-2} + r^{-2}]^{-\frac{1}{2}}$$

From the definition of the Miller indices as the reciprocals of the intercepts of the plane next to the one passing through the origin, measured on a scale in

TABLE 11.2 RELATIVE DIAMETERS OF ELECTRON DIFFRACTION RINGS IN GOLD

(Where reflections from two sets of planes are unresolved, the average predicted diameter is listed)

$(nh\ nk\ nl)$	(111)	(200)	(220)	(113)(222)	(400)	(331)(420)	(422)	(511)(333)	(440)	(531)(600)	(620)	(533)(622)
$\sqrt{(nh)^2+(nk)^2+(nl)^2}$	$\sqrt{3}$	$\sqrt{4}$	$\sqrt{8}$	$\sqrt{11.25}$	$\sqrt{16}$	$\sqrt{19.5}$	$\sqrt{24}$	$\sqrt{27}$	$\sqrt{32}$	$\sqrt{35.4}$	$\sqrt{40}$	$\sqrt{43.5}$
Observed values	$\sqrt{2.96}$	$\sqrt{4.08}$		$\sqrt{11.25}$	$\sqrt{15.7}$	$\sqrt{19.5}$	$\sqrt{22.7}$	$\sqrt{26.6}$		$\sqrt{35.4}$		$\sqrt{43.1}$
	$\sqrt{3.02}$	$\sqrt{4.25}$		$\sqrt{11.2}$		$\sqrt{19.3}$	$\sqrt{24.3}$	$\sqrt{27.8}$		$\sqrt{34.9}$		$\sqrt{42.6}$
	$\sqrt{2.95}$	$\sqrt{4.08}$		$\sqrt{11.7}$		$\sqrt{19.9}$	$\sqrt{24.1}$	$\sqrt{27.5}$		$\sqrt{35.0}$		$\sqrt{43.5}$
	$\sqrt{2.96}$	$\sqrt{3.98}$		$\sqrt{11.2}$		$\sqrt{19.5}$	$\sqrt{24.4}$	$\sqrt{26.7}$		$\sqrt{34.7}$		$\sqrt{43.5}$
	$\sqrt{3.06}$	$\sqrt{3.9}$		$\sqrt{11.0}$		$\sqrt{19.5}$						
				$\sqrt{11.0}$		$\sqrt{19.5}$						
				$\sqrt{11.25}$		$\sqrt{19.4}$						

which the cube edge of length a is taken as unity, we have

$$\frac{d}{a} = \left(\frac{1}{p^2} + \frac{1}{q^2} + \frac{1}{r^2}\right)^{-\frac{1}{2}}$$

or, after simplification,

$$\frac{1}{d} = \frac{\sqrt{h^2 + k^2 + l^2}}{a} \tag{11.9}$$

Substituting this into Eq. 11.5, we have for the diameter of the rings

$$D = \frac{2Ln\lambda}{a} \sqrt{h^2 + k^2 + l^2}$$

$$= \frac{2L\lambda}{a} \sqrt{(nh)^2 + (nk^2) + (nl)^2} \tag{11.10}$$

A comparison of this result with experiment is shown in Table 11.2. In this table the quantity $2L\lambda/a$ is determined from the (220) ring, and then $Da/2L\lambda$, using this and the observed diameter, is tabulated for all the other rings. Some of the rings fall so closely together that their weighted average is taken for comparison with the single ring observed. Not all integral values of the Miller indices represent crystallographic planes in the face-centered cubic lattice. We have shown that the three with the greatest spacings are (111) (200) and (220). A large number of other planes leading to reflections of varying intensity are listed in Table 11.2. The agreement is very satisfactory. The missing rings may be accounted for either by the weakness of the reflection from certain planes or by the absence of the required grain orientation as a result of the hammering process by which the gold foil was produced.

Finally it remains to be shown that the lattice parameter a obtained by electron diffraction is the same as that determined by X rays. The results are shown in Table 11.3.

TABLE 11.3   SIZE OF THE UNIT CUBE, a

	X Rays	Electrons
Aluminum	4.046×10^{-10} meter	4.06×10^{-10} meter
		4.00
Gold	4.06	4.18
		3.99
Platinum	3.91	3.88
		3.89
Lead	4.92	4.99
Iron	2.87	2.85
Silver	4.079	4.11
Copper	3.60	3.66
Tin (white), spacing of (200)	2.91	2.86

The evidence of the wave aspect of an electron beam is complete and overwhelming. There can be no doubt of it. By way of completing the analogy between X ray and electron diffraction Fig. 11.12 is added which shows in a the pattern of spots obtained from a single crystal, and the pattern of curved lines, called Kikuchi lines, and similar to the Kossel lines, found when rays diverge from within a crystal.

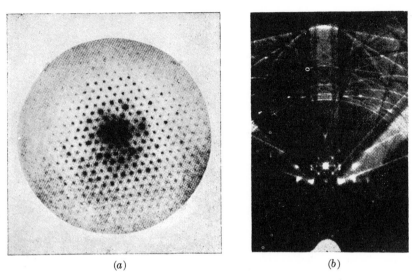

(a) (b)

Fig. 11.12. Electron diffraction patterns from single crystals.

Are electrons the only particles which show diffraction effects when scattered by crystals, or are such effects also shown by heavier particles? To answer this, let us compute the energy of a proton with a wavelength of 10^{-10} meter. Using Eq. 11.4, we get

$$\lambda = \frac{h}{mv} = \frac{h}{\sqrt{2mE}}$$

$$E = \left(\frac{h}{\lambda}\right)^2 \frac{1}{2m}$$

For a proton, the required energy is about 0.08 ev, or the same order of magnitude as thermal energies of motion at room temperature. Protons with such energies cannot penetrate appreciably into crystals, and therefore they cannot be diffracted. Slow neutrons, however, can penetrate into crystals and are diffracted.

Without going into detail at this point, we merely state that the nuclear reactions which proceed inside nuclear reactors liberate many neutrons. These particles are uninfluenced by the electric fields inside atoms and move through solids unimpeded until they collide with a nucleus. Because of the small size of nuclei, the mean free paths of neutrons are very large, even in solid matter. Fast neutrons, having energies of the order of Mev, such as are released in a nuclear reaction,

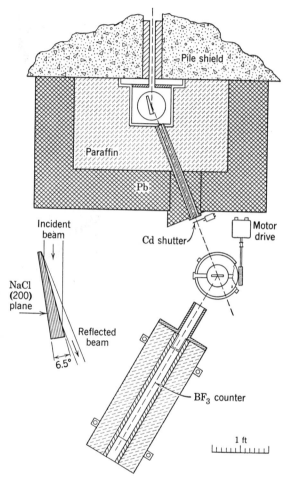

FIG. 11.13. Neutron diffraction apparatus.

may either be slowed down to thermal energies by successive collisions or be absorbed by nuclei and produce new nuclear reactions. Which of the two processes is more likely to occur depends on the kinds of nuclei with which the neutrons collide. Many thermal neutrons are present in a reactor and escape through ports. Here they may be collimated and reflected from crystallographic planes. This process selects a particular wavelength, according to the Bragg relation, and the mono-chromatic beam may then be used for further experimentation.

The experimental arrangement used by Wollan and Shull at the Oak Ridge National Laboratory in 1948 to demonstrate neutron diffraction

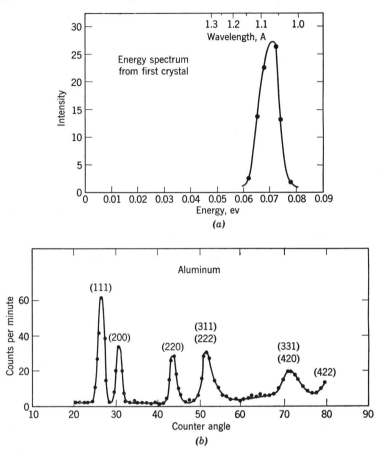

FIG. 11.14. (a) Energy distribution of neutron beam. (b) Diffraction pattern of a neutron beam by powdered aluminum.

is shown in Fig. 11.13. Neutrons are collimated and diffracted from a NaCl crystal. Cadmium is used as a shutter because cadmium nuclei are effective in absorbing slow neutrons. The neutron beam has the energy distribution shown in Fig. 11.14a. The beam is diffracted from a polycrystalline sample $\frac{1}{2}$ in. thick. The beam is detected in a BF_3 counter. This is a device which makes use of nuclear reactions in the BF_3 gas induced by neutrons to measure the intensity of the beam. The results obtained are shown in Fig. 11.14b. The correspondence of this pattern to the electron diffraction pattern obtained for face-centered cubic crystals is obvious. This is an important further demonstration of the wave properties of matter.

11.4 THE QUANTIZATION OF ELECTROMAGNETIC ENERGY

One of the cornerstones of atomic physics is the recognition that particles have wavelike properties. Another is the recognition that electromagnetic waves have some of the properties of particles. Historically, the recognition of the existence of this quantum aspect of electromagnetic radiation came early in this century, when Max Planck discovered that the spectral distribution of the radiation coming from an opening in a hot furnace could be described in terms of a thermal equilibrium of particles having certain peculiar properties, but not as a thermal equilibrium of electrical oscillators radiating according to Maxwell's laws. We shall discuss these facts later on, but, as they are more complex and difficult to understand in detail than are experiments involving single quanta, we shall begin our discussion with the latter.

A *quantum*, or *photon*, is defined in terms of Planck's constant h, which has already been introduced in Eq. 11.4 defining the wavelength of a particle. The energy E of a quantum of electromagnetic radiation of frequency f is

$$E = hf \qquad \blacktriangleright(11.11)\blacktriangleleft$$

The energy of a quantum depends on the frequency only. It does not depend on the amplitude of the electromagnetic wave. We must conclude that, in radiations from two sources of different intensity but of the same frequency, the difference must be accounted for in terms of the density of quanta and not in terms of the energy of individual quanta. From the definition of the energy, Eq. 11.11, we may conclude that the mass of a quantum m is

$$m = E/c^2 = hf/c^2 \qquad (11.12)$$

and that the momentum p of a quantum is

$$p = mc = hf/c = h/\lambda \qquad (11.13)$$

Notice that the relationship between the momentum and wavelength associated with a quantum is the same as the corresponding relationship for a particle.

If electromagnetic radiations consist of particles, then we must expect collisions with particles with which they interact. Electromagnetic fields do not interact with each other. Waves can travel through each other without mutual interference. There can be no collisions between quanta. But the electric field of a quantum does act on a charge, and we might therefore expect to find a collision between a quantum and an electron or proton, if, indeed, there is validity in this quantum concept at all.

Let us first review qualitatively what we might expect of a collision between a quantum of frequency f and a particle of mass m_0 initially at rest. If a collision occurs, the particle after the collision will no longer be at rest. It will have picked up energy and momentum. These must have come from the quantum whose energy and momentum have been decreased. But, if the energy of the quantum is decreased, its frequency, according to Eq. 11.11, must be decreased. We should therefore expect to find, if the quantum concept is correct, that the frequency of the light scattered by a charged particle is decreased relative to the frequency of the incoming light.

Qualitatively, at least, we know that in the visible range this is not true. Scattered light appears to have the same frequency as the incident light. This, however, is no disproof of the idea. We must examine it more carefully and quantitatively. First of all, we should review what we know about the collision of two particles. When a golf ball strikes a large bowling ball, it loses very little energy (apart from that lost in internal friction). Only when two more nearly equal particles collide, such as two billiard balls, will the moving one in general pass on a reasonable fraction of its energy to the one at rest. We should not, therefore, expect any appreciable change in wavelength unless the mass of the quantum hf/c^2 is somewhere near the mass m_0 of the particle. The condition for an appreciable change in frequency or wavelength on scattering is

$$f \simeq mc^2/h$$

or

$$\lambda = c/f = h/mc \tag{11.14}$$

For a change of λ in a collision with a proton to occur, the critical electromagnetic wavelength is

$$\lambda = \frac{6.62 \times 10^{-34}}{1.67 \times 10^{-27} \times 3 \times 10^8} = 1.3 \times 10^{-15} \text{ meter}$$

This is in the range of γ rays, which we shall consider further in Chapter 14. However, if we consider the critical wavelength of collisions with electrons, we get

$$\lambda = \frac{6.62 \times 10^{-34}}{9.1 \times 10^{-31} \times 3 \times 10^8} = 2.4 \times 10^{-12} \text{ meter} \tag{11.15}$$

This falls not too far from the range of X rays whose wavelengths can be accurately determined by diffraction from crystals, and it is therefore in the scattering of X rays that we should expect to find accurately measurable effects. For visible light, on the other hand, whose wavelength is several hundred thousand times as great, $\sim 5 \times 10^{-7}$ meter, the quanta have such small masses compared to electronic masses that no appreciable energy or frequency change is to be expected.

In order to make quantitative predictions we must set up the equations of conservation of energy and momentum. Moreover, if we are to deal with quanta satisfying Eq. 11.12, or for which $hf \sim mc^2$, we see that, if the quanta are to lose an appreciable portion of their energy, the electron must acquire a velocity comparable to that of light. We must therefore set up our conservation equations so that they are relativistically correct. In other words, the mass of the electron is

$$m = \frac{m_0}{\sqrt{1 - \beta^2}}$$

where $\beta = v/c$, the ratio of its velocity to that of light. The total energy of the electron is mc^2, and its kinetic energy is this less the "rest energy,"

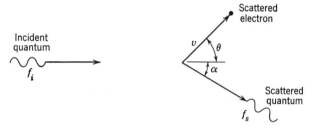

Fɪɢ. 11.15. The Compton effect.

or $(m - m_0)\, c^2$. The momentum in the direction of motion is mv. Using the symbols shown in Fig. 11.15, we have, for the statement that the energy before the collision is equal to that after the collision,

$$hf_i = (m - m_0)c^2 + hf_s \qquad (11.16)$$

and for the statement that the initial and final momenta, in and perpendicular to the direction of the incident quanta, must be equal

$$\frac{hf_i}{c} = mv \cos \theta + \frac{hf_s}{c} \cos \alpha \qquad (11.17)$$

$$0 = mv \sin \theta - \frac{hf_s}{c} \sin \alpha \qquad (11.18)$$

From these three equations, two variables may be eliminated. Since we propose to make observations on the incident and scattered quanta, and not on the scattered electron, we shall eliminate the variables v and θ specifying the motion of the electron. We shall be left with a single equation containing, in addition to the constants h, m_0, and c, the incident and scattered frequencies or wavelengths and the scattering angle α. This relation will then specify, if an incident quantum of frequency f_i and wavelength λ_i is scattered through an angle α, what the frequency or wavelength of the scattered quantum must be. The mathematical steps leading to the expected result are carried out below. The result is

$$\lambda_s = \lambda_i + \frac{2h}{m_0 c} \sin^2 \frac{\alpha}{2} \tag{11.19}$$

Derivation of the Compton Shift in Wavelength

The elimination of θ and v from the above equations is straightforward but somewhat long. We shall indicate a few steps and the final result. First solve Eq. 11.18 explicitly for $\sin \theta$. Then, since $\cos^2 \theta = 1 - \sin^2 \theta$, we may put

$$(mv \cos \theta)^2 = (mv)^2 - \left(\frac{h f_s}{c} \sin \alpha \right)^2 \tag{11.20}$$

But the expression on the left appears also in Eq. 11.17 and may therefore be eliminated. We have from Eqs. 11.17 and 11.19

$$(mv \cos \theta)^2 = \left(\frac{h f_i}{c} - \frac{h f_s}{c} \cos \alpha \right)^2 = (mv)^2 - \left(\frac{h f_s}{c} \sin \alpha \right)^2 \tag{11.21}$$

Solving this for $(mv)^2$ we get

$$(mv)^2 = \left(\frac{h f_i}{c} \right)^2 - 2 \frac{h f_i}{c} \frac{h f_s}{c} \cos \alpha + \left(\frac{h f_s}{c} \right)^2 \tag{11.22}$$

But Eq. 11.16 may be rewritten

$$(mc)^2 = \left(\frac{h f_i}{c} - \frac{h f_s}{c} + m_0 c \right)^2 \tag{11.23}$$

Now, subtracting Eq. 11.22 from Eq. 11.23, we get

$$m^2 (c^2 - v^2) = c^2 m^2 (1 - \beta^2) = m_0^2 c^2$$

$$= -2 \frac{h f_i}{c} \frac{h f_s}{c} (1 - \cos \alpha) + m_0^2 c^2 + 2 \left(\frac{h f_i}{c} - \frac{h f_s}{c} \right) m_0 c \tag{11.24}$$

which, upon simplification, may be put into the form

$$\frac{c}{h f_s} - \frac{c}{h f_i} = \frac{1 - \cos \alpha}{m_0 c} \tag{11.25}$$

This is the required expression, which, using the relations $\lambda f = c$, and

$(1 - \cos \alpha) = 2 \sin^2 \alpha/2$, may be put into the more convenient form

$$\lambda_s = \lambda_i + \left(\frac{2h}{m_0 c}\right) \sin^2 \frac{\alpha}{2} \tag{11.26}$$

But $h/m_0 c$ we have already calculated in Eq. 11.15. We therefore have, numerically,

$$\lambda_s = \lambda_i + 0.05 \times 10^{-10} \sin^2 \frac{\alpha}{2} \text{ meter (approx.)} \tag{11.27}$$

The quantum theory predicts that light scattered by an electron at any given angle will have its wavelength increased by a few hundredths of an angstrom unit, regardless of the incident wavelength. If the incident wavelength is in the visible, and several thousand angstrom units long in the first place, the addition of a few hundredths of an angstrom will be difficult to observe. This conclusion we had already arrived at on qualitative grounds. But when we come to the scattering of X rays having wavelengths comparable to the calculated change, we may expect measurable effects.

In the 1920's this effect was observed by A. H. Compton and was interpreted by him, using the above arguments, as an experimental demonstration of the existence of electromagnetic quanta. It still is one of the most convincing arguments.

We shall now discuss another phenomenon, the photoelectric effect, whose explanation in terms of quanta is very simple, but which is hard to understand on the basis of classical electromagnetic theory. The critical features of the photoelectric effect were discovered by Lenard in 1902 and were explained by Einstein in 1905, some years after Planck's introduction of the quantum concept in 1899.

The photoelectric effect consists of the emission of electrons from metallic surfaces when illuminated by light. That such an effect can exist is readily understandable in terms of electromagnetic theory. Since light, according to this theory, is an electromagnetic wave motion, the electric vector in the wave may be expected to act on the electrons in a metal surface. Oscillations are produced, and energy is consequently absorbed, until the electron has sufficient kinetic energy to overcome the forces of attraction which bind it to the metal. One might expect, on the basis of electromagnetic theory, that the number and velocity of the ejected photoelectrons would depend on the amplitude of the electric vector, and therefore on the intensity of the light, rather than critically on the wavelength.

The relevant experimental facts are that, for a particular surface, light having a frequency below a certain critical frequency produces no photoelectrons, no matter what the incident intensity. Further, for frequencies above the critical frequency, photoelectrons are always produced, even for a very feeble intensity of the incident light. These results are difficult to understand on the basis of a classical model for energy absorption, in which the electric vector produces a force acting on the electron proportional to E, or proportional to the square root of the intensity of the light.

The explanation in terms of the quantum theory is straightforward if we assume that the energy in a beam of light is concentrated in quanta whose magnitude is determined by the frequency, and that all of the

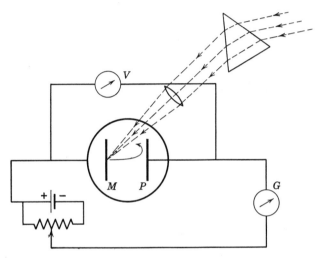

FIG. 11.16.   An apparatus for measuring the maximum kinetic energy of photo-electrons.

energy in a quantum is absorbed by a single electron. If the work required to remove an electron from the metal being illuminated is W, the following condition must be fulfilled if an electron is to escape:

$$hf \geqslant W \qquad (11.28)$$

If we define a frequency f_0 by the relation

$$W = hf_0$$

Eq. 11.28 may be rewritten in the form

$$f \geqslant f_0 = W/h \qquad (11.29)$$

Regardless of the intensity of the incident light, photoelectrons are to be expected if Eq. 11.29 is satisfied. A more detailed verification of the explanation advanced above is contained in the quantitative interpretation of the following experiment illustrated in Fig. 11.16. Light of variable frequency f from a spectrograph falls on a metal plate M in a vacuum tube. Electrons are ejected, some of which will travel to a second plate P and thus produce a current measured by the deflection of the galvanometer G. If the potential of P is just sufficiently negative for no ejected electrons to have a kinetic energy great enough to reach P the observed current will be stopped, and the condition satisfied by the potential difference between the plates will be

$$eV = \tfrac{1}{2} m v_{max}{}^2 \tag{11.30}$$

But the maximum kinetic energy of the emitted electrons will be the energy of a quantum less the energy required to remove the electron from the plate M, or

$$\tfrac{1}{2} m v_{max}{}^2 = hf - W = hf - hf_0 = eV$$

This may be put into the form

$$V = \frac{h}{e}\,(f - f_0) \tag{11.31}$$

Eq. 11.31 is plotted in Fig. 11.17. The experimental results are in accordance with the above, not only to the extent of yielding points

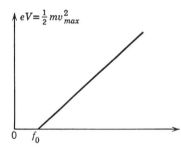

FIG. 11.17. Graph of Eq. 11.21 concerning the photoelectric effect.

along a straight line with a positive slope and a positive intercept f_0, but the slope of the line is just that computed with the value of e obtained from Millikan's oil drop experiment, and with the same value of Planck's constant used in describing the wavelength of a particle and in the Compton effect.

The Compton effect indicated the usefulness of the quantum concept in the X ray region. The photoelectric effect has been studied primarily with ultraviolet and visible light. In the next paragraphs we shall extend the range of quantum phenomena to include the infrared radiation from a furnace to which Planck first applied the quantum concept.

If we look into a small aperture in a closed furnace into which no light can penetrate from outside, we see nothing if the temperature is much below 500°C. We may sense heat, and with suitable thermal measuring devices we may measure the quantity of heat as well as also its spectral distribution, but it is not until the temperature gets higher than 500°C that we begin to see. At first the color is red, then, as the temperature rises, it changes to orange, and next to yellow. What we see in the furnace depends only on the temperature and not on the materials of which the furnace is constructed.

The amount of energy radiated per second per unit of area is called the *radiant emittance*. We designate it by W and express it in watts/meter². The fraction of this energy in the range of wavelengths between λ and $\lambda + d\lambda$ is proportional to $d\lambda$. We may write $dW = W_\lambda d\lambda$, where $W_\lambda = dW/d\lambda$ is called the *spectral emittance* and is here measured

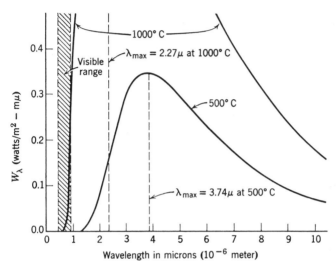

Fig. 11.18. The spectral emittance from a furnace at 500°C and at 1000°C.

in watts/meter³, or often watts/m² - mμ. The electromagnetic energy radiated from a small aperture in a furnace is sometimes called "black-body" radiation because a "black" surface is one which absorbs all the energy which falls on it. A small opening in a large cavity may be thought of as a trap which lets in any energy which strikes it and, being small, makes it difficult for this energy to get out again. That which does get out is then emitted by a "black body." The spectral emittance from a furnace at two temperatures is plotted in Fig. 11.18. Wavelengths are given in microns, 1 micron being designated by the symbol μ,

$$1\mu = 10^{-6} \text{ meter} \qquad (11.32)$$

Notice that at 1000° the total energy radiated is much greater than at 500°C, that at the higher temperature the maximum has shifted to shorter wavelengths, and finally that, whereas there is a negligible amount of energy in the visible at 500°C, there is very much more at 1000°C. Quantitative measurements bear out the qualitative point already made. The curves in Fig. 11.18 depend only on the temperature and not on the material of which the furnace is constructed. The spectral distribution must therefore be explicable by arguments involving the radiation only and not the details of the interaction of the radiation with matter.

By way of introduction to a discussion of the radiation in a furnace, let us review briefly the results obtained for N atoms having a total kinetic energy E and confined to a box. The question to be considered is the distribution of the energy E among the N atoms or, what amounts to the same thing, the distribution of velocities among the atoms. A possible distribution of velocities would be one in which each atom had exactly the same velocity as every other one. To be consistent with our initial assumption, this velocity would have to be given by $E/N = \frac{1}{2}mv^2$. But we should certainly not expect to find such uniformity in a large assembly of atoms. If it existed at some instant, we should expect collisions to occur in which some atoms gained energy and others lost energy. The kinetic theory of gases shows that there is one particular distribution of velocities that is more probable than any other: the Maxwellian distribution. In any gas, this particular distribution may be expected regardless of the nature of the collision processes between individual atoms.

The radiation in a furnace may be treated in a similar way. There is one important difference. Electromagnetic fields do not interact with each other. In order that a quantum may change its energy, it must interact with matter. Without specifying the nature of this interaction in detail, however, it is possible to show by statistical arguments that there is a most probable spectral distribution of a given amount of electromagnetic energy in any given volume, and that for a particular energy density this distribution will be in thermal equilibrium with matter at one particular temperature. Once these conditions are established, it is possible to compute the spectral emittance from a small hole in an enclosure at a temperature T. The result, in frequency units, is

$$dW = W_f \, df = \frac{2\pi h}{c^2} \frac{f^3 \, df}{e^{hf/kT} - 1} \text{ watts/meter}^2 \quad \blacktriangleright(11.33)\blacktriangleleft$$

where h is Planck's constant, k is Boltzmann's constant, and c is the velocity of light. Expressed per unit range of wavelength, we find, since

$$\lambda f = c$$

$$\lambda \, df + f \, d\lambda = 0$$

$$df = -\frac{f}{\lambda}\, d\lambda = -\frac{c}{\lambda^2}\, d\lambda$$

that

$$W_\lambda = \frac{c_1 \lambda^{-5}}{e^{c_2/\lambda T} - 1} \qquad \blacktriangleright(11.34)\blacktriangleleft$$

where $c_1 = 2\pi hc^2 = 3.740 \times 10^{-16}$ and $c_2 = hc/k = 1.438 \times 10^{-2}$ in mks units. This is called *Planck's law* of the spectral emittance of an enclosed furnace or black body. It is in excellent agreement with all observations.

It is interesting to note that a law describing the distribution of energy in a furnace, which is based on purely classical considerations, and in which Planck's constant h therefore does not appear, had previously been derived. It is called the *Rayleigh-Jeans law*. It corresponds to Planck's law at low frequencies, or long wavelengths. In general, for long wavelength radio waves, electromagnetic theory suffices for a complete description, but as we proceed to shorter wavelengths quantum phenomena become more marked. For low frequencies, Planck's law as expressed in Eq. 11.33 may be simplified through putting

$$e^{hf/kT} - 1 = 1 + \frac{hf}{kT} + \cdots - 1 \simeq \frac{hf}{kT}$$

and we get

$$W_f = \frac{2\pi f^2}{c^2}\, kT \qquad \text{for } \frac{hf}{kT} \ll 1 \qquad (11.35)$$

which is the Rayleigh-Jeans law. Planck's constant has dropped out. The Rayleigh-Jeans law is valid only for long wavelengths.

Two aspects of Planck's law that are of particular importance are called *Wien's displacement law* and the *Stefan-Boltzmann law*. The first of these relates the wavelength λ_m, for which the spectral emittance has a maximum, to the absolute temperature. By differentiating Eq. 11.34 with respect to λ and setting the derivative equal to zero one obtains

$$\frac{c_2}{\lambda_m T} = 5(1 - e^{-c_2/\lambda_m T})$$

This equation, solved graphically, gives the final result

$$\lambda_m T = \frac{c_2}{4.965} = 2.897 \times 10^{-3} \qquad \blacktriangleright(11.36)\blacktriangleleft$$

This is Wien's displacement law.

The final law to which we have made reference above relates the radiant emittance to the absolute temperature.

$$W = \int_0^\infty W_\lambda \, d\lambda = \frac{\pi^4}{15} \frac{c_1}{c_2{}^4} \, T^4 = 5.672 \times 10^{-8} T^4 \text{ watts/meter}^2 \quad \blacktriangleright(11.37)\blacktriangleleft$$

This is the Stefan-Boltzmann law. It expresses the fact that the total energy radiated per second per unit of area from an opening in an enclosed furnace is proportional to the fourth power of the absolute temperature. It is not, like Planck's law, a demonstration of the validity of the quantum hypothesis. The fourth power temperature dependence can also be derived from classical electromagnetic theory and thermodynamics (see Problem 27, p. 466). Planck's law, however, from which the Stefan-Boltzmann law may be deduced, cannot be derived from classical electromagnetic theory. In fact, its derivation gave for the first time the value of Planck's constant h. The theoretical conclusions expressed in Eqs. 11.34, 11.36, and 11.37 are completely borne out by experiment, and it is this agreement which led Planck to adopt the quantum hypothesis.

We have now ample evidence that, on an atomic scale, particles have wavelike aspects and waves have particlelike aspects. Electrons are diffracted. Electromagnetic waves are involved in "collision" processes. These two aspects of atomic phenomena may be reconciled by the following considerations.

Classical electromagnetic theory explains interference and diffraction phenomena as being due to waves. In a diffraction pattern produced on a screen by light passing through a small circular opening, for instance, we are able to compute the amplitude of the electric and magnetic field vectors at every point of the pattern. The intensity of the light is then correctly given at every point in terms of the square of the amplitude of the electromagnetic wave.

It is at the same time true that when light is absorbed or scattered it manifests itself in the form of packets of energy hf and momentum hf/c.

These two statements are reconcilable if we assume that the energy in the electromagnetic field is not distributed uniformly but in packets of magnitude hf, which are in turn so distributed that the average density is that given by classical theory. Thus, for example, if we have an electromagnetic wave, having a frequency of 3 megacycles/sec and a wavelength of 100 meters transmitting energy at the rate of 1 microwatt/meter^2, the average density of quanta n will be such that $n(hf)$ will be the energy per unit volume. The energy per unit volume is given classically by the amplitude of the electric and magnetic oscillations. In the quantum theory this idea is not dropped but supplemented. The energy per unit volume is also determined by the density of quanta and the energy of each. For the wave described above we find that, if 10^{-6} watts are transmitted per square meter perpendicular to the direction of propagation, this must be equal to the number of quanta passing a square meter in 1 sec multiplied by the energy per quantum, or

$$10^{-6} = n \cdot c \cdot hf$$

Solved for n, this gives

$$n = \frac{10^{-6}}{3 \times 10^8 \times 6.6 \times 10^{-34} \times 3 \times 10^6} = 1.7 \times 10^{11} \text{ quanta/meter}^3$$

If these quanta are so distributed that their density at every point is given by $(\frac{1}{2}\epsilon_0 E^2 + \frac{1}{2}\mu_0 H^2)/hf$ at that point, then we must assume that the density is twice this value near the troughs and crests of the electromagnetic wave and zero halfway between them. If we are concerned with regions so small that the average number of particles which they contain is less than one, then we must interpret the variations of the electromagnetic field within the region as giving the relative probabilities of finding a quantum at various points.

There is no particular necessity for adopting such a model. The critical part of our understanding of electromagnetic phenomena relates first of all to the propagation of waves. We can describe the phenomena of reflection, refraction, interference, and diffraction in terms of waves. Our predictions are correct, and, in so far as such experiments are concerned, we must be satisfied. We have done all that can be done. The second important aspect of our understanding of electromagnetic phenomena deals with the interaction of light with particles. In predicting results of emission, absorption, or scattering experiments, we make use of packets of energy hf and momentum hf/c. Again, we can predict the results of experiment correctly. In doing so, we have achieved all that can be expected. If the model involved in describing the various processes transcends anything we have ever seen with our eyes, we must not be surprised. We are studying a branch of existence which lies beyond the reach of our eyes. It is not like our familiar surroundings. But we nevertheless can describe it sufficiently to make predictions about observable phenomena. That is all we can hope for.

11.5 THE QUANTIZATION OF ANGULAR MOMENTUM

The experimental facts described above seem most strange when viewed from the point of view of the behavior of macroscopic objects and waves. But on an atomic scale it is abundantly clear that particles have wave properties. Electrons and neutrons are diffracted by crystals.

Also electromagnetic waves are scattered and absorbed in processes very like collisions. We now add a third new and strange property. Atomic angular momentum is quantized, both in magnitude and direction. An atom or molecule will in general possess angular momentum due to the motion of its electrons. This angular momentum cannot have an arbitrary magnitude. The only values of angular momentum found in nature are integral multiples of $\frac{1}{2}(h/2\pi)$, also written $\frac{1}{2}\hbar$. Planck's constant has the dimensions of energy $\times$ time, or $M(L/t)^2 t$, which can also be written $ML^2\omega$, or angular momentum. On a macroscopic scale angular momentum appears to be continuously variable because the units by which it can change are so small compared to the total angular momentum of objects that can be directly observed. On an atomic scale the effects of the quantization of angular momentum are tremendous.

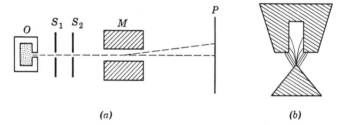

(a)   (b)

FIG. 11.19.   The apparatus used in the Stern-Gerlach experiment.

The experimental facts about atomic angular momentum took several years to unravel completely. The first clear indication was achieved by the experiments of Stern and Gerlach on a beam of atoms in 1921. They were attempting to measure atomic magnetic moments by a new and very direct method. A beam of atoms originating in a furnace O and moving through a vacuum is defined by a slit system S_1, S_2, as shown in Fig. 11.19a. The beam traverses a region between the specially shaped poles of a magnet in which there is a non-uniform, or inhomogeneous field. A cross section of the poles is shown in Fig. 11.19b. Here the beam is moving into the paper midway between the poles. In this field the atoms are deflected by a force perpendicular to the direction of motion in a manner further discussed below. After leaving the field, the atoms travel in straight lines to a photographic plate or other detector where the amount of the deflection is observed.

The Force on a Dipole in an Inhomogeneous Field

The forces which a field exerts on a dipole are most readily visualized in the electric case, in which the dipole consists of two equal poles of opposite sign a

fixed distance apart. In a uniform field, the forces on the two poles are equal
and oppositely directed. This condition may give rise to a torque which might
turn the dipole, but not to a resultant force which could move it or change the
motion of its center of mass. In an inhomogeneous field, there may be a
resultant force on the dipole, as illustrated in Fig. 11.20a. Here the dipole is so
oriented that its moment is in the direction of the field, and in the direction of
increasing field strength, since the field strength is greater when the lines are
closer together. In this condition the force on the positive pole will be greater
than the force on the negative pole, and there will consequently be a resultant
downward force, as shown. When the dipole is at right angles to the field and

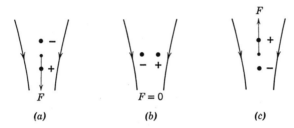

(a)   (b)   (c)

FIG. 11.20. The force on a dipole in an inhomogeneous field.

the direction of increase, the magnitude of the force on the two poles is equal
and the resultant vanishes. For orientations between that shown in a and b,
the force is intermediate in magnitude but in the direction shown in a. If now
the dipole is turned so that it is pointing in a direction opposite to the field
and to the direction of increase, the force on the negative pole will be greater,
and the resultant force on the dipole will be upward, as shown in Fig. 11.20c.

A general expression for the force on a dipole, applicable to the magnetic
case in which we have a current loop rather than two poles, is easily derived
from the expression for the energy of a dipole μ in a field B.

$$E = -\mu B \cos \theta$$

where θ is the angle between B and μ. If we choose an axis, say the x axis, in
the direction of B and assume that B varies from point to point along it, we
get by differentiation

$$\frac{dE}{dx} = -\mu \frac{dB}{dx} \cos \theta \qquad (11.38)$$

But there must be a force F exerted by the field on the dipole opposite to the
direction of increase of potential energy.

$$F = -\frac{dE}{dx} \qquad (11.39)$$

and, therefore, upon combining Eqs. 11.38 and 11.39, we find for the magnetic
force

$$F = \mu \cos \theta \frac{dB}{dx} \qquad (11.40)$$

The magnetic force acting on the atoms as they fly through the magnetic field is either up or down in Fig. 11.19a, depending on their orientation. If, in the beam, all orientations are present, we should expect to find at the detecting plate P all deflections between zero and some maximum deflection obtained for those atoms whose magnetic moment was parallel or antiparallel to the field. Actually, in the experiments with silver atoms, it was found that, upon application of the field, the central spot obtained with no field was split into two, just as though in the field the magnetic moments of all the atoms were either parallel or antiparallel to the field, but never in an intermediate orientation.

Later observations on other atoms showed that more complex conditions exist. The beam is always split up into several parts by the magnetic field, as though only certain orientations in the field are possible, but sometimes instead of splitting into just two beams, as in the case of silver, it splits into three, or four, or some larger number of components.

The discovery of the simple physical laws behind these observations required the correlation of many observations. In the first place, it was necessary to consider not only the magnetic moments of the atoms used but also their angular momenta. It turned out that, whereas the magnitude of the deflection in an atomic beam experiment is determined by the magnetic moment, the number of beams into which the incident beam is split is determined by the angular momentum. For methods of measuring the angular momentum of an atom, J, the reader is referred to Chapter 7. When all the facts were collected, the following very simple pattern in nature appeared.

1. The total angular momentum of an atom or molecule is always some integral multiple of $\frac{1}{2}(h/2\pi)$, including zero.

2. In the presence of a magnetic field, an atom can have only certain discreet orientations such that the difference in the component of the angular momentum in the direction of the field for adjacent orientations is $h/2\pi$.

These two rules lead to the situation which is schematically shown in Fig. 11.21. Apart from the case of zero angular momentum, the smallest possible angular momentum J is $\frac{1}{2}(h/2\pi)$. The only possible orientations of this angular momentum in a field, if the difference in the z component, which we assume parallel to an applied field, is to be $h/2\pi$, are parallel or antiparallel, as shown in Fig. 11.21a. The next possible case, $J = h/2\pi$, is shown in Fig. 11.21b. Here three possible orientations are shown, with the angular momentum parallel to, perpendicular to, or antiparallel to the applied field. If the total angular momentum is $\frac{3}{2}(h/2\pi)$, there are four possible orientations, as shown in Fig. 11.21c.

It is often useful to speak of an angular momentum quantum number which describes the number of units of $h/2\pi$ present. We should have

$$J = j\frac{h}{2\pi}$$

and in Fig. 11.21a, b, and c the values of j are $\frac{1}{2}$, 1, and $\frac{3}{2}$. The reader should extend Fig. 11.21 to higher values of j and note that, if we call

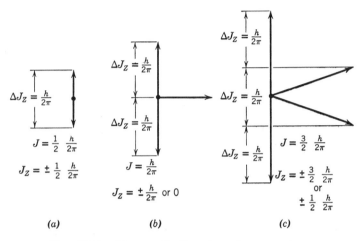

Fig. 11.21. The quantization of angular momentum.

j_z the corresponding quantum number for the z component of the angular momentum, then

$$J_z = j_z\frac{h}{2\pi}$$

The possible values of j_z are

$$j_z = j, \quad j - 1, \quad j - 2, \cdots, \quad -j$$

The total number of possible orientations of an atom having an angular momentum specified by j is $2j + 1$, as can easily be verified numerically.

Returning now to the Stern-Gerlach experiment, we see that, if the beam is split into two components, as for silver, we should expect to be dealing with a case of $j = \frac{1}{2}$ which can be oriented parallel or anti-parallel to the field. But, since the magnetic moment of a silver atom is a consequence of the angular momentum of the charged electronic shell, we should expect the silver atom to be oriented in the field so that not only its angular momentum but also its magnetic moment is parallel or antiparallel to the field. The splitting into *two* beams is determined by the fact that $j = \frac{1}{2}$. The magnitude of splitting is determined by the magnitude of the magnetic moment.

Not all atoms with $j = \frac{1}{2}$ have the same magnetic moment. The beautiful regularity and order which we have found in the description of angular momentum do not extend to magnetic moments. But for any given atom having angular momentum we shall always find some definite magnetic moment, and this will be along the direction of the angular momentum. In other words, the vector magnetic moment may always be calculated from the angular momentum J by means of an equation of the form

$$\mu = \gamma \mathbf{J}$$

where γ is a constant characteristic of an atom and may be positive or negative.

An atomic beam experiment on atoms having some arbitrary angular momentum given by j will involve a beam that splits into $2j + 1$ components, one for each possible orientation. By simply counting the number of traces on the plate P it is possible to specify the j value for the atom being investigated. From the magnitude of the splitting and the constants of the apparatus it is, in addition, possible to specify the magnitude of μ.

We have now described the three main observations concerning atoms which must be incorporated into any theory of atomic structure. They are the wave aspect of particles, the particle aspect of waves, and the quantization of angular momentum. In the next chapters, we shall show how a modification of the laws of mechanics leads to an understanding of these three facts.

SUMMARY

Diffraction patterns can be produced by the interactions between waves and regularly arranged points in a space lattice. The direction in which waves are reflected with maximum intensity from crystallographic planes is given by the Bragg equation

$$2d \sin \theta = n\lambda$$

where d is the separation between the planes, θ is the angle between the incident ray, or the reflected ray, and the plane in question, n is any integer, and λ is the wavelength of the radiation being diffracted. Notice that the Bragg relation can be satisfied only if $\lambda < 2d$. Only waves whose wavelengths are smaller than twice the spacing of atomic planes can be diffracted by crystals. X rays satisfy this condition and have been extensively used to study crystal structure.

Beams of electrons and neutrons may also be diffracted from crystals. The wavelength to be associated with these particles is

$$\lambda = h/mv$$

The counterpart to this wave aspect of particles is to be found in the particle, or quantum, aspect of electromagnetic waves. An electromagnetic quantum of frequency f has an energy given by

$$E = hf$$

a mass given by

$$m = E/c^2 = \frac{hf}{c^2}$$

and a momentum

$$mc = hf/c$$

The equations of conservation of energy and momentum applied to a collision between an incident X ray quantum of wavelength λ_i and an electron of mass m_0 at rest predict an increase in the wavelength when the quantum is scattered through an angle α. The wavelength λ_s of the scattered quantum is

$$\lambda_s = \lambda_i + \left(\frac{2h}{m_0 c}\right) \sin^2 \frac{\alpha}{2} \simeq \lambda_i + 0.05 \times 10^{-10} \sin^2 \frac{\alpha}{2} \text{ meter}$$

The quantum concept is similarly necessary to explain the fact that, in the photoelectric effect involving the ejection of electrons from a metal surface by light, no electrons are ejected for any intensity whatever if the frequency f is such that the energy of a quantum hf is less than the work function of the metal, or the work required to remove an electron from the metal. Further, for frequencies greater than the critical frequency, some electrons are ejected no matter how weak the intensity of the incident light may be. A photoelectric experiment described in the text makes possible an independent determination of h/e.

A furnace in which electromagnetic radiation is in thermal equilibrium with the walls has a spectral emittance given by

$$W_f = \frac{2\pi h}{c^2} \frac{f^3}{e^{hf/kT} - 1}$$

This relation can be derived as the most probable distribution of quanta of energy. It was shown by Planck in 1899 that a law of the above form was consistent with the experimental results, and that it implied quantization. The magnitude of Planck's constant h required to fit the experimental results is of course the same as required by the Compton effect and the photoelectric effect.

It is possible to reconcile the electromagnetic statement that energy is distributed in space according to the square of the electric and magnetic fields with the quantum concept by assuming that energy is not uniformly distributed, but that quanta are so distributed that the average energy density is that given by electromagnetic theory. The electric and magnetic fields at various points then specify the relative probability that there are quanta at these points.

Angular momentum is quantized. The angular momentum of any atomic system is some integral multiple of $\frac{1}{2}(h/2\pi)$. Atomic systems are so oriented in a magnetic field that the difference in the component of the angular momentum in the direction of the field for adjacent possible orientations is $h/2\pi$.

PROBLEMS

1. Analysis of X ray data shows that NaCl crystallizes in the cubic form. How many atoms of Na and of Cl are there per unit cube? Compute the separation between nuclei in NaCl. Density = 2.16. Molecular weight = 58.4. Avogadro's number = 6.02×10^{23}.

2. Analysis of X ray data shows that copper crystallizes in the face-centered cubic form. How many atoms are there per unit cube? Find the dimensions of the unit cube and the distance between nearest neighbors in copper. Density = 8.9. Molecular weight = 63.7.

3. Consider the crystallographic planes shown in Fig. 11.5 for the face-centered cubic lattice. Make drawings showing the arrangement of atoms in these planes. (See Fig. 11.4b for an example.) Make a drawing equivalent to 11.5 but showing the (200) and (202) planes.

4. Make three drawings showing the (111), (200), and (220) planes for a simple cubic lattice. Make a drawing showing the arrangement of atoms in each of these planes.

5. Using the results of Problems 1 and 2, find the distance between successive (111) and (220) planes in NaCl and copper.

6. Using the results of Problem 5 compute the angle at which first order Bragg reflection occurs for the (111) and (220) planes of NaCl and copper for X rays of the following wavelengths: 1, and 0.1 A.

7. Compute the wavelength of electrons accelerated through the following potentials: 0.025 volt, 10 volts, 4 Mev. 100 Mev. What will be their velocities? What energies are suitable for demonstrating electron diffraction by crystals?

8. Determine the approximate energy and velocity a neutron should have for a demonstration of neutron diffraction in NaCl. Choose a reasonable value for the Bragg angle. If the neutrons in a beam do not all have the same energy, how will the spread of neutron energies affect the results of a diffraction experiment?

9. What is the least energy which an electron could have and still be reflected from a face-centered cubic crystal whose unit cell has an edge length of 1.5 A? From what planes, and at what angles, could this reflection take place?

10. Monochromatic X rays of wavelength $\lambda = 0.708$ A are scattered from a carbon block. Calculate the wavelength of the rays scattered by the electrons in the block at 50°, 90°, 150°.

11. (a) Calculate the angle between the direction of motion of the recoil electron and the incident quantum in Problem 10 above. (b) Determine the energy of the recoil electron.

12. Monochromatic X rays of wavelength $\lambda = 0.124$ A are scattered from a carbon block. (a) Determine the wavelength of the X rays scattered through 180°. (b) Determine the maximum kinetic energy of the recoil electrons.

★13. A particle of rest mass M_0 radiates a frequency f_0 toward an observer at rest with respect to the particle. If the radiating particle and observer were approaching each other with a velocity v, the observer would measure a different frequency $f = f_0 + \Delta f$ because of the Doppler effect. Assume $v \ll c$, and $hf/c^2 \ll M_0$. Compute the Doppler shift in frequency, first on the basis of a classical oscillating particle, and second on the basis of the emission of quanta, and show that the two results agree.

The following may be helpful in arriving at a conclusion. Assume that the radiating particle is at rest and that the observer is moving toward the radiator with a velocity v. How many wave crests would have passed the observer in 1 sec if $v = 0$? How many additional wave crests would have passed the observer because of his approach to the radiating particle? Is the same result true if the observer is at rest and the radiating particle is approaching him? What is the value of $\Delta f/f_0$ on the above classical basis?

If we now consider quanta being emitted by a particle having a much greater mass, we must set up the equations of conservation of momentum and energy. We assume that the velocity of the radiating particle before emitting the quantum is v_0 and after emitting the quantum is v. In setting up the equation describing the conservation of momentum it suffices to use the rest mass M_0 of the particle. Verify that this is true for $v/c \ll 1$.

In setting up the equation for the conservation of energy we may take the initial energy to be the rest energy of the particle before radiation, M_0c^2, plus its classical kinetic energy before radiating. By how much has the rest mass of the particle been reduced after the emission of a quantum? What is the new rest energy? What is the new kinetic energy? What is the energy of the emitted quantum in the laboratory coordinate system? Eliminate v from the equations describing the conservation of momentum and energy, and solve for

$$\frac{\Delta f}{f} = \frac{f - f_0}{f}$$

14. The photoelectric thresholds [$\lambda_0 = c/f_0$] of particular samples of certain metals are as follows: aluminum, 4770 A; copper, 3000 A; potassium, 6000 A; sodium 6800 A; tungsten, 2300 A. Determine the photoelectric work function for each of these metals in electron volts.

15. Determine the stopping potential in volts for electrons from each of the metals in Problem 14 when the metal is illuminated (a) with light of wavelength 1849 A and (b) 3500A.

16. The thermionic work functions for particular samples of certain metals are as follows: silver, 3.64 ev; nickel, 4.05 ev; lithium, 2.13 ev. Determine the respective threshold wavelengths.

17. Determine the maximum velocity of the electrons ejected from each of the metals in Problem 16 when the metal is illuminated with light of wavelength 2530 A.

18. X rays are produced in an evacuated tube in which electrons are emitted at

a heated cathode, are accelerated by a difference of potential V between anode and cathode, and finally are stopped at the anode. What is the shortest wavelength to be expected in the X rays produced in a tube in which the accelerating voltage V is 10 kv?

19. The temperature of a black body is 3000°K. Compute the ratio of its spectral emittance at a wavelength 10,000 A (infrared) to its spectral emittance at 5000 A (visible).

20. At what wavelength is the spectral emittance of a black body a maximum if its temperature is (a) 500°K, (b) 5000°K? (c) At what temperature does the maximum spectral emittance lie at a wavelength of 5550 A where the eye is most sensitive?

21. What is the radiant emittance of a black body at a temperature of (a) 300°K, (b) 600°K, (c) 1200°K?

22. (a) What is the average density of quanta in a radio wave having a wavelength of 100 meters transmitting 1 microwatt/meter^2? What is the average number of quanta in a volume λ^3?

(b) Assume that an X ray tube generates X rays having a wavelength of 1 A at the rate of 1 mw. What is the average number of quanta in a volume λ^3 at a distance of 1 meter from the anode of the tube?

★23. Prove that Wien's displacement law, Eq. 11.36, is a consequence of Planck's law, Eq. 11.34.

★24. Prove that the Stefan-Boltzmann law, Eq. 11.37, is a consequence of Planck's law, Eq. 11.34, given the following integral:

$$\int_0^\infty \frac{x^3 \, dx}{e^x - 1} = \frac{\pi^4}{15}$$

★25. Show that, for isotropic radiation, if K is the energy flow per unit area per unit solid angle per second, u is the energy density, and W is the power transmitted per unit area, then $W = \pi K$, and $u = \dfrac{4\pi}{c} K = \dfrac{4W}{c}$.

★26. Show that the pressure p exerted by isotropic radiation on a reflecting wall is equal to one-third the radiation energy density,

$$p = u/3$$

using either the concept of reflected waves carrying energy and momentum as described in Chapter 8 or the concept of reflected quanta.

★27. Prove that the T^4 dependence for the total radiation is a consequence of (a) the thermodynamic relation,

$$dQ = dU + p \, dV = d(uV) + p \, dV$$

(b) the fact that

$$p = u/3$$

and (c) the second law of thermodynamics, according to which the change in entropy dS for reversible processes is

$$dS = dQ/T$$

and is independent of the conditions under which the heat dQ is added, so that we may write

$$dS = \left(\frac{\partial S}{\partial T}\right)_v dT + \left(\frac{\partial S}{\partial V}\right)_T dV$$

The desired result will then be found to follow from the fact that

$$\frac{\partial^2 S}{\partial T \, \partial V} = \frac{\partial^2 S}{\partial V \, \partial T}$$

28. In a Stern-Gerlach experiment a beam of Na atoms is sent through two slits 0.1 mm wide and 0.5 meter apart. The velocity of the atoms in the beam may be assumed to be 8×10^4 cm/sec. Immediately behind the slits is a magnetic field having a gradient dB/dx at right angles to the beam. The field extends over 10 cm of the beam. At a distance 0.5 meter beyond the magnetic field is a photographic plate on which the position of the beam is recorded. The magnetic moment of the sodium atom is 10^{-20} erg/gauss and this is always either parallel or antiparallel to the applied field. The force acting on the Na atoms in the field may be computed from Eq. 11.40. If μ is in ergs per gauss, B is in gauss, and x is in cm, then F is in dynes.

Compute the least value of the magnetic field gradient, dB/dx, which will resolve the two beams of sodium atoms. The mass of a sodium atom is about 23 times the mass of a proton. In doing this problem be sure to use corresponding units throughout. μ is here given in ergs per gauss because this is the customary way of describing atomic moments.

CHAPTER 12

Wave Mechanics

12.1 WAVE FUNCTIONS

A stream of particles fired at a crystal will "bounce" in certain directions only and not in others. We can describe these directions accurately in terms of the diffraction of a wave having a wavelength

$$\lambda = h/mv$$

In order to describe wave phenomena in more detail we must assume something, perhaps analogous to a field, which has a wavelength. This "something" we shall call a wave function, and we shall designate it by ψ. Traveling or standing ψ waves may be described as functions of x, y, z, and t, just as we have described any other kind of wave.

So much is simply concerned with mathematical description. But what can we ask physically of this wave function? Will it have any other observable attribute than a wavelength?

The attributes to be expected of a wave function can perhaps best be understood through considering possible analogies with electromagnetic waves. We have found that the presence of electric and magnetic fields implies an energy density in space. If at some point in a traveling wave we have an electric field E and a magnetic field H, we then have an energy per unit volume

$$u = \frac{\epsilon_0}{2} E^2 + \frac{\mu_0}{2} H^2$$

This function is a continuous function, but it does not necessarily imply that energy is really continuously distributed. It is perfectly consistent with a situation in which energy is distributed in quanta in such a way that $u = $ (number of quanta per unit volume)(hf). This is the same situation we encounter in describing the density of air as being ρ kilograms/meter^3 under given conditions of temperature and pressure. The existence of such a density function in no way contradicts the further fact that air is made up of discrete molecules very far apart compared to their diameters. The density of air may be expressed as the average number of molecules per unit volume multiplied by the average mass of a molecule.

The concept of an "average number per unit volume" may be considered in greater detail. In air there are roughly 30×10^{18} molecules per cubic centimeter. This is the average number that one would find in any sample of air chosen at random. The average number in an element of volume 10^{-6} cm on a side would be $30 \times 10^{18} \times 10^{-18} = 30$. One might find 31, or 29, or other comparable numbers, but the average would be 30. How about an element of volume 10^{-7} cm on a side? The average number $\rho\, dv$ will be $30 \times 10^{18} \times 10^{-21} = 0.03$. What does it mean that the average number is three one-hundredths of a particle? It means that, if one were to examine a series of volume elements of this size, either one would find a molecule within or one would find no molecule. The quantity $\rho\, dv$ must be interpreted not as the average number of particles in dv but as the *probability that a particle will be found in dv*. If $\rho\, dv = 0.03$, this means that the probability of finding a particle in a volume element of this size is 0.03, or that in 3% of the tries one would find a particle. In this sense $\rho\, dv$ is a *probability density*.

We return now to our wave function and assume that we are dealing with a plane wave which at some instant of time has the form $\psi = A \sin 2\pi\, x/\lambda$. We shall interpret the square of this function as being proportional to the probability of finding one of the particles being described. ψ^2 is a probability density, and $\psi^2\, dv$ is the probability of finding a particle in the volume element dv. In this sense the wave function plays a part similar to electromagnetic fields in determining the distribution of mass or energy in space.

Wave functions are often complex functions; that is, they are written in terms of real and imaginary parts. We shall, however, confine ourselves to real functions, and in the main to the simple periodic functions with which we are already familiar. Also, it is possible to describe the flow of matter in a ψ field just as we described the flow of energy in the electromagnetic field in terms of the Poynting vector. An attempt to do so, however, would take us farther into the mathematical theory than seems expedient at this stage.

12.2 STANDING WAVES

A new aspect of ψ waves is manifested when we consider confined, or standing waves, rather than traveling waves. Let us consider a particle confined to a long narrow tube of length L_x, with one end at the origin of a coordinate system, and the other end at a point $X = L_x$. This we shall presume to be a mechanical system like an atom, in which we cannot observe the motion of the particle as a function of time. We therefore cannot apply Newtonian mechanics as we would, for example, to the motion of the earth around the sun. In the case of large bodies,

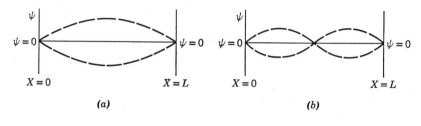

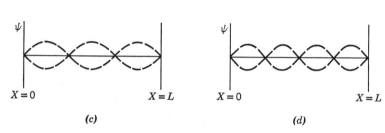

Fig. 12.1.   Standing ψ waves.

we can specify their position and velocities at some initial time and predict the future positions by applying Newton's laws of motion. For an atom we cannot do this, and attempts to build up hypothetical models along these lines did not prove useful. We shall now consider an entirely new approach involving wave functions. We shall make one assumption about these wave functions, namely, that they must be continuous. We shall assume that, like electric or magnetic fields, they vary smoothly from point to point.

If we know that the particle is in our tube, and that the wave function ψ which we use to describe the particle must be zero wherever the particle cannot be, we must conclude that, outside of the tube, $\psi = 0$, as shown in Fig. 12.1a. If the wave function is to be continuous, then it must be zero for $X = 0$ and $X = L_x$. The simplest sort of function satisfying this condition would be a sine wave with $L_x = \lambda/2$. Other possible forms would be waves having shorter wavelengths. In b the length L_x is two half wavelengths. In c and d L_x is three and four half wavelengths. In general we may put

$$L_x = s_x \frac{\lambda}{2} \quad \text{or} \quad \lambda = \frac{2L_x}{s_x} \tag{12.1}$$

where s_x may be any integer but not zero. If s_x were zero, then ψ would have to be constant, and the only constant value of ψ consistent with our boundary conditions is $\psi = 0$, which means that no particle is in the tube, and therefore is not a solution of our problem.

This sort of discussion of standing waves would hardly be worth repeating were it not for the fact that, when we are dealing with ψ waves rather than electromagnetic waves, or acoustic waves, some entirely new conclusions must be drawn. The ψ waves tell us something about a particle which we cannot see. In the first place they specify its energy. If $\lambda = h/mv$, then, since $mv = [2m(\frac{1}{2}mv^2)]^{\frac{1}{2}}$, or $mv = (2mE)^{\frac{1}{2}}$, we have

$$\lambda = \frac{h}{\sqrt{2mE}} \tag{12.2}$$

Combining Eqs. 12.1 and 12.2, we have

$$\lambda = \frac{2L_x}{s_x} = \frac{h}{\sqrt{2mE}}$$

$$E = \frac{h^2}{8mL_x^2} s_x^2 \tag{12.3}$$

The various possible wave forms shown in Fig. 12.1 are called states of the system. With each one is associated an energy. For these waves, in contrast to those we are used to, the energy is given not by their amplitude but by their wavelength. The energies of the four states of the system shown in Fig. 12.1 may be computed from the mass of the particle and the length of the tube in which it is confined, and the values of s_x in Eq. 12.3 equal to 1, 2, 3, and 4.

Notice that, according to wave mechanics, the particle we are discussing has only certain definite energies, and that zero kinetic energy is not one of these allowed energies. The particle cannot come to rest. There is a lowest possible energy and a lowest possible velocity. Since we think of atoms as small solar systems whose size is determined by the motion of the electrons, is there in this inability of the electron to come to rest a clue as to why atoms do not collapse as a result of the slowing down of the electrons in their orbital motions?

Before concluding this introductory discussion we shall make a few additional points concerning possible conclusions. The first of these deals with the magnitude of the parameter $h^2/8mL^2$ of Eq. 12.3, which we shall call E_0. This determines the order of magnitude of the energy intervals of our system. Expressed in electron volts, we have

$$E_0 = \frac{h^2}{8mL^2} \frac{1}{e} = \frac{3.4 \times 10^{-49}}{mL^2} \text{ ev}$$

For a particle having the mass of an electron confined to a box of the order of atomic dimensions, or $L \simeq 2 \times 10^{-10}$ meters, we get $E_0 \simeq 10$ electron volts. This is actually the order of magnitude of the energies involved in atomic interactions and is physically determined by these two parameters m and L. For protons and neutrons confined to regions of nuclear dimensions, on the other hand, we find, for $m = M_p$ and $L \simeq 4 \times 10^{-15}$ meters, that $E_0 \simeq 10$ Mev. This again is just the order of magnitude of the energies involved in nuclear interactions and again is determined by the wave nature of particles, the mass of the particles, and the dimensions of the region to which they are confined. The size of the region to which a wave is confined determines the spacing of the energy levels, and the spacing predicted by these simple considerations is the spacing actually found in atoms and nuclei. Furthermore, if only certain definite energies of our system are possible, this fact must mean that it cannot get rid of arbitrarily small amounts of energy. It must get rid of certain definite amounts or not change its state at all. If we anticipate what this must mean in connection with the process of radiation, is there here perhaps a first clue concerning the quanta of electromagnetic energy which we have had to postulate to explain many of the experimentally observed aspects of the interaction of light and matter?

One point which we have glossed over and should explain at this stage of our discussion relates to the amplitude of the ψ wave. If the energy is determined by the wavelength and not by the amplitude, what physical significance has the amplitude? To understand this, we return to our assumption that $\psi^2 \, dv$, or, in our case, if A is the area of the tube, $\psi^2 \, A \, dx$, represents the probability of finding the particle in a range between x and $x + dx$ of the tube. Then if we know that the particle is in the tube we must have the probability of finding the particle somewhere in the tube equal to unity, or

$$\int_0^{L_x} \psi^2 A \, dx = 1 \qquad\qquad (12.4)$$

This determines the amplitude of ψ. If, for example, $\psi = \psi_0 \sin \dfrac{2\pi x}{\lambda}$, and we are dealing with the state $s_x = 1$, so that $\lambda = 2L_x$, we have

$$\int_0^{L_x} \psi_0{}^2 \sin^2 \frac{\pi x}{L_x} \, dx = 1$$

The value of the left-hand side of this equation depends on the amplitude ψ_0 of the wave function. We must choose this amplitude so that the value of the integral is unity. Having done so, we can use the adjusted wave function to compute the probability of finding the particle in any part of the tube. The process of adjusting the amplitude of the wave function so that the probability of finding the particle being described somewhere in the allowed space is unity is called *normalizing* the wave function.

12.3 CIRCULAR ORBITS

The straight tube we have discussed above becomes much like a circular orbit if we simply bend the tube into a circle of radius r. If the wave function is to fit into the circular orbit smoothly, we must demand that the circumference, $2\pi r$, should be some integral number of wavelengths. Half-integral numbers of wavelengths could be made to fit without producing a discontinuity in ψ but would give rise to a kink at the joining point, which must be excluded. In fact, even the sharp kinks which we have allowed at the boundaries $x = 0$ and $x = L_x$ in Fig. 12.1 are to be considered with a certain skepticism. We shall return to them in the next section. We conclude then that for circular orbits we should expect that

$$j\lambda = 2\pi r$$

where j must be some integer. If, now, we use the expression for the wavelength of the particle moving in the circular orbit as specified by previous diffraction experiments, we get

$$\lambda = h/mv = \frac{2\pi r}{j}$$

$$(mv)r = j\frac{h}{2\pi} \tag{12.5}$$

The left-hand side of our expression is, in fact, the angular momentum of our circulating particle. It is quantized and is always some integral multiple of $h/2\pi$. This begins to reproduce the experimental results summarized in Section 11.5 of the previous chapter; however, we have not yet a complete basis for understanding those results. We have not yet discovered how half-units of the basic $h/2\pi$ of angular momentum arise.

An example of the application of this result is a rigid rotator, like a diatomic molecule. If the moment of inertia of the molecule is I, then its angular momentum is $I\omega = jh/2\pi$. Its energy is

$$E = \tfrac{1}{2}I\omega^2 = \frac{(I\omega)^2}{2I} = \frac{j^2}{2I}\left(\frac{h}{2\pi}\right)^2 \tag{12.6}$$

The energy of the rigid rotator is quantized. As with the particle in a straight tube, the energy of the various levels is proportional to the squares of the integers starting with 1. The lowest energy level for the straight path was

$$\frac{h^2}{8mL_x{}^2}$$

For the rotator it is

$$\frac{h^2}{8\pi^2 I}$$

where I is the moment of inertia.

In order to understand these problems more completely, we must set up some more adequate way of studying our ψ waves in detail. This is provided by the Schroedinger wave equation, which plays a fundamental part in wave mechanics.

12.4 THE SCHROEDINGER EQUATION

Before taking up the wave equation for particles, let us review the wave equation for a stretched string, with special reference to the description of standing waves. We had, for a plane wave, for example, with a displacement in the direction of the y axis and traveling in the direction of the x axis

$$\frac{\partial^2 Y(x, t)}{\partial x^2} = \frac{1}{v^2} \frac{\partial^2 Y(x, t)}{\partial t^2} \tag{12.7}$$

where v is the velocity of propagation of the wave along the string. The general solution of this equation may be expressed as the product of two functions, one containing the space variable x only and the other the time variable t only. For the periodic oscillations in which we are interested the time variation may be written in the form sin $(2\pi ft + \alpha)$. Thus, if we substitute

$$Y(x, t) = Y(x) \sin (2\pi ft + \alpha)$$

into Eq. 12.7, we get

$$\sin (2\pi ft + \alpha) \frac{d^2 Y(x)}{dx^2} = - \left(\frac{2\pi f}{v}\right)^2 Y(x) \sin (2\pi ft + \alpha)$$

or simply

$$\frac{d^2 Y(x)}{dx^2} = - \left(\frac{2\pi f}{v}\right)^2 Y(x)$$

$$= - \left(\frac{2\pi}{\lambda}\right)^2 Y(x) \tag{12.8}$$

This is the equation whose solutions give the amplitude of the standing wave at any point along the string.

Similarly for any electromagnetic wave in space we might write an equation to be satisfied by the electric or the magnetic field. If we limit ourselves to a one-dimensional wave the formulas would be identical. For a three-dimensional field, the equation to be satisfied by a standing magnetic wave would be

$$\frac{\partial^2 H}{\partial x^2} + \frac{\partial^2 H}{\partial y^2} + \frac{\partial^2 H}{\partial z^2} = - \left(\frac{2\pi}{\lambda}\right)^2 H$$

or, in the usual shorthand,

$$\nabla^2 H + \left(\frac{2\pi}{\lambda}\right)^2 H = 0 \tag{12.9}$$

The form of the solutions of this equation depends on the boundary conditions. If these are, for example, to make $H = 0$ on the surface of a cube with sides perpendicular to the x, y, and z axes, the solutions will be simple periodic functions of these variables. If, on the other hand, the boundary conditions fix the value of the function over some other surface, a cylinder with square ends, for example, then other less familiar functions will constitute the desired solution. To return for the moment to our acoustic standing wave problem, the standing waves in a string, or of a square stretched membrane, can be expressed in terms of sine and cosine functions, but the standing waves of a circular stretched membrane cannot. They require other functions with which, however, we shall not further concern ourselves at this point.

We now turn to the wave equation governing the standing waves of the ψ function. We may expect this to be of the form

$$\nabla^2 \psi + \left(\frac{2\pi}{\lambda}\right)^2 \psi = 0 \tag{12.10}$$

This is a promising form for our wave equation since we have already learned how to specify the wavelength λ of the wave function describing a particle with given momentum. As an electron or other particle moves about in a field of force its velocity, and therefore also its momentum and wavelength, must be expected to change. The sort of problem which we shall want to solve is that of an electron moving about with some given total energy E in a field of force, for example, the Coulomb field of the nucleus. This field of force may be specified by the potential energy V of the electron at every point. For a Coulomb law of force we have

$$V = \frac{1}{4\pi\epsilon_0} \frac{e^2}{r}$$

For some other law of force we should have some other form for V. Notice that here V is not a potential, expressed in volts, but a potential energy, expressed in joules. The momentum, and consequently also the wavelength of the particle we are dealing with, can be described in terms of its total energy E and its potential energy V. In the range of velocities for which the Newtonian expression for the kinetic energy is valid, we have

$$\text{Kinetic energy} = \tfrac{1}{2}mv^2 = E - V$$

and consequently the momentum is

$$mv = \sqrt{2m \cdot \tfrac{1}{2}mv^2} = \sqrt{2m(E - V)}$$

or

$$\lambda = \frac{h}{mv} = \frac{h}{\sqrt{2m(E - V)}} \tag{12.11}$$

A possible form for the wave equation would therefore be obtained through substituting Eq. 12.11 into Eq. 12.10 giving

$$\nabla^2\psi + \frac{8\pi^2 m}{h^2}(E - V)\psi = 0 \qquad\qquad \blacktriangleright(12.12)\blacktriangleleft$$

This is, in fact, the famous Schroedinger wave equation for the ψ function describing a particle of mass m in a field of force defined by the potential energy function V.

The above discussion does not constitute a "derivation" of the Schroedinger equation. It merely shows that this wave equation is quite consistent with any wave equation in which the wavelength is specified by Eq. 12.11. In a more advanced presentation of the subject we might start by formulating certain basic general propositions from which the means of solving special problems can be derived. Thus, for Newtonian mechanics Newton's laws of motion constitute these basic propositions, or for electromagnetic theory, it is Maxwell's equations which must always be satisfied, and the electromagnetic wave equations may be derived from these. There are also certain fundamental well-established postulates of quantum mechanics from which the Schroedinger equation may be derived. At this point, however, we shall merely state that it is useful and correct, apart from relativistic effects which it does not take into account. The solution of the Schroedinger equation for a cubical box is given below.

12.5 WAVES IN A BOX

As we have already implied, one of the most important consequences of the adoption of a wave function in describing a particle is the insight which this gives us into the structure of atoms and nuclei. The particles confined in atoms and nuclei are described by particular wave functions describing characteristic modes of motion just as the fundamental and harmonics of a stringed instrument describe it. The details of this description depend on precisely how the particles are held together just as the natural frequencies and tone quality of a horn, or violin, or double bass, depend on its shape and construction.

The simplest problem occurring in nature which we might hope to solve using Eq. 12.12 is the hydrogen atom, consisting of a single electron held by the Coulomb attractive force of a proton. It turns out that even this simple problem involves mathematics with which the student at this stage is unfamiliar. We shall therefore take up an artificial problem whose solution is mathematically simple: that of a particle of mass m and total energy E in a box having the shape of a cube. Though we cannot expect the solutions of this problem to reproduce atomic or nuclear properties in detail, we shall find certain general similarities. In particular we shall be able to understand the effect of the size of the box on the spacing of energy levels and, consequently, some of the differences to be expected between the properties of atoms and the properties of nuclei, already indicated by the discussion of Section 12.2.

The box within which we propose to confine our particle will have edges of length L_x, L_y, and L_z. Corners of the box are located at the origin, at the point $x = L_x, y = 0, z = 0$; $x = 0, y = L_y, z = 0$, etc. In the box the particle is subject to no force, and we may therefore choose the potential energy $V = 0$ inside the box. We shall specify that the particle is always necessarily inside the box by stipulating that its potential energy at all points outside the box is infinite. In other words, since an infinite amount of work must be done in removing the particle from the box, it must necessarily remain inside the box. We have then, within the box

$$0 < x < L_x$$
$$0 < y < L_y$$
$$0 < z < L_z$$
$$V = 0$$

$$\nabla^2\psi = \frac{\partial^2\psi}{\partial x^2} + \frac{\partial^2\psi}{\partial y^2} + \frac{\partial^2\psi}{\partial z^2} = -\frac{8\pi^2 m}{h^2}E\psi \qquad (12.13)$$

and, for points on the surface and outside of the box, $V = \infty$ and therefore $\psi = 0$.

The solution of this problem requires us to find functions $\psi(x, y, z)$ which satisfy Eq. 12.13, for points within the box, and which satisfy the boundary conditions that $\psi = 0$ for $x = 0$ or L_x, for $y = 0$ or L_y, and for $z = 0$ or L_z. The solutions of Eq. 12.13 are products of sine or cosine functions. If the functions are to vanish for $x = 0$, $y = 0$, or $z = 0$, we are restricted to sine functions. If they are also to vanish for $x = L_x$, $y = L_y$, or $z = L_z$, then they must have the form

$$\psi = A \sin \frac{s_x \pi x}{L_x} \sin \frac{s_y \pi y}{L_y} \sin \frac{s_z \pi z}{L_z} \qquad (12.14)$$

where s_x, s_y, and s_z are any positive integers. By substituting Eq. 12.14 into Eq. 12.12 we find that these are in fact solutions if the energy E has certain special values. For other values of E, no solutions exist. We have, for example

$$\frac{\partial^2 \psi}{\partial x^2} = - A \left(\frac{s_x \pi}{L_x}\right)^2 \sin \frac{s_x \pi x}{L_x} \sin \frac{s_y \pi y}{L_y} \sin \frac{s_z \pi z}{L_z} = - \left(\frac{s_x \pi}{L_x}\right)^2 \psi$$

Substituting this and corresponding expressions for the y and z coordinates and canceling ψ from both sides of the equation, we have

$$E = \frac{h^2}{8m} \left(\frac{s_x{}^2}{L_x{}^2} + \frac{s_y{}^2}{L_y{}^2} + \frac{s_z{}^2}{L_z{}^2}\right) \qquad (12.15)$$

If the box is cubic, $L_x = L_y = L_z$, and the energy has the simpler form

$$E = \frac{h^2}{8mL^2} (s_x{}^2 + s_y{}^2 + s_z{}^2) \qquad (12.16)$$

The wave equation and the boundary conditions are satisfied by the functions in Eq. 12.14. The particle in the box can exist only in certain discrete states given by this function with positive integral values of the constants s_x, s_y, and s_z. The energy of the particle in any one of these states is given by Eq. 12.15. The arbitrary constant A is not important in this discussion. It may, however, be evaluated through integrating ψ^2 over the volume of the box. The first four x components of the wave function are those shown in Fig. 12.1. They vanish, as required, for $x = 0$ and $x = L$. As we shall see, the properties of the particle in the box are determined by the wave function. We shall concentrate first on a discussion of the allowed energies in Eq. 12.16 and return to a discussion of wave functions further on.

The characteristic and qualitatively new result brought about by the wave mechanical description of a mechanical system is that it can exist in only certain discrete states. In the problem under discussion these states are given by the set of numbers s_x, s_y, s_z. The various possible different sets of numbers, and the energy of the system for each such

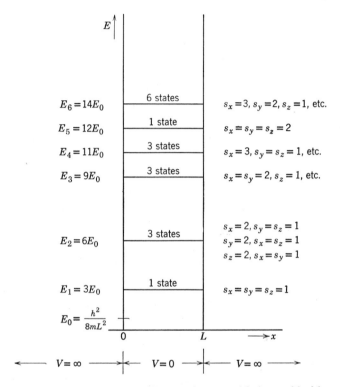

FIG. 12.2. The energy level diagram for a particle in a cubical box.

state, are listed in Table 12.1. For the sake of brevity the symbol E_0 is used to designate $h^2/8mL^2$ throughout. These energies are plotted in an energy level diagram in Fig. 12.2. Such diagrams are characteristic of atomic systems. The detail of the diagram depends on the precise way that the particle is confined. For the cubical box under discussion, we see that certain groups of states have the same energy. Three different states, for example, have the energy $6E_0$. Such states are called "degenerate." It is easy to see that the degeneracy of these states is removed if the lengths L_x, L_y, and L_z of the sides of the box in the x, y, and z directions are not equal.

An important point which we wish to make about the wave aspect of particles is illustrated by the change which is brought about in the

TABLE 12.1   THE STATES AND ENERGIES OF A PARTICLE
IN A CUBICAL BOX

s_x	s_y	s_z	E	s_x	s_y	s_z	E
1	1	1	$3E_0$	2	2	2	$12E_0$
2	1	1		3	2	1	
1	2	1	$6E_0$	3	1	2	
1	1	2		2	3	1	$14E_0$
2	2	1		1	3	2	
2	1	2	$9E_0$	2	1	3	
1	2	2		1	2	3	
3	1	1					
1	3	1	$11E_0$				
1	1	3					

previously discussed problem if we stipulate that the potential outside
of the box is not infinite but has some finite magnitude V_0.

The general rule to be satisfied by the solutions of the wave equation
is that, if we can solve it separately for two regions, then the solution
of the complete problem is obtained through matching the wave functions in the two regions so that at the boundary the function and its
first derivative are continuous. Now we have shown that the solution
of the wave equation in the box where $V = 0$ consists of periodic functions of arbitrary wavelength and amplitude. In the region where
$V = V_0$ the Schroedinger equation has the form

$$\frac{\partial^2 \psi}{\partial x^2} = - \frac{8\pi^2 m}{h^2}(E - V_0)\psi \tag{12.17}$$

Solutions for which E is greater than V_0 represent states in which the
particle can escape from the box. Only if the total energy E is less than
V_0 will the particle be bound. But when E is less than V_0, the right
side of the equation will be positive and our equation has the form

$$\frac{\partial^2 \psi}{\partial x^2} = + \text{constant } \psi$$

This equation is not satisfied by a periodic function. However, we
have encountered it before in our discussion of the propagation of waves
in cables at the end of Section 8.3. If the right side of Eq. 12.17 is
positive, the solution has the form of an exponential. We have, now,
the means for obtaining a complete solution. Inside the well the solutions are periodic functions. Outside the well they are exponentials.
These solutions can be fitted together in such a way that they form a

smooth curve, as shown in Fig. 12.3. Although the mathematics is considerably more complicated than in the case of infinite potential walls, solutions for the complete problem can be found corresponding to energies of the particle below V_0. The particle has not enough kinetic energy to break through the box and get out. However, and this is the crucial point, there is a penetration of the particle into the forbidden

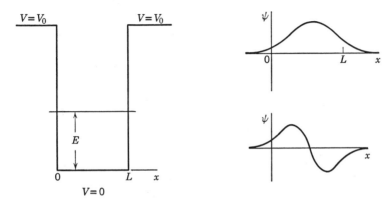

FIG. 12.3. Particle in a potential energy well having a finite depth.

region in which the total energy is less than the potential energy. In Newtonian mechanics a particle can never reach such a point. It is typical of wave mechanics that this limitation is no longer strictly true. There is a fuzziness about the region of space in which a particle can exist. Only for an infinite jump in potential energy is this boundary sharp. For finite boundaries the wave function can penetrate slightly into the classically forbidden region. For a further discussion of this situation, see Problem 10 at the end of this chapter.

12.6 THE UNCERTAINTY PRINCIPLE

Classical Newtonian mechanics leads to the conclusion that from a knowledge of the condition of a mechanical system at some one time we can accurately predict its later behavior. The usefulness of this conclusion depends on our ability to observe the functioning of the system *without disturbing it*. Thus if we can discover the positions and velocities of two suns circling around each other at some one time we can predict their future motion.

When we come to very small objects, objects like atoms and electrons too small for us to see, we must reconsider the above propositions. How shall we observe the position and velocity of such particles? If we shine a light on the particle, as we would on a macroscopic object to measure its position and velocity, we must remember that, in a collision between a light quantum and a particle, the motion of the particle is disturbed. We saw that quanta having short wavelengths will, in a collision, impart velocities comparable to the velocity of light to an electron. If we use long wavelengths, on the other hand, though we do not so violently disturb the motion of the particle we are observing we are lessening the information we can acquire about its position. There seem to be definite limits to what we can measure concerning atomic systems, limits set not by the perfection of the instruments used but by the means available to us for making observations.

Out of a study of this situation has come a new principle of physics, called the "uncertainty principle," or "principle of indeterminacy." It is generally associated with the name of Werner Heisenberg, the man who first enunciated it. It states that certain pairs of variables defining a mechanical system cannot simultaneously be measured with arbitrary accuracy. In fact, it goes farther and specifies the limit of the attainable accuracy. We shall discuss this principle for a particular pair of variables, the x coordinate and the momentum of a particle moving in the x direction.

We saw in Chapter 10 that the wave aspect of light set a limit to the detailed knowledge about external objects that could be acquired by studying their images. Since matter itself must be described in terms of waves, we may expect the wavelength involved to set a limit on our knowledge of the position of a particle. If, for example, an electron is caught by an atom having a diameter of about 10^{-8} cm, then its wavelength must be of this order of magnitude and the uncertainty in our knowledge of the x component of its position, Δx, will be of this order of magnitude. But from our basic definition of λ we have

$$\lambda = \frac{h}{mv} \leqslant \Delta x$$

or, in words, the uncertainty in our knowledge of the position of the particle must be greater than h/mv. But the particle is bouncing around in the atom and changing the direction of its motion all the time. By rewriting the above equation we may conclude that the uncertainty regarding the x component of its momentum Δp_x must be

$$\Delta p_x \geqslant \frac{h}{\Delta x}$$

or finally

$$\Delta p_x \cdot \Delta x \geqslant h \tag{12.18}$$

This is the formulation of the Heisenberg uncertainty principle for the variables x and p_x. We cannot know both simultaneously with arbitrary accuracy. If we measure the position more and more accurately, the uncertainty in our knowledge of the momentum will increase. If we measure the momentum more and more accurately, the uncertainty in our knowledge of its position will increase.

Another pair of variables that cannot be measured simultaneously with arbitrary accuracy are energy and time. The uncertainty principle says that

$$\Delta E \cdot \Delta t \geqslant h \tag{12.19}$$

meaning that, if we would specify the energy of a mechanical system within some interval of time Δt, then there is a limit to the exactness with which we can specify the energy, and the uncertainty in the energy ΔE may be computed from Eq. 12.19. The meaning of this relation is perhaps more understandable if we consider a measurement of the energy of light quanta whose energy in $E = hf$. Equation 12.19 may be expressed in the form

$$\Delta f \, \Delta t \geqslant 1$$

Planck's constant has been canceled out, and we may expect to be able to interpret this statement from a classical point of view. If we observe a gas radiating the frequency being investigated for a time Δt, then there is this much uncertainty about the time at which the radiating atoms were actually emitting. But, if this time interval Δt is of the order of magnitude required for one cycle to pass, then we cannot measure the frequency to much better than one cycle. If on the other hand Δt is long enough for a million cycles to pass, then we can measure the frequency to about a millionth of a cycle. The greater the time interval Δt, the smaller the uncertainty Δf.

Just as the resolving power of an optical instrument is a most useful concept in establishing the limit of what we can reveal about our surroundings by forming images of these surroundings, so the uncertainty principle is most useful in setting a limit to what we can know and predict about the submicroscopic world.

SUMMARY

The motion of particles may be described by wave functions. A wave function ψ, describing the motion of a particle, has the property that, for the wave functions we are concerned with, $\psi^2 \, dv$ represents the probability that the particle being described is within the volume element dv. For standing waves describing steady states, the wave function of a particle of mass m in a field of force such that its potential energy is V must satisfy Schroedinger's equation

$$\nabla^2\psi + \frac{8\pi^2 m}{h^2}(E - V)\psi = 0$$

Schroedinger's equation for particles in a box leads to certain discrete possible values for the energy of the particle. To each of these characteristic energies one or more wave functions correspond. In general, wave functions are not completely confined to the interior of the box but penetrate into the barrier constituting the walls of the box.

Wave mechanics specifies that the orbital angular momentum of a particle always is some integral multiple of $h/2\pi$.

The wave aspect of matter implies certain limitations on our knowledge of atomic systems. These limitations are embodied in Heisenberg's uncertainty principle stating that the uncertainty in our measurement of certain pairs of quantities must necessarily be greater than h. One pair of such quantities is the x coordinates and the x component of the momentum. If Δx and Δp_x represent the uncertainty in our measurements of these quantities, Heisenberg's principle states that

$$\Delta x \cdot \Delta p_x \geqslant h$$

PROBLEMS

1. What is the complete normalized wave function for the particle moving in a tube of length L discussed in Section 12.2?

2. The wavelength of a free particle is given by

$$\lambda = h/mv = h/\sqrt{2m(E - V)}$$

The particle moves from a region of space where $V = V_1$ into another where $V = V_2$, V_1 and V_2 being constant within the two regions. How does the wavelength change when the particle crosses the boundary between the two regions? What does this mean in connection with the classical kinetic energy of the particle?

3. A hydrogen molecule may be approximately described as a rigid body consisting of two hydrogen atoms rigidly held at a distance 10^{-10} meter apart. What is the moment of inertia of this molecule about an axis through its center and perpendicular to the line joining the two atoms? What is the kinetic energy of rotation of such a molecule in its four lowest states of rotation? How does this compare with $\frac{3}{2}kT$, the average translational kinetic energy of molecules of a gas at room temperature? What range of rotational energy levels would you expect to find occupied at room temperature, and at 10° absolute?

4. Find the solutions of Schroedinger's equation for a particle in a cubical box having an edge length L if the box has its center at the origin of coordinates.

5. What are the lowest three energy levels for a particle of mass m in an impenetrable cubical box whose side is L for the following cases: (a) A neutron for $L = 10^{-13}$ cm. (b) A neutron for $L = 10^{-12}$ cm. (c) An electron for $L = 10^{-12}$ cm. (d) An

electron for $L = 10^{-8}$ cm. (e) An electron for $L = 10^{-2}$ cm. Give your answers in electron volts.

6. Solve the problem of a particle in a rectangular box whose sides have the different lengths L_x, L_y, L_z. What are the degeneracies of the lowest six energy levels if $L_x = L_0$, $L_y = 2L_0$, $L_z = 3L_0$?

7. (a) A particle of mass m is confined in a cubical box of length L whose sides are perpendicular to the axes of a rectangular coordinate system. Make a table of λ_x, λ_y, and λ_z, the wavelengths associated with the motion of the particle in the x, y, and z directions, for the four different stationary states of motion having the least energy.

(b) Show how, starting from the experimentally established relation between wavelength and momentum, $\lambda = h/mv$, the energy of the four states in part a may be computed, and compute the above energies in electron volts for a particle of mass $m = 9.1 \times 10^{-31}$ kg in a box for which $L = 2 \times 10^{-10}$ meter.

8. A 60 cycle/sec voltage is applied to the vertical deflector plates of an oscilloscope for 0.1 sec. The horizontal plates are connected to a linear sweep having a repetition rate of five sweeps per second. Make a sketch of what a photograph of the resulting trace would look like. Assuming that you can measure the location of a peak to approximately $\pm$ a quarter of the distance between peaks, what is the fractional uncertainty in your measurement of the applied frequency? What is the magnitude of the uncertainty Δf of your determination of f? If the frequency f had been applied for 10 sec and a moving picture of the trace had been provided for detailed examination, what then would have been the uncertainty Δf in the measurement of f?

★9. A particle of mass m which can move along the x axis only is attracted to the origin by a force such that the potential energy of the particle is $V = \frac{1}{2}kx^2$. If the motion of the particle is calculated according to Newton's laws, one finds that the particle is subject to a force $F = -kx$, and that it performs simple harmonic oscillations about the origin. (a) If the total energy of the particle is E, what is the maximum possible distance X_0 of the particle from the origin?

If the motion of the above particle is calculated by use of Schroedinger's equation

$$\frac{d^2\psi}{dx^2} + \frac{8\pi^2 m}{h^2}(E - V)\psi = 0 \tag{I}$$

its wave function in the ground state is

$$\psi = A e^{-(x/a_0)^2} \tag{II}$$

(b) For what value of a_0 is Eq. II a solution of Eq. I?

(c) What is the value of the normalizing constant A?

(d) What is the energy E of the particle when it is in the state shown in Eq. II? According to Eq. II, the wave function approaches zero rapidly when x/a_0 is greater than 1, and a_0 therefore plays a part in wave mechanics comparable to X_0 in classical Newtonian mechanics. (e) Express both X_0 and a_0 as functions of E and k only, and show that the ratio $X_0/a_0 = 1/\sqrt{2}$.

★10. A particle of mass m is confined to a square potential energy well, illustrated in Fig. 12.4. Its total energy E is therefore less than V_0. Find solutions of the wave equation which are continuous, and have continuous derivatives, at the boundaries $x = a$ and $x = -a$ for the following values of the depth of the well:

$$V_0 = \frac{h^2}{8\pi^2 ma^2}, \qquad 4\frac{h^2}{8\pi^2 ma^2}, \qquad \text{and} \quad 12\frac{h^2}{8\pi^2 ma^2}$$

The solutions for the three regions of space are, for $-a < x < a$,

$$\psi(x) = A \sin \alpha x + B \cos \alpha x \qquad \text{where } \alpha = \sqrt{\frac{8\pi^2 mE}{h^2}}$$

for $x > a$,

$$\psi(x) = Ce^{-\beta x}$$

and, for $x < -a$,

$$\psi(x) = De^{\beta x} \qquad \text{where } \beta = \sqrt{\frac{8\pi^3 m(V_0 - E)}{h^2}}$$

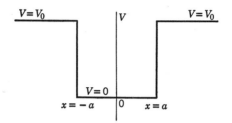

FIG. 12.4.

A, B, C, and D are arbitrary constants. Solutions will be found to be of two kinds:
1. $A = 0$, $C = D$, and then $\alpha \tan \alpha a = \beta$.
2. $B = 0$, $C = -D$, and then $\alpha \cot \alpha a = -\beta$.

Numerical values are best found graphically. Schiff* suggests changing variables to $\xi = \alpha a$, $\eta = \beta a$, and plotting ξ as a function of η in accordance with Eqs. 1 and 2 above, and finding the intersections of these curves with

$$\xi^2 + \eta^2 = \frac{8\pi^2 mV_0 a^2}{h^2}$$

which satisfy the definitions of α and β above.

*L. I. Schiff, *Quantum Mechanics*, p. 37, McGraw-Hill Book Co., 1949.

CHAPTER **13**

Atoms and Electrons

13.1 THE HYDROGEN ATOM AND ITS RADIATIONS

Just as classical Newtonian mechanics provides us with rules for handling macroscopic mechanical problems, so quantum, or wave, mechanics provides us with rules for handling submicroscopic mechanical problems. Let us once more briefly review the formulation of classical mechanics in order to clarify the modifications that are required when we go over to a system for describing invisible atomic particles, in particular, the electron and its motion around the hydrogen nucleus.

Classical mechanics is summarized in Newton's "laws of motion." These have certain consequences that are very generally applicable and that may be very simply expressed. Such consequences are often called principles and may be thought of as underlying the more complex formulation of the laws themselves. Newton's laws of motion are used as follows: given certain material objects having prescribed properties, such as shape, density, elasticity, etc., with given initial positions and velocities, and subjected to given forces, compute the motion. This motion is observable, and the interest and importance of the procedure are that it relates observable quantities, the initial conditions to the subsequent motion. Important aspects of Newton's laws of motion are the principles of conservation of energy and momentum.

What may we expect of atomic mechanics? Fundamentally, to be useful, it must provide us with relationships between observable quantities, but these cannot be "laws of motion" in the Newtonian sense, since these motions are not observable.

To begin with, just as Newtonian mechanics deals with the interaction of objects which are postulated, so quantum mechanics deals with the interaction of "elementary particles" whose attributes must be postulated. In atomic theory these particles are electrons and nuclei, characterized in our previous discussions by mass and charge. We shall see presently that they have important other attributes.

If the energy and momentum of atomic systems are observable, then we should certainly expect the laws of conservation of energy and momentum to hold, but further details about atomic structure must involve a new analysis of the motion of charged particles. This motion must somehow be described in terms of wave functions derived from Schroedinger's equation. An atom will be capable of existing in a series of "states." Each such state will be characterized by a wave function. From the wave function we may expect to calculate the properties of the atom in this state. Particularly, we should be able to compute the energy and the angular momentum.

A most important way of observing the properties of atoms in the various states in which they can exist is to analyze the radiations which they emit. Our first problem in atomic theory will be to account for the spectrum of the radiation of hydrogen atoms. Having done this, we shall have accomplished what we set out to do, namely, to derive or predict observable effects in terms of other observable effects. The starting point of our theory involves electrostatic forces and the wave properties of the electron. These are based on many observations which we have described in detail. The result of our calculations will be the prediction of the optical and other observable properties of matter.

The hydrogen atom consists of a proton and an electron. The proton has so large a mass compared to the electron that we may consider the center of mass of the atom to be at the center of the nucleus. If, then, we put the nucleus at the origin of a coordinate system, and the electron at some distance r from the origin, the force F on the electron will be

$$F = \frac{1}{4\pi\epsilon_0} \frac{e^2}{r^2} \tag{13.1}$$

and the potential enregy V of the system will be

$$V = \frac{-1}{4\pi\epsilon_0} \frac{e^2}{r} \tag{13.2}$$

Since the force between proton and electron is attractive, work must be done in separating them, and, therefore, if we agree to designate the potential energy for infinite separation zero, we must have negative potential energies for finite separations.

To this, we must add the fact that the wave function of the electron must satisfy Schroedinger's wave equation, which for a hydrogen atom with the potential energy function of Eq. 13.2 is

$$\nabla^2\psi + \frac{8\pi^2 m}{h^2}\left(E + \frac{1}{4\pi\epsilon_0}\frac{e^2}{r}\right)\psi = 0 \tag{13.3}$$

The usual analysis of this equation is beyond the scope of our present discussion. However, the most important results can be discussed in very simple terms. In the first place, we must demand of a solution of Eq. 13.3 describing a hydrogen atom a wave function which is different from zero only in the vicinity of the origin, where the attracting proton is located. Wave functions having finite values at remote points must be representations of an ionized hydrogen atom, or a free electron far from the proton. Further, the wave function must be such that the probability of finding the electron in the atom is unity, or that

$$\int \psi^2 \, dv = 1 \tag{13.4}$$

the integral being taken over all space. By analogy with the wave mechanical solution of a particle contained in a box, for which the simplest solution shown in the upper right-hand corner of Fig. 12.3 involved a wave function which had a hump in the middle of the box and tapered off toward the sides, we might expect something similar for the electron confined by the field of a proton. The corresponding solution in fact is

$$\psi_1 = A e^{-r/a_0} \tag{13.5}$$

This function has a maximum at the origin and tapers off as the distance r from the proton at the origin increases. The constant A may be chosen so that the integral of Eq. 13.4 is satisfied. The correct value is

$$A = \frac{1}{\sqrt{\pi a_0{}^3}} \tag{13.6}$$

Finally, as may be shown by substitution into Eq. 13.3, the Schroedinger wave equation is satisfied if

$$a_0 = \frac{\epsilon_0 h^2}{\pi m e^2} \tag{13.7}$$

and if the energy E of the system has a particular value, which we call E_1, where

$$E_1 = -\frac{m e^4}{8\epsilon_0{}^2 h^2} \tag{13.8}$$

The detailed calculation of these quantities is given at the end of this section. The wave function ψ_1, and its square, are plotted at the top of Fig. 13.1. There are various points of interest about this solution. The first is that the size of the atom is here specified by the constant a_0. The probability of finding the electron in a small volume element at a distance greater than $2a_0$ is quite negligible. The electron may be thought of as represented in this ground state of hydrogen in terms of a

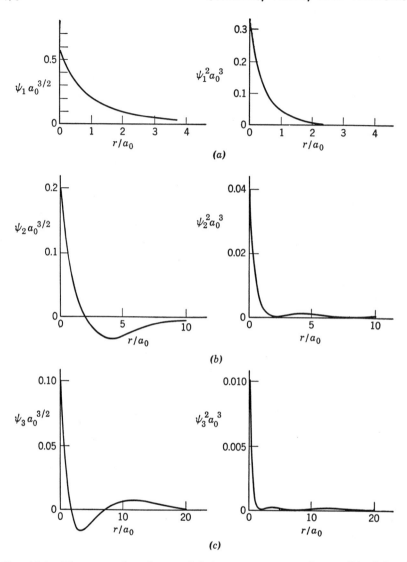

FIG. 13.1.   Three wave functions, and their squares, representing possible states of the hydrogen atom.

spherically symmetrical cloud tapering off from a maximum density at the proton and falling off to zero rapidly at distances greater than a few times a_0.   The magnitude of a_0 may be found through substituting the known constants into Eq. 13.7.   We find

$$a_0 = 0.528 \times 10^{-10} \text{ meter} \tag{13.9}$$

The size of the hydrogen atom is difficult to determine experimentally, but atoms in general are of this magnitude.

Next we come to the energy E_1. Since we have stipulated that the energy of separated electron and proton will be called zero, then it follows that the magnitude of E_1 is just the work required to ionize the hydrogen atom from its ground state. In electron volts, we find upon substituting into Eq. 13.8

$$E_1 = 13.5 \, \text{ev} \tag{13.10}$$

which is the experimental value for this quantity.

In addition to the solution ψ_1 for the ground state of hydrogen, there are many more. Two other particular solutions which depend only on r, and are therefore spherically symmetrical, are

$$\psi_2 = \frac{1}{4} \frac{1}{\sqrt{2\pi a_0^3}} \left(2 - \frac{r}{a_0} \right) e^{-r/2a_0} \tag{13.11}$$

$$\psi_3 = \frac{1}{81} \frac{1}{\sqrt{3\pi a_0^3}} \left(27 - 18 \frac{r}{a_0} + 2 \frac{r^2}{a_0^2} \right) e^{-r/3a_0} \tag{13.12}$$

These wave functions and their squares are plotted in Figs. 13.1b and c. Like ψ_1, they have maxima at the origin, but they change sign. They have additional nodes, just as the wave functions for a particle in a box had additional nodes at higher energies. Notice that, in these states of higher energy, the atom is expanded. There are additional maxima of ψ^2 for larger values of r/a_0.

The value which the energy E must have for these states may be found through substituting into Eq. 13.3. The values are

$$E_2 = -\frac{1}{4} \frac{me^4}{8\epsilon_0^2 h^2} \tag{13.13}$$

and

$$E_3 = -\frac{1}{9} \frac{me^4}{8\epsilon_0^2 h^2} \tag{13.14}$$

A complete analysis of the wave equations shows that there are infinitely many solutions, and that they can all be classified according to a corresponding allowed energy of the atom

$$E_n = -\frac{1}{n^2} \frac{me^4}{8\epsilon_0^2 h^2} \tag{13.15}$$

where n is any integer greater than or equal to unity.

The potential energy of an electron in the field of a proton is plotted

in Fig. 13.2. Since the potential energy for infinite separation is taken
as zero, the attractive forces give rise to a negative value at finite separations. This may be thought of as a potential energy well which con-
fines the electron, much as the walls of the box did in the previous chapter. We should expect the solutions of the Schroedinger equation to
establish certain possible energy levels for the electrons, and one or more

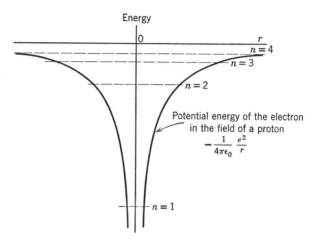

FIG. 13.2.   The energy levels of the hydrogen atom.

wave functions corresponding to each.   The actually found allowed
energy levels are given by Eq. 13.15.   Four of these energy levels are
indicated by dotted lines in Fig. 13.2.   The energy required to remove an
electron from the lowest, or ground state of a hydrogen atom, is E_1, as
given in Eq. 13.8.   The size of the atom in excited states is greater than
in the ground state.   It is shown below that, for the spherically symmetrical states described above, the average value of r is given by the
expression

$$\bar{r}_n = \frac{3a_0}{2} n^2 \tag{13.16}$$

Although the experimental confirmation of the wave mechanical
results obtained above is satisfactory, the overwhelming evidence for
the correctness of our procedures comes from optical considerations.
An atom can exist in any one of many stationary states.   We have
calculated the energies of these states for the hydrogen atom.   In addition, however, an atom can spontaneously make a transition from some
initial state to some final state having a lower energy.   If the numbers n
corresponding to these states are n_i and n_f, the energy lost by the atom

in this transition is $E_{n\ i} - E_{n\ f}$ and this energy is radiated into space as electromagnetic radiation. Since, from Planck's law, the frequency of an electromagnetic quantum having an energy E is hf, we must expect the frequency radiated by an atom in a transition from an initial state designated by n_i to a final state designated by n_f to be

$$hf = E_{n\ i} - E_{n\ f}$$

or, for the hydrogen atom, using Eq. 13.15,

$$f = \frac{me^4}{8\epsilon_0^2 h^3}\left(\frac{1}{n_f^2} - \frac{1}{n_i^2}\right) \tag{13.17}$$

The coefficient above is often written as

$$\frac{me^4}{8\epsilon_0^2 h^3} = Rc \tag{13.18}$$

where R is called Rydberg's constant and c is the velocity of light. In many optical discussions frequencies are replaced by inverse wavelengths, $1/\lambda = f/c$, a quantity proportional to frequency but having dimensions of meter^{-1} or often centimeter^{-1}. The value of the Rydberg constant may be found through substituting the known natural constants. It is

$$R = 1.097 \times 10^7 \text{ meter}^{-1} \tag{13.19}$$

The wavelengths which the hydrogen atom can radiate are then given by

$$\frac{1}{\lambda} = R\left(\frac{1}{n_f^2} - \frac{1}{n_i^2}\right)$$

These wavelengths are grouped in series, depending on the value of n_f. The various possible transitions are shown in Fig. 13.3. All the transitions from excited states to the ground state lead to radiation in the ultraviolet. This series of spectral lines is called the Lyman series, and the radiated wavelengths are given by

$$\text{Lyman series:} \quad \frac{1}{\lambda} = R\left(1 - \frac{1}{n^2}\right) \quad n = 2, 3, 4, \cdots \tag{13.20}$$

Transitions terminating on the first excited level lead to radiation in the visible and ultraviolet. This series of spectral lines is called the Balmer series. The radiated wavelengths are given by

$$\text{Balmer series:} \quad \frac{1}{\lambda} = R\left(\frac{1}{4} - \frac{1}{n^2}\right) \quad n = 3, 4, 5, \cdots \tag{13.21}$$

This part of the spectrum of hydrogen is shown in Fig. 13.3b.

Three other series, terminating on the next higher levels, have also been observed. They are in the infrared. All the observed wavelengths radiated by atomic hydrogen fit into the above description.

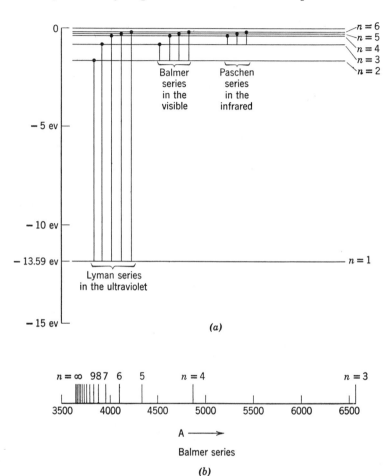

FIG. 13.3. (a) Radiative transitions in the hydrogen atom. (b) The Balmer series.

The Schroedinger Equation for the Hydrogen Atom

We wish to show that the function Ae^{-r/a_0} where A and a_0 are constants is a possible solution of the Schroedinger equation for an electron in the Coulomb field of force of a proton at the origin, as given in Eq. 13.3.

$$\frac{\partial^2 \psi}{\partial x^2} + \frac{\partial^2 \psi}{\partial y^2} + \frac{\partial^2 \psi}{\partial z^2} + \frac{8\pi^2 m}{h^2}\left(E + \frac{1}{4\pi\epsilon_0}\frac{e^2}{r}\right)\psi = 0$$

We have, by simple differentiation,

$$\frac{\partial \psi}{\partial x} = -\frac{1}{a_0}\psi\frac{\partial r}{\partial x}$$

$$\frac{\partial^2 \psi}{\partial x^2} = -\frac{1}{a_0}\psi\frac{\partial^2 r}{\partial x^2} + \frac{1}{a_0^2}\psi\left(\frac{\partial r}{\partial x}\right)^2$$

$$\frac{\partial r}{\partial x} = \frac{x}{r} \qquad \frac{\partial^2 r}{\partial x^2} = \frac{1}{r}\left(1 - \frac{x^2}{r^2}\right)$$

$$\frac{\partial^2 \psi}{\partial x^2} = -\frac{1}{a_0}\frac{1}{r}\left(1 - \frac{x^2}{r^2}\right)\psi + \frac{1}{a_0^2}\frac{x^2}{r^2}\psi$$

$$\frac{\partial^2 \psi}{\partial x^2} + \frac{\partial^2 \psi}{\partial y^2} + \frac{\partial^2 \psi}{\partial z^2} = -\frac{2}{a_0 r}\psi + \frac{1}{a_0^2}\psi$$

On substituting, and combining, we get

$$\left(\frac{8\pi^2 m}{h^2}E + \frac{1}{a_0^2}\right)\psi + \left(-\frac{2}{a_0} + \frac{8\pi^2 m}{h^2}\frac{e^2}{4\pi\epsilon_0}\right)\frac{\psi}{r} = 0$$

Since the equation must be valid for all values of r, we must demand that the constant term, and the coefficient of $1/r$, be each equal to zero. From the first, we find that the energy of the system, E, must have the value

$$E = -\frac{h^2}{8\pi^2 m a_0^2} \tag{13.22}$$

and, from the second, we find that the constant a_0 must satisfy the relation

$$a_0 = \frac{\epsilon_0 h^2}{\pi m e^2} \tag{13.23}$$

or, substituting this value of a_0 into 13.22, that the energy must have the value

$$E = -\frac{m e^4}{8\epsilon_0^2 h^2} \tag{13.24}$$

in agreement with Eq. 13.8.

The magnitude of the constant A in the above expression for the wave function ψ is obtained through "normalizing" the function, or ensuring that

$$\int \psi^2 \, dv$$

over all space is unity. To carry out this integration, we put for dv, our element of volume, the volume of a spherical shell of radius r and thickness dr.

$$dv = 4\pi r^2 \, dr$$

This is acceptable since the wave function we are concerned with is a function of r only and is therefore spherically symmetrical. We have

$$\int \psi^2 \, dv = \int_0^\infty A^2 e^{-2r/a_0} 4\pi r^2 \, dr$$

$$= 4\pi A^2 \int_0^\infty r^2 e^{-2r/a_0} \, dr = 1 \tag{13.25}$$

If we put $x = -2r/a_0$, the expression for $\psi^2 \, dv$ becomes

$$\frac{\pi a_0{}^3}{2} A^2 \int_0^\infty x^2 e^{-x} \, dx = 1$$

This may be evaluated using the general result

$$\int_0^\infty x^n e^{-x} \, dx = n! \tag{13.26}$$

In our case above, $n = 2$, and we get

$$\frac{\pi a_0{}^3}{2} A^2 \cdot 2 = 1$$

$$A = \frac{1}{\sqrt{\pi a_0{}^3}} \tag{13.27}$$

in conformity with Eq. 13.6.

The average value of r for the ground state may be computed from Eq. 13.16 putting $n = 1$. This result follows from the definition of the mean value of r,

$$\bar{r} = \int r\psi^2 \, dv$$

$$= \frac{1}{\pi a_0{}^3} \int_0^\infty r e^{-2r/a_0} 4\pi r^2 \, dr$$

$$= \frac{a_0}{4} \int_0^\infty x^3 e^{-x} \, dx$$

where again $x = 2r/a_0$. The definite integral may be evaluated using Eq. 13.26 with $n = 3$, or $n! = 3 \cdot 2 = 6$. We get for the average value of r

$$\bar{r} = \frac{a_0}{4} \cdot 6 = \frac{3}{2} a_0 \tag{13.28}$$

13.2   THE ANGULAR MOMENTUM OF THE HYDROGEN ATOM

We have shown that there are certain spherically symmetrical wave functions that are solutions of Schroedinger's wave equation. In addition to these, there are many others which are not spherically symmetrical but in which the probability density ψ^2 is concentrated along an axis, or in ring-shaped regions around an axis. A closer study shows that an important basis for classifying these wave functions is according to their angular momentum. It turns out that wave functions describe not only the probability density, but also motion within this "cloud" of probability density. The situation is quite analogous to that which we encountered in describing energy in electric and magnetic fields. The fields determine the energy density in space, but in addition it was found possible to specify the Poynting vector defining certain aspects of the motion of energy in space. Similarly, it is possible to compute not only a probability density from a known wave function but also a flow. In particular, by means which we shall not go into, it is possible to compute the angular momentum associated with a stationary state.

For a hydrogen atom, and also for other atoms, the angular momentum due to the motion of the electrons about their nuclei is specified by a number, called a quantum number l. An atom having a total angular momentum defined by the quantum number l, which is always some integer or zero, can have components along some axis, say along a magnetic field,

$$l\frac{h}{2\pi} \qquad (l-1)\frac{h}{2\pi} \qquad (l-2)\frac{h}{2\pi} \cdots -l\frac{h}{2\pi}$$

The complete description of the orbital angular momentum of an atom requires the specification of two numbers, l and m, where the additional number m specifies the orientation of the atom. The magnetic quantum number, m, satisfies the relation

$$l \geqslant m \geqslant -l \tag{13.29}$$

In this description we are approaching the experimental facts summarized in Section 11.5. In fact, this is exactly equivalent to the situation taken up in Fig. 11.21b for the special case of $l = 1$. In this case m may have the values $+1$, 0, -1, corresponding to three possible orientations of the atom in a field.

The classification of the wave functions of the hydrogen atom now proceeds as follows. We first of all make use of the quantum number n appearing in the energy expression, Eq. 13.15,

$$E_n = -\frac{1}{n^2}\frac{me^4}{8\epsilon_0^2 h^2} \tag{13.30}$$

For $n = 1$ there is only one possible wave function. It is that given in Eq. 13.5 and has zero angular momentum or, in other words, is characterized by the orbital angular momentum quantum number $l = 0$. For $n = 2$, or for the next higher energy level, there are wave functions with two possible values of l, namely, 0 or 1. There are thus one solution for $n = 1$, $l = 0$, and then three solutions with $n = 2$, $l = 1$, the three corresponding to different magnetic quantum numbers $m = \pm 1$, 0. This first excited state, therefore, has a fourfold degeneracy, with four possible different wave functions having the same energy. The next energy level, with $n = 3$, has solutions with $l = 0, 1,$ or 2, or, as shown in Fig. 13.4, a total of nine different possible wave functions. In general it can be shown that all positive values of l are possible up to $n - 1$.

The correct description of the hydrogen atom is somewhat more complicated because the electron itself has been found to have an intrinsic angular momentum of $\frac{1}{2}(h/2\pi)$ of its own. This is called its spin and is often characterized by the quantum number $s = \frac{1}{2}$. At this stage in our study of atoms we must simply accept this as an experimental fact.

	$l = 0$	$l = 1$	$l = 2$	$l = 3$
$n = 4$	1 state $m = 0$	3 states $m = \pm 1, 0$	5 states $m = \pm 2,$ $\pm 1, 0$	7 states $m = \pm 3,$ $\pm 2, \pm 1, 0$
$n = 3$	1 state $m = 0$	3 states $m = \pm 1, 0$	5 states $m = \pm 2,$ $\pm 1, 0$	
$n = 2$	1 state $m = 0$	3 states $m = \pm 1, 0$		
$n = 1$	1 state $m = 0$			

FIG. 13.4. The classification of possible states of the hydrogen atom according to the Schroedinger wave equation.

In any state of motion of the electron in the hydrogen atom, the total angular momentum will be the orbital angular momentum, plus or minus the spin angular momentum. The spin has only two possible orientations. Protons and neutrons also are found to have an intrinsic angular momentum $\frac{1}{2}(h/2\pi)$.

The inclusion of the spin in the description of the degeneracy of the energy levels of the hydrogen atom results in our multiplying the previously obtained degeneracy, shown in Fig. 13.4, by two. The final result is shown in Fig. 13.5.

The lowest level is doubly degenerate. The first excited state has eight different wave functions. The next 18, and so on. These results are fully confirmed by experiments on the Zeeman effect, described in the next section.

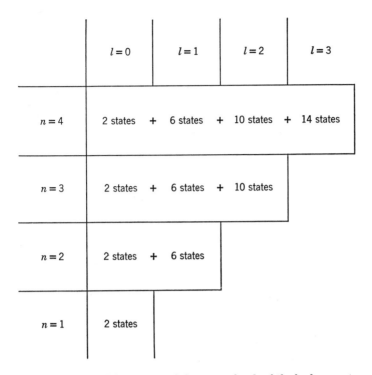

Fig. 13.5. The actual degeneracy of the energy levels of the hydrogen atom.

The Bohr Model of the Hydrogen Atom

Before the advent of wave mechanics Niels Bohr derived an expression for the energy levels of the hydrogen atom in a different way. He assumed that the electron moved around the nucleus in elliptical orbits, just as the planets move around the sun in elliptical orbits. In order to restrict the motion of the electron to a few possible orbits he applied certain quantum conditions which yielded the same expression for the energy levels found in the treatment of Section 13.1. The discussion of these elliptic orbits is not simple, especially if we try to obtain an insight into the degeneracy of the various possible energy levels. Some authors of physics texts have attempted to present the Bohr theory in a considerably oversimplified form. A brief review of this kind of discussion is included here for the benefit of those students who may look up the treatment of the hydrogen atom in other texts.

The assumption is made that we may consider only circular orbits of the electron around the nucleus. In a circular orbit, we must equate the radial acceleration required for circular motion to the electrostatic force between proton and electron.

$$\frac{mv^2}{r} = \frac{1}{4\pi\epsilon_0}\frac{e^2}{r^2} \qquad (13.31)$$

If now we make an additional assumption, that the angular momentum of the electron in its circular orbit must be some integral number of times $h/2\pi$, and if we write for this integer the quantity n (in our previous discussion this was called l), we have

$$mvr = n\frac{h}{2\pi} \qquad (13.32)$$

These equations may be solved for r and v. The results are

$$r = \epsilon_0 \frac{n^2 h^2}{\pi m e^2} = n^2 a_0 \qquad (13.33)$$

$$v = \frac{1}{\epsilon_0} \frac{e^2}{2nh} \qquad (13.34)$$

Here, as above, $a_0 = \epsilon_0 h^2/\pi m e^2$. The radii of the circular orbits are nearly the same as the mean value of r for the spherically symmetrical wave functions. The energy of the system may be computed from the radius and the velocity of the electron.

$$E_{total} = E_{kinetic} + E_{potential}$$

$$= \frac{1}{2} mv^2 - \frac{1}{4\pi\epsilon_0} \frac{e^2}{r} \qquad (13.35)$$

On substituting values of v and r from Eqs. 13.33 and 13.34 into Eq. 13.35, we get the following values for possible energy levels,

$$E_n = -\frac{1}{n^2} \frac{me^4}{8\epsilon_0^2 h^2} \qquad (13.36)$$

in complete agreement with the previously obtained result in Eq. 13.15. Although this treatment gives the correct energy levels, it gives wrong results for the angular momentum. In fact, we have seen that, if n is the quantum number specifying the energy, the maximum possible angular momentum in this state is $(n-1)h/2\pi$. The treatment of the Bohr atom assuming circular orbits therefore leads to conclusions at variance with the facts. We must therefore conclude that circular orbits are inadmissible.

If we drop circular orbits and treat only elliptic orbits using Bohr's methods, we obtain essentially correct results, but the discussion of elliptic orbits is too difficult for us to pursue in detail here.

13.3   ANGULAR MOMENTUM AND THE ZEEMAN EFFECT

The detailed study of energy levels is beyond the scope of the present text. It is found that the energy levels of most atoms have a complex structure. They consist of many levels that are almost, but not quite, degenerate. This comes about as a result of small magnetic interactions which have been neglected. The spinning electron has a magnetic moment. It is a little magnetic dipole. The orbital motion of the electron produces a magnetic field. These interact, and it is only reasonable to expect that the energy when l and s are parallel will be somewhat different from the energy in the corresponding state when l and s are antiparallel. This gives rise to a splitting of energy levels and a corresponding splitting of spectral lines radiated in transitions between these levels.

However, if we focus our attention on a single one of these lines, there is one important characteristic that we may profitably pursue further. The upper state involved in a radiative transition will have some definite total angular momentum, specified by the quantum number j. Similarly, the lower level will also be characterized by some particular value of the resultant angular momentum. We proceed to describe the effect of an externally applied magnetic field on the single spectral line being considered. We shall see that it splits into several components. This splitting is accurately described by the quantum theory and is called the Zeeman effect in honor of its discoverer.

By way of illustrating the Zeeman effect, let us consider a transition from an excited level with $j = 1$ to a ground state with $j = 0$. In the absence of a magnetic field, the atom will radiate a single line whose frequency is f. In the presence of a magnetic field, the ground state will be unaltered, and in the excited state the atom can have any one of three orientations, with its angular momentum parallel to, at right angles to, or antiparallel to the applied field, as in Fig. 11.21b. An atom with angular momentum will also have a magnetic moment, as shown in the discussion leading up to Eq. 7.67. The atom will therefore also have three different energies. If its magnetic moment in the excited state is μ, these energies will be the unperturbed energy E, in the absence of a magnetic field plus ΔE, where

$$E = \pm \mu B \qquad \text{or } 0$$

The excited state is therefore split into three states, as shown in Fig. 13.6a. Further, the single frequency radiated in the absence of a field giving rise to a single spectral line will be modified to include three frequencies and three spectral lines having the frequencies f, $f + \mu B/h$, and $f - \mu B/h$.

Spectral lines may split up in more complex ways. The Zeeman effect of a line involving a transition from an excited level with $j = \frac{1}{2}$ to a ground state with $j = \frac{1}{2}$ is shown in Fig. 13.6b. In the presence of a magnetic field each level will split into two, corresponding to the two possible orientations of j. (See Fig. 11.21a.) If the magnetic moments of the atom in the ground and excited states are different, the amount of the splitting will be different, and we may expect to find the single line of frequency f without a field split into four components by a magnetic field.

The Zeeman effect provides us with a convenient way to supplement Stern-Gerlach atomic beam experiments for studying the angular momentum of atoms. The analysis of atomic energy levels has provided us with very complete rules for combining the contributions of orbital motion and spin, but these rules are too complicated for us to spell out here. We mention only that one fact previously described, that systems with an even number of electrons have integral values of j and systems with an odd number of electrons have half-integral values of j, has an easy explanation in terms of the electron spin. No matter how the components of orbital angular momentum are coupled together, their resultant always leads to an integral multiple of $h/2\pi$. Then, if we are dealing with an even number of electrons, the vector sum of all the spins turns out also to be an integral multiple of $h/2\pi$, and therefore leads to an integral value of j, and on the other hand to a half-integral value of j for systems with an odd number of electrons.

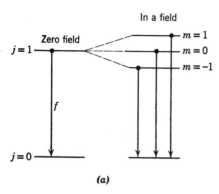

(a)

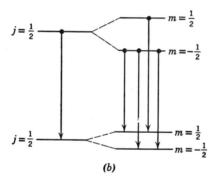

(b)

Fig. 13.6.   The Zeeman effect.

Thus, for example, the splitting of a spectral line into a triplet in the presence of a magnetic field, as in Fig. 13.6a, is found in atoms containing an even number of electrons, like zinc with 30, or cadmium with 48, or mercury with 80. The situation illustrated in Fig. 13.6b, on the other hand, with $j = \frac{1}{2}$, is to be found in atoms with an odd number of electrons, like hydrogen with 1, lithium with 3, or sodium with 11. (See also appendix VIII, c)

13.4 THE EXCLUSION PRINCIPLE

In Newtonian mechanics it is axiomatic that two objects cannot exist at the same place at the same time. We describe the contact force which we use to move objects from one point to another simply as a consequence of this fundamental postulate. An incautious observer might even conclude that this is "an established fact." It would be more correct to state that, as we bring microscopic objects closer and closer together, a greater and greater repulsive force is brought into play. This force is more or less what one might expect if a material object were to exclude other material objects from the space it occupies. But in point of fact, when we examine the situation in detail, from an atomic point of view, we find that there is no such exclusion. We cannot even specify exactly where a particle is at any given time. Our knowledge covers the statistical, or average, aspects of the motion of electrons within atoms, and statistically they move as though collisions did not take place.

From the quantum mechanical point of view, an electron or other similar particle must be described in terms of a wave function. For the problems of interest in connection with the present discussion, the particle is restrained by attractive forces, so that the motion of the particle is characterized by a number of stationary states. The wave functions of the particle in these states are localized. If the particle is in a potential energy box, the wave functions are predominantly within the box, though they may penetrate the walls to some extent. If the wave functions describe an electron in the field of force of an atom, they are localized within a volume having linear dimensions of the order of a few times 10^{-10} m. If the wave functions describe the motions of a proton inside a nucleus, they are localized within a much smaller volume. We can, in each of these cases, specify that the particle is in the region occupied by the wave functions, but we cannot specify where, within such a region, the particle is at any one instant.

What, now, is characteristically different or new about the problem if we have present two or more identical particles in the same system at the same time? Without specifying how the result is arrived at, and without attempting to state this result in rigorous form, we may summarize its significance in the following statement. This is the *exclusion principle* of quantum mechanics. *Two or more identical particles, such as electrons (or protons, or neutrons), cannot exist in the same state at the same time.* The state of any one of these particles is entirely specified by the spatial wave function which we have discussed and one more item, the orientation of its intrinsic angular momentum, or spin. There are always two different possible orientations of the $\frac{1}{2}(h/2\pi)$ spin angular momentum of electrons, protons, or neutrons. Consequently for every wave function there are two possible states. If in the box problem discussed at the end of Chapter 12 we have one wave function corresponding to the lowest energy, then we may put two particles in the box and they can both exist in stationary states having this lowest energy. If, however, we put a third particle in the box, all three particles cannot get into states having this energy. One of them must occupy a higher energy level. In this particular problem there are three different wave functions which characterize a particle with the next higher energy. If we put more particles into the lowest possible states, we can add six more before this energy level is "filled," and so on. The exclusion principle, as we shall see, is most important to our understanding of the properties of matter.

13.5 THE PERIODIC TABLE

A good deal about the structure of atoms in general may be inferred from the hydrogen atom and the exclusion principle. For example, if we have an atom consisting of a nucleus with a double nuclear charge and a single electron, this single electron will have hydrogenlike states, but the potential energy well will be deeper and narrower, the energy levels will be lower and farther apart, and the wave functions will cover a smaller volume. If now we add a second electron, the problem is much more complicated electrostatically. However, it turns out that the hydrogen energy level scheme is still approximately applicable. The electrons tend to keep out of each other's way. The second electron, if its spin is oppositely oriented to that of the first, may have the same spatial wave function as the first and may therefore also occupy the lowest energy level. This results in a particularly stable atom that is hard to excite. The ground state is separated from the next higher level by a greater gap than in any other atom. This atom is the helium atom, with $Z = 2$. It is chemically very inert. Helium atoms interact with each other so little that helium gas at a pressure of one atmosphere must be cooled to within a few degrees of the absolute zero before the very slight attractive forces between them will cause the gas to condense.

The degeneracy of the hydrogen energy levels is shown in Fig. 13.7. With a nuclear charge $Z = 2$, and two electrons, the lowest level is filled. The corresponding substances are hydrogen and helium.

If now we consider atoms with more and more electrons, we may think of the energy level with $n = 2$ being filled. Since there are four spatial wave functions and each may contain two electrons with oppositely oriented spins, we may expect to find another stable heliumlike atom with eight more, or altogether ten, electrons. From the periodic table we find the following:

$Z = 3$	4	5	6	7	8	9	10
Element Li	Be	B	C	N	O	F	Ne

The element whose atomic number is 10, neon, is indeed a heliumlike gas.

The filling of the third shell proceeds in like manner. However, the energy levels are now closer together, as shown in Fig. 13.2, and the interaction of the electrons with each other is no longer negligible. As a result the addition of only eight more electrons, to give a total of 18,

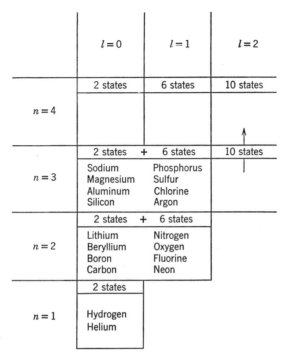

	$l = 0$	$l = 1$	$l = 2$
$n = 4$	2 states	6 states	10 states
$n = 3$	2 states +	6 states	10 states
	Sodium Magnesium Aluminum Silicon	Phosphorus Sulfur Chlorine Argon	
$n = 2$	2 states +	6 states	
	Lithium Beryllium Boron Carbon	Nitrogen Oxygen Fluorine Neon	
$n = 1$	2 states		
	Hydrogen Helium		

FIG. 13.7. The degeneracy of the hydrogen energy levels and the periodic table.

produces the next noble gas, argon, with $Z = 18$. The energy of the ten states with $n = 3$ and $l = 2$ is raised, and the corresponding substances occur in the next period of the periodic table. An alphabetic list of the chemical elements and their arrangement in a periodic table are reproduced in Appendices IV and V. The further details of the periodic table become much more difficult to understand because of the greater influence of electron-electron interactions, and we shall not pursue them further but turn our attention to another feature of atomic structure nicely explained by our simple analysis, namely, the X-ray line spectrum of the elements.

13.6 X RAYS

Let us consider the energy levels of a single electron in the field of a nucleus having a charge Ze. The expression for the potential energy becomes $-(Ze^2)/4\pi\epsilon_0 r$, and the energy levels of the atoms may easily be shown to be

$$E = -\frac{m(Ze^2)^2}{8\epsilon_0{}^2 h^2}\frac{1}{n^2}\qquad(13.37)$$

or just Z^2 times the energy values obtained for the hydrogen atom. The frequency radiated in a transition from the second to the first level is then

$$f = \frac{E_2 - E_1}{h} = \frac{mZ^2 e^4}{8\epsilon_0{}^2 h^3}\left(\frac{1}{1} - \frac{1}{4}\right)\qquad(13.38)$$

It will be seen that, as Z increases, f increases, and upon substituting numbers into Eq. 13.38 one finds frequencies in the X-ray region for not very great values of Z.

Highly ionized atoms to which Eq. 13.38 is applicable are difficult to produce, and we must consider how such transitions may be generated in neutral atoms. In a heavy atom with large Z, the electrons in the lowest level are held in a small shell close to the nucleus. The larger the atomic number, the smaller the shell. This inner shell is called the K shell. Outside this inner K shell, with two electrons, is a larger shell, called the L shell, with eight electrons. Outside this, in turn, are other shells. In a normal atom shells are filled from the bottom up. Because of the exclusion principle, transitions from one to another of these low-lying levels are not possible *unless a vacancy in some state is created by the removal of an electron.* If a K shell electron, for example, is removed from an atom, say by a collision with a fast-moving electron, then an electron in any one of the shells with higher energy may "drop" into the K shell. In doing so, it will emit a quantum, which may be in the X-ray region. X-ray spectra may be computed by using Eq. 13.38 with one modification, for reasons that may be understood on the basis of the following considerations. The field within a spherically symmetrical shell of charge is zero. The outer electrons contribute nothing to the field of which an inner electron in an atom is aware. In fact, we might estimate that an electron in the L-shell of an atom from which one inner-most K electron was missing would be moving in the attractive field of force of $Z - 1$ protons, the -1 being due to the one remaining K electron down nearer the nucleus than the L-shell electron. In general, we might expect to use a formula like Eq. 13.38 for the computation of X-ray frequencies and wavelengths if we replace the atomic number Z by some smaller number Z^*, the actual value of Z^* depending on which electron is missing and which transitions we are considering.

Further, because the shielding of inner electrons is slightly different for various values of n, we might expect a best description of the radiated frequencies using not integers but other numbers near the integers representing hydrogen energy levels. A theoretical investigation has shown that, for transitions in all but the lightest elements from an L shell to a singly ionized K shell, the numerical factor on the right of Eq. 13.38 $\frac{1}{1} - \frac{1}{4} = \frac{3}{4}$ should be replaced by 0.865. The dependence of the fre-

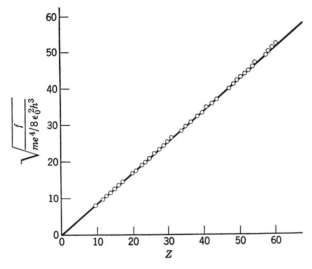

FIG. 13.8.   A Moseley diagram.

quency of X rays for this $L \rightarrow K$ transition as a function of the atomic number Z should then be given by the expression

$$\sqrt{f} = \sqrt{\frac{me^4}{8\epsilon_0{}^2 h^3}} \cdot 0.865 (Z^*) \qquad (13.39)$$

where Z^* is the atomic number Z less some constant approximately equal to unity. The degree to which this expression is satisfied is shown in Fig. 13.8, in which

$$\frac{\sqrt{f}}{\sqrt{\dfrac{me^4}{8\epsilon_0{}^2 h^3}}}$$

is plotted as a function of the atomic number Z, f being the experimentally observed frequency. The predicted line according to Eq. 13.39 is shown as well as the experimental points. The agreement between theory and experiment is seen to be excellent. A plot of this kind is called a Moseley diagram in honor of the scientist, who was killed during the First World War, and who first discovered the linear relationship between the $\sqrt{f}$ and Z for corresponding X ray lines of the elements.

13.7 FREE ELECTRONS IN METALS

We stated in the first chapter of this book that metals could conduct, or carry a current, because of the presence of free electrons that could move from point to point within the metal. These free electrons are essentially particles in a box. They are free to move about but confined to the body of the metal by restraining surface forces. We may therefore expect to be able to apply the analysis of the previous chapter.

In our discussion of the electrical conductivity of metals in Chapter 3, we showed that an ideal metal would have no resistance at all. In the absence of irregularities in the structure of the atomic planes of single crystals due to thermal agitation, impurities, strains, and so on, there would be no obstacles to the free motion of the electrons within the metal. Resistivity is due entirely to these irregularities. A study of the resistivity of metals is therefore a study of the manner in which a metal differs from an empty box confining the electrons. We shall not attempt an analysis of such effects but confine ourselves to another aspect of the problem not dependent on the presence of lattice imperfections. This has to do with the specific heat of metals.

It is an observed fact that the specific heats of the solid elements are generally in the vicinity of 6 calories per mole per degree centigrade. In other words, for most elements, 6 calories are required to raise the temperature of 6.02×10^{23} atoms by 1°C in the vicinity of room temperature. This result, sometimes referred to as Dulong and Petit's law, can be satisfactorily accounted for by the kinetic theory of solids as just the amount of heat required by this number of independent atoms oscillating about their mean positions in a crystal lattice. The point that is difficult to understand is why this same value of 6 should hold for conducting as well as non-conducting elements. If conductivity is due to the presence of free electrons, we should expect that, as the temperature is raised, additional energy would be required to increase the average thermal kinetic energy of the free electrons. Further, since the number of free electrons in metals is comparable to the number of atoms, we should expect metals to have an appreciably greater specific heat. Why is this not the case?

For an understanding of this point we return to the wave functions of a particle in a cubic box and apply the results previously obtained to the free electrons in a cubic centimeter of copper. In this cubic centimeter there are roughly 10^{23} atoms and, we may assume, in the vicinity of 10^{22}

free electrons.   To begin with, we consider the box at the absolute zero of temperature.   By this we mean that all particles are in the lowest possible energy state.   According to Newtonian mechanics, in which particles can have any kinetic energy at all, atomic particles are gradually slowed down as the temperature is reduced.   At the absolute zero of temperature, the particles are all at rest with no kinetic energy.   In quantum mechanics particles can have only certain prescribed energies.   For the particles in the box, these are, according to Eq. 12.16,

$$E = \frac{h^2}{8mL^2} \left(s_x^2 + s_y^2 + s_z^2\right) \tag{13.40}$$

where the quantities s_x, etc., are positive integers.   As the temperature of the box is decreased, energy is removed, and the particles occupy lower and lower energy levels.   In quantum mechanics, however, particles can never come to rest.   There is a lowest energy level which is above the point of zero kinetic energy.   Furthermore, because of the operation of the exclusion principle, only two particles of the kind we are discussing with a spin of $\frac{1}{2}(h/2\pi)$ can be in this state of motion.   Additional particles must exist in states of higher kinetic energy.   The maximum energy of a free electron in a metal when all the lowest states are filled in this way is called the Fermi energy.   We designate it by E_f.   Electrons having energies below this critical value cannot slow down, and can change their state of motion only by being "lifted" energetically to unoccupied states having an energy greater than E_f.   Another way of describing the situation is that, under these circumstances, electrons cannot undergo collisions except with particles having sufficient energy to boost the electron over the top of the Fermi level.   There is, in quantum mechanics, something almost like a guiding force which prevents a particle from slowing down or undergoing collisions except under prescribed conditions.   This guiding force is really the ψ wave, which controls the behavior of the particle just as the electromagnetic wave controls the motion of quanta.

We have, here, the explanation of the fact that free electrons do not contribute to the specific heats of metals.   The average kinetic energy of the atoms of a metal in the vicinity of room temperature is of the order of a few hundredths of an electron volt.   If the Fermi energy of the electrons is much smaller than this, we may expect that collisions in which they are accelerated will occur at room temperature.   This acceleration process will go on until the average kinetic energy per degree of freedom of the electrons is just equal to that of the atoms.   As the temperature of the metal is raised, the average energy of both electrons and atoms will increase, and the electrons will contribute to the specific heat

as in Newtonian mechanics.   If, however, the Fermi energy is much
greater than a few hundredths of an electron volt, collisions with atoms
having such a low energy cannot occur.   The energy of the electrons is
constant, and their motions contribute nothing to the specific heat.

It is easy to see that E_f may be large compared to kT.   Let us compute
the lowest energy of an electron in a 1 cm cube.   In electron volts, we
have

$$E = \frac{h^2 \cdot 3}{8mL^2 e} = \frac{(6.6 \times 10^{-34})^2 (3)}{(8)(9 \times 10^{-31})(10^{-4})(1.6 \times 10^{-19})} \simeq 1.13 \times 10^{-14} \text{ ev}$$

Of course, as we put in more and more electrons, there are more and
more states per unit energy range, but even so we might well expect
that by the time we put 10^{22} electrons into the box, the lowest unfilled
energy levels will be well above 10^{-2} electron volts.   The derivation of
the formula for the Fermi energy is carried out below.

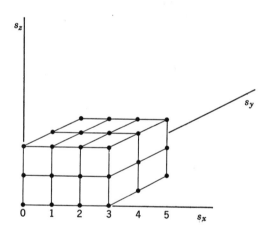

FIG. 13.9.   The distribution of integral values of s_x, s_y, and s_z.

The Fermi Energy of Free Electrons

Each state of an electron, apart from spin, is characterized by a particular
set of values of s_x, s_y, s_z.   Let these points be represented in the positive
octant of a rectangular coordinate system, as shown in Fig. 13.9.   It will be
seen that the points fill this space with uniform density.   Further, if we draw a
sphere, centered at the origin, in this octant, the radius R of this sphere, shown
in Fig. 13.10, has the following property.   Since

$$R^2 = s_x{}^2 + s_y{}^2 + s_z{}^2$$

all the representative points within this sphere have energies less than
$h^2 R^2 / 8mL^2$.   But we can easily determine how many points there are within

the sphere and, therefore, how many states there are corresponding to an energy less than any preassigned quantity.

The volume of a sphere of radius R is $(4\pi/3)R^3$. If, in our sphere shown in Fig. 13.10 we let

$$R^2 = s_x{}^2 + s_y{}^2 + s_z{}^2$$

we have for the volume of the octant, or for the number of points which an octant contains,

$$N = \frac{1}{8}\frac{4\pi}{3}(s_x{}^2 + s_y{}^2 + s_z{}^2)^{3/2}$$

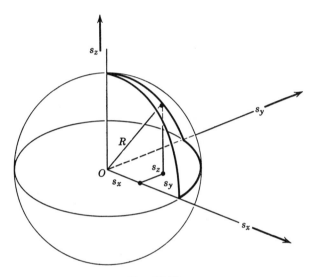

Fig. 13.10.

But, from Eq. 13.40, if the value of R is such that the energy has some particular value, say E_f, then

$$N = \frac{1}{8}\frac{4\pi}{3}\left(\frac{E_f \cdot 8mL^2}{h^2}\right)^{3/2} \tag{13.41}$$

But $(L^2)^{3/2} = L^3 = V$, the volume of the metal. N/V is the number of states per unit volume of the metal. If these are all filled with electrons and if we put two electrons in each, then the number of electrons per unit volume, n, may be written $2N/V = n$, and Eq. 13.41 may be rewritten

$$E_f = \left(\frac{3}{\pi}n\right)^{2/3}\left(\frac{h^2}{8m}\right) \tag{13.42}$$

If we take n to be of the order of the number of atoms per unit volume, approximately 10^{29} per cubic meter, the Fermi energy becomes

$$E_f = 12.7 \times 10^{-19} \text{ joules}$$
$$= 8 \text{ ev}$$

This is very large compared to thermal energies at normal temperatures, and it is therefore to be expected that heating a metal at room temperature will contribute little, if anything, to the motion of the free electrons.

SUMMARY

The Schroedinger wave equation applied to a hydrogen atom has solutions for values of the energy

$$E = -\frac{1}{n^2}\frac{me^4}{8\epsilon_0{}^2h^2}$$

where n is any positive integer.

Transitions between these levels give rise to the observed frequencies of the atomic hydrogen spectrum, the radiated frequency being related to the energy change in the atom by

$$\Delta E = hf$$

The various energy levels are degenerate, in that there are several distinct wave functions for all except the lowest energy level. If we classify the wave functions in a given energy level by their orbital angular momenta, then we find that the orbital angular momentum quantum number l can have any integral value and zero, up to and including $n - 1$.

The electron itself has an intrinsic or spin angular momentum $\frac{1}{2}(h/2\pi)$, and this may be parallel or antiparallel to the orbital angular momentum. As a result, there are actually two possible different states of the electron for each of the spatial wave functions.

The Zeeman effect, or the splitting of spectral lines by a magnetic field, results from the spatial quantization of the angular momentum.

The exclusion principle states that no more than one electron can occupy any given quantum mechanical state.

The main features of the periodic table, especially for light elements, are very simply explained in terms of the hydrogen energy level scheme and the exclusion principle.

Atoms can radiate X rays when an inner electron is removed and an outer electron undergoes a transition into the vacant state. The fact that, if f is the frequency of a particular transition of this kind, $\sqrt{f}$ is very nearly proportional to the atomic number Z is called Moseley's law and is accounted for by the energy levels computed for electrons moving in the fields of partly shielded nuclei.

Free electrons in metals have energy levels so widely spaced that when all the lowest levels are filled, the upper levels have energies of several electron volts. This maximum energy is called the Fermi energy. Free electrons do not take part in thermal agitation because the Fermi energy is much greater than the kinetic vibrational energy of the atoms of solids.

PROBLEMS

1. An electron is moving in the field of a nucleus containing Z protons. (a) What is the wave function in the ground state? (b) What is the ionization potential of singly ionized helium? Of doubly ionized lithium? (c) Find the mean value of r for a single electron in the field of an iron nucleus ($Z = 26$); of a silver nucleus ($Z = 47$); of a lead nucleus ($Z = 82$).

2. Balmer observed the following two lines in the spectrum of hydrogen: $\lambda = 6562$ A, and 4862 A. (a) What is the difference in energy between the states of the hydrogen atom which gives rise to these lines? Express your answer in electron volts. (b) What energy levels are involved in the radiation of these two lines?

3. What are the wavelengths of the first two lines of the Balmer series? Of the Lyman series?

4. What is the ionization potential of tne hydrogen atom from the state with $n = 2$?

5. Calculate the diamagnetic susceptibility of atomic hydrogen gas at normal temperature and pressure. (See Eq. 6.18.) A hint concerning the number of atoms per unit volume is given in Problem 15. The additional magnetic contributions due to the electron spin would in fact make atomic hydrogen paramagnetic.

6. Assuming that the magnetic moment of the atom shown in Fig. 13.6a in the excited state is 10^{-23} amp-meter^2 (see Eq. 5.61), and that the wavelength radiated in the transition shown, in zero field, is 2536.000 A, compute the three wavelengths radiated in a field of 2 webers/meter^2.

★7. If a spectral line is examined with a spectroscopic instrument having a large resolving power, it is possible to find the shape of the radiated line, that is, the intensity as a function of wavelength. This is found to have a central maximum which falls off on either side. The width of the intensity curve at half the maximum intensity is called the width of the line. In most spectral lines this width is determined by the Doppler effect. If the atoms were at rest they would radiate a much sharper line, but, because of their thermal velocities, they radiate an apparently higher frequency when they are approaching an observer and a lower frequency when they are receding from an observer. The width of the spectral line observed from a radiating gas is determined by the mean velocities of the gas atoms. The change in frequency due to the motion of a radiating source moving in the direction of radiation is

$$\Delta f/f = v/c$$

where v is the velocity of the source toward the observer and c is the velocity of light. If the probability that an atom has a velocity component along an arbitrary axis between v and $v + dv$ is

$$dw = \sqrt{\beta/\pi} \exp\left(-\beta v^2\right) dv$$

$$\beta = M/2kT$$

(a) Show that the spectral distribution is

$$I(f) = I_0 \exp\left[-\beta(c^2/f^2)(f - f_0)^2\right]$$

and that the width of the line, defined as the width at half maximum, as shown in
Fig. 13.11, is $\Delta_D = 2\dfrac{f_0}{c}\sqrt{\dfrac{2kT}{M}}\ln 2$.

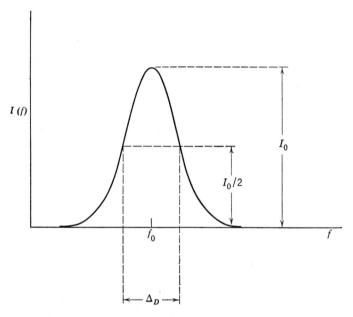

$$\text{Fig. } 13.11.$$

(b) Noting that $\lambda f = c$, and therefore that $d\lambda/\lambda = -df/f$, show that the Doppler
width in wavelength units is

$$\frac{2\lambda_0}{c}\sqrt{\frac{2kT}{M}}\ln 2$$

8. The width of a spectral line Δ_D broadened by the random motion of the radiating atoms, in frequency units, is

$$\Delta_D = \frac{2f_0}{c}\sqrt{\frac{2kT}{M}}\ln 2$$

Compute the smallest field that can be used to show the Zeeman effect of the line
discussed in Problem 6, assuming that the radiating atom is mercury ($A = 200$),
that the absolute temperature of the radiating gas is 350° absolute, and that the
Zeeman components must be separated by at least the Doppler width to be resolved.

9. How large a magnetic field would be required to show the Zeeman effect of
the spectral line discussed in Problem 6 above if the spectroscope used is the prism
spectroscope described at the end of Section 10.5? Neglect Doppler broadening.

10. A low-pressure mercury arc is operated so that the temperature of the electrons
is 11,000°K and the ratio of the number of atoms in the first excited state to the
number in the ground state corresponds to thermal equilibrium at approximately

this temperature. Under these conditions the spectral intensity of the emitted radiation in the middle of the spectral line resulting from transitions from the above excited state to the ground state may be estimated by assuming it is equal to that of a black body at the electron temperature. The radiation in the interior of the lamp is absorbed and reemitted as though it were in an insulated container, and comes to thermal equilibrium with the electrons. If the radiation is a single spectral line having the Doppler width appropriate to mercury atoms with a translational energy corresponding to 40°C, approximately 5×10^{-4} mμ, and if the wavelength of the line is 253.7 mμ, what is the total power radiated per meter of length of a tubular lamp 1.5 in. in diameter?

11. Twenty-one electrons are placed in a cubic box with impenetrable walls 10^{-10} meter long in each dimension. The electrons settle into the lowest possible energy levels. A single electron is now removed from the lowest level by some means. What are the possible wavelengths that this hypothetical system could radiate?

12. The wavelengths of a series of corresponding X ray lines from several elements are given below:

λ, in A	Element	Atomic Number, Z
17.6	Fe	26
12.22	Zn	30
5.39	Mo	42
4.15	Ag	47
3.59	Sn	50
1.47	W	74
1.17	Pb	82
0.908	U	92

Make a plot of $\sqrt{f}$ as a function of Z using these data, and estimate the effective nuclear charge Z^* for this series of lines. Discuss the significance of this result.

13. Assume that an insulator may be considered as a rectangular box within which electrons which are added in some way are perfectly free to move about. If free electrons are gradually added in this way and occupy all the lowest energy levels, at what concentration will the maximum energy of an electron (the Fermi energy), be just equal to $\frac{3}{2}kT$, with $T = 300°$K? At this concentration the free electrons would behave more or less like the atoms of an ordinary gas at 300°K. Would they have an appreciable effect on the observed specific heat of the insulator?

14. At approximately what temperature would the Fermi energy of free electrons in copper be equal to kT?

15. Compute the number of atoms per unit volume of helium at 300°K, and a pressure of 1 atmosphere. To do so, remember that a perfect gas containing N atoms at a temperature T in a volume V will exert a pressure p on the walls where $pV = NkT$. Suitable units must be used in the above expression. The usual gas constant R is just k times the number of atoms per mole, or $R = 6.02 \times 10^{23}k$. What would be the maximum energy of a helium atom in such a gas if each had a spin $s = \frac{1}{2}$ like an electron, due to the nuclear contribution, and if all the lowest energy levels were occupied? At what temperature could this happen?

CHAPTER 14

Atomic Nuclei and
Nuclear Radiations

14.1 NUCLEAR STRUCTURE; THE PROTON-NEUTRON MODEL

This last chapter of our physics course is not so much a last chapter concluding the description of protons and electrons and their electrical interactions as it is the first chapter concerning a new set of problems: problems associated with new particles and high energies. We have described a cycle in the evolution of physical ideas, namely, the cycle beginning with electrons and nuclei, the Coulomb law of force between them, and the magnetic forces between them; a cycle then continuing with a description of the electric and magnetic fields associated with electrons and nuclei, and the revelation of the electromagnetic nature of light; a cycle concluding with the establishment of wave mechanics, or quantum mechanics, to supplement Newtonian mechanics in the realm of atomic magnitudes. This completes our description of electromagnetic phenomena and of the electric and magnetic properties of charged particles. There is, of course, a tremendous amount of detail to be filled in around the few basic concepts which we have mentioned. The student of physics must spend many years in acquiring a full understanding of the subject matter discussed in this book. But the basis for an understanding is there. The main chain of ideas is complete.

Sometimes, when one chapter of a story is complete, we must wait a long time for the next. In the case of physics, in this particular instance, there has been no waiting period at all. From quantum theory and atomic physics we have proceeded directly to nuclear physics, and the interaction of "heavy" particles with each other over nuclear, rather than atomic, dimensions.

The new ideas must somehow be built on the old. We shall expect to find the principles of Newtonian physics valid, particularly in the form of the laws of conservation of energy and momentum, modified by relativity. We shall expect to use our electromagnetic laws and the principles of quantum theory. But as we go farther and farther into small dimensions and high-energy collisions, we shall find new forces acting between particles and indeed new kinds of particles and fields. Of this new subject we can say very little. We shall confine ourselves to a few comments about nuclear physics which should serve as an introduction to those aspects of the subject which are becoming of increasing importance to all of us.

Nuclear physics deals with atomic nuclei, which we shall describe in terms of their *atomic number* Z, which specifies the number of positive charges in the nucleus, or the number of electrons in the neutral atom, and the *mass number* A, which for the moment we define as the approximate number of hydrogen atom masses in the neutral atom. We shall presently arrive at a more specific definition of A. A plot of known kinds of nuclei, also called *nuclides*, is shown in Fig. 14.1. In this illustration the quantity $(A - Z)$ is plotted as a function of Z.

The chemical properties of an atom are determined by its atomic number, Z. It is apparent that most chemical species consist of atoms with a variety of mass numbers. These are called the *isotopes* of a chemical species. A common way of designating a particular isotope is to put its atomic number below and to the left of its chemical symbol, and its mass number above and to the right of the chemical symbol. Thus the isotope of tin, Sn, with $Z = 50$ and $A = 120$ would be written

$$_{50}Sn^{120}$$

For this isotope $(A - Z) = 120 - 50 = 70$, and it occupies the black square having the coordinates $(50, 70)$ in Fig. 14.1. Three kinds of nuclei are shown differently on the chart. Those which are stable, and do not spontaneously emit particles, and so transform themselves into other nuclides, are black. The others are radioactive. Those that occur naturally on the earth are represented by a small dot in a hollow square in the chart. Those which now occur on the earth only as the result of man-made nuclear reactions are shown as open hollow squares. An alphabetic list of the chemical elements, the currently used symbols for the elements, and their atomic numbers is contained in Appendix IV. A periodic table is reproduced in Appendix V

A fundamental problem of nuclear theory is to explain the regularities shown in Fig. 14.1. As a first step we might consider two alternative hypotheses. The first is that nuclei are made up of protons and electrons. It might seem that this is the only possibility, since we have so far introduced only these two elementary particles. Furthermore, certain radioactive nuclei emit electrons, and this fact might be taken

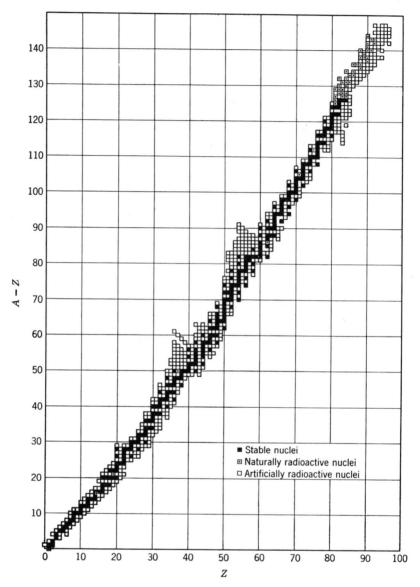

FIG. 14.1.   Chart of the known nuclei.   From F. Bitter, *Nuclear Physics*, Addison-
Wesley, Cambridge, Mass., 1950.

as evidence that electrons exist in the nucleus.   There are, however,
great difficulties with this hypothesis.   We shall review some of these
below and shall conclude that nuclei are not made up of protons and

electrons, even though electrons may be emitted. This apparently paradoxical statement is further discussed in Section 14.6.

An alternative hypothesis is that nuclei are made up of protons and *neutrons*. In the 1930's the neutron was recognized in the radiations accompanying certain nuclear reactions. Its mass is very nearly that of the proton, and, like the proton, its intrinsic angular momentum is $\frac{1}{2}(h/2\pi)$, but, unlike the proton, it is uncharged, or electrically neutral. Hence its name, the neutron.

Is there any basis for preferring one hypothesis to the other? There is, first of all, an argument about size. We know that nuclei have radii of 10^{-15} to 10^{-14} m. We also know something of the spacing of energy levels in the nucleus. They are of the order of Mev. From our wave mechanical description of the energy levels of particles in a potential energy well, we know certain conditions that must be satisfied. In particular the wavelength associated with the motion of the particle must be less than twice the dimensions of the confining box. As we have seen, this requirement leads to energy levels whose spacing is of the order

$$E_0 = \frac{h^2}{8mL^2}$$

and, if we take $L = 10^{-14}$ and $m = 9.1 \times 10^{-31}$ for an electron, we get $E_0 \simeq 3000$ Mev, which is far beyond the observed range. However, if instead of the electron mass we take the proton mass we get $E_0 \simeq$ Mev. This would seem to be a much more reasonable assumption.

The clinching argument about the composition of nuclei comes from considerations of angular momentum. We shall not discuss how nuclear angular momentum is actually measured; we merely point out that nuclear angular momentum is comparable in magnitude to the electronic angular momentum of atoms, and that these forms of angular momentum are coupled together through atomic and nuclear magnetic fields and can be inferred from the structure of atomic spectra. (See the frontispiece and appendix VIII, d) The three particles with which we are concerned, protons, neutrons, and electrons, each have an intrinsic or spin angular momentum of $\frac{1}{2}(h/2\pi)$, or, in units of $h/2\pi$, a spin of $\frac{1}{2}$. These spins are always coupled parallel or antiparallel to each other, so that the resultant spin of two particles may be 1 or 0, and of three particles may be $\frac{1}{2} + \frac{1}{2} + \frac{1}{2} = \frac{3}{2}$, or $\frac{1}{2} + \frac{1}{2} - \frac{1}{2} = \frac{1}{2}$, and so forth. It will be noticed that the resultant spin angular momentum of an odd number of particles of any kind must be a half-integer, and the resultant spin angular momentum of an even number of particles of any kind must be an integer in units of $(h/2\pi)$, or zero.

To these considerations of spin angular momentum we must add the contributions due to orbital motions of the particles. These, it turns out, are always integral multiples of $(h/2\pi)$. The resultant total angular

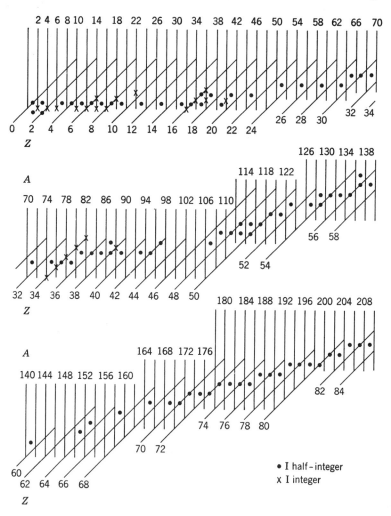

FIG. 14.2.   Nuclear angular momenta.   From F. Bitter, *Nuclear Physics*, Addison-Wesley, Cambridge, Mass., 1950.

momentum of an odd number of particles is therefore a half-integral plus an integral, or a total half-integral number of units. Similarly, the resultant total angular momentum of a system containing an even number of particles is necessarily an integral number of units. Measurements of total angular momentum therefore reveal whether we are dealing with an odd or an even number of particles.

The observed results are plotted in Fig. 14.2. The intersections of the vertical and diagonal lines in the illustration assign a place to a nucleus with given A and Z. Thus, for example, to find $_2He^4$, or an alpha particle with $Z = 2$ and $A = 4$, we find the intersection of the vertical line marked 4 and of the diagonal line marked 2. At the intersection is a cross, indicating that the resultant angular momentum of this nuclide is an integer (actually zero). For $_2He^3$, the resultant angular momentum on the line $Z = 2$, and in the space reserved for $A = 3$, is indicated by a dot. It is half-integral.

If the first hypothesis about nuclear structure were correct, namely, that nuclei are made up of protons and electrons, the total number of particles would be the total number of protons, or the number A, plus the number of electrons $(A - Z)$, or $(2A - Z)$ particles all told. But, since $2A$ is always even, we should expect $(2A - Z)$ to be odd or even depending only on whether Z is odd or even. Looking back at the figure, we note that the crosses certainly are not restricted to the diagonal lines with even Z. Dots and crosses appear more or less randomly for odd or even values of Z. We conclude that the number of particles in a nucleus is not correctly given by the assumption that the nucleus contains protons and electrons.

If, on the other hand, the nucleus is made up of protons and neutrons, the total number of particles is given by the mass number A. Upon examining Fig. 14.2 once more, we find that, without exception, the vertical lines corresponding to even values of A are occupied by crosses, or nuclei having an integral number of units of angular momentum, and the spaces between the lines, corresponding to odd values of A, are occupied by dots, or nuclei having a half-integral number of units of angular momentum. This is an impressive bit of evidence. We conclude that nuclei are indeed composed of neutrons and protons. These particles, of which nuclei are constructed, are called *nucleons*. Thus nucleons are the constituents of nuclei, either protons or neutrons.

Once the proton-neutron model of the nucleus has been adopted, one of the striking features of Fig. 14.1 becomes plausible. Here we have plotted the number of neutrons $(A - Z)$ vertically and the number of protons Z horizontally. For light elements the number of neutrons is approximately equal to the number of protons. For heavy elements there is a slight neutron excess. Particles in nuclei must be held together by very strong short-range attractive forces to overcome the repulsive Coulomb forces. The potential energy of a particle in the vicinity of a nucleus must be very much like that of a particle in a box, discussed in Section 12.5. In such a box, there is a succession of energy levels and these will be successively filled as particles are added. The exclusion principle prevents two identical particles from occupying the same state. Although two protons or two neutrons cannot occupy the same state, there is no exclusion for different particles. It would seem, therefore, that in order to fill successively the lowest-lying energy levels in a nucleus, we should expect to require equal proportions of protons and neutrons. Moreover, we should expect the energy levels of protons in heavy nuclei to lie somewhat higher than the corresponding levels for neutrons because of the Coulomb forces. This accounts for the small excess of neutrons over protons in the heavy atoms. Though this argument indicates that the observed stable nuclei are energetically favored, there are many features of Fig. 14.1 not accounted for. Especially, it is to be noticed, we have no understanding as yet of why only this small range of nuclei exist, why stable nuclei with a large excess of protons, or a large excess of neutrons, are not found.

14.2 NUCLEAR SIZE

Rutherford showed that alpha particles were scattered by nuclei as though a Coulomb law of force were effective provided the distance of closest approach was not less than a critical value, of the order of $10^{-14} - 10^{-15}$ meter. At such small distances other forces are effective.

A similar estimate of nuclear size, or of the range of nuclear forces, is obtained through observing neutron scattering. Fast neutrons are deflected in going through matter only if they make a nuclear collision. It is therefore possible to measure nuclear sizes by observing the attenuation of a beam of neutrons in passing through a slab of matter containing a known number of nuclei, as illustrated in Fig. 14.3. Let I_0 be the number of neutrons incident on the absorber per unit area per second. We wish to compute the intensity of the beam which passes without a collision through an absorber of thickness t. The following is an elaboration of the discussion of the mean free path in Section 3.3. Let us first assume that the neutrons are points, and that the projected area of the nuclei in the absorber is σ. The beam will be attenuated in going through the slab. At a depth x, let the intensity of the beam be $I(x)$. The fraction of the beam removed in going through a further thickness dx is

$$\frac{I(x) - I(x + dx)}{I(x)} = -\frac{dI(x)}{I(x)} \tag{14.1}$$

This fraction may also be expressed in terms of the fraction of the area of the slab blocked out by nuclei. If there are n nuclei per unit volume in the slab, then the number in a slab of area A and thickness dx is $nA\,dx$, and the number per unit area of the absorber is $n\,dx$. The fraction of the area A which is opaque to neutrons is then $\sigma n\,dx$, and we may write

$$dI(x)/I(x) = -\sigma n\,dx \qquad (14.2)$$

The solution of this equation is

$$\ln I(x) = -\sigma nx + \text{constant} \qquad (14.3)$$

The arbitrary constant must be so chosen that, when $x = 0$, the intensity is the incident intensity I_0. Equation 14.3 may be put into the

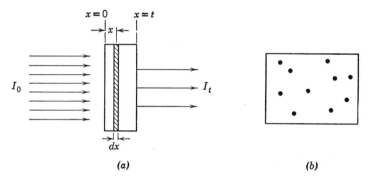

(a)   (b)

FIG. 14.3.   (a) Incident and transmitted intensities of a beam of neutrons in passing through an absorber.   (b) The black dots represent the area $n\sigma\,dx$ which is opaque to the beam of neutrons.

following form, expressing the intensity I_t which can penetrate a slab of thickness t,

$$I_t = I_0 e^{-n\sigma t} \qquad (14.4)$$

If the impinging particle is not a point but behaves like a rigid particle of finite size, then a correction has to be made. As was pointed out in Chapter 3, the collision cross section between two rigid spheres having radii R and R' is $\pi(R + R')^2$.

The cross section σ need not be interpreted in terms of the collisions of rigid spheres. The attenuation of a beam due to any interaction with the particles in its path may be described in terms of an effective cross section, but we must not then expect this cross section to have the properties of a rigid sphere cross section. For example, a study of the absorption cross section of nuclei for slow neutrons having velocities comparable to those of gas atoms at normal temperatures shows a marked dependence on velocity and even "resonance" maxima. These

phenomena can be explained in terms of the detailed energy level structure of the nuclei in question and the wave nature of the impinging
neutrons. We shall not study these processes here, but merely point
out the generalized meaning of the term cross section.

In nuclear physics, cross sections are generally expressed in *barns*.

$$1 \text{ barn} = 10^{-24} \text{ cm}^2 = 10^{-28} \text{ meter}^2$$

This term originated during World War II when the very large slow
neutron cross sections were first observed. They were said to be "as
big as a barn," and this term has now been officially adopted.

The elastic scattering of fast neutrons by nuclei can be accurately
described in terms of classical collisions between spheres. The attenuation of a fast neutron beam in aluminum, silver, and uranium is shown

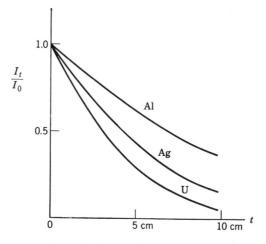

Fig. 14.4.   The attenuation of a beam of fast neutrons in aluminum, silver, and
uranium.

in Fig. 14.4. We have here three curves indicating that nuclear size
increases as Z and A increase. A detailed examination of these and
other results has shown that the nuclear size may be very simply interpreted as resulting from the agglomeration of incompressible particles.
The nuclear volume is proportional to the number of nucleons which it
contains. If R is the nuclear radius

$$\tfrac{4}{3}\pi R^3 = \text{constant} \cdot A$$

where A is the mass number. This may be rewritten

$$R = 1.4 \times 10^{-15} A^{\frac{1}{3}} m \tag{14.5}$$

The numerical constant has been chosen for a best fit with the experimental data over a wide range of masses. The approximate nuclear radius of stable nuclides is plotted as a function of the atomic number in Fig. 14.5.

14.3 NUCLEAR MASSES; BINDING ENERGY

Nuclear masses may be determined very precisely by means of an instrument called the mass spectrograph. A beam of ions of known

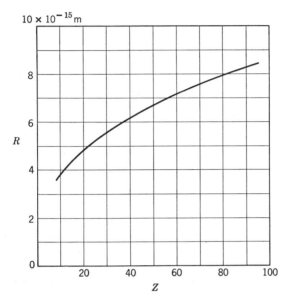

FIG. 14.5. The approximate nuclear radius of stable nuclides as a function of the atomic number Z.

velocity is directed into a magnetic field, and the radius of the circular path of the beam depends on the mass of the ion. We found in Eq. 5.7 that

$$R = mv/qB \qquad (14.6)$$

Thus in an instrument such as that illustrated in Fig. 14.6, ions of mass M_1 and M_2 will travel along circular paths of radius R_1 and R_2 and the point of termination of the path may be detected, for example, by means of a photographic plate whose emulsion is blackened by the ions in question. This sort of instrument determines the ratio of masses particularly reliably, since neither the absolute value of the field nor that of the velocity need then be known. If they are the same for both particles, we have

$$M_1/M_2 = R_1/R_2 \qquad (14.7)$$

for equally charged ions. It is customary to base all measurements on a scale in which the mass of the isotope of oxygen having $A = 16$ is taken as exactly 16 units. Thus the mass of $_8O^{16}$ is 16, but the mass of the hydrogen atom with $A = 1$, or $_1H^1$, is not 1, but 1.008123, and the mass of the helium atom with $A = 4$, or $_2He^4$, is not 4, but 4.00390.

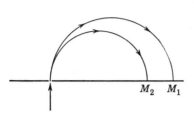

$M_2 \quad M_1$

Fig. 14.6. Illustration of the principle of a mass spectrograph.

These masses are the masses of neutral atoms, and the observed ionic masses must be corrected by the addition of the proper number of electron masses.

The knowledge of these numbers is most important in nuclear physics because they tell us something about the binding energy of nuclei, or the work that would have to be done to break heavy atoms up into hydrogen atoms and neutrons. Thus if the mass of an atom is M, and if by some means it can be broken up into two or more atoms having masses M_1, M_2, $\cdots$, then if

$$M > M_1 + M_2 + M_3 \cdots \qquad (14.8)$$

mass has been lost. The product atoms have less mass than the initially present atom. This loss in mass must necessarily show up as energy, for example, kinetic energy of the particles M_1, M_2, M_3, $\cdots$, as they fly apart. If the loss in mass is ΔM, the energy liberated, Q, must be

$$Q = \Delta M c^2 \qquad (14.9)$$

On the other hand, if

$$M < M_1 + M_2 + M_3 \cdots \qquad (14.10)$$

mass would have to be created through the breaking up of the atom. This means that the energy would have to be supplied, and that work would have to be done to pull the constituents apart.

If the condition in Eq. 14.10 is satisfied, the mass M could not possibly fly apart spontaneously into the parts having the masses M_1, M_2 $\cdots$, etc., as this would be in contradiction to the principle of conservation of energy. On the other hand, if the condition in Eq. 14.8 is satisfied, the atom *may* fly apart spontaneously but it need not. Some triggering mechanism may have to be applied to cause it to fly apart. If it does fly apart for some reason, the energy liberated will be given by Eq. 14.9.

To see this more clearly, let us consider a ball on a surface with hills and valleys. If the ball is in the lowest valley, it could not possibly spontaneously appear on a hill top. For it to do so would contradict the principle of conservation of energy. However, if the ball was on a hill, it could roll down into a valley, and if it did it would certainly release its original potential energy as kinetic energy. But it need not roll down the hill at all. It may be caught in a little local valley, and until it is pushed over the lip of this valley it can not roll down to the lowest valley. Or again, an explosive is capable of releasing energy, but it will not do so until certain auxiliary conditions are satisfied. It has energy stored within itself but will not release it until it is "triggered."

The energy content in atoms is determined by their masses. The binding energy of an atom is defined as the work required to separate it into its component hydrogen atoms and neutrons. Thus the binding

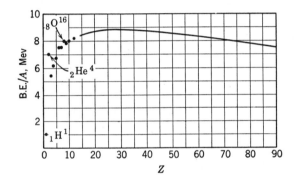

FIG. 14.7.   The binding energy per nucleon for stable atoms.

energy of an atom in mass units is the difference in mass between its Z protons and $(A - Z)$ neutrons, and the actual mass of the atom $_ZM^A$. Thus

$$\text{B.E.} = ZM_p + (A - Z)M_n - {_Z}M^A \qquad (14.11)$$

To express the binding energy in joules we must multiply by c^2, and to convert this into Mev, which is the generally more useful form, we must divide by $10^6 e$.

The binding energy per particle, which is a measure of the average loss in mass of a nucleon when it is held in a nucleus, is shown in Fig. 14.7. Among the light atoms there are great irregularities. The two protons and two neutrons in an alpha particle are more strongly bound than are the nucleons in other light atoms. In the vicinity of $Z = 30$ the nucleons are more firmly bound than in light or heavy atoms. In this region of the periodic table (iron, nickel, copper, zinc) the average mass per nucleon has its lowest value. For heavier nuclei the trend is reversed, and the binding energy per particle decreases again. We shall return to these considerations further on in connection with radio-activity, or the spontaneous disintegration of atoms, and nuclear reactions induced by bombardment. It is already clear, however, that nuclear energy can be released in two ways, by the *fission*, or splitting up of the heaviest stable atoms, or by the *fusion*, or combining, of the lightest atoms.

14.4 NUCLEAR REACTIONS

Nuclear reactions, like chemical reactions, involve a rearrangement of constituents. In chemical reactions the atoms forming the molecules of the reagents are rearranged. In nuclear reactions the nucleons (pro-tons and neutrons) forming the reagents are rearranged. Chemical reactions can usually be initiated through simply mixing the substances which are to react. The contact of the electronic structures of the molecules with each other is sufficient to bring the interatomic forces into play and so produce the rearrangement.

Nuclei cannot be brought into contact through simply mixing chem-ical substances. The electrons around the nuclei and the Coulomb repulsive forces between nuclei serve as a barrier preventing neighbor-ing nuclei from colliding, and so preventing the short-range nuclear forces from acting to produce a rearrangement. In order to initiate a nuclear reaction it is necessary to bring a particle up to or into contact with a nucleus. The commonest particles used to induce nuclear reac-tions, and the symbols used to designate them, are gamma rays (γ), neutrons (n), protons, or nuclei of $_1\text{H}^1$ atoms (p), deuterons, or nuclei of $_1\text{H}^2$ atoms (d), tritons, or nuclei of $_1\text{H}^3$ atoms (t), and the alpha particle, or $_2\text{He}^4$ nucleus (α).

Neutrons of any energy can penetrate a nucleus. In nuclear reactors many neutrons are liberated, and some of these are slowed down to thermal velocities by repeated collisions. These slow neutrons may bounce elastically from a nucleus, or they may be violently attracted when they get up to a nucleus. The attractive force is so violent that the newly formed nucleus is highly excited and must get rid of energy by the emission of particles or of electromagnetic quanta, called gamma rays when emitted by atomic nuclei. Gamma rays may likewise be absorbed by a nucleus which is put into an excited state from which it settles down into a stable state by emitting a gamma ray or a particle.

Charged particles must have sufficient energy to overcome the Coulomb repulsive force of the nucleus with which they are to react.

Heavier bombarding particles than alpha particles are not often used.
A target nucleus T struck by a bombarding particle B forms a compound nucleus C which breaks up into a product nucleus P and a secondary particle S. A nuclear reaction might be indicated schematically by the symbols

$$T + B \rightarrow C \rightarrow P + S$$

An example of a reaction written in this way would be

$$_1\mathrm{H}^1 + {}_0n^1 \rightarrow {}_1\mathrm{H}^{2^*} \rightarrow {}_1\mathrm{H}^2 + \gamma$$

The asterisk in the symbol for the compound nucleus indicates that it is an excited nucleus. A shorter and commonly used way of designating a reaction is

$$T(B, S)P$$

or, in the case of the above example,

$$_1\mathrm{H}^1(n, \gamma)_1\mathrm{H}^2$$

In this notation the compound nucleus is not specifically mentioned, and the product nucleus is sometimes also omitted, as the reaction itself specifies the product. Thus $_1\mathrm{H}^1(n, \gamma)_1\mathrm{H}^2$ is sometimes abbreviated to $_1\mathrm{H}^1(n, \gamma)$. Common reactions are

(n, γ)	(α, p)	(p, n)
(n, p)	(d, n)	(p, α)
(n, α)	(d, p)	(p, γ)
(α, n)	(d, α)	(γ, n)

Like chemical reactions, nuclear reactions either require energy to make them go, or liberate energy. Chemical reactions are called endothermic or exothermic, and nuclear reactions are called endoergic or exoergic, depending on whether they require or liberate energy. The energy balance in a nuclear reaction is called the Q of the reaction, and may be computed if the masses of all the particles before and after the reaction are known. Thus, if a mass M has disappeared from the reacting particles, it must have been transformed into energy. If $\sum M_i$ is the sum of the masses of all the initially present particles, and $\sum M_f$ is the sum of the masses of all the finally present particles, then the energy liberated in the reaction is

$$Q = (\sum M_i - \sum M_f)c^2 \qquad (14.12)$$

The masses of some of the lightest neutral atoms are given in Table 14.1. These may be used instead of nuclear masses in evaluating Eq. 14.12 whenever the same number of electrons are present in the initially and finally present neutral atoms.

The Q of a reaction may also be computed from the kinetic energies of the reacting particles if no positive electrons and no gamma rays are involved. We then have that the kinetic energies of the finally present particles must have come from the initially present kinetic energy of the bombarding particle and from the energy Q liberated in the reaction.

$$E_B + Q = E_P + E_S \qquad (14.13)$$

The products of a nuclear reaction are in general not stable. They are often radioactive and decay into other substances in a manner further discussed in the next section.

TABLE 14.1 THE MASSES OF SOME OF THE LIGHTEST NEUTRAL ATOMS

Particle	Mass in Atomic Mass Units	Particle	Mass in Atomic Mass Units
$_0n^1$	1.00893	$_3Li^8$	8.02502
$_1H^1$	1.008123	$_4Be^7$	7.01906
$_1H^2$	2.013708	$_4Be^8$	8.00785
$_1H^3$	3.01702	$_4Be^9$	9.01503
$_2He^3$	3.01700	$_4Be^{10}$	10.01677
$_2He^4$	4.00390	$_5B^9$	9.01620
$_2He^6$	6.0209	$_5B^{10}$	10.1618
$_3Li^6$	6.01697	$_6C^{10}$	10.0210
$_3Li^7$	7.01822		

In addition to the reactions mentioned above in which a single particle is emitted by the compound nucleus, there is the important "fission" reaction, in which the nucleus blows up into several pieces of comparable size. This is of particular importance in connection with *chain reactions*.

A chain reaction is one in which the products of the reaction induce the reaction itself, and this process continues until the reacting substance is used up. A chain reaction may take place as a result of fission of heavy elements, already mentioned. A particular fission process, for example, is the breaking up of U^{235} upon the addition of a neutron. The breaking up may occur in a variety of ways, of which one is

$$_{92}U^{235} + _0n^1 \rightarrow _{56}Ba^{144} + _{36}Kr^{89} + 3_0n^1$$

These fission products are not stable. The radioactive barium will decay with the emission of four successive electrons into stable $_{60}Nd^{144}$, and the radioactive krypton will decay with the emission of three successive electrons into stable $_{39}Y^{89}$. The details of these transformations and the conditions for their occurrence are further discussed in Section 14.5.

Whether some or all of the three free neutrons liberated produce fission in other U^{235} nuclei obviously depends on the physical conditions present. For example, if no other U^{235} nuclei are present, no further fission can take place. On the other hand, even if there is a large concentration of other fissionable nuclei near a nucleus undergoing fission, we cannot say whether the available neutrons will actually produce a chain reaction in the available nuclei until we have considered all the other things that the neutrons can do, such as escape from the region in question, or be absorbed by these or other nuclei without producing fission.

The energy released in the fissioning of a U^{235} nucleus can be determined from measurements on the fission products. It turns out to be about 200 Mev. This energy appears as kinetic energy of the fission products, including the neutrons, each of which initially has kinetic energy of the order of many Mev.

In a sufficiently large piece of sufficiently pure U^{235} or of other suitable fissionable material, an explosive chain reaction may be produced. Essentially each neutron liberated produces fission, and the 200 Mev per fission produce such a high temperature that rapid melting, evaporation, and ionization of the constituents results. Before the U^{235} explosion is to take place, the material must be kept in sufficiently small pieces so that the neutrons produced by a nucleus undergoing fission will escape without producing enough further fission processes to maintain a chain reaction. When the explosion is to take place, two or more pieces are brought together to form a block of sufficient size to initiate the reaction. The effectiveness of an arrangement of this kind depends on maintaining the critical geometry for a sufficiently long time so that as large a number of nuclei as possible will undergo fission before the assembly disintegrates.

We have stated above that the very light elements, containing only a few nucleons per atom, and the very heavy elements, containing over 200 nucleons per atom, have a greater average mass per nucleon than the elements near the middle of the periodic table. In other words, mass will be lost by heavy nuclei when they are divided, as by fission, or mass may be lost by the lightest elements when they are fused into larger groups. The fusion of hydrogen nuclei to form helium nuclei can also be made to liberate energy, and this is the basis of the hydrogen bomb. Reagents at very high temperatures, millions of degrees centigrade, are required to make the light nuclei collide and react. Again it is necessary to hold the reagents together long enough so that many collisions occur before the components fly apart. Important reactions in this connection might be, for instance, the result of collisions between deuterons if the reacting gases are heavy hydrogen, giving

$$_1\text{H}^2 + {}_1\text{H}^2 \rightarrow {}_1\text{H}^3 + {}_1\text{H}^1 \tag{14.14}$$

or

$$_1\text{H}^2 + {}_1\text{H}^2 \rightarrow {}_2\text{He}^3 + {}_0n^1 \tag{14.15}$$

or, if the colliding nuclei include tritium, a radioactive isotope of hydrogen having a half-life of 12 years and therefore usable in reagents that are not stored too long,

$$_1\text{H}^3 + {}_1\text{H}^3 \rightarrow {}_2\text{He}^4 + 2{}_0n^1 \tag{14.16}$$

or

$$_1\text{H}^3 + {}_1\text{H}^2 \rightarrow {}_2\text{He}^4 + {}_0n^1 \tag{14.17}$$

Each of these reactions can liberate an amount of energy calculable from the masses of the light elements given in Table 14.1.

In addition to explosive reactions, reactions that proceed at a controllable rate are also possible. Of these the first one discovered applied to stars. The origin of the energy in stars, energy which is continually being radiated away and must therefore be continually replenished, was a mystery until it was realized that the temperatures in the stars might be sufficient to allow atomic collisions of such violence that nuclear forces come into play, so that nuclear reactions can occur. The stars are held together by gravitational forces in spite of these enormous temperatures, and their temperatures rise until the amount of energy radiated is just equal to the amount generated. They are then in a steady state.

The stars are known to contain hydrogen and helium. In fact, the element helium is named for the sun, "helios" in Greek, as it was first discovered spectroscopically as radiation from an unknown element, in light from the sun. A series of reactions in which the fuel $_1\text{H}^1$ may be converted into the "ashes" $_2\text{He}^4$ are

$$_1\text{H}^1 + {}_1\text{H}^1 \rightarrow {}_1\text{H}^2 + {}_1e^0 \tag{14.18}$$

$$_1\text{H}^2 + {}_1\text{H}^1 \rightarrow {}_2\text{He}^3 \tag{14.19}$$

$$_2\text{He}^3 + {}_1\text{H}^1 \rightarrow {}_2\text{He}^4 + {}_1e^0 \tag{14.20}$$

This is currently assumed to be responsible for the energy production in faint, not-too-hot stars. In others, corresponding sequences involving also heavier elements are responsible.

Man-made nuclear reactors, or nuclear chain-reacting piles, as they are also called, derive their energy not from the synthesis of light elements, but from the fission of heavy elements. However, in order to produce a controlled reaction, that is, one in which the number of fissioning nuclei per second is subject to control or adjustment, it is necessary to use slow neutrons rather than fast neutrons. We have pointed out above that the neutrons emitted by a U^{235} nucleus undergoing fission have kinetic energies of millions of electron volts. The vibrational kinetic energy of nuclei in solids at room temperature is a few hundredths of an electron volt. Every time a fast-moving neutron hits a slow nucleus one of two things can happen. It can stick and produce a nuclear reaction, or it can bounce and in the process impart some kinetic energy to the nucleus which was struck and therefore lose some energy itself. The amount of energy lost by the fast-moving particle in an elastic collision with a slow-moving particle depends on the ratio of their masses. The quantitative results may readily be derived through setting up the expressions for the energy and momentum of the colliding nuclei and equating these to the energy and momentum after collision. Qualitatively the result is intuitively obvious. A ping-pong ball striking a bowling ball at rest will lose very little of its energy. A neutron striking a much heavier nucleus similarly will retain most of its kinetic energy in a collision. On the other hand, a billiard ball striking another billiard ball at rest may lose a large fraction of its energy, the actual amount depending on whether the collision was a head-on collision, or a glancing collision. Similarly, a neutron striking a nucleus of a light element may lose a large fraction of its energy.

We return now to a controlled nuclear reaction in a reactor in which uranium metal is used. The isotopic composition of natural uranium contains 99.3% U^{238} and 0.7% U^{235}. Such material may be used as fuel in a reactor. The fuel may be in the form of rods of such size that most of the fast neutrons produced by U^{235} fission escape from the rod. Surrounding the fuel rods there must be a moderator, a substance whose sole function is to slow down neutrons as a consequence of elastic collisions while absorbing as few as possible in $n - \gamma$ reactions, or other reactions. Very pure carbon, for example, has been used as a moderator. Heavy water has also been used. Here the neutrons are slowed down to thermal velocities, with kinetic energies of a few hundredths of an electron volt, and diffuse back again into the uranium. Here some are absorbed by U^{235} nuclei, and as a result more fission processes take place, and more neutrons are liberated. In an assembly of fuel rods surrounded by moderators, and a coolant which carries away the heat generated, a reaction once started will proceed at a pace such that, for every neutron absorbed and thus producing fission, exactly one will go through the above cycle and return to produce fission. The others escape from the reactor or are absorbed by nuclei in other reactions. The construction details which assure stable rather than unstable or

explosive operation need not concern us here. The control is essentially like the control of the rate of burning of a fire. The more oxygen
we admit to the hot, or burning coal, the hotter it gets. Similarly,
the more neutrons we allow to diffuse back into the uranium, the
"hotter" it gets. This control of neutron density in the uranium involves the use of a neutron-absorbing substance, such as cadmium, for
instance. If there is a high probability of neutron capture in the body
of a control rod inserted into the reactor, the insertion or withdrawal of
such a control rod can alter the neutron density and thus the rate of
reaction in the reactor.

The nuclear reactor has several important functions in addition to the
production of heat, already mentioned. Perhaps, from the atomic
energy point of view, the most important is that new fissionable material
may be generated in the reactor as a byproduct of its operation. For
example, the radiative capture of slow neutrons by the abundant isotope
U^{238} in the uranium rods leads to the following reactions:

$$_{92}U^{238} + {_0}n^1 \rightarrow {_{92}}U^{239} \tag{14.21}$$

Radioactive $_{92}U^{239}$ decays with the emission of an electron into an
element not found in the rocks and minerals of the earth. It has atomic
number 93 and is called neptunium. It is the first of the so-called
transuranic elements. None are found on the earth because there are
no sufficiently long-lived parent substances for them to have survived
since our world and the atoms of which it is composed were formed.
We have

$$_{92}U^{239} \rightarrow {_{93}}Np^{239} + {_{-1}}e^0 \tag{14.22}$$

This isotope of neptunium decays by the emission of another electron
into a further transuranic element, with $Z = 94$, called plutonium.

$$_{93}Np^{239} \rightarrow {_{94}}Pu^{239} + {_{-1}}e^0 \tag{14.23}$$

Like U^{235}, it will undergo fission upon the capture of a slow neutron
and may be used as a nuclear fuel or explosive.

Another nuclear species capable of undergoing fission upon slow
neutron capture, and therefore also useful as a fuel or explosive, is
another isotope of uranium, U^{233}. This also does not occur on the
earth in rocks and minerals. It can be produced from thorium by the
following series of events:

$$_{90}Th^{232} + {_0}n^1 \rightarrow {_{90}}Th^{233} \tag{14.24}$$

$$_{90}Th^{233} \rightarrow {_{91}}Pa^{233} + {_{-1}}e^0 \tag{14.25}$$

$$_{91}Pa^{233} \rightarrow {_{92}}U^{233} + {_{-1}}e^0 \tag{14.26}$$

A further important use for a nuclear reactor is that it can be used to produce radioactive substances. There are first of all highly active fission fragments which can be recovered from the fuel rods. Other substances may be placed within the reactor where they are subjected to neutron bombardment, and therefore will undergo nuclear reactions. Finally, a reactor may be used as an intense source of neutrons. Reactors have been, and will doubtless continue to be, of very great, scientific as well as economic and military importance.

14.5 THE FORMAL DESCRIPTION OF RADIOACTIVE PROCESSES

We have spoken of stable and unstable nuclei. Unstable nuclei can transform themselves spontaneously into a new form by emitting a particle. This spontaneous transformation is called radioactivity. There is one single law which describes the rate at which all radioactive transformations take place. *The number of transformations per second is proportional to the number of decaying unstable atoms present.* If N is the number of atoms of the decaying species present, then

$$dN/dt = - \lambda N \qquad (14.27)$$

The proportionality constant λ is called the *decay constant*. Its reciprocal, τ, is called the *mean life* of the decaying substance. Thus, the solution of Eq. 14.3 is

$$N = N_0 e^{-\lambda t} = N_0 e^{-t/\tau} \qquad (14.28)$$

where N_0 is the number of decaying atoms present at the time $t = 0$. A quantity related to the mean life τ is the *half-life* $\tau_{1/2}$ or the time required for half of the original number of atoms to decay.

$$N = \frac{N_0}{2} = N_0 \exp\left(-\tau_{1/2}/\tau\right)$$

or

$$\tau_{1/2} = \tau \ln 2 \qquad (14.29)$$

The activity of radioactive substances is measured in terms of the number of disintegrations per second. The unit of activity is the *curie*. The activity of 1 gram of radium is approximately 3.7×10^{10} disintegrations per second, and this rate of disintegration is commonly used as the measure of 1 curie of any radioactive substance. The *millicurie* and *microcurie*, being a thousandth and a millionth of a curie, are often used. Another important unit is the *rutherford*. One rutherford is exactly 10^6 disintegrations per second.

Radioactive substances emit three kinds of rays, alpha, beta, and gamma rays. Alpha particles are helium nuclei and have a mass num-

TABLE 14.2   THE NATURALLY OCCURRING RADIOACTIVE SERIES

(Y = years; D = days; H = hours; M = minutes; S = seconds)

Nuclear Symbol	Other Designation		Half-Life
The Thorium Series			
$_{90}Th^{232}$	Th	Thorium	$1.39 \times 10^{10}\ Y$
$_{88}Ra^{228}$	MsTh$_1$	Mesothorium 1	$6.7\ Y$
$_{89}Ac^{228}$	MsTh$_2$	Mesothorium 2	$6.13\ H$
$_{90}Th^{228}$	RdTh	Radiothorium	$1.90\ Y$
$_{88}Ra^{224}$	ThX		$3.64\ D$
$_{86}Rn^{220}$	Tn	Thoron	$54.5\ S$
$_{84}Po^{216}$	ThA		$0.158\ S$
$_{85}At^{216}$			$3 \times 10^{-4}\ S$
$_{82}Pb^{212}$	ThB		$10.6\ H$
$_{83}Bi^{212}$	ThC		$60.5\ M$
$_{84}Po^{212}$	ThC'		$3 \times 10^{-7}\ S$
$_{81}Tl^{208}$	ThC''		$3.1\ M$
$_{82}Pb^{208}$			
The Uranium Series			
$_{92}U^{238}$	UI	Uranium	$4.51 \times 10^9\ Y$
$_{90}Th^{234}$	UX$_1$		$24.1\ D$
$_{91}Pa^{234}$	UX$_2$ and UZ		$1.14\ M$ and $6.7\ H$
$_{92}U^{234}$	UII		$2.35 \times 10^5\ Y$
$_{90}Th^{230}$	Io	Ionium	$8.0 \times 10^4 Y$
$_{88}Ra^{226}$	Ra	Radium	$1622\ Y$
$_{86}Rn^{222}$	Rn		$3.825\ D$
$_{84}Po^{218}$	RaA		$3.05\ M$
$_{85}At^{218}$			Several S
$_{82}Pb^{214}$	RaB		$26.8\ M$
$_{83}Bi^{214}$	RaC		$19.7\ M$
$_{84}Po^{214}$	RaC'		$1.5 \times 10^{-4}\ S$
$_{81}Tl^{210}$	RaC''		$1.32\ M$
$_{82}Pb^{210}$	RaD		$22\ Y$
$_{83}Bi^{210}$	RaE		$5.0\ D$
$_{84}Po^{210}$	RaF	Polonium	$138\ D$
$_{81}Tl^{206}$			$4.23\ M$
$_{82}Pb^{206}$			
The Actinium Series			
$_{92}U^{235}$	AcU	Actinouranium	$8.91 \times 10^8\ Y$
$_{90}Th^{231}$	UY		$25.65\ M$
$_{91}Pa^{231}$	Pa		$3.43 \times 10^4\ Y$
$_{89}Ac^{227}$	Ac		$21.7\ Y$
$_{90}Th^{227}$	RdAc	Radioactinium	$18.6\ D$
$_{87}Fr^{223}$	AcK		$21\ M$
$_{88}Ra^{223}$	AcX		$11.2\ D$
$_{85}Rn^{219}$	An	Actinon	$3.92\ S$

TABLE 14.2 (*Continued*)

Nuclear Symbol	Other Designation	Half-Life
$_{84}Po^{215}$	AcA	$1.83 \times 10^{-3}\ S$
$_{82}Pb^{211}$	AcB	$36.1\ M$
$_{83}Bi^{211}$	AcC	$2.16\ M$
$_{84}Po^{211}$	AcC'	$0.005\ S$
$_{81}Tl^{207}$	AcC''	$4.76\ M$
$_{82}Pb^{207}$		

ber of 4. A substance decaying by alpha emission changes its mass number by four units, or $\Delta A = 4$. Beta particles are electrons. Positive as well as negative electrons are found in radioactive radiations. Gamma rays consist of electromagnetic quanta. Substances undergoing radioactive transformations by beta or gamma decay do so with $\Delta A = 0$. It follows that all radioactive transformations will take place with either $\Delta A = 4$ or $\Delta A = 0$.

Naturally occurring radioactive elements are concentrated at the heavy end of the table of nuclei. They decay in series. Thus a substance A decays into B and this into C and so on until a stable product is formed. As a consequence of the law $\Delta A = 4$ or 0, two radioactive series never have a common member. For example, a series originating with U^{238} can decay through nuclei with mass numbers 234, 230, 226, $\cdots$, but never to any of the intermediate mass numbers. There are, therefore, four possible radioactive series. However, only those series will be found on the earth which have at least one member whose half-life is longer than the age of the earth. Three of the possible four series satisfy this condition. They are listed in Table 14.2 and illustrated in Fig. 14.8.

Here nuclides having a given mass number are shown in a vertical column. The elements, for which the atomic number Z is constant, form a staggered sequence rising at an angle of 45° to the right. The horizontal arrows showing transitions with $\Delta A = 4$, represent the transformations resulting from the emission of an alpha particle. The arrows pointing down represent transformations involving the emission of an electron. Some nuclides, for instance, $_{82}Pb^{212}$, called thorium B as it is a member of the thorium series, although actually an isotope of lead, can decay in either of the two ways shown. A certain fraction of the nuclei decay by alpha emission, the rest by beta emission. The ratio of the two modes of decay is called the *branching ratio*.

When substances decay in series, the amount of any one substance present at any one time may be calculated through solving a series of equations like Eq. 14.27 with an additional term representing the rate at which the nuclide in question is being created. Thus if we have

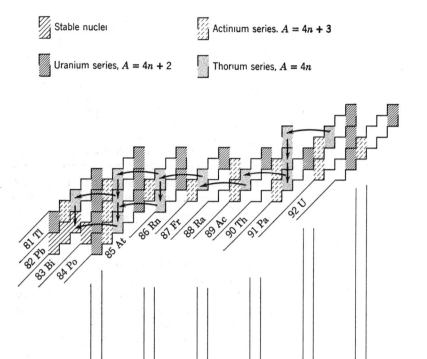

FIG. 14.8.   The three series of naturally occurring radioactive substances. Decay is by alpha or beta emission, as is indicated for the thorium series by arrows. From F. Bitter, *Nuclear Physics*, Addison-Wesley, Cambridge, Mass., 1950.

a substance 1 which decays at a rate determined by a constant λ_1 into a substance 2 which in turn decays at a rate determined by a constant λ_2 into a substance 3, and so on, we should have

$$dN_1/dt = -\lambda_1 N_1$$

$$dN_2/dt = \lambda_1 N_1 - \lambda_2 N_2$$

$$dN_3/dt = \lambda_2 N_2 - \lambda_3 N_3 \qquad (14.30)$$

$$\cdot \qquad \cdot \qquad \cdot$$
$$\cdot \qquad \cdot \qquad \cdot$$
$$\cdot \qquad \cdot \qquad \cdot$$

and so on. The explicit solution of these equations is given at the end of this section for a special case, illustrated in Fig. 14.9 which is taken from Rutherford, Chadwick, and Ellis, *Radiations from Radioactive Substances.*

The curves shown in Fig. 14.9 show the number of atoms of each of four substances formed in series by a parent substance which was initially present in the pure state. This situation might be physically realized through exposing a test body for a few seconds to a radioactive gas, radon, or $_{86}Rn^{222}$, a member of the uranium series. Some number of atoms, N_0, of the decay product of radon, which is RaA, or $_{84}Po^{218}$, with a half-life of 3.05 min, are deposited on the test body. The curves

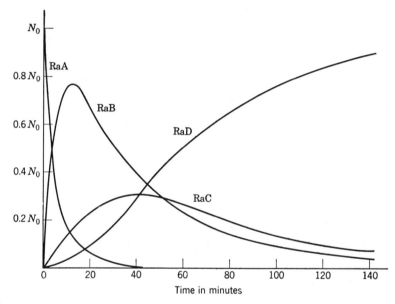

FIG. 14.9. The decay on N_0 atoms of a parent substance into a series of substances which also decay. From *Radiations from Radioactive Substances*, Ernest Rutherford, James Chadwick, and C. D. Ellis, Cambridge University Press, 1930.

of Fig. 14.9 follow these N_0 atoms for 140 min during which they are partially transformed into RaB, or $_{82}Pb^{214}$, with a half-life of 26.8 min, RaC, or $_{83}Bi^{214}$, with a half-life of 19.7 min, and finally into RaD, or $_{82}Pb^{210}$, with a half-life of 22 years. The substances RaC' and RaC''; formed from RaC, are not shown because too few atoms are present at any one time to show in the figure. The curve that is simplest to understand is that for RaA which shows a decay with a 3.05-min half-life. These atoms accumulate at first as RaB, but as the number of atoms of RaB increases, the number decaying into RaC per second also increases. After a little over 10 min the amount of RaB has reached a maximum value. After this the rate of decay exceeds the rate of production. In the same way the amount of RaC present reaches a maximum after about 35 min, and both RaB and RaC finally disappear and RaD is accumulated. Because of its very long half-life, 22 years, its decay would be apparent only in much longer times than 140 min. Note that the sum of all the atoms present at any one time is just N_0, the initial number of atoms of RaA.

If RaA is produced at a constant rate, for example, in a vessel in which the pressure of radon is kept constant, then after a sufficient time an equilibrium concentration of the decay products will be set up. Let us assume that the rate at which RaA is generated is n_0 atoms per second. Then the decay products will build up to just that number required to make their rate of decay equal to this rate of production of RaA, and therefore of every decay product. If the successive decay products are 1, 2, 3, $\cdots$, and the equilibrium numbers are $N_{1\,0}$, $N_{2\,0}$, $N_{3\,0}$, $\cdots$, then we must have

$$n_0 = \lambda_1 N_{1\,0} = \lambda_2 N_{2\,0} = \lambda_3 N_{3\,0} \cdots \qquad (14.31)$$

or

$$N_{1\,0} = \frac{n_0}{\lambda_1}, \; N_{2\,0} = \frac{n_0}{\lambda_2}, \cdots$$

The ratios of any two decay products are inversely proportional to the decay rates, or directly proportional to the half-lives. Substances with short half-lives will be present in much smaller quantities than substances with long half-lives.

The Decay of N_0 Atoms of a Parent Substance into a Series of Substances Which Also Decay

The equations to be solved are given in Eq. 14.30.

$$dN_1/dt = -\lambda_1 N_1$$

$$dN_2/dt = \lambda_1 N_1 - \lambda_2 N_2$$

$$dN_3/dt = \lambda_2 N_2 - \lambda_3 N_3$$

The solution of the first equation is given in Eq. 14.28.

$$N_1 = N_0 e^{-\lambda_1 t}$$

This may be substituted into the second equation above. The solution will be of the form

$$N_2 = ae^{-\lambda_1 t} + be^{-\lambda_2 t} \qquad (14.32)$$

where a and b are constants. To find them we substitute into the equation to be solved and get

$$-\lambda_1 ae^{-\lambda_1 t} - \lambda_2 be^{-\lambda_2 t} = \lambda_1 N_0 e^{-\lambda_1 t} - \lambda_2(ae^{-\lambda_1 t} + be^{-\lambda_2 t})$$

Collecting terms we have

$$(-\lambda_1 a - \lambda_1 N_0 + \lambda_2 a)e^{-\lambda_1 t} + (-\lambda_2 b + \lambda_2 b)e^{-\lambda_2 t} = 0$$

If this equation is to be satisfied at all times, the coefficients of the two exponentials must vanish. From the first we get

$$a = \frac{\lambda_1 N_0}{\lambda_2 - \lambda_1} \tag{14.33}$$

The second vanishes for any value of b. We must therefore evaluate b from another consideration, namely, that $N_2 = 0$ for $t = 0$, or, from Eq. 14.32,

$$a + b = 0 \tag{14.34}$$

This process may be extended to any number of equations. The general solution for the nth decay product is

$$N_n = C_1 e^{-\lambda_1 t} + C_2 e^{-\lambda_2 t} + \cdots C_n e^{-\lambda_n t} \tag{14.35}$$

$$C_1 = \frac{\lambda_1 \lambda_2 \lambda_3 \cdots \lambda_{n-1} N_0}{(\lambda_2 - \lambda_1)(\lambda_3 - \lambda_1) \cdots (\lambda_n - \lambda_1)}$$

$$C_2 = \frac{\lambda_1 \lambda_2 \lambda_3 \cdots \lambda_{n-1} N_0}{(\lambda_1 - \lambda_2)(\lambda_3 - \lambda_2) \cdots (\lambda_n - \lambda_2)}$$

14.6 NUCLEAR TRANSFORMATIONS; ALPHA AND BETA RADIATIONS

We now return to a discussion of the known nuclei plotted in Fig. 14.1 and the reasons for the existence of the particular isotopes shown. Experimentally it is found that of all the stable nuclei, the average mass per particle is least in the vicinity of $Z = 30$. In other words, as we combine neutrons and protons into the various stable forms, starting with small Z, we find that the mass per nucleon is less than the sum of the masses of the individual nucleons. Light nucleons, once brought together, fuse with the liberation of much energy. Such synthesis is one basis for liberating atomic energy. It cannot occur spontaneously on the earth because of the Coulomb repulsive fields.

Beyond $Z = 30$ the mass per nucleon, though less than the mass calculated from the masses of the constituent protons and neutrons, increases as the particles get larger. In other words, it would require work to pick them apart into their constituents, but it would require less work per particle to pull a uranium nucleus with 235 nucleons apart than, say, to pull an iron nucleus with 70 nucleons apart. However, there is clearly here a tendency which will make the heavier nuclei less stable. We have seen that, if excited, they can undergo fission and break up into smaller pieces which are more stable. It turns out that these heavier nuclei can also get into more stable configurations spontaneously by emitting an alpha particle. This change, involving a decrease of $(A - Z)$ by two and of Z by two will move them down along a 45° line in Fig. 14.1 toward the region of more stable nuclei.

We now come to the beta rays in radioactive decay. How, in the first place, can we understand the emission of electrons from nuclei which, we have indicated, are composed of neutrons and protons only? The answer is that, although electrons do not exist in the nucleus, they can be created in a disintegration. A neutron can, if it is energetically favorable, transform itself into a proton and an electron. In other words, if we have an atom composed of Z protons, Z electrons, and $(A - Z)$ neutrons having a mass greater than the mass of an atom containing $(Z + 1)$ protons, $(Z + 1)$ electrons, and $(A - Z - 1)$ neutrons, then the atom will spontaneously transform itself. If, therefore, we somehow make atoms above the stable curve in Fig. 14.1 with an excess of neutrons, for example, by fission, these atoms will spontaneously transform themselves by beta decay, or by the radioactive emission of electrons, into more and more stable atoms having the same mass number.

For atoms containing an excess of protons there are similar considerations. Let us consider the transformation of an atom containing Z protons, Z electrons, and $(A - Z)$ neutrons. A proton can transform itself into a neutron, if this is energetically favorable, by emitting a positive electron, or positron. The resulting neutral atom would contain $(Z - 1)$ protons, $(Z - 1)$ electrons, and $(A - Z + 1)$ neutrons, and we should have also left over a positive and a negative electron. If, then, the original atom had a greater mass than the resulting atom plus two electrons, it will spontaneously emit a positron and change over to the more stable form. Positron-emitting nuclei are found below the curve of stable isotopes in Fig. 14.1.

A proton can transform itself into a neutron in yet another way. Instead of emitting a positron, it can absorb an electron, if this is energetically possible, and if an electron is present. The latter condition is always fulfilled, because atomic electrons are continually penetrating the nucleus in the course of their motion, particularly electrons in the inner or K shell. Transformation by K capture, as it is called, is recognized from the presence of X rays emitted as one of the atomic electrons falls into the K shell to fill up the vacancy left by the captured electron. A part of a nuclear chart is shown in Fig. 14.10. The lightly shaded squares represent stable nuclei. The black square for $_{19}K^{40}$ represents one of a few, naturally occurring, light radioactive atoms. The white squares represent artificially produced radioactive atoms. The masses and modes of decay are also shown.

In order to complete our picture of the stability of nuclei, we must consider the binding energy per particle not only along the line of stable

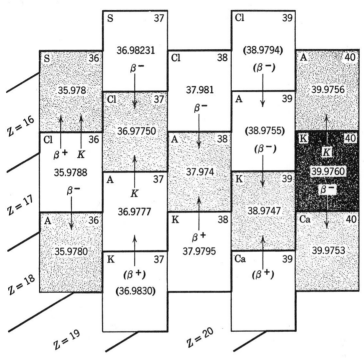

FIG. 14.10. A portion of a nuclear chart. From F. Bitter, *Nuclear Physics*, Addison-Wesley, Cambridge, Mass., 1950.

nuclei, as in Fig. 14.7, but as a function of $(A - Z)$ and Z. A contour map showing this relation is reproduced in Fig. 14.11. Along the dashed line the values of B.E./A agree with those plotted in Fig. 14.7. If we think of these binding energies as negative potential energies, we should have here a narrow valley with its trough set approximately 45° to the axes shown, with its lowest point around $Z = 28$ and $(A - Z) = 32$. Transformations of protons into neutrons and neutrons into protons appear to be possible whenever this is energetically favorable. So transformations with $\Delta A = 0$ are called *isobaric transformations*, and would shift a nuclide along a line on which A is constant, shown in Fig. 14.11. One might expect then, that only one stable nuclide occurs for each value of A. This condition is almost fulfilled for odd values of A. Among the few exceptions is $A = 87$, for which two nuclei occur in nature, $_{37}Rb^{87}$ and $_{38}Sr^{87}$. The reason is that the mass per particle for these two nuclides is almost identical, and there is very little tendency for transformation one way or the other. Actually, however, the mass per particle in Rb^{87} is slightly greater, and it is radioactive, a beta emitter with a half-life of 6.3×10^{10} years. The

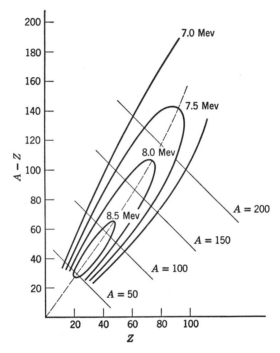

FIG. 14.11. A contour plot of B.E./A in the vicinity of stable nuclei.

cross section of the binding energy surface with a plane at constant A appears to be smooth, as shown in Fig. 14.12a.

For even mass numbers the situation is more complicated in that the binding energy curve for Z even and $(A - Z)$ even seems to lie below that for Z odd and $(A - Z)$ odd, as shown in Fig. 14.12b. Such a picture is theoretically justifiable and accounts for the fact that isobars with even A often contain two stable nuclides with an unstable one between. The stable ones are then always even-even nuclides, with an odd-odd form between them. The occurrence of three even-even stable nuclides with odd-odd forms between them can also be expected if the troughs of Fig. 14.12 are steep enough, with minima occurring not at an odd value of Z, as in Fig. 14.12b, but at an even value of Z.

Although it is difficult to say much about alpha or gamma decay without undertaking a detailed quantum mechanical discussion of nuclear structure, there is one point about alpha decay, or the spon-

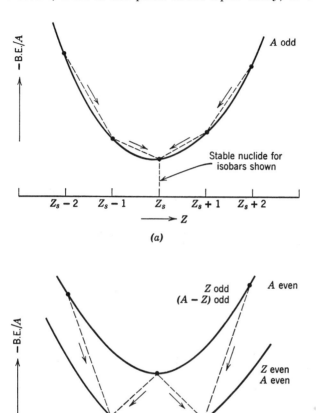

Fig. 14.12. The binding energies of a series of isobars, or nuclides having the same mass number.

taneous emission of alpha particles, which deserves special mention even in an elementary discussion. Table 14.3 lists some characteristic facts about this form of radioactivity. There are two outstanding

TABLE 14.3   REPRESENTATIVE DATA CONCERNING ALPHA DECAY

Nucleus	Half-Life	Energy of Emitted Alpha Rays in Mev
$_{90}Th^{232}$	1.39×10^{10} years	3.98
$_{92}U^{238}$	4.51×10^{9} years	4.18
$_{92}U^{235}$	8.91×10^{8} years	4.56 and 4.40
$_{92}U^{234}$	2.35×10^{5} years	4.76
$_{90}Th^{230}$	8.0×10^{4} years	5.01 and 4.74
$_{88}Ra^{226}$	1622 years	4.79
$_{89}Ac^{227}$	21.7 years	4.95
$_{90}Th^{228}$	1.9 years	5.42 and 5.34
$_{86}Rn^{222}$	3.825 days	5.486
$_{93}Np^{231}$	53 min	6.2
$_{92}U^{228}$	9.3 min	6.72
$_{86}Rn^{217}$	10^{-3} sec	7.74
$_{85}At^{216}$	3×10^{-4} sec	7.79

features of this table which should be noticed. The first is that, although the half-life varies by a wide range of orders of magnitude, actually in the vicinity of 10^{20}, the energies of the alpha particles vary by a factor of only about 2. The second is that high energies are associated with short lives, whereas low energies are associated with long lives.

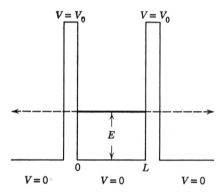

FIG. 14.13.   A leaky potential barrier.

For an explanation of these facts we return to our wave mechanical discussion of a particle in a box at the end of Section 12.5. When the box was bounded by an infinite potential energy barrier, the wave function had nodes at the surface of the box. For a box with a finite potential energy barrier, however, it was found that the wave penetrated to some extent into the energetically forbidden region outside of the box, as shown in Fig. 12.3.

If now we modify the problem still further by limiting the thickness of the potential energy barrier which retains the particle, as shown in Fig. 14.13, the barrier penetration leads to a new result. The box is "leaky." We must match wave functions in the box, in the barrier, and outside the barrier. But outside the barrier the particle is unconfined and can move off arbitrarily, and a new formulation of the problem is required. When this is done, we find that solutions of the problem again correspond to certain characteristic energy levels but there is a finite probability that in any given interval of time the particle will appear outside the box. It has been able to penetrate the potential energy barrier. The nearer the energy level is to the top of the barrier, and the thinner the barrier, the greater the probability of having the particle appear beyond the barrier in any given time interval.

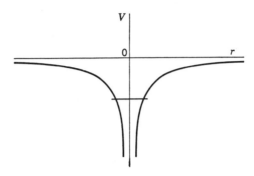

Fig. 14.14.   The potential energy of an electron in the field of a nucleus.

For electrons in atoms the attractive Coulomb force provides a potential energy barrier of the form shown in Fig. 14.14. The electron can have certain characteristic energies. There will be energy levels within the well, and the wave functions will be limited in space, as for the well shown in Fig. 12.3. Electrons cannot leak out of atoms. For nuclei, however, the Coulomb forces on a positively charged particle are repulsive. Inside the nucleus there are strong short-range attractive forces which may be represented by a steep-sided potential energy well as is shown in Fig. 14.15. These forces do not extend outside the nucleus. Here the Coulomb repulsive forces take over, and we have left a potential energy barrier of finite height and thickness. Positively charged particles having energy levels near the top of such a barrier can leak out. We shall now apply these ideas to the problems of alpha particle emitting radioactive substances.

We may think of the alpha particles as retaining their identity to some extent within a nucleus. They may be thought of as existing in energy levels of which two are shown in Fig. 14.16. Remembering that particles near the top of a thin barrier may be expected to escape rapidly, whereas particles having energies far below the top of a thick barrier will be much more effectively retained, we proceed to consider the range of energies to be expected of escaping alpha particles. Particles having energies over 10 Mev are not found because they are effectively not bound at all. They escape "at once." Particles having energies

less than 3 or 4 Mev are not found because they cannot escape at all.
The barrier is too high and thick.   Between these limits lie the observed
radioactive substances, with the understandable trend of higher energies

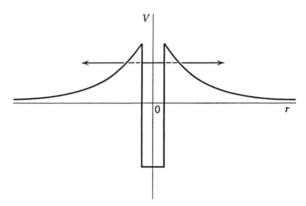

FIG. 14.15.   The potential energy of a positively charged particle in the vicinity of
a nucleus.

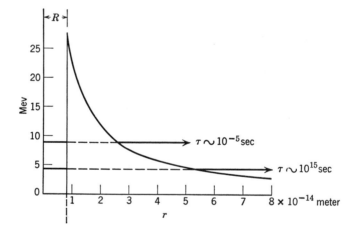

FIG. 14.16.   The mechanism of alpha decay.

associated with shorter lives.   For an explanation of the irregularities
in Table 14.3 one would have to consider variations in radius and
nuclear charge among the nuclei listed.

14.7   POSITIVE ELECTRONS, NEUTRINOS, MESONS, AND OTHER
PARTICLES

The discussions of the last four chapters will serve to illustrate the
broadening in our thinking required to understand atomic phenomena

and the simplifying concepts made possible by quantum mechanics. We begin our experience of the world by observing macroscopic objects directly through the senses, and so we form our first ideas of what existence in the material world involves. This experience we then use in constructing a model of the invisible atomic world not directly accessible to our senses. Finally we see that the evidence of our senses must not be extrapolated too far beyond the area in which it was gathered. Electrons, atoms, quanta, all these manifestations of nature which we have learned to perceive with our minds are qualitatively unlike the objects which we see around us. This insight into the nature of creation, going so very far beyond the direct evidence of our senses, is the great contribution of modern physics to civilization. We close this discussion with a brief mention of a few more of the conceptual innovations to which theory and experiment invite us. The first of these is the positively charged electron, already referred to above.

The experimental facts are these. Hard gamma rays, having frequencies such that the energy hf of the gamma ray quanta is in excess of a million volts, can disappear and leave in their place two particles, which, on detailed examination turn out to be two electrons, one of which is positively charged. The greater the energy of the quantum in excess of 1 Mev, the greater the kinetic energy with which the electrons fly apart. The positive electron, also called a *positron*, does not remain in existence indefinitely. Sooner or later it combines with a negative electron. Both of these electrons are apparently destroyed, and from the point of collision two or more gamma rays emerge having a total energy of at least 1 Mev.

We have here an example of the kind of complete transformation which the investigation of particles with high energy is bringing to light. In these transformations charge is conserved and so is momentum. Energy is conserved only if we include mass. The rest mass of an electron is equivalent to an energy m_0c^2 which is approximately 0.5 Mev. It is understandable, then, that, to create two electrons, twice this amount, or approximately 1 Mev, should be required. It is further understandable that, if a positive and a negative electron destroy each other, quanta having a total energy of 1 Mev or more should be emitted. The creation of two or more quanta rather than a single one follows from the laws of conservation of energy and momentum. If the two electrons produced a single quantum then the law of conservation of energy, expressed relativistically, would demand that

$$m_1c^2 + m_2c^2 = hf$$

and the law of conservation of momentum would require that

$$m_1v_1 + m_2v_2 = hf/c$$

which would be satisfied only if $v_1 = v_2 = c$, which condition cannot be satisfied. A possible solution involving the creation of two quanta is shown in Fig. 14.17. We can understand that, if such pair production and annihilation processes take place, they should take place in the way they do. But how can we understand the occurrence of such an event in the first place?

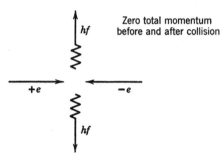

FIG. 14.17. Two quanta produced by the annihilation of a positive and a negative electron.

Here is the argument. It must obviously have some connection with the relativistic conception of mass and energy. For an electron whose rest mass is m_0, and having a momentum $p = mv$, we had previously stated that

$$E = mc^2 \qquad (14.36)$$

$$m = \frac{m_0}{\sqrt{1 - \beta^2}} \qquad \beta = v/c$$

The energy may be expressed in terms of the momentum in a way which follows from the above

$$\frac{E^2}{m_0{}^2 c^4} = 1 + \left(\frac{p}{m_0 c}\right)^2 \qquad p = mv$$

or

$$E = \pm m_0 c^2 \sqrt{1 + \left(\frac{p}{m_0 c}\right)^2}. \qquad (14.37)$$

The plus or minus sign is a direct consequence of the relativistic expressions (14.36) which up to this point have yielded correct results. For many years the minus sign in Eq. 14.37 was regarded as having no significance. What could be the meaning of a particle with negative mass and negative energy?

The matter, however, took on a different light when P. A. M. Dirac studied the quantum theory of the relativistic electron. A result similar to Eq. 14.37 was obtained, with the difference that, as in our previous consideration, the electron can exist only in certain states. The meaning of these statements is illustrated in Fig. 14.18. According to the theory the electron can exist in states having a total energy equal to or greater than m_0c^2, or in states having a total energy less than $-m_0c^2$. Between these two bands of states is a range of energies in which there are no allowed states and in which the electron can therefore not exist. It would seem, at first glance, that this is essentially equivalent to the

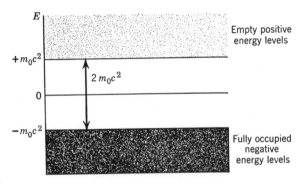

FIG. 14.18.   The energy levels of the relativistic electron.

previously described situation.   One further assumption, however, puts an entirely different light on the matter.   What if we assume that all the negative energy states are occupied?   A particle in such a completely filled band cannot undergo a collision in which less than $2m_0c^2$ of energy is supplied, because there is no "nearer" vacant state for it to go into. The situation is analogous to that of the free electrons in a metal in which, because of the exclusion principle, an electron could not change its state of motion except in a process which raised its energy to the Fermi level.   Here the electrons in the filled negative energy band, because of the exclusion principle, cannot change their state of motion except in processes which can lift them to empty states in the positive energy band. But, since in our normal surroundings no particles have enough energy to supply 1 Mev of energy in a collision, no collisions occur, and the electrons in the negative energy levels are unobserved. All space may therefore be filled with such electrons, and we should never observe any interaction between them and normal matter.

If, however, we include in our observations the effects produced by 1 Mev gamma rays, we should suppose that the absorption of such a quantum can lift an electron from the negative energy band into the positive energy band, where it is free to move off and interact with matter in the usual way. But what about the vacancy left in the negative energy band? Since this vacancy can be filled, or canceled, by a negative electron, it must have the field of a positive electron. Further considerations show that this hole will have the inertial and energetic properties of a particle of rest mass m_0. The hole will be indistinguishable from a positron. The absorption of the gamma ray quantum therefore results, from an experimental point of view, in the creation of a pair of electrons, one positive, and one negative.

Positrons behave, while they exist, just like negative electrons, except for the sign of their charge. They will in general be slowed down by collisions, and in the end they may capture a negative electron or negatron. A pair of electrons, one positive and one negative, circling around each other constitutes a new kind of neutral particle. One might designate it an atom of zero mass number. This new "element" has been observed and studied in some detail. It has been called positronium. It is not stable. Eventually the positronium particle disappears with the emission of two or more gamma ray quanta. In the terms of our model, the negative electron has fallen into the hole which was observed as a positron.

Then there is the strange and interesting case of the neutrino, a particle which has proved to be extraordinarily elusive, but which is nevertheless firmly established among particles that we are quite certain exist.

We have shown that alpha particles have certain discrete energies corresponding to radioactive decay to certain states of the parent and daughter nuclides. This is not true of beta rays. Beta ray spectra show a continuous spread of energies.

It is true that no beta particle has an energy greater than that which would be computed from the masses of the decaying and product nuclei, but the emitted beta rays are found to have all possible energies between this maximum and zero. This startling fact seems to violate the principle of conservation of energy unless some way is discovered for carrying off the lost energy. It is now accepted that there is in fact an additional unobserved particle, called a neutrino, emitted during beta decay. The energy lost in the transformation is shared by the electron and the neutrino. The maximum possible energy of the electron is to be expected if the neutrino goes off with little or none. The minimum energy of the electron is to be expected when the neutrino goes off with it all. It is assumed that the neutrino is unobserved because it is electrically neutral and does not sufficiently interact with matter. The probability of interaction is so small that it escapes far from the apparatus within which it was created, and so is not observed. This arbitrary assumption can rescue our law of conservation of energy, but is the assumption justified by additional evidence? The answer is in the affirmative. There are, in fact, three independent kinds of evidence supporting the assumption of the existence of this so far undetected particle.

The first has to do with the shape of the beta ray spectrum. What distribution of energies would be expected for electrons if a fixed total energy were shared in a random way between it and a neutrino? This can be computed, and leads to the observed distribution.

Secondly, if the neutrino carries away energy, it must also carry away momentum. In other words, if we examine the two observable fragments of a decaying atom in detail, that is, the recoiling atom and the electron, we should find that their momenta are not equal and opposite, but that a quantity of momentum as well as of energy has disappeared. Experiments in cloud chambers to prove this point are extremely difficult but have been carried out. They indicate that both energy and momentum are carried off by a neutrino in beta decay.

Finally, there is angular momentum to be considered. In beta decay, the mass number does not change. Since it is observed that all nuclei with an odd mass number have a half-integral angular momentum, and all nuclei with an even mass number have an integral angular momentum we may conclude that in beta decay the angular momentum of a nucleus must change by zero or an integral number of units. Now an electron, because of its translational motion, may carry off an integral number of units of angular momentum, but, in addition, it carries off a half-unit in its spin. An additional half-unit must have been carried off by our unobserved particle, the neutrino.

Other unstable particles have been found in the radiations from matter subject to very high-energy bombardment. Of these we mention here only the mesons, of which there are several kinds, and which are, in some respects, like heavy electrons, as their masses are intermediate between that of the electron and the proton, and that of the recently announced negative proton. The succession of new particles discovered as higher and higher bombardment energies become available indicates that a new chapter of physics is now being written.

SUMMARY

Nuclei are made up of protons and neutrons in approximately equal proportions. The short-range attractive forces which nucleons exert on each other may be thought of as producing a potential energy well, within which the protons and neutrons occupy the states with the lowest possible energy consistent with the exclusion principle. The proton states are more spread out in energy, especially for heavy atoms, because of the Coulomb repulsive force. Hence the neutron excess in heavy atoms. The validity of the proton-neutron model of nuclei is particularly clearly demonstrated by considerations involving the nuclear angular momentum. Nuclei containing an integral number of nucleons have a spin which is an integral number of times $h/2\pi$, or zero. Nuclei containing an odd number of particles have a spin which is a half-integral number of times $h/2\pi$.

The nuclear volume is proportional to the number of nucleons present. This fact leads to the expression for the nuclear radius R

$$R = 1.4 \times 10^{-15} A^{\frac{1}{3}} \text{ meters}$$

Nuclear energies may be computed from observed nuclear masses by use of the relation $E = mc^2$. The work required to separate a nucleus into two or more parts may therefore be calculated if the mass of the original nucleus, and that of the components into which it is to be divided, are all known. The work required to separate a nucleus into separate protons and neutrons or, what amounts to the same thing, the work required to separate an atom into hydrogen atoms and neutrons, is called the binding energy of the atom. Atoms of intermediate mass, or with atomic number around 30, have the greatest binding energy, or the least mass per nucleon.

Nuclear reactions involve a rearrangement of nucleons. In order to induce a nuclear reaction, an incident particle must come within the range of nuclear forces or must be absorbed. The resulting excited compound nucleus will then settle down to its stable state by emitting a particle or a quantum. Light nuclei, or neutrons, or gamma rays, are commonly used to induce nuclear reactions. These are also found among the particles emitted by the compound nucleus. An important reaction of another type is fission, in which a struck heavy nucleus flies apart into two fragments of comparable size. Chain reactions are reactions in which the products initiate further reactions, either explosively or at a controllable rate.

Some nuclei are stable, whereas others are unstable and transform themselves spontaneously into other forms. The radiations given off in this way consist either of alpha rays (helium nuclei), beta rays (electrons), or gamma rays (electromagnetic quanta). The rate of radioactive decay is given by the following law

$$dN/dt = -\lambda N$$

$$N = N_0 e^{-\lambda t}$$

Three of the four possible radioactive series occur on the earth. The fourth has disappeared because no member has a sufficiently long life $\tau = 1/\lambda$.

Isobaric transformations are nuclear transformations without change of mass number. If a nucleus can become more stable, or if it can get rid of energy, by the transformation of a neutron into a proton, this transformation will take place with the emission of an electron and an additional neutral particle called a neutrino. The excess energy is shared by these two particles, each of which has an intrinsic angular momentum of $\frac{1}{2}h/2\pi$. If, on the other hand, a nucleus can become more stable by the transformation of a proton into a neutron, it will do so either by capturing a negative electron (K capture) or by emitting a positive electron, and also a neutrino.

With a few exceptions, alpha decay occurs only among the heaviest elements, or $Z > 82$ (lead). The outstanding fact about this process is that all alpha rays have energies of from 4 to 8 Mev, but half-lives range from a few microseconds to 10^{10} years. The long half-lives are associated with the low energies, and the short half-lives are associated with the higher energies. These facts are accounted for by the wave mechanical explanation of barrier penetration. The Coulomb barrier surrounding the nucleus is transparent near its lip to high-energy alpha particles, but it rapidly becomes opaque at lower energies where it is thicker.

High-energy physics, up in the Bev range, is revealing a complex set of new particles and is providing us with a first glimpse of the next chapters of physics, dealing with the constituents of matter and the forces which they exert on each other.

PROBLEMS

1. A hypothetical metal having a specific gravity of 8 and mass number 120 is placed in a beam of neutrons. The scattering cross section is 0.8 barns. (a) What thickness is needed to reduce the intensity of the beam to 10% of its incident value? (b) Another sample of the above metal contains an unknown percentage of an impurity having an absorption cross section of 12,000 barns. A slab having the same thickness as that used in part a is found to reduce the beam intensity to 5% of its initial value. What is the concentration of the impurity?

★2. The masses of nuclei are fairly accurately given by the following expression,

$$ZM_p + (A - Z)M_n - a_1A + a_2A^{2/3} + a_3\frac{Z^2}{A^{1/3}} + a_4\frac{(A/2 - Z)^2}{A} + \delta$$

where M_p and M_n are the masses of the proton and neutron respectively, A is the mass number, Z is the atomic number, a_1, a_2, a_3, and a_4 are constants, and δ is a small correction term depending on whether A and Z are even or odd. Apart from the last term, the form of the above expression can be understood using only concepts with which the student is familiar if we consider the nucleus as a "liquid drop" of closely packed neutrons and protons held together by strong short-range forces to form spherical aggregates whose radii are given by Eq. 14.5. Discuss briefly the origin of each term. Can you account for the fact that $a_3 \fallingdotseq 7 \times 10^{-4}$ if masses are expressed in atomic mass units?

3. By which of the reactions listed on p. 529 could $_1H^1$, $_1H^2$, $_1H^3$, $_2He^3$, or $_2He^4$ be produced from stable elements? The stable elements at the beginning of the periodic table are $_1H^1$, $_1H^2$, $_2He^3$, $_2He^4$, $_3Li^6$, $_3Li^7$, $_4Be^9$, $_5B^{10}$, $_5B^{11}$, $_6C^{12}$, $_6C^{13}$. Write your answers in the form

$$_1H^1 \; (n, \gamma) \; _1H^2$$

4. How much energy in Mev is released in the following reactions?

$$_1H^3 \; (p, \gamma) \; _2He^4$$
$$_1H^2 \; (n, \gamma) \; _1H^3$$
$$_3Li^6 \; (d, n) \; _4Be^7$$
$$_3Li^7 \; (\gamma, n) \; _3Li^6$$

5. Could a cyclotron producing 4 Mev protons initiate the reaction

$$_{53}I^{127} \; (p, \gamma) \; _{54}Xe^{128}$$

6. The luminous dials of watches and similar instruments are usually made by mixing a zinc sulfide phosphor with an alpha emitter. The phosphor emits light when bombarded by the alpha particles. A typical airplane altimeter dial contains 180 mμg of radium whose half-life is 1622 years. How much radiothorium (RdTh; $\tau_{1/2} = 1.9$ years) would be required to produce the same luminescence? What is the disadvantage, if any, in using RdTh?

7. If the age of the earth is taken as 2.5×10^9 years, how much of the original U^{238} has decayed since the earth was formed?

8. Assuming that, in a mineral containing uranium, the decay products of the uranium series are in equilibrium with each other and with the parent substance, how much uranium would have to be processed to recover 10 grams of radium?

9. From experiment it is known that 1 gram of pure radium forms 0.042 cc of helium per year. It is also known from counting the number of alpha particles emitted that 3.7×10^{10} alpha particles are emitted per second. From this information and the fact that 1 gram-molecule of helium has a volume of 22.4 liters under standard conditions, compute Avogadro's number.

10. Through bombarding Be^9 by various particles the following products may be obtained:

$$He^6, \; Be^8, \; Be^{10}, \; B^{10}$$

What projectile may be used in each case and what would be its minimum energy and the energies of the products?

11. (a) Calculate the potential energy in Mev of a system consisting of a spherical $_{36}Kr^{92}$ nucleus touching a spherical $_{56}Ba^{144}$ nucleus.

(b) Compare this energy with the energy released in the reaction

$$_{92}U^{235} + _0n^1 \rightarrow _{92}U^{236} \rightarrow _{36}Kr^{91} + _{56}Ba^{142} + 3(_0n^1)$$
$$_{92}U^{236} = 236.132 \text{ amu}$$
$$_{36}Kr^{91} = 90.936 \text{ amu}$$
$$_{56}Ba^{142} = 141.939 \text{ amu}$$
$$_0n^1 = 1.009 \text{ amu}$$

★12. In a pile the neutrons released in the fission process are "moderated" in graphite. On colliding with a C atom, a neutron is sometimes captured but usually bounces off with reduced energy in accordance with the laws of conservation of energy and momentum.

(a) If, on the average, a neutron gives up 15% of its energy at each collision, retaining 85%, how many collisions are required to reduce a 1-Mev (10^6 ev) neutron to an energy of 1 ev?

(b) Assume that, of a large number of neutrons making one collision each with a C atom, about 99.90% would bounce off, the rest being captured. For 10^{10} neutrons starting off at 1 Mev, how many will be reduced to 1 ev in energy without being captured?

(c) If no other neutron losses were involved, what minimum number of neutrons would have to be released, on the average, per fission, to sustain the chain reaction in the pile, assuming that every neutron that reaches an energy of 1 ev will produce fission?

(d) What other losses would be present in an actual pile?

13. How much energy in Mev is released in the reactions listed in Eqs. 14.14 and 14.17?

14. How much energy is released in the series of reactions in Eqs. 14.18 to 14.20?

15. The first atomic bombs made were said to be the equivalent in destructive power to 20,000 tons of T.N.T. Assuming that destructive power is a measure of the energy released, and that 1 lb of T.N.T. releases about 1.7×10^6 joules, estimate the number of pounds of U^{235} consumed in the explosion. The density of uranium metal is about 18.5 grams/cc. Estimate the total decrease of nuclear mass resulting from the explosion.

16. A nuclear reactor is operating at a level of 1000 kw. Assuming that 200 Mev are released per U^{235} fission, how many fissions are occurring per second? How long will it take to use up 10 grams of fissionable material?

17. Compute the "heat of fission" of U^{235} in calories per gram. (See Problem 16.)

★18. Assume that when the sun is directly overhead, the power radiated to the earth by the sun is 80 kw per meter^2.

(a) If the radius of the earth is 6000 km, what is the equivalent mass of the energy falling on the earth per second?

(b) Compute the mass of the earth from the known acceleration due to gravity at the earth's surface. Compute, then, the mass of the sun from the fact that it is moving in an almost circular orbit having a radius of 150 million km, and that the time taken for one revolution is 365 days. Compute, finally, the total radiation from the sun. What fraction of its mass does the sun radiate per year?

(c) If the temperature of the sun were not maintained by a nuclear reaction, but if the sun could be regarded as a reservoir of energy containing $\frac{3}{2}kT$ for every nucleon in it, and if the average temperature of the sun were X million degrees centigrade, how long would it take the sun to lose all of its energy at the present rate of loss? Express your answer in terms of the unknown X above.

19. If a positron and electron pair are annihilated and two photons of equal energy are given off, what are the wavelengths of the photons?

20. A 5-Mev quantum generates a positron-electron pair, and these share the excess energy available equally. What is the kinetic energy of each particle? What is its velocity?

Damped
Simple Harmonic Motion

The oscillations which we wish to study are solutions of the equation

$$\frac{d^2x}{dt^2} + \frac{1}{T}\frac{dx}{dt} + \omega_0{}^2 x = A \qquad (\text{I.1})$$

where T and ω_0 are constants, and A is either a constant or a periodic function of t. For those who would like to relate this equation to a familiar physical situation, we first set up the equation of motion of a mass M free to move along the x axis subject to a restoring force of magnitude $-kx$ directed toward the origin. We have from Newton's laws of motion

$$Ma = F$$

$$M\frac{d^2x}{dt^2} = -kx \qquad (\text{I.2})$$

The solution of this equation is

$$x = X_0 \sin (\omega_0 t + \alpha)$$

with $\omega_0 = \sqrt{K/M}$, and X_0 and α arbitrary constants which can be adjusted to satisfy prescribed initial conditions. For example, if we stipulate that, at the time $t = 0$, the position and velocity of the particle have particular values x_0 and v_0, the two constants X_0 and ψ can be given values satisfying

$$x_0 = X_0 \sin \alpha$$

$$v_0 = \left(\frac{dx}{dt}\right)_{t=0} = \omega_0 X_0 \cos \alpha$$

Now suppose that the mass M is subject to a damping force proportional to the velocity. For example, for a sphere of radius r in a medium of viscosity η the damping force is $6\pi\eta rv$, as we saw at the beginning of Chapter 3 in connection with Millikan's oil drop experiment. In general we shall assume the damping force to be some constant times the velocity, and the equation of motion becomes

$$M \frac{d^2x}{dt^2} = -kx - c \frac{dx}{dt} \tag{I.3}$$

If the velocity is in the direction of increasing x, so that dx/dt is positive, the damping force will be negative. If there is some additional force F, we get

$$M \frac{d^2x}{dt^2} = -kx - c \frac{dx}{dt} + F \tag{I.4}$$

Rearranging terms and dividing by M reduces Eq. I.4 to the form of Eq. I.1. Note that ω_0 is the natural frequency of the free undamped system, and that T is a characteristic time related to the damping.

We shall discuss first the solutions of Eq. I.1 for the case that A is a constant. We first show that a function of the form

$$x = X_0 e^{-t/\tau} \sin (\omega_D t + \alpha) + X \tag{I.5}$$

is a solution. This is damped simple harmonic motion, damped with a characteristic time τ, and oscillating with an angular frequency ω_D characteristic of the damped system. By differentiation we find

$$\frac{dx}{dt} = -\frac{1}{\tau} X_0 e^{-t/\tau} \sin (\omega_D t + \alpha) + \omega_D X_0 e^{-t/\tau} \cos (\omega_D t + \alpha)$$

$$\frac{d^2x}{dt^2} = \frac{1}{\tau^2} X_0 e^{-t/\tau} \sin (\omega_D t + \alpha) - \frac{\omega_D}{\tau} X_0 e^{-t/\tau} \cos (\omega_D t + \alpha)$$

$$\frac{-\omega_D}{\tau} X_0 e^{-t/\tau} \cos (\omega_D t + \alpha) - \omega_D{}^2 X_0 e^{-t/\tau} \sin (\omega_D t + \alpha)$$

Combining terms reduces the last equation to

$$\frac{d^2x}{dt^2} = \left(\frac{1}{\tau^2} - \omega_D{}^2 \right) X_0 e^{-t/\tau} \sin (\omega_D t + \alpha) - \frac{2\omega_D}{\tau} X_0 e^{-t/\tau} \cos (\omega_D t + \alpha)$$

On substituting these expressions into Eq. I.1 we find terms that depend on t in three different ways. One set of terms contains a factor $e^{-t/\tau} \sin (\omega_0 t + \alpha)$. Another set contains the factor $e^{-t/\tau} \cos (\omega_0 t + \alpha)$. The third set comprises constants, independent of time. Combining these terms we get

$$C_1 e^{-t/\tau} \sin (\omega_D t + \alpha) + C_2 e^{-t/\tau} (\cos \omega_D t + \alpha) + C_3 = 0 \quad \text{(I.6)}$$

$$C_1 = \frac{1}{\tau^2} - \omega_D{}^2 - \frac{1}{\tau T} + \omega_0{}^2$$

$$C_2 = -\frac{2\omega_D}{\tau} + \frac{\omega_D}{T}$$

$$C_3 = X\omega_0{}^2 - A$$

Eq. I.6 can be satisfied for all values of t only if the three constants C_1, C_2, and C_3 are each equal to zero. The last equation requires that $X\omega_0{}^2 = A$. The second equation can be satisfied in two different ways. One possibility is that $\omega_D = 0$, in which event the system does not oscillate. In this case the first equation reduces to

$$\frac{1}{\tau^2} - \frac{1}{\tau T} + \omega_0{}^2 = 0$$

which can be satisfied by two different values of $1/\tau$.

$$1/\tau = \frac{1}{2T} \pm \frac{1}{2} \sqrt{\frac{1}{T^2} - 4\omega_0{}^2}$$

$$= \frac{1}{2T} [1 \pm \sqrt{1 - 4\omega_0{}^2 T^2}] \quad \text{(I.7)}$$

This in turn provides a real solution for τ only if $4\omega_0{}^2 T^2 < 1$. Let us call the two values of τ which satisfy Eq. I.7 τ_1 and τ_2. If exp $(-t/\tau_1) + A/\omega_0{}^2$ and exp $(-t/\tau_2) + A/\omega_0{}^2$ are separate solutions of Eq. I.1, then, as may be verified by substitution,

$$X_1 \exp (-t/\tau_1) + X_2 \exp (-t/\tau_2) + A/\omega_0{}^2$$

is also a solution, with arbitrary values for the constants X_1 and X_2. These may be chosen so as to satisfy initial conditions. We conclude then, that if

$$4\omega_0{}^2 T^2 < 1$$

a solution of Eq. I.1 with two arbitrary constants is

$$x = X_1 \exp (-t/\tau_1) + X_2 \exp (-t/\tau_2) + A/\omega_0{}^2$$

$$\frac{1}{\tau_1} = \frac{1}{2T} [1 + \sqrt{1 - 4\omega_0{}^2 T^2}] \quad \text{(I.8)}$$

$$\frac{1}{\tau_2} = \frac{1}{2T} [1 - \sqrt{1 - 4\omega_0{}^2 T^2}]$$

These two characteristic decay times are plotted in Fig. I.1 as functions of the dimensionless quantity $\omega_0 T$.

To illustrate the significance of this solution we consider an overdamped system, such as a pendulum suspended in a liquid of such high viscosity that oscillations do not occur. The initial conditions will be

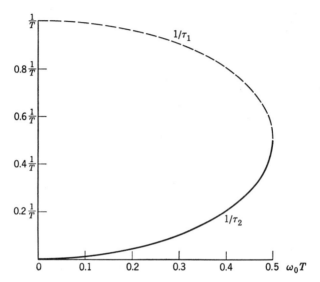

FIG. I.1. The characteristic decay times for non-oscillatory solutions of Eq. I.1.

assumed to consist of a displacement D, with the pendulum released from rest, and with no external force acting after the pendulum is released. Furthermore, let us assume $\omega_0 T = 0.4$, so that $1/\tau_1 = 0.8/T$ and $1/\tau_2 = 0.2T$

$$A = 0$$

$$X_1 + X_2 = D$$

$$\left(\frac{dx}{dt}\right)_{t=0} = 0 = -\frac{X_1}{\tau_1} - \frac{X_2}{\tau_2}$$

These conditions are satisfied if

$$X_1 = \frac{D}{1 - \tau_2/\tau_1} = -\frac{D}{3}$$

$$X_2 = \frac{D}{1 - \tau_1/\tau_2} = \frac{4D}{3}$$

and the solution in Eq. I.8 therefore reduces to

$$x = \frac{D}{3}\left(-e^{-0.8t/T} + 4e^{-0.2t/T}\right) \tag{I.9}$$

This function is plotted in Fig. I.2.

We shall now proceed with the case of oscillatory motion, for which $\omega_D \neq 0$. As previously, if C_3 in Eq. I.6 is to vanish, we must have $X = A/\omega_0^2$. The second condition is

$$1/\tau = 1/2T \tag{I.10}$$

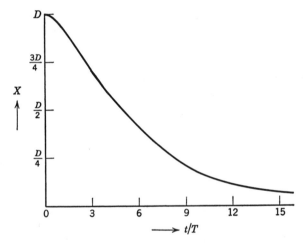

Fig. I.2. The motion of an overdamped pendulum starting from a displaced position at rest.

and, on substituting this into the first, we find that

$$\frac{1}{4T^2} - \omega_D^2 - \frac{1}{2T^2} + \omega_0^2 = 0$$

$$\omega_D^2 = \omega_0^2 - \frac{1}{4T^2}$$

$$\omega_D = \omega_0\sqrt{1 - \frac{1}{4\omega_0^2 T^2}} \tag{I.11}$$

The expression for the natural frequency of the damped system is real only if $4\omega_0^2 T^2 > 1$. The solution for this case has the form of Eq. I.5, with $1/\tau$ and ω_D having the values I.10 and I.11 above. X_0 and α are arbitrary constants which must be chosen to satisfy the initial conditions. For large values of $\omega_0 T$ the frequency of the damped oscillations approaches that of the free oscillations. The quantity $\omega_0 T/2\pi$ specifies the number of oscillations the system will execute before the amplitude of the oscillations is reduced to $1/e$ of their initial value.

We come now to a consideration of forced oscillations, or the response of a system such as has been discussed above to a periodic driving force. In Eq. I.4 we may consider F to be a prescribed periodic function, and the equation to be solved, after division by M, becomes

$$\frac{d^2x}{dt^2} + \frac{1}{T}\frac{dx}{dt} + \omega_0{}^2 x = A_0 \cos \omega t \qquad (I.12)$$

We shall confine our attention to solutions having the periodicity ω of the applied force. In general, if we start the motion of our system in an arbitrary way, for example, from rest, the driving force will produce oscillations whose amplitude varies with time. However, after sufficient time has elapsed, the "transients," as they are called, will be damped out, and we arrive at a condition in which the oscillations have the frequency of the driving force, and a constant amplitude. We may assume that the displacement has the form

$$x = X_0 \cos (\omega t - \psi) \qquad (I.13)$$

and the solution of the problem consists of finding the values of X_0 and ψ, the amplitude and phase of the function x in terms of the amplitude and phase of the driving force. In this connection a geometrical description of the situation is illuminating. We are concerned with the two functions

$$A = A_0 \cos \omega t$$

$$x = X_0 \cos (\omega t - \psi) \qquad (I.14)$$

The choice of the cosine rather than the sine or some combination of sine and cosine functions for A is purely arbitrary. It specifies that we shall choose as our initial time $t = 0$, an instant for which A has its maximum positive value. We represent our function A as the horizontal projection of a vector of magnitude A_0 rotating in a counterclockwise direction with the angular velocity ω, as shown in Fig. I.3. The horizontal projection of A_0 is $A_0 \cos \omega t = A$ in accordance with Eq. I.14. We now draw a second vector of magnitude X_0 making an angle ψ with A_0. We adopt the usual convention of calling ψ the angle by which A_0 leads X_0. When ψ is positive A_0 leads X_0 as they both rotate at the same angular velocity. We then have from Fig. I.3 that the horizontal projection of the vector X_0 is $X_0 \cos (\omega t - \psi) = x$, in accordance with Eq. I.13. The solution of Eq. I.12 will consist of finding the vector X_0, given A_0.

To find the values of X_0 and ψ which will make the function x in Eq. I.13 a solution of Eq. I.12, we note that if

$$x = X_0 \cos (\omega t - \psi)$$

it can also be written in the form

$$x = X_0 \cos \psi \cos \omega t + X_0 \sin \psi \sin \omega t \qquad (\text{I.15})$$
$$= K_1 \cos \omega t + K_2 \sin \omega t$$

where

$$K_1 = X_0 \cos \psi$$
$$K_2 = X_0 \sin \psi \qquad (\text{I.16})$$

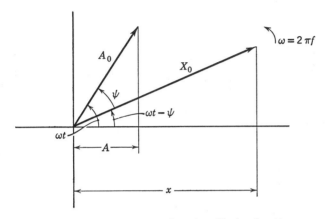

FIG. I.3.   Vector representation of oscillating functions.

By differentiation we find

$$dx/dt = -\omega K_1 \sin \omega t + \omega K_2 \cos \omega t$$

$$\frac{d^2x}{dt^2} = -\omega^2 K_1 \cos \omega t - \omega^2 K_2 \sin \omega t = -\omega^2 x$$

Substituting this result into Eq. I.12, and combining the first and third terms, we get

$$(\omega_0{}^2 - \omega^2)(K_1 \cos \omega t + K_2 \sin \omega t) - \frac{\omega}{T}(K_1 \sin \omega t - K_2 \cos \omega t) = A_0 \cos \omega t$$

This expression may be simplified through collecting all the terms involving cos ωt, and all the terms involving sin ωt, as in the above discussion. The resulting expression will have the form

$$F_1 \cos \omega t + F_2 \sin \omega t = 0$$

where F_1 and F_2 are factors not involving the time which must vanish if the equation is to be true at all times. We have, then,

$$F_1 = (\omega_0{}^2 - \omega^2)K_1 + \frac{\omega}{T} K_2 - A_0 = 0 \tag{I.17}$$

$$F_2 = (\omega_0{}^2 - \omega^2)K_2 - \frac{\omega}{T} K_1 = 0 \tag{I.18}$$

From Eqs. I.16 and I.18 we get

$$\frac{K_2}{K_1} = \tan \psi = \frac{\omega/T}{\omega_0{}^2 - \omega^2} = \frac{1/\omega_0 T}{\dfrac{\omega_0}{\omega} - \dfrac{\omega}{\omega_0}}$$

and from this, since

$$\cos^2 \psi = \frac{1}{1 + \tan^2 \psi}$$

$$\cos \psi = \frac{\omega_0{}^2 - \omega^2}{\sqrt{(\omega/T)^2 + (\omega_0{}^2 - \omega^2)^2}} = \frac{\omega_0 T \left(\dfrac{\omega_0}{\omega} - \dfrac{\omega}{\omega_0} \right)}{\sqrt{1 + \omega_0{}^2 T^2 \left(\dfrac{\omega_0}{\omega} - \dfrac{\omega}{\omega_0} \right)^2}} \tag{I.19}$$

and since $\sin \psi = \cos \psi \tan \psi$

$$\sin \psi = \frac{\omega/T}{\sqrt{(\omega/T)^2 + (\omega_0{}^2 - \omega^2)^2}} = \frac{1}{\sqrt{1 + \omega_0{}^2 T^2 \left(\dfrac{\omega_0}{\omega} - \dfrac{\omega}{\omega_0} \right)^2}} \tag{I.20}$$

Similarly, by squaring Eq. I.17 and I.18 and adding, we get
$$X_0{}^2 = K_1{}^2 + K_2{}^2$$

$$X_0 = \frac{A_0}{\sqrt{(\omega/T)^2 + (\omega_0{}^2 - \omega^2)^2}} = \frac{A_0 T/\omega}{\sqrt{1 + \omega_0{}^2 T^2 \left(\dfrac{\omega_0}{\omega} - \dfrac{\omega}{\omega_0} \right)^2}} \tag{I.21}$$

These results are plotted in Fig. I.4. Note that the quantity $\omega_0 T$ plays an important part in these equations. It is given a special designation, Q.

$$Q = \omega_0 T \tag{I.22}$$

Note that when Q or $\omega_0 T \gg 1$ we have marked "resonance" phenomena in the neighborhood of $\omega/\omega_0 = 1$. The phase angle between force and displacement changes rapidly from 0 to 180°, and the amplitude of X_0 has a pronounced maximum. This is the situation for systems which have only slight damping. In systems with such pronounced damping that Q or $\omega_0 T \lesssim 1$, resonance phenomena are suppressed. Note finally that resonance occurs when the applied frequency is equal to that of the undamped system, even though the system is actually damped.

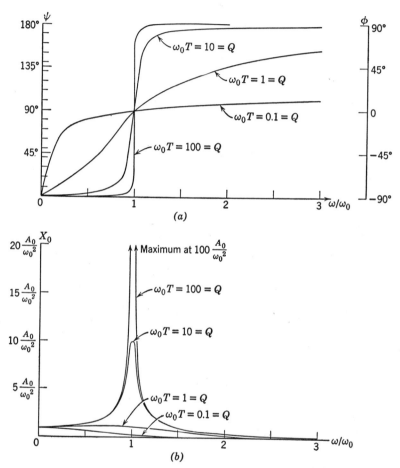

FIG. I.4. (a) The phase angle, and (b) the amplitude of forced oscillations as a function of ω/ω_0, the ratio of the applied frequency to the natural frequency of the undamped system.

Whereas for some purposes it is important to know the relation between the displacement and the applied force, for others it is important to emphasize the velocity and the force. For instance, if we are studying energy relationships, Fv is the rate at which the force F does work, and the average power supplied by this force and converted into heat through the damping is simply the average of Fv over a cycle.   If

$$F = MA_0 \cos \omega t = F_0 \cos \omega t$$

$$x = X_0 \cos (\omega t - \psi)$$

then

$$v = dx/dt = -\omega X_0 \sin (\omega t - \psi)$$

Which can be rewritten, since $\sin \alpha = -\cos (\alpha + \pi/2)$ and therefore $-\sin (\omega t - \psi) = \cos (\omega t - \psi + \pi/2)$

$$v = v_0 \cos (\omega t - \phi)$$

$$v_0 = \omega X_0 = \frac{A_0 T}{\sqrt{1 + \omega_0{}^2 T^2 \left(\dfrac{\omega_0}{\omega} - \dfrac{\omega}{\omega_0} \right)^2}} \tag{I.23}$$

$$\phi = \psi - \pi/2$$

The rate at which energy is fed into the system is

$$Fv = MA_0 \cos \omega t \cdot \omega X_0 \cos (\omega t - \phi)$$

and the average power input is

$$W = Fv = MA_0 X_0 \, \omega \, \frac{1}{t} \int_0^t \cos \omega t \cdot \cos (\omega t - \phi) \, dt$$

the integration being extended over any integral number of cycles, for example, one cycle, in which case $t = 2\pi/\omega$.   But $\cos (\omega t - \phi)$ may be written (see Eq. I.15)

$$\cos (\omega t - \phi) = \cos \phi \cos \omega t + \sin \phi \sin \omega t$$

The integral of $\cos \omega t \sin \omega t$ over a cycle vanishes, and the integral $\cos^2 \omega t$ over a cycle is $\frac{1}{2}(2\pi/\omega)$, so that

$$W = \frac{F_0 V_0}{2} \cos \phi \tag{I.24}$$

where

$$F_0 = MA_0$$

and

$$X_0 \frac{2\pi}{t} = X_0 \omega = v_0$$

Using Eq. I.23 and, noting that $\cos \phi = \cos (\psi - \pi/2) = \sin \psi$, which in turn is given in Eq. I.20, one may write out this expression explicitly in terms of the applied frequency and the physical parameters characterizing the motion.

$$W = \frac{F_0^2 T}{2M} \frac{1}{1 + \omega_0^2 T^2 \left(\dfrac{\omega_0}{\omega} - \dfrac{\omega}{\omega_0}\right)^2} = \frac{F_0^2 \omega_0}{2k} \frac{\omega_0 T}{1 + \omega_0^2 T^2 \left(\dfrac{\omega_0}{\omega} - \dfrac{\omega}{\omega_0}\right)^2} \quad (I.25)$$

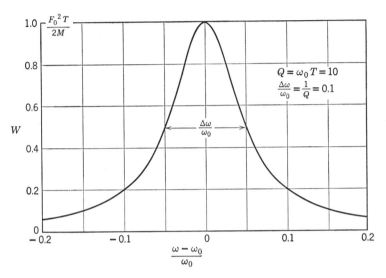

FIG. I.5.   A power resonance curve for $Q = 10$.

For systems showing marked resonance phenomena the region of inter-
est is in the vicinity of resonance, or ω nearly equal to ω_0.   In this range
we may make the following approximations:

$$\frac{\omega_0^2 - \omega^2}{\omega\omega_0} = \frac{(\omega_0 + \omega)(\omega_0 - \omega)}{\omega\omega_0} \simeq \frac{2\omega_0(\omega_0 - \omega)}{\omega_0^2} = 2\frac{\omega_0 - \omega}{\omega_0}$$

Eq. I.25 under these conditions becomes

$$W = F_0^2 \frac{T}{M} \frac{1}{1 + 4Q^2 \left(\dfrac{\omega_0 - \omega}{\omega_0}\right)^2} \quad (I.26)$$

This expression is plotted in Fig. I.5.   Notice that, if the width of the
power resonance curve at half maximum is $\Delta\omega$, then for $\omega = \omega_0 \pm \dfrac{\Delta\omega}{2}$

$$\frac{1}{1 + 4Q^2 \left(\dfrac{\omega_0 - \omega}{\omega_0}\right)^2} = \frac{1}{2}$$

$$4Q^2 \left(\frac{\Delta\omega}{2\omega_0}\right)^2 = 1$$

$$Q = \frac{\omega_0}{\Delta\omega} \qquad\qquad (I.27)$$

Q, or $\omega_0 T$, measures the width of the resonance curve in a system undergoing forced oscillation, whereas in a system undergoing free oscillations it measures the rate at which the oscillation is damped out.

Table of
Physical Constants

APPROXIMATE VALUES

Electronic charge	e	1.6×10^{-19} coulomb
Electronic mass	m	9.1×10^{-31} kilogram
Mass of the proton	M_p	1.67×10^{-27} kilogram
Planck's constant	h	6.62×10^{-34} joule-sec
Velocity of light	c	3×10^8 meter/sec
Avogadro's number	A	6.02×10^{23} particles
Permittivity of free space	ϵ_0	8.85×10^{-12} farad/meter
Permeability of free space	μ_0	$4\pi \times 10^{-7}$ henry/meter
Boltzmann's constant	k	1.38×10^{-23} joule/$^\circ K$

APPENDIX III

Commonly Used
Conversion Factors

1 angstrom unit = 10^{-8} cm = 10^{-10} meter

1 micron = 0.001 mm = 10^{-6} meter

1 centimeter = 0.39370 in.

1 inch = 2.5400 cm

1 foot = 30.480 cm

1 newton = 0.224 lb = 10^{5} dynes

1 pound (wt) = 445,000 dynes

1 atmosphere = 14.697 lb per sq in.

1 joule = 10,000,000 ergs

1 calorie = 4.186 joules

1 foot-pound = 1.3549 joules

1 Btu = 252.00 cal

1 Btu = 778 ft-lb

1 electron volt = 1.6 × 10^{-19} joules

1 horsepower = 746 watts

APPENDIX IV

Alphabetic List of the Elements

Element	Symbol	Atomic No. Z	Element	Symbol	Atomic No. Z
Actinium	Sc	89	Gadolinium	Gd	64
Aluminum	Al	13	Gallium	Ga	31
Americium	Am	95	Germanium	Ge	32
Antimony	Sb	51	Gold	Au	79
Argon	A	18	Hafnium	Hf	72
Arsenic	As	33	Helium	He	2
Astatine	At	85	Holmium	Ho	67
Barium	Ba	56	Hydrogen	H	1
Berkelium	Bk	97	Indium	In	49
Beryllium	Be	4	Iodine	I	53
Bismuth	Bi	83	Iridium	Ir	77
Boron	B	5	Iron	Fe	26
Bormine	Br	35	Krypton	Kr	36
Cadmium	Cd	48	Lanthanum	La	57
Calcium	Ca	20	Lead	Pb	82
Californium	Cf	98	Lithium	Li	3
Carbon	C	6	Lutetium	Lu	71
Cerium	Ce	58	Magnesium	Mg	12
Cesium	Cs	55	Manganese	Mn	25
Chlorine	Cl	17	Mendelevium	Mv	101
Chromium	Cr	24	Mercury	Hg	80
Cobalt	Co	27	Molybdenum	Mo	42
Copper	Cu	29	Neodymium	Nd	60
Curium	Cm	96	Neon	Ne	10
Dysprosium	Dy	66	Neptunium	Np	93
Einsteinium	E	99	Nickel	Ni	28
Erbium	Er	68	Niobium	Nb	41
Europium	Eu	63	Nitrogen	N	7
Fermium	Fm	100	Osmium	Os	76
Fluorine	F	9	Oxygen	O	8
Francium	Fr	87	Palladium	Pd	46

Element	Symbol	Atomic No. Z	Element	Symbol	Atomic No. Z
Phosphorus	P	15	Strontium	Sr	38
Platinum	Pt	78	Sulfur	S	16
Plutonium	Pu	94	Tantalum	Ta	73
Polonium	Po	84	Technetium	Tc	43
Potassium	K	19	Tellurium	Te	52
Praseodymium	Pr	59	Terbium	Tb	65
Promethium	Pm	61	Thallium	Tl	81
Protactinium	Pa	91	Thorium	Th	90
Radium	Ra	88	Thulium	Tm	69
Radon	Rn	86	Tin	Sn	50
Rhenium	Re	75	Titanium	Ti	22
Rhodium	Rh	45	Tungsten	W	74
Rubidium	Rb	37	Uranium	U	92
Ruthenium	Ru	44	Vanadium	V	23
Samarium	Sm	62	Xenon	Xe	54
Scandium	Sc	21	Ytterbium	Yb	70
Selenium	Se	34	Yttrium	Y	39
Silicon	Si	14	Zinc	Zn	30
Silver	Ag	47	Zirconium	Zr	40
Sodium	Na	11			

Periodic Table
of the Elements ▶

Outer Electrons are in the	I	II	III	IV	V	VI	VII	VIII			O
1st or K shell	1 H 1.0078										2 He 4.003
2nd or L shell	3 Li 6.940	4 Be 9.02	5 B 10.82	6 C 12.00	7 N 14.008	8 O 16.0000	9 F 19.00				10 Ne 20.183
3rd or M shell	11 Na 22.994	12 Mg 24.32	13 Al 26.97	14 Si 28.06	15 P 30.98	16 S 32.06	17 Cl 35.457				18 A 39.944
4th or N shell	19 K 39.096	20 Ca 40.08	21 Sc 45.10	22 Ti 47.90	23 V 50.95	24 Cr 52.01	25 Mn 54.93	26 Fe 55.85	27 Co 58.94	28 Ni 58.69	
	29 Cu 63.57	30 Zn 65.38	31 Ga 69.72	32 Ge 72.60	33 As 74.91	34 Se 78.96	35 Br 79.916				36 Kr 83.7
5th or O shell	37 Rb 85.48	38 Sr 87.63	39 Y 88.92	40 Zr 91.22	41 Nb 92.91	42 Mo 95.95	43 Tc	44 Ru 101.7	45 Rh 102.91	46 Pd 106.7	
	47 Ag 107.880	48 Cd 112.41	49 In 114.76	50 Sn 118.70	51 Sb 121.76	52 Te 127.61	53 I 126.92				54 Xe 131.3
6th or P shell	55 Cs 132.91	56 Ba 137.36	57 La 138.92 *	72 Hf 178.6	73 Ta 180.88	74 W 183.92	75 Re 186.31	76 Os 190.2	77 Ir 193.1	78 Pt 195.23	
	79 Au 197.2	80 Hg 200.61	81 Tl 203.39	82 Pb 207.21	83 Bi 209.00	84 Po 210	85 At 212.?				86 Rn 222
7th or R shell	87 Fr 223.?	88 Ra 226.05	89 Ac 227.05	90 Th 232.12	91 Pa 231.?	92 U 238.07	93 Np	94 Pu	95 Am 96 Cm	97 Bk	98 Cf†

TRANSURANIC ELEMENTS (93 Np, 94 Pu, 95 Am, 96 Cm, 97 Bk, 98 Cf†)

* The rare earths	58 Ce 140.13	59 Pr 140.92	60 Nd 144.27	61 Pm 146.0	62 Sm 150.43	63 Eu 152.0	64 Gd 156.9	65 Tb 159.2	66 Dy 162.46	67 Ho 164.94	68 Er 167.20	69 Tm 169.4	70 Yb 173.04	71 Lu 174.99

† Recent additions are 99 E, 100 Fm, 101 Mv. See Appendix IV.

Natural
Trigonometric Functions

Angle	Sine	Cosine	Tangent	Angle	Sine	Cosine	Tangent
0°	0.000	1.000	0.000	32°	0.530	0.848	0.625
1°	0.018	1.000	0.018	33°	0.545	0.839	0.649
2°	0.035	0.999	0.035	34°	0.559	0.829	0.675
3°	0.052	0.999	0.052	35°	0.574	0.819	0.700
4°	0.070	0.998	0.070	36°	0.588	0.809	0.727
5°	0.087	0.996	0.088	37°	0.602	0.799	0.754
6°	0.105	0.995	0.105	38°	0.616	0.788	0.781
7°	0.122	0.993	0.123	39°	0.629	0.777	0.810
8°	0.139	0.990	0.141	40°	0.643	0.766	0.839
9°	0.156	0.988	0.158	41°	0.656	0.755	0.869
10°	0.174	0.985	0.176	42°	0.669	0.743	0.900
11°	0.191	0.982	0.194	43°	0.682	0.731	0.933
12°	0.208	0.978	0.213	44°	0.695	0.719	0.966
13°	0.225	0.974	0.231	45°	0.707	0.707	1.000
14°	0.242	0.970	0.249	46°	0.719	0.695	1.03€
15°	0.259	0.966	0.268	47°	0.731	0.682	1,072
16°	0.276	0.961	0.287	48°	0.743	0.669	1.111
17°	0.292	0.956	0.306	49°	0.755	0.656	1.150
18°	0.309	0.951	0.325	50°	0.766	0.643	1.192
19°	0.326	0.946	0.344	51°	0.777	0.629	1.235
20°	0.342	0.940	0.364	52°	0.788	0.616	1.280
21°	0.358	0.934	0.384	53°	0.799	0.602	1.327
22°	0.375	0.927	0.404	54°	0.809	0.588	1.376
23°	0.391	0.921	0.425	55°	0.819	0.574	1.428
24°	0.407	0.914	0.445	56°	0.829	0.559	1.483
25°	0.423	0.906	0.466	57°	0.839	0.545	1.540
26°	0.438	0.899	0.488	58°	0.848	0.530	1.600
27°	0.454	0.891	0.510	59°	0.857	0.515	1.664
28°	0.470	0.883	0.532	60°	0.866	0.500	1.732
29°	0.485	0.875	0.554	61°	0.875	0.485	1.804
30°	0.500	0.866	0.577	62°	0.883	0.470	1.881
31°	0.515	0.857	0.601	63°	0.891	0.454	1.963

Angle	Sine	Cosine	Tangent	Angle	Sine	Cosine	Tangent
64°	0.899	0.438	2.050	77°	0.974	0.225	4.331
65°	0.906	0.423	2.145	78°	0.978	0.208	4.705
66°	0.914	0.407	2.246	79°	0.982	0.191	5.145
67°	0.921	0.391	2.356	80°	0.985	0.174	5.671
68°	0.927	0.375	2.475	81°	0.988	0.156	6.314
69°	0.934	0.358	2.605	82°	0.990	0.139	7.115
70°	0.940	0.342	2.747	83°	0.993	0.122	8.144
71°	0.946	0.326	2.904	84°	0.995	0.105	9.514
72°	0.951	0.309	3.078	85°	0.996	0.087	11.43
73°	0.956	0.292	3.271	86°	0.998	0.070	14.30
74°	0.961	0.276	3.487	87°	0.999	0.052	19.08
75°	0.966	0.259	3.732	89°	1.000	0.018	57.29
76°	0.970	0.242	4.011	90°	1.000	0.000	∞

The Greek Alphabet

Alpha	A	α
Beta	B	β
Gamma	Γ	γ
Delta	Δ	δ
Epsilon	E	ϵ
Zeta	Z	ζ
Eta	H	η
Theta	Θ	θ
Iota	I	ι
Kappa	K	κ
Lambda	Λ	λ
Mu	M	μ
Nu	N	ν
Xi	Ξ	ξ
Omicron	O	o
Pi	Π	π
Rho	P	ρ
Sigma	Σ	σ
Tau	T	τ
Upsilon	Υ	υ
Phi	Φ	ϕ
Chi	X	χ
Psi	Ψ	ψ
Omega	Ω	ω

Discussion
of Spectra Shown
in the Frontispiece

(a)[1] The lamp used to produce this spectrum radiates light with a
continuous distribution of frequencies as does a furnace, or black body,
described at the end of Section 11.4. The instrument used to show this
spectrum consists of a grating crossed with an echelle. The grating has
low dispersion and low resolving power and serves to spread the wavelengths in broad bands into a vertical spectrum as shown in the frontispiece, with the red at the top and violet (which looks bluish) at the
bottom. The echelle, developed by G. R. Harrison, and made by
Bausch & Lomb, is a type of grating with broad flat rulings, shaped like
stairs, each step being about $\frac{1}{8}$ mm wide, and relies on high orders of
interference to achieve a great resolving power. In the frontispiece,
the echelle spreads the wavelengths horizontally, as shown for a few of
the broad stripes in which the wavelengths in angstroms are marked at
the left and right extremities. Notice that the entire visible spectrum
is contained in the small band of wavelengths roughly between 4000 A
and 7000 A.

(b)[2] This spectrum was obtained with the instrument described
above but by use of light from a thorium arc in a helium atmosphere.
The thorium atoms have been vaporized and are excited in inelastic
collisions, chiefly by electrons accelerated by the electric field in the
arc. The frequencies radiated are all the result of transitions between
energy levels in the thorium atom. The complexity of the spectrum
indicates a complex system of energy levels. One of the tasks of spectros-
copy is to determine where these levels lie and which lines are radiated

[1]This paragraph should be read after study of Chapters 10 and 11.
[2]This paragraph should be read after study of Chapter 13.

from or to a single level. It is a great help in this determination to observe how the lines split up in a magnetic field, and thus to determine the angular momentum and magnetic moment of the atom in the upper and lower states of a transition, as discussed below.

$(c)^3$ The magnetic field used to split the spectral lines in this photograph is produced at the center of an air core solenoid having an inner diameter of 1.25 in. and a length of 10 in. A current of 8000 amp generates heat at the rate of 1200 kw which is carried off by a water flow of 700 gal a minute. The magnetic field strength achieved is 75,000 gauss. The lines shown in c are in the spectrum of neon. Three of the lines, whose wavelengths are shown, have a common lower level with $j = 1$, and arise from transitions from upper levels with $j = 0, 1, 2$, as shown in Fig. VIII.1. In a magnetic field, levels with $j = 0$, having no angular momentum and therefore no magnetic moment, are unaffected. Levels with $j = 1$ are split into three, with m values $+1$, 0, and -1. The magnitude of the splitting depends on the magnitude of the magnetic moment and the magnitude of the field. Although the upper and lower levels of the line at 6382.99 A both have $j = 1$, they do not have the same magnetic moments. The lower level, with the greater splitting, has the greater magnetic moment.

Only some of the possible transitions actually take place. Quantum theory can account for observed intensities. Notice that the frequency differences between the outer components of the three lines reproduced are equal and are determined by the splitting of the lower level. The expected Zeeman effect of these three lines is shown in the lower part of Fig. VIII.1. The lines are drawn immediately below the arrows representing the corresponding transitions. The weak lines above and below strong lines in c of the frontispiece are due to secondary diffraction maxima of the grating, and may be disregarded.

$(d)^4$ This is an example of the detailed structures of spectral lines as revealed with high resolving powers and a light source radiating sufficiently narrow lines. It is a strong green line of mercury, which appears also in the continuous spectrum a. The explanation of the effects observed is quite complex. We shall here indicate only a few of the main points which illustrate the bearing of the observed patterns on our understanding of nuclear structure. The element mercury has several stable isotopes, having mass numbers 198, 199, 200, 201, 202, and 204. Those having even mass numbers have no angular momentum and no magnetic moment. We shall first consider spectral lines radiated by these isotopes. An electron near the nucleus moves in the Coulomb

³This paragraph should be read after study of Chapter 13.
⁴This paragraph should be read after study of Chapter 14.

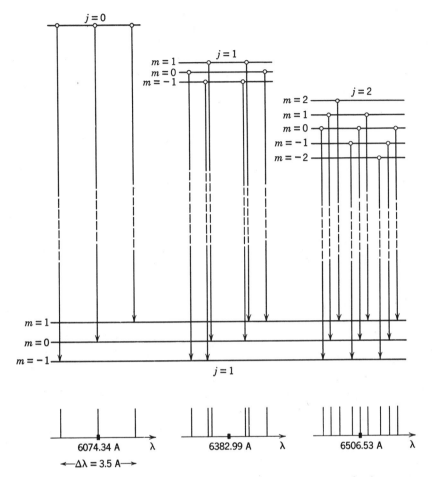

FIG. VIII.1   The Zeeman effect of three lines in the neon spectrum having a common lower level.

field of force of the protons. Its potential energy is inversely proportional to the distance from the center of the atom, as shown in the solid curve in Fig. VIII.2. If this law of force held for arbitrarily small values of r, the energy levels of the atom would have certain values, indicated by E_1 and E_2, for example. If the nucleus is not an infinitesimal point at the origin, but has a finite radius R within which the nuclear charge is distributed, the potential energy of the electron will not approach $-\infty$ inside the nucleus but will change only little from its value at the nuclear surface. This behavior is indicated by the dotted part of the potential energy curve. The energy levels of the atom will be modified because of the departure from the Coulomb "point charge" potential, the new values being indicated by E'_1 and E'_2. Some levels will be shifted more than others, depending on whether or not the electron in the corresponding state spends much of its time inside of the nucleus. This, in turn, depends on whether ψ^2 has a maximum or a minimum for $r = 0$. Different isotopes will have slightly different radii, and therefore

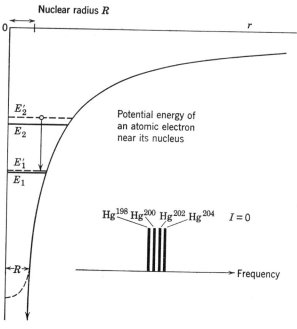

FIG. VIII.2. The origin of the isotope shift of heavy atoms.

the energy levels will be shifted by slightly different amounts. The spectral lines emitted by the mercury isotopes with even mass number are schematically indicated in Fig. VIII.2. The actual frequency differences are very small. This phenomenon is spoken of as an isotope shift.

Another effect is observed if the nucleus has an angular momentum, and consequently also a magnetic moment, as, for example, in the case of Hg^{199}, with a nuclear angular momentum quantum number $I = \frac{1}{2}$. The green line of mercury is emitted in a transition from an upper state with electronic angular momentum described by $j = 1$ to a lower state with $j = 2$. The electronic and nuclear magnetic moments will interact. There will be a certain number of possible orientations with respect to each other, depending on their angular momenta. The energy of the atom for these various orientations will differ by an amount depending on the magnetic moments. These effects can be rigorously calculated by use of a more complete form of quantum mechanics than has been developed in the text. Approximately, however, we might say that the

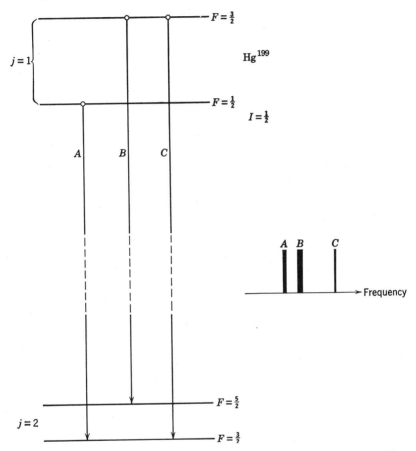

Fig. VIII.3.   The origin of the hyperfine structure of the green line of Hg^{199}.

atomic electrons produce a magnetic field at the nucleus, and that the nuclear spin can take on only certain orientations in this field.   In Hg^{199}, this leads to a splitting of the energy levels into two, one having a resultant angular momentum quantum number $F = j + \frac{1}{2}$, the other with $F = j - \frac{1}{2}$, as shown in Fig. VIII.3.   Again not all transitions are allowed.   The calculated transition probabilities lead to the three lines A, B, and C.   Finally, the isotope Hg^{201} with $I = \frac{3}{2}$ can be treated in a similar fashion.   Because of the greater angular momentum the levels split into a larger number of components, which leads to lines designated by a, b, c, d, e, f, g, h. This form of splitting due to nuclear and electronic magnetic interactions is called hyperfine structure. The complete structure of the mercury green line as calculated is reproduced in Fig.

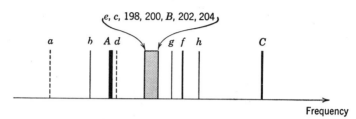

Fig. VIII.4.   The predicted hyperfine structure of the green line of natural mercury.

VIII.4. This structure, together with that of other lines in the spectrum, may be used to calculate nuclear moments and sizes, as outlined above. Extensions of these ideas lead to the possibility of estimating nuclear shapes, and certain aspects of charge and current distribution in nuclei as well.

Problem Answers

CHAPTER 1

2. 9.2×10^5 ton.

4. 2.5×10^{-2} meter from the 1 μc charge, and 12.5×10^{-2} meter from the 25 μc charge.

6. (a) $F = 0.173$ newton normal to the line joining the two positive charges.
(b) $F = 0.1$ newton parallel to the line connecting the other two charges.

8. (a) For $x > 0.05$ meter, $\qquad 0.45 \dfrac{0.05^2 + x^2}{(0.05^2 - x^2)^2}$ newton

For $x < -0.05$ meter, $\qquad -0.45 \dfrac{0.05^2 + x^2}{(0.05^2 - x^2)^2}$ newton

For -0.05 meter $< x < +0.05$ meter, $\dfrac{-0.045x}{(0.05^2 - x^2)^2}$ newton

(b) $F_y = \dfrac{0.45y}{(0.05^2 + y^2)^{3\!/\!2}}$

12. (a) 0.5 amp. (b) 1 volt and 5 volts.

14. (a) 121 ohms. (b) 25 watts.

16. (a) $f = \dfrac{1}{2\pi} \sqrt{\dfrac{k}{I}}$. (b) $\tau = 2.56 \times 10^{-11}$ newton-meter. (c) $Q = 122\,\mu$c.

CHAPTER 2

2. (a) -18×10^3 volt/meter. (b) -6.36×10^3 volt/meter.
(c) 8×10^3 volt/meter.

6. (a) $\dfrac{k(Q_1 + Q_2)x}{(x^2 + R^2)^{3\!/\!2}}$. (b) Unchanged. (c) $\dfrac{2}{\pi} \dfrac{k(Q_1 - Q_2)R}{(x^2 + R^2)^{3\!/\!2}}$; 0.

8. (a) $\dfrac{kQL}{s(s^2 - L^2/4)}$ for $s > L/2$. (b) $\dfrac{-4kQ}{L} \left[\dfrac{1}{(s^2 + L^2/4)^{1\!/\!2}} - \dfrac{1}{s} \right]$.

10. (a) $\dfrac{1}{2\pi\epsilon_0} (t/r)$. (b) 3.6×10^6; 3.6×10^5; 3.6×10^3 volt/meter.

16. (a) For $r < R$, $\dfrac{\rho r}{3\epsilon_0}$; for $r > R$, $\dfrac{1}{4\pi\epsilon_0}\dfrac{Q}{r^2}$.

(c) For $r < R$, $\dfrac{Q(3R^2 - r^2)}{8\pi\epsilon_0 R^3}$; for $r > R$, $\dfrac{1}{4\pi\epsilon_0}\dfrac{Q}{r}$.

20. (a) 100 volts, 200 μc; 100 volts, 500 μc. (b) 86 μc, 43 volts; 214 μc, 43 volts.
(c) 3.5×10^{-2} joules. (d) 3.5×10^{-2} joules. (e) 0.64×10^{-2} joules.

22. (a) 218 μc. (b) 109 volts, 54.5 volts, 36.3 volts. (c) 11.9×10^{-3} joule;
5.95×10^{-3} joule; 3.96×10^{-3} joule.

26. (a) 1.73 $\mu\mu$f. (b) 1.2 $\mu\mu$f.   28. (a) 1800 volts. (b) 2860 volts.

30. 33 sec.   32. (a) 0.011 μc. (b) -333 $\mu\mu$c.

CHAPTER 3

2. (a) 1.24×10^8 meters.   (b) 6.64×10^4 meters.
   (c) 4.45×10^{-7} meter.   (d) 2.42×10^{-10} meter.

6. (a) 9.2×10^{-8} newton.   (b) 4.1×10^{-47} newton.

8. (a) 9.52 Mev   (b) 4.27×10^7 meters/sec.

10. (a) 28.4 Mev.   (b) Yes.

12. One in 7.9×10^7.

14. $n = \dfrac{j}{e\sqrt{\dfrac{2eV_0 x}{md}}}$; $jd^2 V^{-3/2} < 2.7 \times 10^{-3}$

16. $4\,\dfrac{m}{M_A}\cos^4(\theta/2)$.   18. 95,000 coulombs/mole.

20. (a) 3.12×10^{12}. (b) 1.17×10^5 meter/sec. (c) 4.73×10^{-4} meter/sec.

22. (a) 2.56×10^6 ohm/km.   (b) 7.81×10^{-5} amp/km.

24. 0.125°C/sec.   26. ± 0.25°C.

28. (a) 2×10^{-36} coulomb-meter.   (b) 1.000066.

30. (a) 10^7 volt/meter. (b) 4×10^7 volt/meter. (c) 0. (d) 2.95×10^{-10} amp.
    (e) 295 volts.

32. 8μf.   34. $\dfrac{2C}{1 + 1/K_e}$.

36. (a) $1.061\ 10^{-9}$f. (b) 3×10^5 volts/meter, 4×10^5 volts/meter,
1.061×10^{-5} coulomb/meter^2.

38. 1.25×10^{-6} meter.   40. (a) 0.0975 amp. (b) 96.2 volt.

42. 3.65 cm.

44. (a) $\dfrac{Q^2 x}{2K_e\epsilon_0 A}$ · (b) $\dfrac{Q^2\,dx}{2\epsilon_0 A}$ · (c) $F = \dfrac{-Q^2}{2\epsilon_0 A}$ ·

CHAPTER 4

2. 16,467 ohms.   4. 0.024 ohm.

6. 2 volts, 200 amp; 4 volts, 200 amp.

8. 2 ohms.   10. 4.9 ohms.

12. (a) 1.88 ohm. (b) 4.9 ma.

14. (a) $\dfrac{1.44 \times 10^6}{(4 + 0.1x)^2}$ watts.

(b) $6 \times 10^4 \dfrac{60x - 920}{x^2 - 12x - 480}$ watts.

(c) $5.5 \times 10^4 \dfrac{200 - 55x}{x^2 - 12x - 488}$ watts.

(d) $4 \times 10^4 \left[\dfrac{5x - 720}{x^2 - 12x - 480} \right]^2$ watts.

20. (a) 4.06 amp, 40.6 volts, 107.6 volts. (c) $-69° 20'$.
22. 265 μf; 69 volts, 92.5 volts.
24. (a) 160 volts, 157.3 volts. (b) 6.18 μc. (c) 158.7 volts.

26. $V_0 \left(1 - \dfrac{1}{4Crf} \right).$ 28. (a) V/E_c. (b) 3.33 meters.

CHAPTER 5

2. $x = 5.92$ cm, $y = 5.36$ cm.
4. (a) 656 gauss. (b) 12.1 cm.
6. 42.2 gauss.
8. (a) Nearly 3×10^8 meters/sec. (b) 7.7×10^4 Mev. (c) Eastward.
14. 1.633 amp.   16. iaB.
18. 6.4×10^{-6} weber/meter^2.   20. 0.209; $\alpha = 6$, $\beta = 2$.

22. $\dfrac{\mu_0}{\pi} \left(\dfrac{id}{d^2 - x^2} \right).$

24. For $r > R$, $B = \dfrac{10^{-3}}{r}$; for $r < R$, $B = 10r$.

26. $H_i = 0$, $B_i = 4\pi \times 10^{-3}$ weber/meter^2; $B_0 = 4\pi \times 10^{-3}$ weber/meter^2, $H_0 = 10^4$ amp/meter.
28. 55.7 amp.
30. (a) $28.9 \times 10^{-7} M_s \sin^2 \phi \cos \phi \log_{10} (r_2/r_1)$; (b) $54° 44'$.

CHAPTER 6

2. $0.0655 \sin (524t)$ volt.   4. (a) 0.0149 μv. (b) 0.0149 μv.
6. $C_H B/\rho$.   8. (a) 0.003%. (b) 0.036%.

10. $\dfrac{V_0 \pi r^2}{d} \left(\dfrac{1}{\rho} \sin 2\pi \text{ft} + \epsilon\omega \cos 2\pi \text{ft} \right).$ 12. 1 volt, 8 volts.

14. (a) 8 henrys. (b) 4 henrys.   16. 6.78×10^{-7} henrys.
22. 0.1836 amp, 91.8 volts, 69.2 volts; $37° 1'$; 16.85 watt.
24. (a) 22 volts. (b) 160.6 watts.   26. 261 volt, 6.15 kw, 1.25 amp.

CHAPTER 7

2. 7.04 henrys; 115 ma, 305 volts, 115 volts, $\phi = 0$, 13.22 watt, 2.65, 22.6 cycles/sec.
6. (a) 3.5 amp. (b) 0.86.

8. $\dfrac{BX_c R}{\sqrt{2}\, A \sqrt{R^2 + X_c{}^2}\, \sqrt{R^2 + (X_L + X_c)^2}}.$

10. (a) 140 ma, 4.25, 580 ohms, 0.00725 mho, 0.00172 mho. (b) 1.5 volt, 0.75 ma.
12. 0.0045 sec.

590   CURRENTS, FIELDS, AND PARTICLES

CHAPTER 8

2. 0.135 watts/meter, 1.35×10^{-2} volt/meter, 7.96×10^{2} amp/meter, 1.35×10^{-2}volt/meter,3.98×10^{2}amp/meter,10.74watts/meter^2,5.37watts/meter^2, 0.0338 watts/meter, 0.135 watts/meter, 0.0338 watts/meter.

6. $S_0 = E_0 H_0/2$.

10. (a) 5×10^7, 10^8, and 1.5×10^8 cycles/sec. (b) 2.5×10^7, 7.5×10^7, and 1.25×10^8 cycles/sec.

12. (a) 1.82 amp. (b) 600 cycles/sec, 3.37×10^5 meters. (c) 91.5 watts.

14. (a) 30, 10, 1 meter. (b) 3×10^6, 3×10^9, 10^{11} cycles/sec.

16. 15.9 amp.

18. (a) 90°. (b) $14° 29'$, $48° 35'$. (c) $7° 11'$, $22° 1'$, $38° 41'$, $61° 3'$ from the normal to the line joining the antennas.

20. $33° 33'$, 60°, $80° 24'$, $99° 36'$, 120°, $146° 27'$.

22. Principal maxima at 0°, $19° 28'$, $41° 49'$, 90°. Secondary maxima at $9° 36'$, 30°, $56° 27'$. Minima at $6° 23'$, $12° 50'$, $26° 22'$, $33° 43'$, 51°, $62° 38'$.

CHAPTER 9

2. (a) $48° 46'$. (b) $33° 39'$.   4. $28° 6'$, 45°, 1.65 mm.

8. (a) $I = \dfrac{I_0}{2} \cos^2 \theta$.   (b) $I = \dfrac{I_0}{8} \sin^2 2\psi$.

10. $\left(\dfrac{\sqrt{K_e} - 1}{\sqrt{K_e} + 1}\right)^2$.   12. 7.4%.

14. 25 ft, red light on the left.

18. -6.66, -10, -13.3, ∞, 3.33, 0 cm; $-\frac{1}{3}$, -1, -1.66, ∞, 1.66, 1.

20. At a point $nR/(n-1)$ beyond the first vertex if $n > 2$. At a point $\dfrac{2-n}{2(n-1)} R$ beyond the second vertex if $n < 2$.

22. 112.87 cm.   24. 16.6 $\times$.

26. 0.14 cm further from the objective.

28. 13 in., 156 in.   30. 37.5 cm, 0.67.

CHAPTER 10

2. 367, 37.   4. 6705 A.

6. (a) 6π, (b) 0, $\pm11° 33'$, $\pm23° 35'$, $\pm36° 53'$, $\pm53° 8'$, $\pm90°$.

8. (a) 7.58×10^{-8} meter.   (b) 1.516×10^{-7} meter.

10. (a) Dark. (b) 4.24×10^{-4} meter. (c) 3×10^{-4} meter.

12. (a) $1.55 \times 10^{-3}\sqrt{n}$ meter.   (b) 0.55 meter, 1.67 meter, ∞.

14. (a) 0, 10°, $20° 20'$, $31° 20'$, 44°, $60° 10'$. (b) 4075 A.

16. $\pm36° 5'$; $66° 5'$, $-6° 5'$.   20. 5880 A.

22. 4 mm, 12 mm.

24. (a) True. (b) True. (c) False. (d) True. (e) False. (f) True.

26. 7.27 meter.

28. (a) 5.95×10^{-2} sec of arc.   (b) 2.73×10^{10} meters.

30. 152.5 km.   32. 6.4×10^{-3} mm.

34. 60 meters.

CHAPTER 11

2. 4; 3.62 A, 2.56 A.
6. NaCl (111), 17° 51′, 1° 45′; (220), 14° 29′, 1° 26′.
   Cu (111), 13° 50′, 1° 22′; (220), 22° 59′, 2° 14′.
8. 0.05 ev, 3 × 10³ meter/sec.   10. 0.717 A, 0.733 A, 0.755 A.
12. (a) 0.714 A. (b) 2.9 × 10⁴ ev.   14. 2.6, 4.14, 2.07, 1.83, 5.39 ev.
16. 3410, 3070, 5830 A.   18. 12.4 A.
20. (a) 579.4 A. (b) 5794 A. (c) 5220° K.
22. (a) 1.68 × 10¹² quanta/meter³; 1.68 × 10¹⁸ quanta/λ³.
    (b) 134 quanta/meter³; 1.34 × 10⁻²⁸ quanta/λ³.
28. 490 gauss/cm.

CHAPTER 12

4. $$\left(\frac{2}{L}\right)^{3/2} \frac{\sin}{\text{or}}\left(\frac{s_x\pi x}{L}\right) \frac{\sin}{\text{or}}\left(\frac{s_y\pi y}{L}\right) \frac{\sin}{\text{or}}\left(\frac{s_z\pi z}{L}\right)$$

The sin is to be used if s is even, and the cos is to be used if s is odd.

$$\frac{h^2}{8mL^2}\,(s_x{}^2 + s_y{}^2 + s_z{}^2)$$

6. No degeneracies.
8. 1/12, ±5 cycles/sec; 1/1200, ±0.05 cycles/sec.

CHAPTER 13

2. (a) 1.88 ev, 2.54 ev.   (b) $n = 3$ to 2, 4 to 2.
4. 3.41 ev.   6. 2536.064 A, 2536.000 A, 2535.936 A.
8. 0.0736 weber/meter².   10. 120 watts/meter.
12. $Z^* = Z - 7$.   14. 81,200°K.

CHAPTER 14

4. 18.63 Mev, 4.93 Mev, 2.36 Mev, −6.73 Mev.
6. 0.212 mμg.   8. 29.3 × 10³ kg.
10. $_4Be^9$ (n, α) $_2He^6$ with 0.737 Mev neutrons.
    $_4Be^9$ (γ, n) $_4Be^8$ with 1.53 Mev gamma rays.
    $_4Be^9$ (n, γ) $_4Be^{10}$ or $_4Be^9$ (d, p) $_4Be^{10}$ gives 6.30 Mev gamma rays or 3.37 Mev
    protons.
    $_4Be^9$ (p, γ) $_5B^{10}$ or $_4Be^9$ (d, n) $_5B^{10}$ gives 6.11 Mev gamma rays or 3.18 Mev
    neutrons.
12. (a) 85 collisions. (b) 9.19 × 10⁹ neutrons. (c) 1.09 neutrons per fission.
14. 24.1 Mev.
16. 3.125 × 10¹⁶ fissions per sec, 9.45 days.
18. (a) 10² kg/sec. (b) 3.95 × 10⁻¹² per year. (c) 3.58 × 10⁴ × X years.
20. 1.989 Mev, almost 3 × 10⁸ meters/sec, in fact, v/c = .979.

Index